Animals

Book-Specific Resources
Student Edition
StudentExpress™ CD-ROM
Interactive Textbook Online
Teacher's Edition
All-in-One Teaching Resources
Color Transparencies
Guided Reading and Study Workbook
Student Edition in MP3 Audio
Discovery Channel School® Video
Consumable and Nonconsumable Materials Kits

Program Print Resources
Integrated Science Laboratory Manual
Computer Microscope Lab Manual
Inquiry Skills Activity Books
Progress Monitoring Assessments
Test Preparation Workbook
Test-Taking Tips With Transparencies
Teacher's ELL Handbook
Reading Strategies for Science Content

Differentiated Instruction Resources
Adapted Reading and Study Workbook
Adapted Tests
Differentiated Instruction Guide for Labs and Activities

Program Technology Resources
TeacherExpress™ CD-ROM
Interactive Textbooks Online
PresentationExpress™ CD-ROM
ExamView®, Test Generator CD-ROM
Lab zone™ Easy Planner CD-ROM
Probeware Lab Manual With CD-ROM
Computer Microscope and Lab Manual
Materials Ordering CD-ROM
Discovery Channel School® DVD Library
Lab Activity Video Library—DVD and VHS
Web Site at PearsonSchool.com

Spanish Print Resources
Spanish Student Edition
Spanish Guided Reading and Study Workbook
Spanish Teaching Guide With Tests

Acknowledgments appear on page 214, which constitutes an extension of this copyright page.

Cover
A herd of Masai giraffes in Kenya, Africa (top) and mother and calf (bottom)

13-digit ISBN 978-0-13-365119-5
10-digit ISBN 0-13-365119-3
2 3 4 5 6 7 8 9 10 V092 12 11

PEARSON

Program Authors

Michael J. Padilla, Ph.D.
Associate Dean and Director
Eugene T. Moore School of Education
Clemson University
Clemson, South Carolina

Michael Padilla is a leader in middle school science education. He has served as an author and elected officer for the National Science Teachers Association and as a writer of the National Science Education Standards. As lead author of Science Explorer, Mike has inspired the team in developing a program that meets the needs of middle grades students, promotes science inquiry, and is aligned with the National Science Education Standards.

Ioannis Miaoulis, Ph.D.
President
Museum of Science
Boston, Massachusetts

Originally trained as a mechanical engineer, Ioannis Miaoulis is in the forefront of the national movement to increase technological literacy. As dean of the Tufts University School of Engineering, Dr. Miaoulis spearheaded the introduction of engineering into the Massachusetts curriculum. Currently he is working with school systems across the country to engage students in engineering activities and to foster discussions on the impact of science and technology on society.

Martha Cyr, Ph.D.
Director of K–12 Outreach
Worcester Polytechnic Institute
Worcester, Massachusetts

Martha Cyr is a noted expert in engineering outreach. She has over nine years of experience with programs and activities that emphasize the use of engineering principles, through hands-on projects, to excite and motivate students and teachers of mathematics and science in grades K–12. Her goal is to stimulate a continued interest in science and mathematics through engineering.

Book Author

Jan Jenner, Ph.D.
Science Writer
Talladega, Alabama

Contributing Writers

Fred Holtzclaw
Science Instructor
Oak Ridge High School
Oak Ridge, Tennessee

Theresa K. Holtzclaw
Former Science Instructor
Clinton, Tennessee

Evan P. Silberstein
Science Instructor
The Frisch School
Paramus, New Jersey

Consultants

Reading Consultant

Nancy Romance, Ph.D.
Professor of Science Education
Florida Atlantic University
Fort Lauderdale, Florida

Mathematics Consultant

William Tate, Ph.D.
Professor of Education and Applied Statistics and Computation
Washington University
St. Louis, Missouri

B • iii

Reviewers

Tufts University Content Reviewers

Faculty from Tufts University in Medford, Massachusetts, developed *Science Explorer* chapter projects and reviewed the student books.

Astier M. Almedom, Ph.D.
Department of Biology

Wayne Chudyk, Ph.D.
Department of Civil and Environmental Engineering

John L. Durant, Ph.D.
Department of Civil and Environmental Engineering

George S. Ellmore, Ph.D.
Department of Biology

David Kaplan, Ph.D.
Department of Biomedical Engineering

Samuel Kounaves, Ph.D.
Department of Chemistry

David H. Lee, Ph.D.
Department of Chemistry

Douglas Matson, Ph.D.
Department of Mechanical Engineering

Karen Panetta, Ph.D.
Department of Electrical Engineering and Computer Science

Jan A. Pechenik, Ph.D.
Department of Biology

John C. Ridge, Ph.D.
Department of Geology

William Waller, Ph.D.
Department of Astronomy

Content Reviewers

Paul Beale, Ph.D.
Department of Physics
University of Colorado
Boulder, Colorado

Jeff Bodart, Ph.D.
Chipola Junior College
Marianna, Florida

Michael Castellani, Ph.D.
Department of Chemistry
Marshall University
Huntington, West Virginia

Eugene Chiang, Ph.D.
Department of Astronomy
University of California – Berkeley
Berkeley, California

Charles C. Curtis, Ph.D.
Department of Physics
University of Arizona
Tucson, Arizona

Daniel Kirk-Davidoff, Ph.D.
Department of Meteorology
University of Maryland
College Park, Maryland

Diane T. Doser, Ph.D.
Department of Geological Sciences
University of Texas at El Paso
El Paso, Texas

R. E. Duhrkopf, Ph.D.
Department of Biology
Baylor University
Waco, Texas

Michael Hacker
Co-director, Center for Technological Literacy
Hofstra University
Hempstead, New York

Michael W. Hamburger, Ph.D.
Department of Geological Sciences
Indiana University
Bloomington, Indiana

Alice K. Hankla, Ph.D.
The Galloway School
Atlanta, Georgia

Donald C. Jackson, Ph.D.
Department of Molecular Pharmacology, Physiology, & Biotechnology
Brown University
Providence, Rhode Island

Jeremiah N. Jarrett, Ph.D.
Department of Biological Sciences
Central Connecticut State University
New Britain, Connecticut

David Lederman, Ph.D.
Department of Physics
West Virginia University
Morgantown, West Virginia

Becky Mansfield, Ph.D.
Department of Geography
Ohio State University
Columbus, Ohio

Elizabeth M. Martin, M.S.
Department of Chemistry and Biochemistry
College of Charleston
Charleston, South Carolina

Joe McCullough, Ph.D.
Department of Natural and Applied Sciences
Cabrillo College
Aptos, California

Robert J. Mellors, Ph.D.
Department of Geological Sciences
San Diego State University
San Diego, California

Joseph M. Moran, Ph.D.
American Meteorological Society
Washington, D.C.

David J. Morrissey, Ph.D.
Department of Chemistry
Michigan State University
East Lansing, Michigan

Philip A. Reed, Ph.D.
Department of Occupational & Technical Studies
Old Dominion University
Norfolk, Virginia

Scott M. Rochette, Ph.D.
Department of the Earth Sciences
State University of New York, College at Brockport
Brockport, New York

Laurence D. Rosenhein, Ph.D.
Department of Chemistry
Indiana State University
Terre Haute, Indiana

Ronald Sass, Ph.D.
Department of Biology and Chemistry
Rice University
Houston, Texas

George Schatz, Ph.D.
Department of Chemistry
Northwestern University
Evanston, Illinois

Sara Seager, Ph.D.
Carnegie Institution of Washington
Washington, D.C.

Robert M. Thornton, Ph.D.
Section of Plant Biology
University of California
Davis, California

John R. Villarreal, Ph.D.
College of Science and Engineering
The University of Texas – Pan American
Edinburg, Texas

Kenneth Welty, Ph.D.
School of Education
University of Wisconsin–Stout
Menomonie, Wisconsin

Edward J. Zalisko, Ph.D.
Department of Biology
Blackburn College
Carlinville, Illinois

Teacher Reviewers

David R. Blakely
Arlington High School
Arlington, Massachusetts

Jane E. Callery
Two Rivers Magnet Middle School
East Hartford, Connecticut

Melissa Lynn Cook
Oakland Mills High School
Columbia, Maryland

James Fattic
Southside Middle School
Anderson, Indiana

Dan Gabel
Hoover Middle School
Rockville, Maryland

Wayne Goates
Eisenhower Middle School
Goddard, Kansas

Katherine Bobay Graser
Mint Hill Middle School
Charlotte, North Carolina

Darcy Hampton
Deal Junior High School
Washington, D.C.

Karen Kelly
Pierce Middle School
Waterford, Michigan

David Kelso
Manchester High School Central
Manchester, New Hampshire

Benigno Lopez, Jr.
Sleepy Hill Middle School
Lakeland, Florida

Angie L. Matamoros, Ph.D.
ALM Consulting, Inc.
Weston, Florida

Tim McCollum
Charleston Middle School
Charleston, Illinois

Bruce A. Mellin
Brooks School
North Andover, Massachusetts

Ella Jay Parfitt
Southeast Middle School
Baltimore, Maryland

Evelyn A. Pizzarello
Louis M. Klein Middle School
Harrison, New York

Kathleen M. Poe
Fletcher Middle School
Jacksonville, Florida

Shirley Rose
Lewis and Clark Middle School
Tulsa, Oklahoma

Linda Sandersen
Greenfield Middle School
Greenfield, Wisconsin

Mary E. Solan
Southwest Middle School
Charlotte, North Carolina

Mary Stewart
University of Tulsa
Tulsa, Oklahoma

Paul Swenson
Billings West High School
Billings, Montana

Thomas Vaughn
Arlington High School
Arlington, Massachusetts

Susan C. Zibell
Central Elementary
Simsbury, Connecticut

Safety Reviewers

W. H. Breazeale, Ph.D.
Department of Chemistry
College of Charleston
Charleston, South Carolina

Ruth Hathaway, Ph.D.
Hathaway Consulting
Cape Girardeau, Missouri

Douglas Mandt, M.S.
Science Education Consultant
Edgewood, Washington

Activity Field Testers

Nicki Bibbo
Witchcraft Heights School
Salem, Massachusetts

Rose-Marie Botting
Broward County Schools
Fort Lauderdale, Florida

Colleen Campos
Laredo Middle School
Aurora, Colorado

Elizabeth Chait
W. L. Chenery Middle School
Belmont, Massachusetts

Holly Estes
Hale Middle School
Stow, Massachusetts

Laura Hapgood
Plymouth Community Intermediate School
Plymouth, Massachusetts

Mary F. Lavin
Plymouth Community Intermediate School
Plymouth, Massachusetts

James MacNeil, Ph.D.
Cambridge, Massachusetts

Lauren Magruder
St. Michael's Country Day School
Newport, Rhode Island

Jeanne Maurand
Austin Preparatory School
Reading, Massachusetts

Joanne Jackson-Pelletier
Winman Junior High School
Warwick, Rhode Island

Warren Phillips
Plymouth Public Schools
Plymouth, Massachusetts

Carol Pirtle
Hale Middle School
Stow, Massachusetts

Kathleen M. Poe
Fletcher Middle School
Jacksonville, Florida

Cynthia B. Pope
Norfolk Public Schools
Norfolk, Virginia

Anne Scammell
Geneva Middle School
Geneva, New York

Karen Riley Sievers
Callanan Middle School
Des Moines, Iowa

David M. Smith
Eyer Middle School
Allentown, Pennsylvania

Gene Vitale
Parkland School
McHenry, Illinois

Contents

Animals

Reference Section

VIDEO

Enhance understanding through dynamic video.

Preview Get motivated with this introduction to the chapter content.

Field Trip Explore a real-world story related to the chapter content.

Assessment Review content and take an assessment.

Get connected to exciting Web resources in every lesson.

SciLinks NSTA Find Web links on topics relating to every section.

Active Art Interact with selected visuals from every chapter online.

Planet Diary® Explore news and natural phenomena through weekly reports.

Science News® Keep up to date with the latest science discoveries.

Experience the complete textbook online and on CD-ROM.

Activities Practice skills and learn content.

Videos Explore content and learn important lab skills.

Audio Support Hear key terms spoken and defined.

Self-Assessment Use instant feedback to help you track your progress.

B • vii

Activities

Lab zone™ Chapter Project — Opportunities for long-term inquiry

Lab zone Discover Activity — Exploration and inquiry before reading

Lab zone Try This Activity — Reinforcement of key concepts

Lab zone Skills Activity — Practice of specific science inquiry skills

Lab zone Labs — In-depth practice of inquiry skills and science concepts

Lab zone At-Home Activity — Quick, engaging activities for home and family

• Tech & Design • — Design, build, test, and communicate

Math — Point-of-use math practice

active art — Illustrations come alive online

B • ix

Careers in Science

An Alligator's Sensitive Side

Inquiry and Vocabulary

Biologist Dr. Daphne Soares currently works at the University of Maryland. She studies the nervous system of animals and how the structure of the nervous system affects an animal's behavior and its ability to survive in the wild. By reading about her work with alligators, students can gain insights about how Dr. Soares investigates animal behavior and the lab work involved in her investigations, including setting up experiments and testing hypotheses. The skills that Dr. Soares uses every day are the same inquiry skills that students need to become successful young scientists.

Build Background Knowledge

Knowledge about Alligators Have students write *What I Know about Alligators* on the top of a sheet of paper. Give them five minutes to record whatever facts and information they know or think they know about alligators. At the end of the five minutes, have students share the items on their lists. Make a cumulative list on the board.

Introduce the Career

Before students read the features, direct them to read the title and to look at the pictures of the animals on these pages. Ask: **What questions came to mind as you looked at the pictures?** *(Sample answers: Why does an alligator have claws? How are the owl and the alligator related? How do alligators float on water?)* Point out that just as students had questions about the animals they observed, scientists too have questions about animals they observe. Tell students that biologists are scientists that study living organisms.

Careers in Science

An Alligator's Sensitive Side

The first time biologist Daphne Soares got really close to an adult alligator was in a Louisiana swamp. She was bouncing around in the back of a pickup truck, helping to hold down an eight-foot American alligator. She was with a team of scientists doing fieldwork to learn how to protect alligators and their habitat. At the time, she was more curious than frightened.

"I was so interested in how alligators interact with the world around them," she remembers. "Why do these animals float half in and half out of the water? When I stick a branch in the water, why do they come toward it?" she wondered.

Daphne studies how the structure of an animal's nervous system influences its behavior and helps it survive. "When I got very close to the alligator in the back of that truck, I saw that its face was covered with little black dots. I thought, 'I wonder what those dots are.'" That simple question led her to make a surprising new discovery about why alligators are such good hunters.

Daphne in her lab

Career Path

Daphne Soares was born in Brazil. She received a Ph.D. in biology from the University of Maryland. Her investigation of the sensory dots of alligators began while she was still a university student. Currently, she holds a research position at the University of Maryland. Her plans for the future include becoming a university professor and doing more research on crocodilians.

Background

Facts and Figures Biology is the study of living organisms and their relationship with the environment. Many biologists specialize in some area of biology, including ecology, botany, zoology, cell biology, microbiology, anatomy, and genetics. Within each field, biologists can specialize in specific areas.

Many biological scientists work in research and development. Their work may involve finding new drugs, increasing crop yields, or cleaning up the environment. Biologists also work in managerial positions, where they may plan and administer programs, such as those for testing foods, or direct activities at zoos. Some work as consultants to business firms or government. Today many biologists are involved in biotechnology, such as those who worked on the Human Genome Project.

Daphne's study of the brains of barn owls led to her study of crocodilians, the closest living relatives of owls and other birds.

Talking With Dr. Daphne Soares

How did you get interested in science?

I grew up on a horse farm in Brazil. Living on the farm made me curious about how animals interact with their environment. Later, while attending university in the United States, I became interested in the nervous systems of animals. One of the first animals I studied was the barn owl. These birds can hear so well they can locate a mouse in the dark, just by listening. I wanted to know how barn owls developed such a fine sense of hearing.

What led you to study alligators?

I wanted to compare the brains of owls and other birds to the brains of their closest living relatives, a group of reptiles called crocodilians. The crocodilians include alligators and crocodiles. By comparing the nervous systems of birds and crocodilians, you can look for things they have in common. This can tell you what is most important in the development of sensory systems like hearing, vision, or touch.

How did you begin your study of alligator dots?

I went to the library. By reading books and scientific journals, I learned that people had noticed the dots before and thought they were probably some kind of sense organ. They could have been smell detectors or taste buds. But no one knew for certain what the dots did for the alligator.

Alligators float partly above and partly below the waterline.

B ◆ 1

Explore the Career

Choose from among the teaching strategies on these pages as you help your students explore the practical application of inquiry skills.

Discuss After students read the information on this page about Dr. Soares, ask: **What traits does Dr. Soares have that might make her a good scientist?** *(Sample answers: She is curious; she searches for answers.)* **What led to her to study alligators?** *(She wanted to compare the brains of birds and crocodilians.)* **What step did she take to begin her search for information?** *(She read books and journals to find out what people already knew about alligators.)*

Use Maps Use a map to show where alligators live in the United States: Alabama, Arkansas, North Carolina, South Carolina, Florida, Georgia, Louisiana, Mississippi, Oklahoma, and Texas. Ask: **What is similar about these areas that make them appropriate for alligators?** *(These areas have warm winters and contain wetlands, allowing alligators to survive.)*

Connect Culture Early in the 20th century, many alligators were hunted for their skin, which provided hunters with a high-quality leather. This led to a severe population decrease. However, recent conservation efforts have led to an increase in alligator population. Now, some human populations are living on the edge of alligator populations, which has caused problems, but captive and wild sustainable harvest programs are helping to monitor alligator numbers while keeping human populations safe.

Build Inquiry Skills

Dr. Soares' study of barn owl brains led her to study crocodilians, or specifically alligators. Ask: **In what ways might Dr. Soares use what she learned about barn owls to better understand alligators?** *(By understanding how a barn owl's nervous system works, she can make connections to how an alligator's nervous system works. She can make those connections because birds and crocodilians are close living relatives.)*

Research Interested students may want to investigate other reptiles or birds and how the development of their sensory systems, such as hearing, vision, or touch, help them hunt for and capture prey.

Background

Facts and Figures Alligators are reptiles that are mainly found in freshwater swamps and marshes, but can also be found in rivers, lakes, and smaller bodies of water. In the United States, alligators are found primarily in the Southeast. Adult males are typically 13 to 14 ½ feet long while females grow no longer than 10 feet long. Alligators have anywhere from 74 to 80 teeth. When they close their mouths, the upper jaw overlaps teeth in the lower jaw. Alligators eat a variety of food including insects, crabs, fish, frogs, turtles, snakes, birds, raccoons, and even deer. If an alligator is hungry enough, it will even eat carrion, or dead animals. Alligators most often feed during times when air temperatures are between 73°F and 90°F.

Discuss Before students read the information on this page about Dr. Soares's first experiment, discuss how nerves travel throughout an organism's body. Point out that information about the environment is detected by an organism's sensory nerves, such as those found in the eyes, ears, nose, skin, or mouth. This information is converted to electrical signals and sent to the brain for interpretation. Explain that scientists can detect the transmission of nerve impulses by using an electrode, which collects the electric signal. After students read about the experiment, ask: **How did Dr. Soares know when a nerve fired in an animal that was hooked up to the electrode apparatus?** *(She would hear a buzzing sound.)* **What happened when she used the electrode apparatus on the alligators?** *(Food, light, and heat near the dots on the alligator's face did not cause the buzzer to fire. When she made ripples in the water, the buzzer would sound.)* **What did she conclude from these observations?** *(The dots must be sensitive to changes in water pressure.)*

Use Visuals Show students photos of the Florida Everglades. Ask: **Why might it be difficult for a scientist to understand how an alligator's nervous system works if only observing them in this environment?** *(Conditions in a laboratory are more easily controlled. Because of all that is happening in the swamps, it would be difficult to isolate how exactly alligators become aware of their prey. In the laboratory, Dr. Soares was better able to test out the various senses used by the gator.)*

Discuss Ask: **What is it about Daphne's job that sounds interesting and exciting?** *(Daphne gets to study animals close up. She is able to observe them in their natural habitats and in her laboratory. As she tests her hypothesis, she must try to eliminate all possibilities that may lead to false understandings. Her work takes time, but once she figures out that her hypothesis is correct, she can feel a real sense of accomplishment.)*

? What was your first alligator experiment?

It was designed to find out whether the dots were connected to nerve cells. I put some red tracer dye on all the dots on the faces of a few baby alligators. This type of dye is picked up by nerve cells. If the dots were connected to nerves, then the dye would travel along the nerves to the brain. To my surprise, a lot of dye moved into the brain. The experiment proved that the dots are part of the alligator's nervous system. But it didn't tell me what kind of information is transmitted to the alligator's brain.

The dots that line an alligator's jaw are located where the surface of the water touches the alligator's face. They can detect and locate movements in the water.

? How did you discover what the dots are for?

I conducted another series of lab experiments. For each experiment, I put the small alligator to sleep, just as a veterinarian puts a dog or cat to sleep during surgery. Then I placed electrodes on nerves coming from some of the sensory dots. Whenever the nerves fired—sent a message to the brain—they created a tiny electric current. When this happened, I would hear a buzzing sound over an audio speaker I had hooked up.

I used this experimental setup with the electrodes in place to see what would cause those nerves to fire. I brought food near the spots, to see if the dots were like taste buds. I tried light to see if the spots acted like eyes. I even tried heat, to see if they were temperature sensors. Nothing worked!

One day I accidentally dropped a tool into the alligator's tank. The alligator was resting half in and half out of the water, as usual. When I stuck my hand in to get the tool out, I made ripples in the water. When the ripples reached the alligator's face, I heard a buzz on the speaker. I thought, "What's going on?" I realized that the dots must be sensitive to the changes in pressure that take place when they are hit by ripples of water.

Background

Integrating Science Alligators are an important part of the ecosystem in Florida, even though their numbers have declined in the 20th century. They build ponds called gator holes. These gator holes are not only home to alligators, but they provide a habitat for other animals of the wetlands. The nests that alligators build are also used by other species, such as the Florida Red-bellied turtle.

If you look at the skull of an alligator, you can see many tiny holes in the bone where some nerves run from the alligator's face to the brain.

Did you do any more experiments?

Oh yes, I wasn't finished yet. My hypothesis was that the dots tell the alligator where ripples in the water are coming from. To test that I was right, I had to make certain that alligators respond to ripples. Sure enough, whenever ripples in the tank reached the sensory dots, the alligator always moved toward the ripples.

I also had to rule out the possibility that the alligators were responding to sight or sound, rather than pressure changes. So I did the experiments again. I darkened the laboratory so the alligators couldn't see, and I blocked up their ears so they couldn't hear. And I got the same result. I was ready to announce my discovery. I had found a new kind of sense receptor in alligators!

How do the dots help alligators hunt?

Alligators feed on frogs, birds, and other animals that disturb the water when they come to drink or swim. The movements of these prey animals create ripples in the water. The dots detect the ripples and help the alligator locate the disturbance that caused them. I now call the dots "dome pressure receptors," because they are shaped like little domes. Along with keen eyesight and hearing, the dome pressure receptors help alligators capture prey.

What research are you working on now?

I am studying blind cavefish from Mexico, trying to learn whether they are blind from birth or lose their sight as they grow up. I'm also looking forward to more research on crocodilians. I want to find out how the genes of alligators with dome pressure sensors only on their faces differ from the genes of crocodilians that have pressure sensors all over their bodies.

Writing in Science

Career Link Suppose you are a reporter for a newspaper, radio, or a TV broadcast, and you've conducted this interview. Write several paragraphs about Daphne Soares, emphasizing how curiosity and accidental discoveries can play a role in a science career.

For: More on this career
Visit: PHSchool.com
Web Code: ceb-2000

Discuss Ask: **How did Dr. Soares use the information from her first experiments to continue her research?** *(She formed a hypothesis and then performed more experiments to eliminate other possible causes of the nerves firing.)* Point out that Dr. Soares was testing and eliminating other possible variables. Ask: **What variables did she test?** *(Sight and sound; she wanted to make sure that the reaction of the alligators was not due to sight or sound.)*

Research Have students work in small groups or pairs to research additional information about Mexico's blind cavefish.

Writing in Science

Writing Mode Description
Scoring Rubric
4 Includes detailed, accurate information; writing is organized and engaging
3 Includes all criteria but writing is uninteresting or disorganized
2 Includes most criteria; may be disorganized
1 Includes inaccurate, disorganized information

For: More on this career
Visit: PHSchool.com
Web Code: ceb-2000

Students can do further research on this career and others related to zoology.

The BIG Idea

The Big Idea is the major scientific concept of the chapter. It is followed by the Essential Question. Read aloud the question to students. As students study the chapter, tell them to think about the Essential Question. Explain that they will discover the answer to the question as they read. The chapter Study Guide provides a sample answer.

L3

Objectives

This project will give students an opportunity to pose questions about how to meet the needs of a particular animal by designing a suitable habitat for that animal. After completing this Chapter Project, students will be able to

- identify the important needs of an animal
- design and build a suitable habitat for the animal
- communicate their findings about the animal and its habitat requirements

Skills Focus

Observing, drawing conclusions, communicating

Project Time Line 3 to 4 weeks

All in One Teaching Resources

- Chapter Project Teacher Notes
- Chapter Project Overview
- Chapter Project Worksheet 1
- Chapter Project Worksheet 2
- Chapter Project Scoring Rubric

Safety

Review the Safety Guidelines in Appendix A. **CAUTION:** *Do not release animals used in this project outdoors after the conclusion of the project (unless they were obtained locally, in which case they can be returned to the location where they were collected). Otherwise, they should be returned to the pet store or supply house from which they were obtained, or kept as classroom pets. It is irresponsible to release animals into a new environment as it can disrupt the local flora and fauna or harm the released animal.*

Chapter 1 Sponges, Cnidarians, and Worms

The BIG Idea

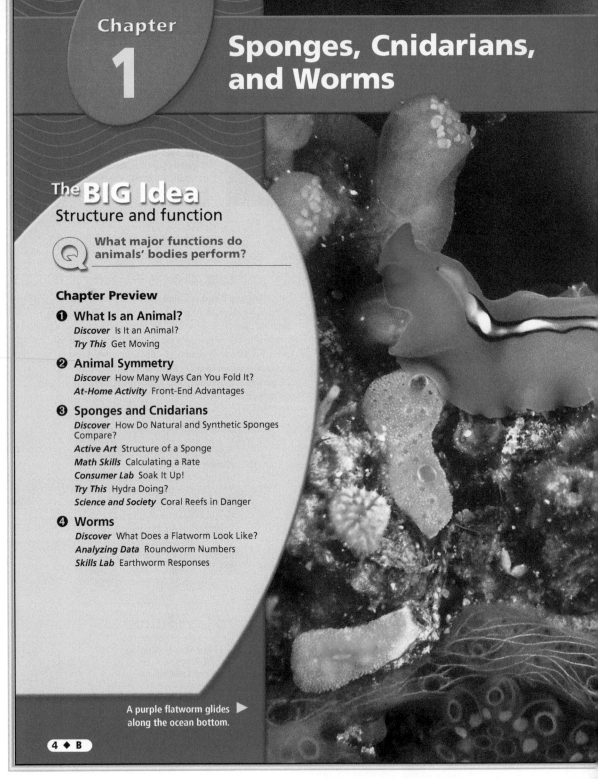

Structure and function

What major functions do animals' bodies perform?

Chapter Preview

1 What Is an Animal?
Discover Is It an Animal?
Try This Get Moving

2 Animal Symmetry
Discover How Many Ways Can You Fold It?
At-Home Activity Front-End Advantages

3 Sponges and Cnidarians
Discover How Do Natural and Synthetic Sponges Compare?
Active Art Structure of a Sponge
Math Skills Calculating a Rate
Consumer Lab Soak It Up!
Try This Hydra Doing?
Science and Society Coral Reefs in Danger

4 Worms
Discover What Does a Flatworm Look Like?
Analyzing Data Roundworm Numbers
Skills Lab Earthworm Responses

A purple flatworm glides along the ocean bottom.

Developing a Plan

Students choose their animals, design their habitats, and have their habitats ready for the animals to live in before obtaining their animals. Students can then place their animals in their habitats and observe the behaviors for one to two weeks.

Possible Materials

- Suitable project animals include snails, earthworms, pill bugs, spiders, millipedes, crickets, guppies, and anole lizards. Before students choose their animals, explain any school rules about live animals in the classroom, limitations on classroom storage space, and building conditions such as nighttime and weekend temperatures.

Chapter at a Glance

PRENTICE HALL TeacherEXPRESS™ Plan • Teach • Assess

Lab zone Chapter Project *Design and Build an Animal Habitat*

Technology | **Local Standards**

All in One **Teaching Resources**
- Chapter Project Teacher Notes, pp. 38–39
- Chapter Project Student Overview, pp. 40–41
- Chapter Project Student Worksheets, pp. 42–43
- Chapter Project Scoring Rubric, p. 44

Section 1

What Is an Animal?

2–3 periods
1–1 1/2 blocks

B.1.1.1 Describe levels of organization in animal bodies.
B.1.1.2 Identify four functions that enable animals to meet their basic needs.
B.1.1.3 Explain how animals are classified.

Section 2

Animal Symmetry

1–2 periods
1/2–1 block

B.1.2.1 Define symmetry.
B.1.2.2 Infer general characteristics of an animal based on its symmetry.

Section 3

Sponges and Cnidarians

4–5 periods
2–2 1/2 blocks

B.1.3.1 Identify the characteristics of sponges.
B.1.3.2 Describe the characteristics of cnidarians.
B.1.3.3 Explain the importance of coral reefs.

Section 4

Worms

3–4 periods
1 1/2–2 blocks

B.1.4.1 Identify the three main phyla of worms.
B.1.4.2 Describe the characteristics of each worm phylum.

Review and Assessment

Teaching Resources
- Key Terms Review, p. 79
- Transparency B12
- Performance Assessment Teacher Notes, p. 88
- Performance Assessment Scoring Rubric, p. 89
- Performance Assessment Student Worksheet, p. 90
- Chapter Test, pp. 91–94

Test Preparation

Test Preparation Blackline Masters

Chapter Activities Planner

For more activities

Student Edition	Inquiry	Time	Materials	Skills	Resources
Chapter Project, p.5	Open-Ended	3–4 weeks	All in One Teaching Resources See p. 38	Observing, drawing conclusions, communicating	Lab zone Easy Planner All in One Teaching Resources Support pp. 38–39
Section 1					
Discover Activity, p. 6	Guided	15 minutes	Crickets, earthworms, ferns, minnows, pill bugs, potted plants, or sponges	Forming operational definitions	Lab zone Easy Planner
Try This Activity, p. 9	Guided	15 minutes	Aluminum cans, drawing materials, modeling clay, paper, wire pipe cleaners	Making models	Lab zone Easy Planner
Section 2					
Discover Activity, p. 12	Guided	10 minutes	Circular object, pen or pencil, scissors, tracing paper	Classifying	Lab zone Easy Planner
Section 3					
Discover Activity, p. 15	Directed	20 minutes	Hand lens or microscope, natural sponges, scissors, synthetic kitchen sponges	Observing	Lab zone Easy Planner
Consumer Lab, p. 18	Directed	Prep: 20 minutes Class: 25 minutes	Piece of cellulose sponge, piece of natural sponge, piece of foam sponge, balance, bowl of tap water, graduated cylinder, beaker, paper towel	Observing, predicting, communicating	Lab zone Easy Planner Lab Activity Video All in One Teaching Resources Consumer Lab: *Soak It Up!*, pp. 66–67
Try This Activity, p. 19	Directed	25 minutes	Hand lens or microscope, live hydra, small glass bowl or petri dish, toothpicks	Classifying	Lab zone Easy Planner
Section 4					
Discover Activity, p. 26	Directed	15 minutes	Bottled water, hand lens, live planarian, plastic dropper, small paintbrush, small transparent container or petri dish	Observing	Lab zone Easy Planner
Skills Lab, p. 33	Directed	Prep: 20 minutes Class: 30 minutes	Plastic dropper, clock or watch, 2 earthworms, water, paper towels, storage containers, cardboard, flashlight, tray	Observing, interpreting data	Lab zone Easy Planner Lab Activity Video All in One Teaching Resources Skills Lab: *Earthworm Responses*, pp. 76–78

ABILITY LEVELS
- L1 Basic to Average
- L2 For All Students
- L3 Average to Advanced

Section 1 What Is an Animal?

 *2–3 periods, 1–1 1/2 blocks*

Objectives

B.1.1.1 Describe levels of organization in animal bodies.
B.1.1.2 Identify four functions that enable animals to meet their basic needs.
B.1.1.3 Explain how animals are classified.

Local Standards

Key Terms

• cell • tissue • organ • adaptation • sexual reproduction • fertilization
• asexual reproduction • phylum • vertebrate • invertebrate

Preteach

Build Background Knowledge

Use student sketches to help students identify characteristics of animals.

 *Is It an Animal?* L1

Targeted Print and Technology Resources

All in One Teaching Resources
- L2 Reading Strategy Transparency B1: Asking Questions

Instruct

Structure of Animals Define the levels of organization in animals and prompt students to cite examples of each.

Functions of Animals Ask leading questions for a discussion on how different kinds of animals meet their basic needs.

Classification of Animals Use diagrams to show how animals are classified and how different animals are related.

Targeted Print and Technology Resources

All in One Teaching Resources
- L2 Guided Reading, pp. 47–50
- L2 Transparencies B2, B3

www.SciLinks.org Web Code: scn-0211

Student Edition on Audio CD

Assess

Section Assessment Questions

Have students use their Asking Questions graphic organizer to help answer the questions.

Reteach

Use photos of animals to review animals' features.

Targeted Print and Technology Resources

All in One Teaching Resources
- Section Summary, p. 46
- L1 Review and Reinforce, p. 51
- L3 Enrich, p. 52

Section 2 Animal Symmetry

 *1–2 periods, 1/2–1 block*

ABILITY LEVELS
L1 Basic to Average
L2 For All Students
L3 Average to Advanced

Objectives

B.1.2.1 Define symmetry.
B.1.2.2 Infer general characteristics of an animal based on its symmetry.

Key Terms

• bilateral symmetry • radial symmetry

Local Standards

Preteach

Build Background Knowledge

Separate objects into those that exhibit symmetry and those that do not.

 *How Many Ways Can You Fold It?* L1

Targeted Print and Technology Resources

All in One Teaching Resources

L2 Reading Strategy Transparency B4: Comparing and Contrasting

PresentationExpress™ CD-ROM

Instruct

The Mathematics of Symmetry Contrast bilateral and radial symmetry.

Symmetry and Daily Life Describe how the kinds of symmetry relate to animals' general characteristics.

Targeted Print and Technology Resources

All in One Teaching Resources

L2 Guided Reading, pp. 55–56

 Web Code: scn-0212

Student Edition on Audio CD

Assess

Section Assessment Questions

Have students use their Venn diagram on symmetry to help answer the questions.

Reteach

Ask leading questions to elicit from students examples of animals having radial, bilateral, and no symmetry.

Targeted Print and Technology Resources

All in One Teaching Resources

• Section Summary, p. 54
L1 Review and Reinforce, p. 57
L3 Enrich, p. 58

Section 3 Sponges and Cidarians

 *4–5 periods, 2–2 1/2 blocks*

ABILITY LEVELS
L1 Basic to Average
L2 For All Students
L3 Average to Advanced

Local Standards

Objectives

B.1.3.1 Identify the characteristics of sponges.
B.1.3.2 Describe the characteristics of cnidarians.
B.1.3.3 Explain the importance of coral reefs.

Key Terms

• larva • cnidarian • polyp • medusa • colony • coral reef

Preteach

Build Background Knowledge

Question students about the features of sponges.

 *How Do Natural and Synthetic Sponges Compare?* L1

Targeted Print and Technology Resources

L2 Reading Strategy Transparency B5: Comparing and Contrasting

PresentationExpress™ CD-ROM

Instruct

Sponges Use diagrams to identify the parts of a sponge and the stages of sponge reproduction.

Cnidarians Use diagrams to show how body structure governs cnidarian movement and food gathering.

Life in a Colony Discuss the characteristics of animals that live in colonies.

 *Soak It Up!* L2

Targeted Print and Technology Resources

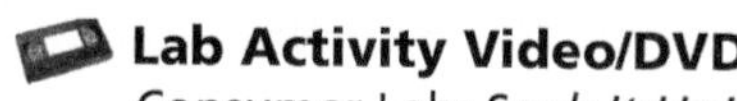

L2 Guided Reading, pp. 61–63
L2 Transparencies B6, B7, B8
L2 Consumer Lab: *Soak It Up!*, pp. 66–67

Lab Activity Video/DVD
Consumer Lab: *Soak It Up!*

PHSchool.com Web Code: cep-2013

Discovery Channel School Video Field Trip

PHSchool.com Web Code: ceh-2010

Student Edition on Audio CD

Assess

Section Assessment Questions

Have students use their table comparing sponges and cnidarians to answer the questions.

Reteach

Use figures to review structures involved in the reproduction of sponges.

Targeted Print and Technology Resources

• Section Summary, p. 60
L1 Review and Reinforce, p. 64
L3 Enrich, p. 65

Section 4 Worms

 *3–4 periods, 1 1/2–2 blocks*

ABILITY LEVELS
L1 Basic to Average
L2 For All Students
L3 Average to Advanced

Objectives

B.1.4.1 Identify the three main phyla of worms.
B.1.4.2 Describe the characteristics of each worm phylum.

Key Terms

• parasite • host • free-living organism • scavenger • anus • closed circulatory system

Local Standards

Preteach

Build Background Knowledge

Use examples of familiar experiences with worms to discuss the characteristics of worms.

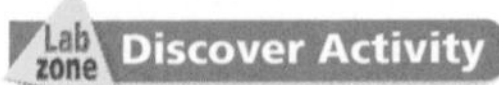 *What Does a Flatworm Look Like?* L1

Targeted Print and Technology Resources

Teaching Resources

L2 Reading Strategy Transparency B9: Using Prior Knowledge

PresentationExpress™ CD-ROM

Instruct

Characteristics of Worms Use photographs to identify body shapes of three worm phyla.

Flatworms Use a diagram to identify host and parasite in a tapeworm life cycle.

Roundworms Ask leading questions to discuss the importance of one-way digestion.

Segmented Worms Note where different organs are found in a segmented worm.

 Skills Lab *Earthworm Responses* L2

Targeted Print and Technology Resources

All in One Teaching Resources

L2 Guided Reading, pp. 70–73
L2 Transparencies B10, B11
L2 Skills Lab: *Earthworm Responses*, pp. 76–78

Lab Activity Video/DVD
Skills Lab: *Earthworm Responses*

PHSchool.com Web Code: ced-2014

Student Edition on Audio CD

Assess

Section Assessment Questions

Have students use their Using Prior Knowledge graphic organizers to answer the questions.

Reteach

Use pictures to compare and contrast the three worm phyla.

Targeted Print and Technology Resources

All in One Teaching Resources

• Section Summary, p. 69
L1 Review and Reinforce, p. 74
L3 Enrich, p. 75

Chapter 1 Content Refresher

Section 1 What Is an Animal?

Movement A defining characteristic of animals is that they are heterotrophs, organisms that acquire nutrients by consuming other organisms. In order to feed, most animals must move, and to move, animals must overcome two forces —gravity and friction.

The particular adaptations for movement depend on which of the three media—air, land, or water—the animal is moving in. Animals encounter less friction in air than in water. However, water provides buoyancy and thereby reduces the effect of gravity. Animals that fly have adaptations, such as wings, for overcoming gravity. They also tend to be less massive than animals that run. Aquatic animals tend to be streamlined, which reduces friction.

Overall, swimming requires the least energy for those animals that are adapted to an aquatic lifestyle. The amount of energy used is also related to the animal's size. Larger animals expend less energy per unit of body mass than do smaller animals—for example, elephants use less energy per unit mass than do dogs. Overall, however, elephants use much more energy than dogs because they are so much bigger.

Section 2 Animal Symmetry

Types of Symmetry There are three basic kinds of symmetry among living things—spherical, radial, and bilateral. Animals that lack these basic symmetries, such as sponges, are said to be asymmetrical. Spherical symmetry (not mentioned in the student text) is rare but may be observed in free-floating organisms, such as some protozoans. Amoebas become spherical at rest.

Some animals exhibit both radial and bilateral symmetry but at different stages in their life cycles. For example, echinoderms are radially symmetrical as adults, but the larvae are bilaterally symmetrical. The presence of bilateral symmetry in the larval stage is one characteristic that shows the relation between echinoderms and chordates.

Section 3 Sponges and Cnidarians

Coral Reef Ecology Coral reefs are the most productive ecosystems, even more productive than tropical rain forests, in terms of the amount of organic matter available for consumption. More productive ecosystems typically support longer food chains and thereby more species diversity.

Another factor that contributes to the enormous species diversity of coral reefs is the large number of habitats the reef supports. The coral reef skeleton provides a structure that supports the corals themselves. In addition, the coral reef provides a substrate for sponges, anemones, and other sessile (nonmoving, attached) organisms. These organisms attract dozens of fish species, including predators such as sharks and rays.

Corals contain symbiotic photosynthetic algae from which the coral obtains some of its nutrients. Corals can survive without the algae, though the rate at which the corals lay down reef is diminished. An increase in water temperature can cause the corals to expel their symbiotic algae and die. This fact is behind the well-known concern that coral reefs may be at risk from global warming.

Section 4 Worms

Germ Layers and Body Cavities As the embryos of most animals develop, they form three layers called germ layers. Each germ layer gives rise to specific organs and tissues. The ectoderm, which is the outermost layer, is the source of sense organs, nerves, and the outermost layer of the skin. The middle layer, which is called the mesoderm, produces the muscles and parts of the excretory, circulatory, and reproductive systems. The innermost germ layer, or endoderm, gives rise to the lining of the digestive tract as well as much of the respiratory system. The illustration shows a simplified version of how these germ layers are arranged in flatworms, roundworms, and segmented worms.

Address Misconceptions

Students may think that the skin disease ringworm is caused by a worm. Ringworm is caused by a fungus, which is in a different kingdom altogether from roundworms. For more on this misconception, see **Address Misconceptions** in the section *Worms.*

Body cavities also form during embryonic development. Flatworms have no body cavity other than the digestive cavity. In addition to the digestive cavity, roundworms have a body cavity called a pseudocoelom that is partly lined with tissue derived from mesoderm. Segmented worms, like animals in most complex animal phyla, have a true coelom, which is a fluid-filled body cavity completely lined with mesoderm. Body cavities are important because they provide a space in which organs and organ systems can be located.

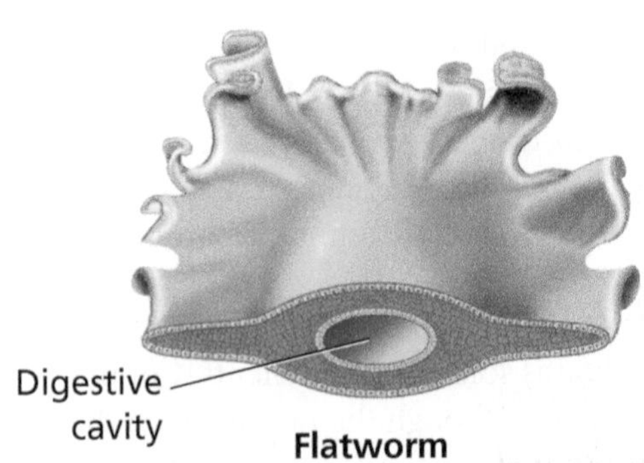

Flatworm

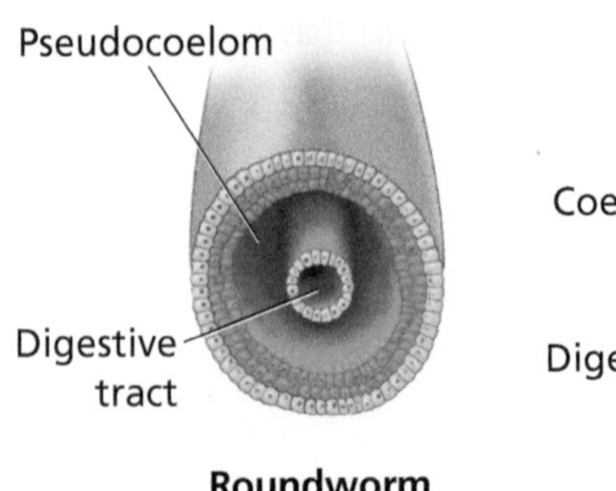

Roundworm

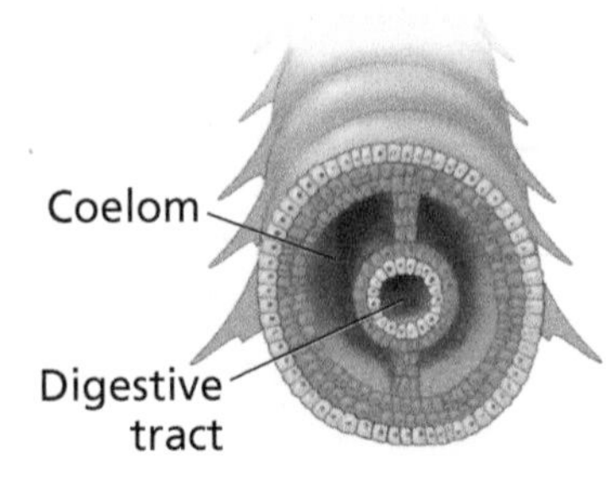

Segmented worm

Help Students Read

Previewing Visuals

Visualize Important Concepts While Reading

Strategy Help students understand and visualize the steps in a process, or the order in which events occur. Locate a figure showing a process that involves several steps, such as the diagrams of reproduction in sponges or cnidarians, or the tapeworm life cycle. Copy the figure and make blank cycle diagrams for students to fill in as they read the passage and study the diagram.

Example

1. First, have students read the passage and/or study the figure, thinking about what takes place first, second, third, and so on.
2. Point out that the text may sometimes use order words such as *next, then,* or *finally.*
3. Draw a cycle diagram on the board and have students tell the sequence while you write each part in a separate box.
4. Put students in groups and have them locate additional examples of sequential relationships in the chapter and depict them using graphic organizers.

Discovery Channel School

Sponges, Cnidarians, and Worms

▶ Video Preview
Video Field Trip
Video Assessment

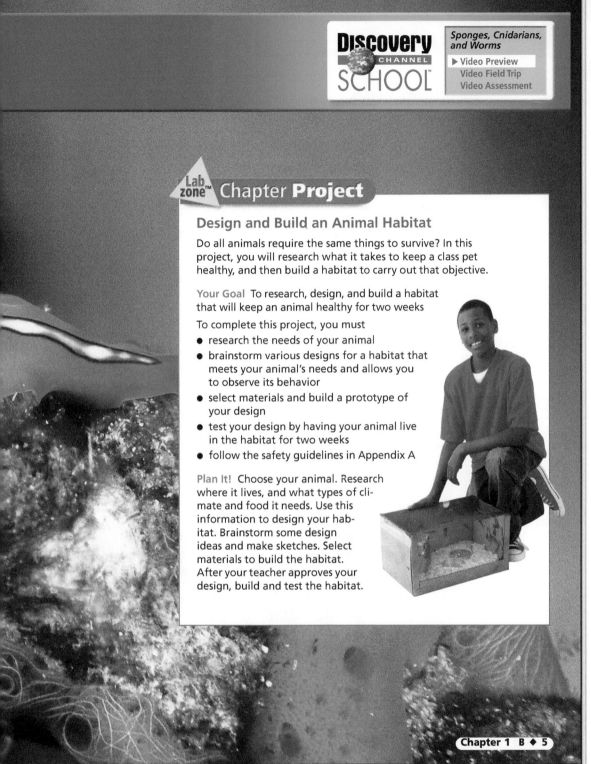

Lab zone™ Chapter **Project**

Design and Build an Animal Habitat

Do all animals require the same things to survive? In this project, you will research what it takes to keep a class pet healthy, and then build a habitat to carry out that objective.

Your Goal To research, design, and build a habitat that will keep an animal healthy for two weeks

To complete this project, you must

- research the needs of your animal
- brainstorm various designs for a habitat that meets your animal's needs and allows you to observe its behavior
- select materials and build a prototype of your design
- test your design by having your animal live in the habitat for two weeks
- follow the safety guidelines in Appendix A

Plan It! Choose your animal. Research where it lives, and what types of climate and food it needs. Use this information to design your habitat. Brainstorm some design ideas and make sketches. Select materials to build the habitat. After your teacher approves your design, build and test the habitat.

Sponges, Cnidarians, and Worms

Show the Video Preview to introduce cnidarians and overview the chapter content. Discussion question: **What substances make up the protective shells of polyps?** *(Calcium carbonate)*

Launching the Project

Bring an animal into the classroom. Ask: **What does this animal need to live?** *(Food, water, a place to live, a certain range of temperatures)* **Where could you find this information?** *(Possible answers: In the library, on the Internet, or in a pet store)* **What kinds of things do you think you can learn by watching this animal's behavior?** *(What the animal eats, how it moves, when it is active, where it stays in its habitat)*

Performance Assessment

The Chapter Project Scoring Rubric will help you evaluate how well students complete the Chapter Project. You may want to share the rubric with your students so that they will know what is expected of them. Students will be assessed on

- how well they plan for their animal's care
- how well they observe and record their animal's behavior
- the thoroughness and organization of their presentation
- how well they participate in their groups

Portfolio

- Leaves, vegetable trimmings, and insects are possible food sources. All habitats must have an adequate supply of water.
- A two-liter soft-drink bottle could serve as a terrarium for an insect. Cut off the top of the bottle, fill it with soil, leaf litter, and plants; then, cover the bottle with plastic wrap and cut holes in the wrap for ventilation.

Possible Shortcuts

- You may wish to choose the animal for the students, or keep one animal for the entire class and have student groups care for and observe it on different days.
- Have students observe the animals for only one week.

Section 1

What Is an Animal?

Objectives

After this lesson, students will be able to

B.1.1.1 Describe levels of organization in animal bodies.

B.1.1.2 Identify four functions that enable animals to meet their basic needs.

B.1.1.3 Explain how animals are classified.

Target Reading Skill

Asking Questions Explain that changing a head into a question helps students anticipate the ideas, facts, and events they are going to read about.

Answers

Possible student question and answers are these: **What is a cell?** *(A cell is the basic unit of structure and function in living things.)* **What is the structure of animals?** *(The cells of animals are organized into tissues, organs, and systems.)* **What are the functions of animals?** *(Animals must obtain food and oxygen, keep a stable environment within their bodies, reproduce, and move about to meet their needs.)* **How are animals classified?** *(Animals are classified according to how they are related to other organisms.)*

All in One Teaching Resources

- Transparency B1

Preteach

Build Background Knowledge L2

Defining an Animal

Ask: **What does an animal look like? How is it different from a flower or a tree?** *(Sample answer: An animal must eat other living things.)* Have students sketch an animal on a piece of paper and list three things that make it an animal. Lead students to realize that there is tremendous diversity among animals.

Section 1

What Is an Animal?

Reading Preview

Key Concepts

- How are animal bodies typically organized?
- What are four major functions of animals?
- How are animals classified?

Key Terms

- cell • tissue • organ
- adaptation
- sexual reproduction
- fertilization
- asexual reproduction
- phylum • vertebrate
- invertebrate

Target Reading Skill

Asking Questions Before you read, preview the red headings. In a graphic organizer like the one below, ask a *what* or *how* question for each heading. As you read, write the answers to your questions.

Structure of Animals

Question	Answer
What is a cell?	A cell is . . .

Lab zone Discover Activity

Is It an Animal?

1. Carefully examine each of the organisms that your teacher gives you.
2. Decide which ones are animals. For each organism, write down the reasons for your decision. Wash your hands after handling each of the organisms.

Think It Over

Forming Operational Definitions

Use your notes about each organism to write a definition of "animal."

Your parents may have told you not to eat with your fingers, but they probably never worried that you'd eat with your feet! But animals called barnacles do just that.

A barnacle begins life as a many-legged speck that floats in the ocean. After a while, it settles its head down on a hard surface and fixes itself in place. Then it builds a hard cone around its body. To feed, the barnacle flicks its feathery feet in and out of the cone, as shown below. The feet trap tiny organisms, or living things, that float in the water.

A barnacle may look like a rock, but it is actually an animal. Animals are many-celled organisms that feed on other organisms.

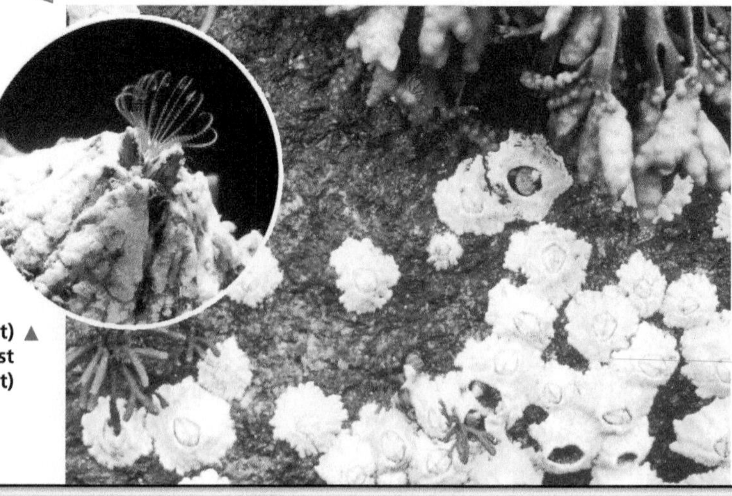

A barnacle feeding (inset) ▲ and many barnacles at rest (right)

Lab zone Discover Activity

Skills Focus Forming operational definitions L1

Materials crickets, earthworms, ferns, minnows, pill bugs, potted plants, or sponges

Time 15 minutes

Tips Make sure students record their observations while looking at the specimen. Remind students to treat all living things with care.

Expected Outcome Earthworms and minnows will be recognizable as animals; sponges may not.

Think It Over Students may note behavioral characteristics, such as eating, or physical features, such as mouths, hair, or legs.

Structure of Animals

Animals are composed of many cells. A **cell** is the basic unit of structure and function in living things. **The cells of most animals are organized into higher levels of structure, including tissues, organs, and systems.** A group of similar cells that perform a specific function is called a **tissue.** One type of tissue is nerve tissue, which carries messages in the form of electrical signals from one part of the body to another. Another type of tissue is bone tissue, a hard tissue that gives bones strength.

Tissues may combine to form an **organ,** which is a group of several different tissues. For example, a frog's thigh bone is composed of bone tissue, nerve tissue, and blood. An organ performs a more complex function than each tissue could perform alone.

Groups of structures that perform the broadest functions of an animal are called systems. One example of a system is the skeletal system of a frog shown in Figure 1.

Go Online SCI LINKS NSTA
For: Links on the animal kingdom
Visit: www.SciLinks.org
Web Code: scn-0211

Reading Checkpoint **What is an organ?**

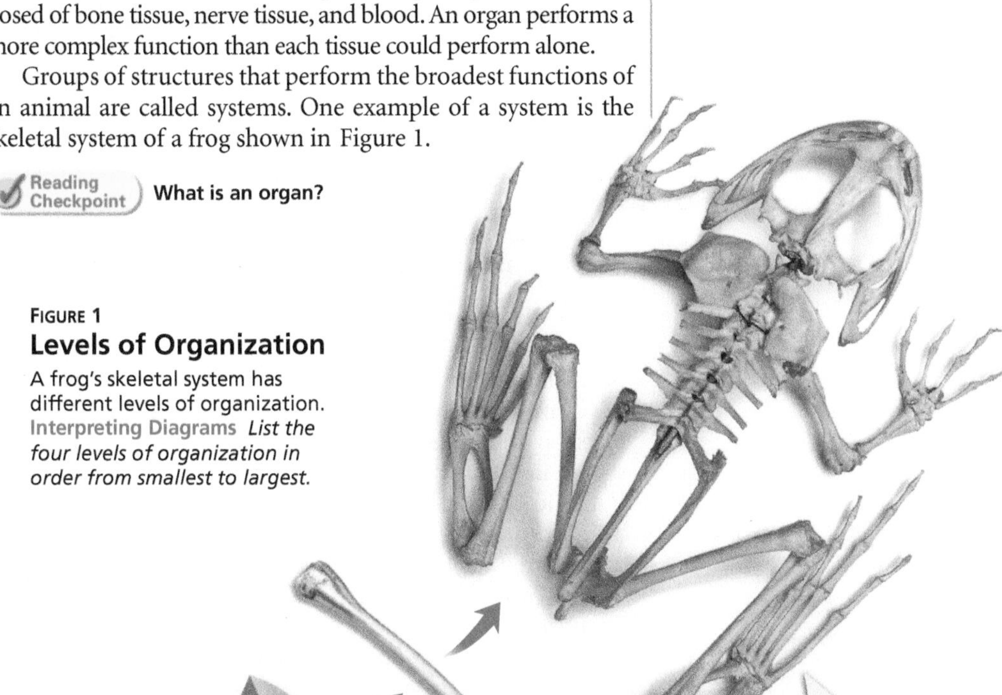

System
Together, all of the bones form the skeletal system.
Organ
A group of different kinds of tissues make up an organ such as the thigh bone.
Tissue
Many bone cells make up bone tissue.
Cells
Cells are the basic unit of animal structure.

FIGURE 1
Levels of Organization
A frog's skeletal system has different levels of organization.
Interpreting Diagrams *List the four levels of organization in order from smallest to largest.*

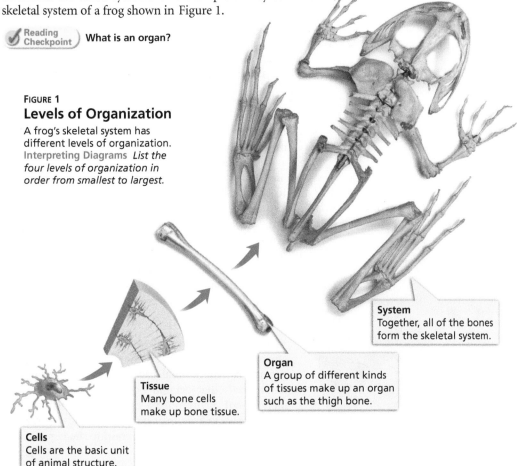

Instruct

Structure of Animals

Teach Key Concepts L1

Levels of Organization in Animals

Focus Tell students that the cells of most animals are organized into levels of structure, including tissues, organs, and systems.

Teach Point out the levels of organization in Figure 1. Ask: **What are cells?** *(Working units that carry out the basic activities of life)* **What are tissues made of?** *(Cells)* Stress that these levels of organization can be observed in nearly all animals with few exceptions (sponges and cnidarians, for example).

Apply Brainstorm with students examples of these levels of organization in different animals. Include as many animals and body systems as time allows. **learning modality: visual**

Independent Practice L2

 **Teaching Resources**

- Transparency B2
- Guided Reading and Study Worksheet: *What Is an Animal?*

Student Edition on Audio CD

Go Online SCI LINKS NSTA
For: Links on the animal kingdom
Visit: www.SciLinks.org
Web Code: scn-0211

Download a worksheet that will guide students' review of Internet sources on the animal kingdom.

Differentiated Instruction

Gifted and Talented L3

Observing Tissues Give students a chicken drumstick with the thigh still attached, a dissection kit, and hand lens. **CAUTION:** *Beforehand, soak chicken overnight in diluted bleach solution, and then rinse and store in the refrigerator. Have students wear disposable gloves and use dissecting probes and scalpels carefully. Tell students not to taste the chicken, put their hands in their mouths, or touch the chicken with their bare hands.* Ask them to disassemble, sketch, and count the muscles of the thigh and lower leg. Have students carefully slice through one of the larger muscles to make a cross section and then observe it with a hand lens. **learning modality: logical/mathematical**

Monitor Progress L2

Answers

Figure 1 cell, tissue, organ, system

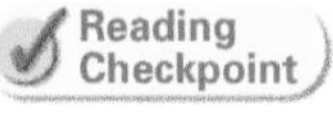 A group of several different tissues

Functions of Animals

Teach Key Concepts

L2

Classifying Animal Adaptations

Focus Tell students that all animals have the same basic needs.

Teach Review with students the major functions of animals: obtain food and oxygen, keep internal conditions stable, move, and reproduce. Ask: **What are adaptations?** *(Structures and behavior that enable an animal to perform basic functions in the environment)* **Why do animals need food?** *(To get energy for growth and body activities)* **Why must animals maintain a stable environment within their bodies?** *(If balance is lost, they will not survive long.)*

Apply Ask: **How do sexual and asexual reproduction differ?** *(Sexual reproduction involves two parents; asexual reproduction involves a singe organism.)* **learning modality: verbal**

L2

Inferring What an Animal Eats

Materials Pictures of animal jawbones showing the shapes of teeth

Time 15 minutes

Focus Tell students that tooth shape helps to determine diet.

Teach Give students several pictures to study. Have students describe the tooth shapes in the pictures. Ask: **What are sharp, pointed teeth adapted to do?** *(Tear skin or flesh)* **What are broad, flat teeth adapted to do?** *(Grind or shred plants)*

Apply Have students compare their own teeth and jaws to those in the pictures. Have them describe the characteristics of their teeth. *(Sample answer: Some of my front teeth are sharp and pointed; some of my teeth are broad and flat.)* Explain that humans are adapted to eating both meat and plants. **learning modality: visual**

Help Students Read

L1

Identifying Details As students read, have them make four index cards with one of the functions of animals on each card. While reading the section *Functions of Animals*, have students record on the back of each card characteristics that help animals to carry out each function.

FIGURE 2
Obtaining Food
This tarantula uses its fangs to kill a grasshopper.

Functions of Animals

From tiny worms to giant whales, animals are diverse. Animals vary not only in size but also in body structure, outward appearance, and the environments in which they live. Despite their diversity, however, all animals carry out the same basic functions. **The major functions of animals are to obtain food and oxygen, keep internal conditions stable, move, and reproduce.** Structures or behaviors that allow animals to perform these basic functions in their environments are called **adaptations.**

Obtaining Food and Oxygen An animal cannot make food for itself—it obtains food by eating other organisms. Animals may feed on plants, other animals, or a combination of plants and animals. They have adaptations that allow them to eat particular kinds of food. For example, the tarantula shown in Figure 2 has an adaptation called fangs—structures it uses to pierce other animals and suck up their juices.

Food provides animals with raw materials for growth and with energy for their bodies' activities, such as breathing and moving. Most animals take food into a cavity inside their bodies. Inside this cavity the food is digested, or broken down into substances that the animal's body can absorb and use. To release energy from food, the body's cells need oxygen. Some animals, like birds, get oxygen from air. Others, like fish, get oxygen from water.

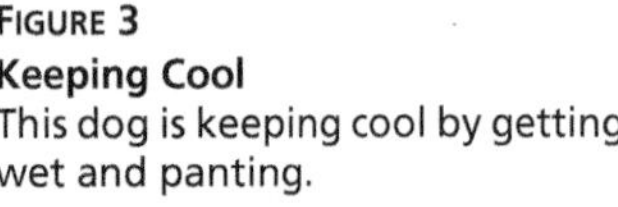

FIGURE 3
Keeping Cool
This dog is keeping cool by getting wet and panting.

Keeping Conditions Stable Animals must maintain a stable environment within their bodies. If this balance is lost, the animal cannot survive for long. For example, cells that get too hot start to die. Therefore, animals in hot environments are adapted, meaning they have adaptations, to keep their bodies cool. Earthworms stay in moist soil during hot days, lizards crawl to shady places, and dogs pant.

8 ◆ B

Differentiated Instruction

English Learners/Beginning L1

Link to Visual Use the photographs to help students understand the boldface sentence. Read the boldface sentence aloud, slowly, pointing to the appropriate photo as you recite the relevant phrase. For example, when you say "obtain food," point to the spider and grasshopper. Then pair beginners with students who are more proficient in English. Have the pairs discuss the Key Concept. **learning modality: visual**

English Learners/Intermediate L2

Link to Visual Do the same exercise that you did for beginners. However, instead of pairing students, have each student write, in English, sentences that explain how animals perform the functions. **learning modality: visual**

Movement All animals move in some way at some point in their lives. Most animals move freely from place to place throughout their lives; for example, by swimming, walking, or hopping. Other animals, such as oysters and barnacles, move from place to place only during the earliest stage of their lives. After they find a good place to attach, these animals stay in one place.

Animal movement is usually related to meeting the basic needs of survival and reproduction. Barnacles wave feathery structures through the water and trap tiny food particles. Some geese fly thousands of miles each spring to the place where they lay eggs. And you've probably seen a cat claw its way up a tree trunk to escape from a barking dog.

Reproduction Because no individual animal lives forever, animals must reproduce. Most animals reproduce sexually. **Sexual reproduction** is the process by which a new organism develops from the joining of two sex cells—a male sperm cell and a female egg cell. The joining of an egg cell and a sperm cell is called **fertilization.** Sperm and egg cells carry information about the characteristics of the parents that produced them, such as size and color. New individuals resulting from sexual reproduction have a combination of characteristics from both parents.

Some animals can reproduce asexually as well as sexually. **Asexual reproduction** is the process by which a single organism produces a new organism identical to itself. For example, animals called sea anemones sometimes split down the middle, producing two identical organisms.

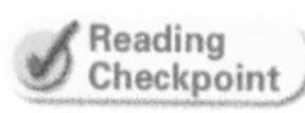
What is asexual reproduction?

Lab zone Try This Activity

Get Moving

Design an animal with a new and different way of moving. Your design should help your animal obtain food or get out of danger.

1. Make and label a drawing that shows how the animal would move.
2. Using clay, aluminum cans, construction paper, pipe cleaners, and whatever other materials are available, create a three-dimensional model of your animal.
3. Compare your animal to those of other classmates. What are some similarities? What are some differences?

Making Models What features of your design help your animal obtain food or escape danger?

FIGURE 4
Owl Family
Baby owls are produced by sexual reproduction. Classifying *Which kind of reproduction involves fertilization?*

Lab zone Build Inquiry L2

Modeling Feeding Adaptations

Materials birdseed, butter knife, cardboard tube (one-half of a paper towel tube or a toilet paper tube), chopsticks, masking tape, plastic dropper, plastic wrap, rubber band, tweezers

Time 15 minutes

Focus Identify some of the feeding adaptations of animals, for example, sticky structures, structures that spear or suck up food, jaws, and structures that filter nutrients from water.

Teach Seal one end of a cardboard tube with plastic wrap and the rubber band. Place about 2 centimeters of birdseed in the tube. Then, tape the sealed end of the tube to a table. Challenge students to find the best way to remove the birdseed using the remaining materials. Allow students to be creative, such as wrapping the knife in masking tape.

Apply Ask: **What real-life adaptations do students' solutions to the problem stand for?** *(Sample answer: The sticky masking tape is like a frog's tongue.)* **learning modality: kinesthetic**

Lab zone Try This Activity

Skills Focus Making models L2

Materials aluminum cans, drawing materials, modeling clay, paper, wire pipe cleaners

Time 15 minutes

Tips Encourage students to concentrate on the purposes of moving, such as obtaining food or avoiding danger.

Expected Outcome Models may resemble familiar animals with adaptations such as long limbs.

Extend Challenge students to design an animal with a new way of moving underwater. **learning modality: kinesthetic**

Monitor Progress L2

Writing Have each student choose an animal and write a description of its adaptations for feeding, protection, or reproduction. Students can save their presentation materials in their portfolios.

Answers

Figure 4 Sexual reproduction

Reading Checkpoint: Asexual reproduction is the process by which a single organism produces a new organism identical to itself.

Classification of Animals

Teach Key Concepts

L2

Classification Systems

Focus Tell students that classification systems are ways of organizing information reasonably and realistically.

Teach Ask: **What characteristics do scientists use to classify an animal?** *(How it looks, how it develops, and the content of its DNA)* **What can scientists tell about different groups of animals based on their classification?** *(Their relationship to each other)*

Apply Ask: **If scientists discover a new animal, how would they go about classifying it?** *(They would look at its characteristics to see if they are similar to a particular group of animals.)* **learning modality: verbal**

All in One Teaching Resources

- Transparency B3

Use Visuals: Figure 5

L1

Classifying Living Things

Focus Tell students that the figure shows one way to illustrate relationships among living things. The more closely related groups are, the closer together they will be in the diagram.

Teach Have students read aloud the names on the limbs of the tree. Some of the names will be unfamiliar to students. Tell students that they will learn more about these animals as they study this book.

Apply Ask: **Are insects more closely related to spiders or to mollusks?** *(Spiders)* **Which group probably arose earlier, crustaceans or echinoderms?** *(Echinoderms)* Continue in this fashion with other animal groups. **learning modality: visual**

Classification of Animals

Biologists have already identified more than 1.5 million species, or distinct types, of animals. Each year they discover more. Classifying, or sorting animals into categories, helps biologists make sense of this diversity. Biologists have classified animals into about 35 major groups, each of which is called a **phylum** (FY lum) (plural *phyla*). In Figure 5 you can see some animals from the largest phyla. Notice that the phyla are arranged like branches on a tree.

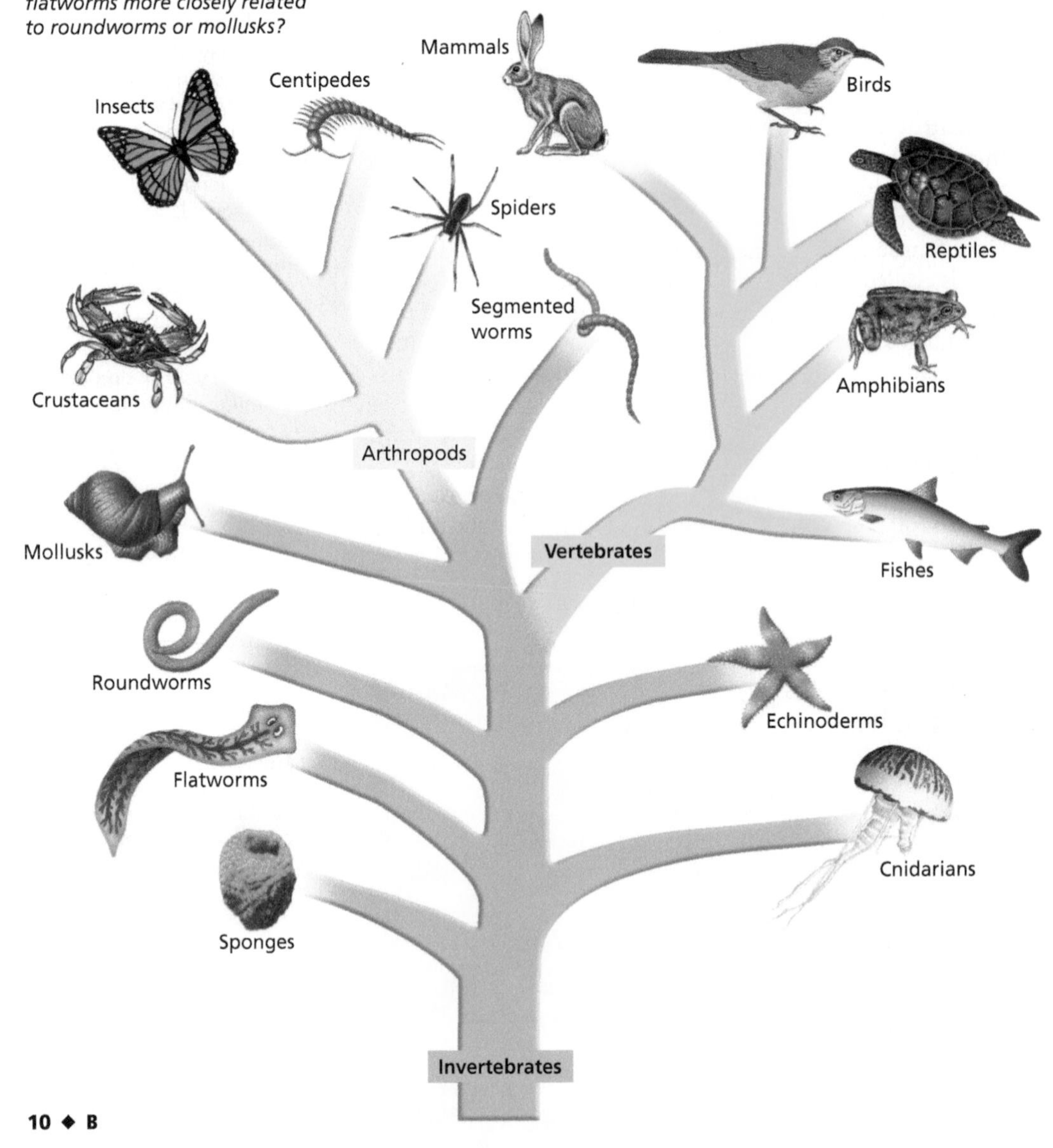

FIGURE 5
Major Animal Groups
This branching tree shows one hypothesis of how the major animal groups are related.
Interpreting Diagrams *Are flatworms more closely related to roundworms or mollusks?*

The branching pattern of the tree in Figure 5 shows how many biologists think the major groups of animals are related. For example, you can see that segmented worms are more closely related to arthropods than to sponges from their positions on the tree.

A branching tree can also show how biologists think animal life has evolved, or changed over time. This process has resulted in all the different phyla that exist today. Biologists do not know the exact way in which evolution took place. Instead, they can only make inferences on the basis of the best evidence available. Biologists hypothesize that all animals arose from single-celled ancestors.

Animals are classified according to how they are related to other animals. These relationships are determined by an animal's body structure, the way the animal develops, and its DNA. DNA is a chemical in cells that controls an organism's inherited characteristics. All **vertebrates,** or animals with a backbone, are classified in only one phylum. All the other animal phyla contain **invertebrates,** or animals without backbones. Of all the types of animals, about 97 percent are invertebrates!

What is a phylum?

FIGURE 6
Discovering New Species
This biologist is surveying the leaves of rain forest plants, looking for new insect species.

Section 1 Assessment

Target Reading Skill Asking Questions Use the answers to the questions you wrote about the headings to help you answer the questions below.

Reviewing Key Concepts

1. a. Defining What is the basic unit of structure and function in an animal?
   b. Sequencing Arrange in order from simplest to most complex structure: tissue, system, cell, organ.
2. a. Reviewing What are four major functions of animals?
   b. Summarizing How do animals obtain food?
   c. Drawing Conclusions Why is movement important for animals?
3. a. Defining What is a vertebrate?
   b. Classifying How do biologists classify animals?
   c. Interpreting Diagrams According to the branching tree shown in Figure 5, are reptiles more closely related to mammals or to fishes? Explain your answer.

Writing in Science

Functional Description Write a few paragraphs about how your classroom pet or a pet at home performs the basic functions of an animal.

Monitor Progress L2

Answers
Figure 5 Flatworms are more closely related to roundworms.

A phylum is one of the 35 major groups of animals.

Assess

Reviewing Key Concepts

1. a. Cell **b.** Cell, tissue, organ, system
2. a. Obtain food and oxygen, keep internal conditions stable, move, and reproduce
b. By eating other organisms **c.** Animals need to move to meet the basic needs of survival and reproduction.
3. a. Vertebrates are animals with backbones. **b.** Biologists classify animals according to their body structures, how they develop, and their DNA. **c.** Reptiles are more closely related to mammals. Reptiles are closer to mammals than to fishes on the diagram.

Reteach L1

Have each student observe a picture of an animal and choose two characteristics that could be used to classify it as an animal.

All in One Teaching Resources
- Section Summary: *What Is an Animal?*
- Review and Reinforce: *What Is an Animal?*
- Enrich: *What Is an Animal?*

Lab zone Chapter Project

Keep Students on Track Group students who have researched and planned habitats for the same kind of animal. Have students discuss plans for acquiring, housing, and caring for the animal. Verify that all students meet the planning requirements of the project and will be able to care for the needs of their animals. Then allow students to prepare the habitats. Check habitats for safety before allowing students to obtain animals.

Writing in Science

Writing Mode Description
Scoring Rubric
4 Includes an accurate and detailed description of all the basic functions the student was able to observe
3 Includes an accurate description and some details
2 Includes sufficient information but lacks details
1 Includes incomplete or inaccurate descriptions

Section 2
Animal Symmetry

Objectives
After this lesson, students will be able to

B.1.2.1 Define symmetry.

B.1.2.2 Infer general characteristics of an animal based on its symmetry.

Target Reading Skill
Comparing and Contrasting Explain that comparing and contrasting information shows how ideas, facts, and events are similar and different. The results of the comparison can have importance.

Answers

Radial symmetry—many lines of symmetry, no distinct front end, live in water, move slowly

Bilateral symmetry—one line of symmetry, halves that are mirror images, front end with sense organs, quick movement

Both—balanced arrangement of parts, perform all the basic life functions

All in One Teaching Resources
- Transparency B4

Preteach

Build Background Knowledge
L1

Observing Symmetry

Bring to class several objects, such as leaves, shells, keys, gloves, and scissors. Sort them into two groups—symmetrical and asymmetrical. Ask: **What characteristics were used to group the objects?** *(Possible answers: round or long and thin; irregular or regular)* After you introduce the section, make sure students understand you sorted the objects based on symmetry.

Section 2

Animal Symmetry

Reading Preview
Key Concepts
- What is symmetry?
- What can you infer about an animal based on its symmetry?

Key Terms
- bilateral symmetry
- radial symmetry

Target Reading Skill

Comparing and Contrasting
As you read, compare and contrast the characteristics of animals with bilateral symmetry and radial symmetry in a Venn diagram like the one below. Write the similarities where the circles overlap, and write the differences on the left and right sides.

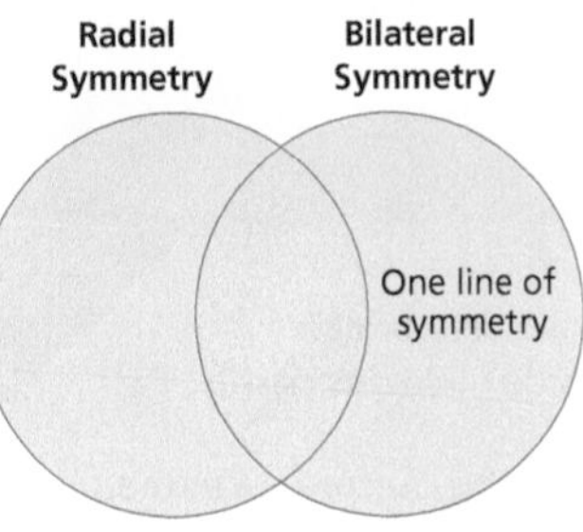

Lab zone Discover Activity

How Many Ways Can You Fold It?
1. Trace the triangle onto a sheet of paper and cut it out. Then draw a circle by tracing the rim of a glass or other round object. Cut out the circle.
2. Fold the triangle so that one half matches the other. Do the same with the circle.
3. See how many different ways you can fold each figure so that the two halves are identical.

Think It Over

Classifying Name an animal whose body shape can be folded in the same number of ways as the triangle.

Have you ever stopped to look at a butterfly perched on a flower? You probably noticed that bright colors and dark lines criss-cross its wings, making a pretty pattern. Did you also see that the pattern on the left side of the butterfly is a mirror image of the pattern on the right?

The Mathematics of Symmetry
As you can see from the photo of the butterfly in Figure 7, a butterfly's body has two halves. Each half looks like a reflection of the other. **This balanced arrangement of parts, called symmetry, is characteristic of many animals.** A butterfly's symmetry contributes to its pleasing appearance. But, more important, the balanced wings help the butterfly to fly easily.

FIGURE 7
Butterfly Halves
This butterfly's body has two mirror-image halves.
Applying Concepts *What is this balanced arrangement called?*

Lab zone Discover Activity

Skills Focus Classifying L1

Materials circular object, pen or pencil, scissors, tracing paper

Time 10 minutes

Tips Suggest that students first determine how many ways the triangle can be folded before they attempt to fold the circle.

Expected Outcome Students will conclude that the triangle can be folded one way into identical halves, and that the circle can be folded in an infinite number of ways.

Think It Over Students may say that the body shapes of butterflies, tigers, and dogs could be folded the same number of ways as a triangle. The body shapes of a sea urchin and jellyfish could be folded the same number of ways as a circle.

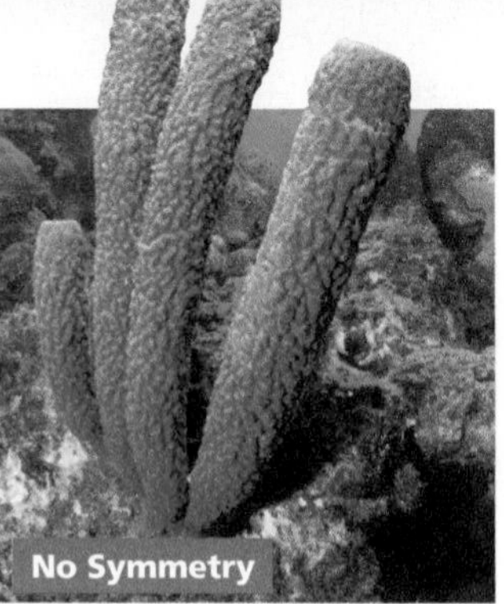

FIGURE 8
Types of Symmetry
Animals have either bilateral or radial symmetry, except for most sponges, which usually have no symmetry.

Animals have different types of symmetry, as shown in Figure 8. In the case of a fish, you can draw a line lengthwise down the middle of its body. This line is called a line of symmetry. An object has **bilateral symmetry** if there is just one line that divides it into halves that are mirror images. In contrast, objects with **radial symmetry** have many lines of symmetry that all go through a central point. For example, the sea star is circular if you look at it from the top. Any line drawn through its center can divide the sea star into two symmetrical halves. A few animals, such as most sponges, have no symmetry.

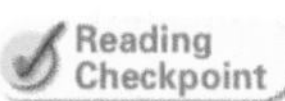
Reading Checkpoint **How many lines divide an animal with bilateral symmetry into halves?**

Symmetry and Daily Life

Animals without symmetry tend to have simple body plans. In contrast, the bodies of animals with bilateral symmetry or radial symmetry are complex. **Depending on their symmetry, animals share some general characteristics.**

Animals With Radial Symmetry The external body parts of animals with radial symmetry are equally spaced around a central point, like spokes on a bicycle wheel. Because of the circular arrangement of their parts, animals with radial symmetry, such as sea stars, jellyfishes, and sea urchins, do not have distinct front or back ends.

Animals with radial symmetry have several characteristics in common. All of them live in water. Most of them do not move very fast. They stay in one spot, are moved along by water currents, or creep along the bottom.

FIGURE 9
Radial Symmetry
The sea stars in this tide pool have radial symmetry.

Instruct

The Mathematics of Symmetry

Teach Key Concepts L2

Observing Symmetry

Focus Ask: **Can you identify a person by looking at either side of his or her face? Why?** *(Yes; both sides appear almost the same.)*

Teach Ask: **When does an object have bilateral symmetry?** *(When one line can divide it into halves that are mirror images)* **How does radial symmetry differ from bilateral symmetry?** *(An object with radial symmetry has many lines that go through a central point.)*

Apply Ask: **What is an example of an object with radial symmetry?** (Possible answer: a paper star) **learning modality: verbal**

Symmetry and Daily Life

Teach Key Concepts L2

Symmetry in Animals

Focus Tell students that symmetry can be observed in animals.

Teach Ask: **Why do animals with radial symmetry not have a front or back end?** *(Because their parts are arranged in a circle around a center)* **What are some characteristics of animals with radial symmetry?** *(Live in water; move slowly)*

Apply Ask: **What advantage is bilateral symmetry to a land animal?** *(It enables them to have sense organs in the front and to be streamlined, letting them move quickly yet be aware of what is in front.)* **learning modality: verbal**

Independent Practice L2

All in One **Teaching Resources**

- Guided Reading and Study Worksheet: *Animal Symmetry*

Student Edition on Audio CD

Monitor Progress L2

Answers

Figure 7 The balanced arrangement is called symmetry.

Reading Checkpoint One

Differentiated Instruction

Less Proficient Readers L1

Building Vocabulary/Word Analysis Point out that the word *bilateral* comes from Latin words meaning "two-sided." Ask students to list other English words that include the root *bi-* and discuss their meanings. *(Sample:* Bicycle *means "two-wheeled.")* Ask students to think of words similar to the word *radial. (Sample:* radius, radiation*)* Suggest that when students read the section, they look for a connection between these words and the definitions of *radial* and *bilateral symmetry*. **learning modality: verbal**

For: Links on animal symmetry
Visit: www.SciLinks.org
Web Code: scn-0212

Download a worksheet that will guide students' review of Internet sources on animal symmetry.

Monitor Progress L2

Answer

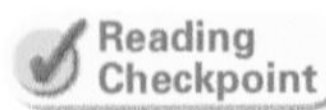
On their front ends

Assess

Reviewing Key Concepts

1. a. The balanced arrangement of parts in animals and other objects **b.** In both types of symmetry, there is a balanced arrangement of parts. In bilateral symmetry, there is only one line of symmetry. In radial symmetry, there are many. **c.** Bilateral symmetry. A grasshopper has a distinct front end and its body parts on one side (such as the legs) are a mirror image of those on the other side.

2. a. They have no distinct front end, live in water, and move slowly. **b.** They are larger and more complex, they have a front end, they move more quickly and efficiently than animals with radial symmetry, and they have sense organs in their front ends. **c.** Having sense organs in their front ends help bilaterally symmetrical animals obtain food and avoid predators.

Reteach L1

Write the words *bilateral symmetry, radial symmetry,* and *no symmetry* on the board. Ask students to call out names of animals for each category as you write them under the appropriate heading.

All in One Teaching Resources

- Section Summary: *Animal Symmetry*
- Review and Reinforce: *Animal Symmetry*
- Enrich: *Animal Symmetry*

Figure 10
Bilateral Symmetry
Animals with bilateral symmetry, like this tiger, have a front end with sense organs that pick up information.

Animals With Bilateral Symmetry Most animals you know have bilateral symmetry, including yourself! In general, animals with bilateral symmetry are larger and more complex than those with radial symmetry. They have a front end that typically goes first as the animal moves along. These animals move more quickly and efficiently than most animals with radial symmetry. This is partly because bilateral symmetry allows for a streamlined body. In addition, most animals with bilateral symmetry have sense organs in their front ends that pick up information about what is in front of them. For example, a tiger has eyes, ears, a nose, and whiskers on its head. Swift movement and sense organs help animals with bilateral symmetry obtain food and avoid enemies.

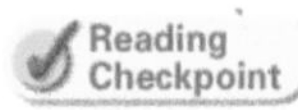
Where are the sense organs of an animal with bilateral symmetry typically found?

For: Links on animal symmetry
Visit: www.SciLinks.org
Web Code: scn-0212

Section 2 Assessment

Target Reading Skill Comparing and Contrasting
Use the information in your Venn diagram about symmetry to help you answer Question 1 below.

Reviewing Key Concepts

1. a. Reviewing What is symmetry?
   b. Comparing and Contrasting How are bilateral symmetry and radial symmetry alike? How are they different?
   c. Applying Concepts What kind of symmetry does a grasshopper have? Explain.
2. a. Identifying What general characteristics do animals with radial symmetry share?
   b. Summarizing What four body characteristics do animals with bilateral symmetry usually have?
   c. Making Generalizations How would having sense organs in front be helpful to an animal?

Lab zone At-Home Activity

Front-End Advantages With a family member, observe as many different animals as possible in a yard or at a park. Look in lots of different places, such as in the grass, under rocks, and in the air. Explain the advantages an animal with a distinct front end has. Tell the person what this type of body arrangement is called.

14 ◆ B

Lab zone At-Home Activity

Front-End Advantages L1 Direct students' attention to the paragraph that explains the advantages of having a distinct front end. Ask students to list these advantages. *(Animals move more quickly because of streamlined, balanced bodies. Sense organs in the front end pick up information about what is in front of the animal, such as food or predators.)* Suggest students show their lists to a family member when explaining bilateral symmetry. When observing animals at home, students can sketch the animals they see.

Section 3

Sponges and Cnidarians

Reading Preview

Key Concepts

- What are the main characteristics of sponges?
- What are the main characteristics of cnidarians?
- Why are coral reefs important?

Key Terms

- larva • cnidarian • polyp
- medusa • colony • coral reef

Target Reading Skill

Comparing and Contrasting As you read, compare and contrast sponges and cnidarians by completing a table like this one.

Sponges and Cnidarians

Feature	Sponge	Cnidarian
Body structure	Hollow bag with pores	
Cell type that traps food		
Method(s) of reproduction		

Lab zone Discover Activity

How Do Natural and Synthetic Sponges Compare?

1. Examine a natural sponge, and then use a hand lens or a microscope to take a closer look. Look carefully at the holes in the sponge. Draw what you see through the lens.
2. Cut out a small piece of sponge and examine it with a hand lens. Draw what you see.
3. Repeat Steps 1 and 2 with a synthetic kitchen sponge.

Think It Over

Observing What are three ways a natural and a synthetic sponge are similar? What are three ways they are different?

Eagerly but carefully, you and the others in your group put on scuba gear as you prepare to dive into the ocean. Over the side of the boat you go. As you descend through the water, you see many kinds of fishes. When you get to the bottom, you notice other organisms, too. Some are as strange as creatures from a science fiction movie. A few of these unusual organisms may be invertebrate animals called sponges.

Sponges don't look or act like most animals you know. In fact, they are so different that for a long time, people thought that sponges were plants. Like plants, adult sponges stay in one place. But unlike most plants, sponges take food into their bodies.

Sponges

Sponges live all over the world—mostly in oceans, but also in freshwater rivers and lakes. Adult sponges are attached to hard surfaces underwater. Water currents carry food and oxygen to them and take away their waste products. Water currents also play a role in their reproduction and help transport their young to new places to live.

◀ Diver investigating a barrel sponge

Section 3 Sponges and Cnidarians

Objectives

After this lesson, students will be able to

B.1.3.1 Identify the characteristics of sponges.

B.1.3.2 Describe the characteristics of cnidarians.

B.1.3.3 Explain the importance of coral reefs.

Target Reading Skill

Comparing and Contrasting Explain that comparing and contrasting information shows how ideas, facts, and events are similar and different. The results of the comparison can have importance.

Answers

Possible answers:

Sponge—hollow body with pores; collar cells; sexual and asexual

Cnidarian—polyp or medusa, central body cavity, tentacles; stinging cells; sexual and asexual

All in One Teaching Resources

- Transparency B5

Preteach

Build Background Knowledge

L2

Features of Sponges

Ask: **How are sponges used around the house?** *(Mopping floors, wiping up spills, washing dishes)* **What feature of sponges makes them useful?** *(They soak up liquids.)* Tell students that natural sponges were once live animals, and that divers have harvested sponges for thousands of years.

Lab zone Discover Activity

Skills Focus Observing L1

Materials hand lens or microscope, natural sponges, scissors, synthetic kitchen sponges

Time 20 minutes

Tips Provide students with sponge specimens. Direct students' attention to the pores on the sponge's surface. Tell them that pores in a natural sponge are the openings of pathways. In a synthetic sponge, the openings are not connected by regular pathways. Students can diagram natural and synthetic sponges and compare their features.

Expected Outcome Students will observe similarities and differences between natural and synthetic sponges.

Think It Over Both have pores, hold liquid, and are soft. They are different in material, color, texture, and shape.

Instruct

Sponges

Teach Key Concepts

L2

Sponge Structure and Function

Focus Have students study Figure 11.

Teach Ask: **How do pores help a sponge feed?** *(They allow water (food) into the sponge.)* **How do collar cells help a sponge feed?** *(They move water through the sponge and trap food.)*

For: Structure of a Sponge activity
Visit: PHSchool.com
Web Code: cep-2013

Students learn about a sponge and how it is dependent on water for survival.

All in One Teaching Resources

- Transparency B6

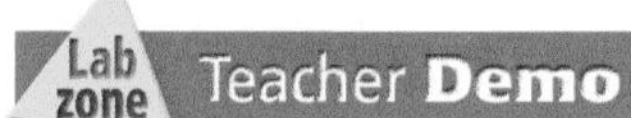

L2

Observing Sponge Spikes

Materials 50% bleach solution, binocular microscope, large jar, natural dried sponge

Time 10 minutes for setup, 1–2 days to complete demonstration

Focus Tell students that spikes are made of calcium carbonate (like chalk or limestone) or silicon dioxide (glass).

Teach Prepare 600 mL of bleach solution by pouring bleach into an equal amount of water. **CAUTION:** *Wear goggles and an apron.* Fill the jar with solution and place the sponge in the jar. Seal and let stand overnight. Carefully pour out the liquid making sure not to pour out the gel and spikes on the bottom. Place some gel under a microscope for students to observe.

Apply Have students draw the shapes they see. **learning modality: visual**

Independent Practice

L2

All in One Teaching Resources

- Guided Reading and Study Worksheet: *Sponges and Cnidarians*

Student Edition on Audio CD

For: Structure of a Sponge activity
Visit: PHSchool.com
Web Code: cep-2013

Body Structure **Sponges are invertebrate animals that usually have no body symmetry and never have tissues or organs.** A sponge looks something like a hollow bag with a large opening at one end and many tiny pores covering its surface. In fact, the name of the phylum to which sponges belong—phylum Porifera—means "having pores."

Look at Figure 11. A sponge's body has different kinds of cells and structures for different functions. For example, most sponges have spikes. The network of spikes throughout the sponge supports its soft body, keeping it upright in the water. The spikes also help a sponge defend itself against an animal that might eat it, which is called a predator. The spikes can be as sharp as needles. Even so, some fish eat sponges.

FIGURE 11
Structure of a Sponge
Structures surrounding the central cavity of a sponge are adapted for different functions. Interpreting Diagrams *Which kind of cell in the sponge digests and distributes food?*

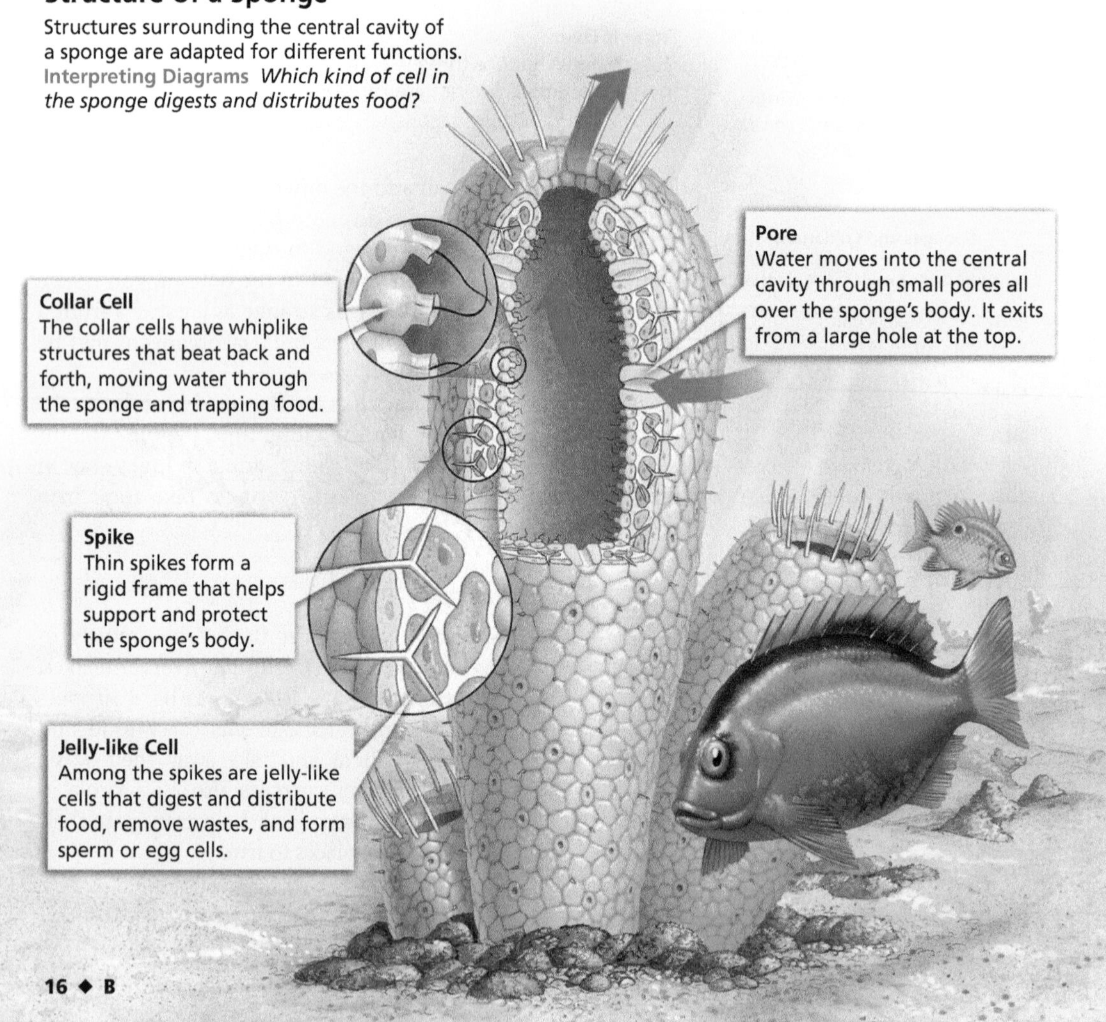

Collar Cell
The collar cells have whiplike structures that beat back and forth, moving water through the sponge and trapping food.
Pore
Water moves into the central cavity through small pores all over the sponge's body. It exits from a large hole at the top.
Spike
Thin spikes form a rigid frame that helps support and protect the sponge's body.
Jelly-like Cell
Among the spikes are jelly-like cells that digest and distribute food, remove wastes, and form sperm or egg cells.

Differentiated Instruction

Special Needs L1

Interpreting Visuals As students examine Figure 11, make sure they understand that the enlargement feature on the diagram helps them to better see the collar cells and spikes. Have students note the arrows and describe what they indicate. *(The path of water through a sponge)* **learning modality: visual**

FIGURE 12
Reproduction of a Sponge
The sexual reproduction of sponges involves a larval stage that moves. Adult sponges stay in one place.

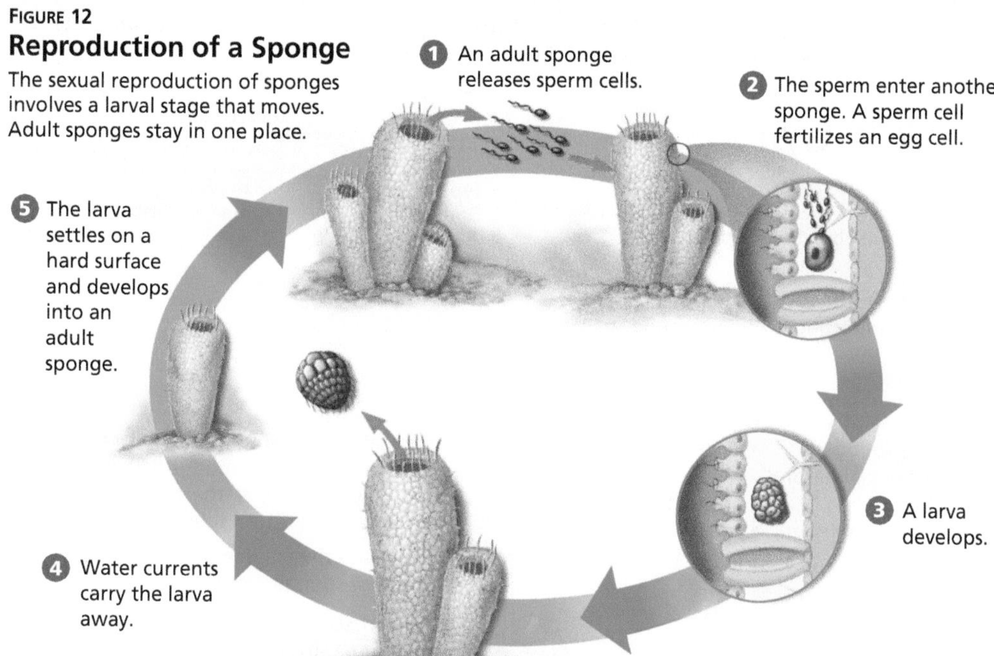

1 An adult sponge releases sperm cells.
2 The sperm enter another sponge. A sperm cell fertilizes an egg cell.
3 A larva develops.
4 Water currents carry the larva away.
5 The larva settles on a hard surface and develops into an adult sponge.

Obtaining Food and Oxygen A sponge eats tiny single-celled organisms. The sponge filters these organisms from the water moving through it. The collar cells that line the central cavity trap the tiny organisms. Jelly-like cells inside the sponge then digest, or break down, the food. Larger sponges can filter thousands of liters of water per day!

A sponge gets its oxygen from water, too. After the water moves through a sponge's pores, it passes over cells inside the sponge. Oxygen in the water then moves into the sponge's cells.

Reproduction Sponges reproduce both asexually and sexually. Budding is one form of asexual reproduction in sponges. In budding, small new sponges grow from the sides of an adult sponge. Eventually, the buds break free and begin life on their own.

Sponges reproduce sexually, too, but they do not have separate sexes. A sponge produces both sperm cells and egg cells. The sperm cells are released into the water. They enter another sponge and fertilize its eggs, as shown in Figure 12. After fertilization, a larva develops. A **larva** (plural *larvae*) is an immature form of an animal that looks very different from the adult.

Reading Checkpoint **What is a larva?**

Math Skills

Calculating a Rate
To calculate the rate of water flow in a sponge, divide the volume of water that the sponge filters by the time it takes the water to pass through the sponge.

$$\text{Flow rate} = \frac{\text{Volume of water}}{\text{Time}}$$

For example, a marble-sized sponge filters 15.6 liters of water in a day. How many liters does it filter per hour?

$$\frac{15.6 \text{ L}}{24 \text{ h}} = 0.65 \text{ L/h}$$

Practice Problem In 4 days, a sponge filters 1,200 L. What is its rate of water flow per day?

Math Skills Calculating a Rate

Focus Tell students they will divide volume by time to get a rate in liters per hour.

Teach Remind students that it is often necessary to use conversions to find rates. In the example, days must be converted to hours. Then, divide volume by time to get the rate.

Answers
300 L/day

Lab zone Build Inquiry L2

Diffusion in Sponges

Materials clock or watch, food coloring, large plastic beaker, plastic dropper, water

Time 20 minutes

Focus Explain to students that diffusion is movement of a material from an area of higher concentration to an area of lower concentration.

Teach Have student groups fill a beaker three-quarters full of water and allow the water to stand for 2 minutes. Then, put eight drops of food coloring into the water. Ask: **What does the food coloring look like as it enters the water?** *(It is dark and concentrated.)* Have students observe the water every 2 minutes over a 10-minute period. Ask: **What happened to the food coloring?** *(It spread evenly through the water.)*

Apply Tell students the way the food coloring spreads through the water is diffusion, and is similar to the way oxygen in water diffuses into a sponge's cells. **learning modality: kinesthetic**

All in One Teaching Resources
- Transparency B7

Monitor Progress L2

Oral Presentation Ask students to compare and contrast the pores and large opening at the top of a sponge. *(Water enters the sponge through the pores and exits through the larger opening.)*

Answers

Figure 11 Jelly-like cells

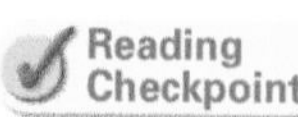
Reading Checkpoint An immature form of an animal that looks very different from the adult

Lab zone **Consumer Lab**

Soak It Up! L2

Prepare for Inquiry

Key Concept
Natural and artificial sponges can be compared for their ability to absorb water.

Skills Objectives
After this lab, students will be able to
- observe which sponge absorbed the most water
- predict how a change in a sponge's mass would affect the absorption of water
- communicate a recommendation to consumers

Prep Time 20 minutes
Class Time 25 minutes

Advance Planning
Buy sponges and soak them in water. Just prior to the lab, squeeze all the excess water out of the sponges so that they are still damp, but so that no water drips from them.

Safety 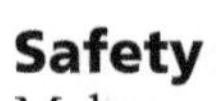 
Make sure students wipe up any spills.

All in One Teaching Resources
- Lab Worksheet: *Soak It Up!*

Guide Inquiry

Invitation
What type of sponge is best absorbing spilled liquids? Show several types of sponges.

Introduce the Procedure
Before students begin, have them carefully examine all three types of sponges to compare their structures.

Troubleshooting the Experiment
Make sure students do not squeeze sponges as they remove them from the bowls. Also make sure that when students remove each sponge from the water, they place it in the beaker as quickly as possible to minimize how much absorbed water drips back into the bowl.

Expected Outcome
The foam sponge will hold more water.

Lab zone **Consumer Lab**

Soak It Up!

Problem
Which sponge absorbs the most water?

Skills Focus
observing, predicting, communicating

Materials
- damp piece of cellulose sponge
- damp piece of natural sponge
- damp piece of foam sponge
- balance
- large bowl of tap water
- graduated cylinder
- beaker
- paper towel

Procedure  
1. Copy the data table on a separate sheet.
2. Examine the size of the pores in each sponge. Record your observations.
3. Make a prediction about which sponge will absorb the most water. Record your prediction and give a reason.
4. Place a damp piece of cellulose sponge on a balance and measure its mass. Record the mass in the data table. Remove the sponge from the balance.
5. Repeat Step 4 with the natural sponge and then the foam sponge.
6. Submerge the cellulose sponge in a bowl of water. Squeeze it several times to remove all air bubbles. Release the sponge and let it absorb water. Then remove the sponge and place it in the beaker.
7. Squeeze out as much water as possible from the sponge into the beaker. (*Hint:* Squeeze and twist the sponge until no more drops of water come out.)
8. Pour the water from the beaker into the graduated cylinder. Measure the volume of water and record the volume in the data table. Pour the water from the graduated cylinder back into the bowl. Dry the graduated cylinder and beaker with a paper towel.

Data Table

Type of Sponge	Mass of Damp Sponge	Size of Pores	Volume of Absorbed Water	
			Total (mL)	Per Gram (mL/g)
Cellulose				
Natural				
Foam				

9. Repeat Steps 6–8 using the natural sponge and then the foam sponge. When you are finished, squeeze all the water from your sponges, and return them to your teacher.
10. Calculate the volume of water absorbed per gram of sponge, using this formula:

$$\frac{\textbf{Volume of absorbed water}}{\textbf{Mass of damp sponge}} = \textbf{Volume absorbed per gram}$$

Analyze and Conclude
1. **Observing** Which sponge absorbed the most water per gram of sponge? The least? Was your prediction confirmed?
2. **Drawing Conclusions** What can you conclude about the relationship between pore size and the ability of the sponge to absorb water?
3. **Predicting** How would the volume of absorbed water change if each of the sponges had twice the mass of the sponges you studied? Explain.
4. **Communicating** Natural sponges can cost more than cellulose and foam sponges. Consider that information and the results of your investigation. Which sponge would you recommend to consumers for absorbing water spills? Explain your choice.

Design an Experiment
Design an experiment to test the prediction you made in Question 3 above. Write your hypothesis as an "If ... then ..." statement. *Obtain your teacher's permission before carrying out your investigation.*

Analyze and Conclude
1. The foam sponge will absorb the most water per gram of sponge. The cellulose sponge will absorb the least. Answers about predictions will vary.
2. Student answers should show an understanding that sponges with smaller pore sizes generally absorb the most water.
3. Doubling the mass of the sponge pieces would increase the volume of water absorbed by each sponge.
4. Student recommendations should take into account the volume of absorbed water per gram of sponge as well as the cost of each sponge. The foam sponge is the best deal.

Extend Inquiry

Design an Experiment
Students hypotheses might take the form of an "If . . . , then . . ." statement. For example, "If three sponges with different pore sizes are tested, then the sponge with the smallest pore size will absorb the most water." Student experimental designs should list the materials they will need and should include clear, logical procedure steps that will test the hypothesis.

Cidarians

Some other animals you might notice on an underwater dive are jellyfishes, corals, and sea anemones. These animals are **cnidarians** (ny DEHR ee unz), invertebrates that have stinging cells and take food into a central body cavity. **Cnidarians use stinging cells to capture food and defend themselves.**

Body Structure Cnidarians have two different body plans, which you can see in Figure 13. Notice that one form looks something like a vase and the other form looks like an upside-down bowl. Both body plans have radial symmetry, a central hollow cavity, and tentacles that contain stinging cells.

The vase-shaped body plan is called a **polyp** (PAHL ip). The sea anemone you see in Figure 13 is a polyp. A polyp's mouth opens at the top and its tentacles spread out from around the mouth. Most polyps are adapted for a life attached to an underwater surface.

The bowl-shaped body plan is called a **medusa** (muh DOO suh). The jellyfish you see in Figure 13 is a medusa. A medusa, unlike a polyp, is adapted for a swimming life. Medusas have mouths that open downward and tentacles that trail down. Some cnidarians go through both a polyp stage and a medusa stage during their lives. Others are either polyps or medusas for their entire lives.

Lab zone Try This Activity

Hydra Doing?

1. Put a drop of water containing hydras in a small unbreakable bowl or petri dish. Allow it to sit for about 15 minutes.
2. Use a hand lens to examine the hydras as they swim. Then gently touch the tentacles of a hydra with the end of a toothpick. Watch what happens.
3. Return the hydras to your teacher. Wash your hands.

Classifying Is a hydra a polyp or a medusa? Describe its method of movement.

FIGURE 13
Cnidarian Body Plans

Cnidarians have two basic body forms, the vase-shaped polyp and the bowl-shaped medusa. **Comparing and Contrasting** *Contrast the location of the mouth in the polyp and the medusa.*

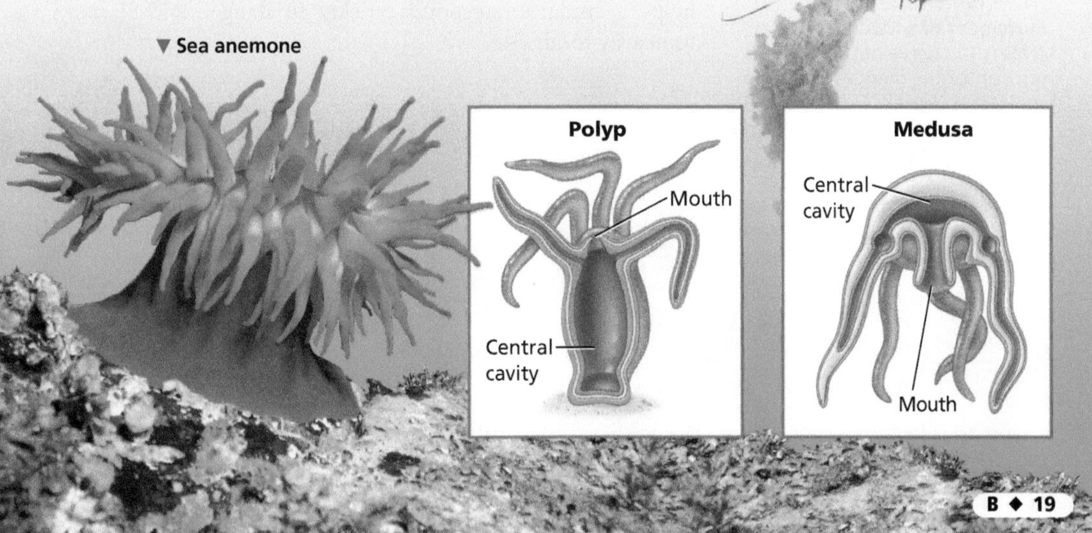

Lab zone Try This Activity

Skills Focus Classifying L2

Materials hand lens or microscope, live hydra, small glass bowl or petri dish, toothpicks

Time 25 minutes

Tips You can order hydras from a biological supply house. Guide students to observe characteristics of a cnidarian.

Expected Outcome The hydras will respond by wrapping their tentacles around the toothpick. A hydra is a polyp. It moves from place to place by somersaulting.

Extend Ask if anyone sees a hydra with a bulb (bud) developing on its stalk. If so, explain that the hydra is reproducing asexually. **learning modality: visual**

Cnidarians

Teach Key Concepts L2

Jellyfish Texture

Focus Ask: **How would you describe a bag full of gelatin?** *(Possible answer: solid but not hard)* Tell students that the body of a jellyfish has the texture of firm gelatin.

Teach Direct students' attention to the pictures of the cnidarian polyp and medusa. Ask: **How do they differ?** *(The opening to the central cavity is at the top of a polyp and on the bottom in the medusa.)* Point out that some cnidarians go through both stages during their life. **How do cnidarians reproduce?** *(Both sexually and asexually)*

Apply Ask: **How is the medusa body plan adapted to life in the water?** *(Possible answer: The shape enables the animal to float and be carried easily by the water.)* **learning modality: kinesthetic**

Help Students Read L1

Previewing Visuals Refer to the Content Refresher, which provides guidelines for Previewing Visuals. Draw students' attention to Figure 13. Point out that a medusa may be thought of as a polyp turned upside down, or vice versa. Have students note that both have tentacles, a central cavity, and a mouth.

Monitor Progress L2

Writing Ask students to write two diary entries, the first from the viewpoint of a sponge, and the second from the viewpoint of a cnidarian. Entries should include what and how the animals eat, and a description of the animals' physical features. Students can save their diary entries in their portfolios. Portfolio

Answer

Figure 13 Polyps have mouths that face upward; medusas have mouths that face downward.

L2

Modeling Movement in Cnidarians

Materials balloon, umbrella
Time 10 minutes

Focus Remind students that adult sponges do not move, as compared to cnidarians, which are highly mobile by comparison.

Teach Give each student group a balloon partially filled with water. (Note: You may wish to do this activity as a demonstration.) Tell students that the balloon represents a cnidarian gastrovascular cavity. Have students gently squeeze the balloon to make it change shape, with one part growing larger while the other shrinks. Next, have students take turns rapidly opening and closing the umbrella. Tell them that this action models the movement of a medusa.

Apply Explain that medusas have muscles that contract the bell in a similar way. Just as the umbrella pushes air backward, a medusa's bell pushes water backward, thus propelling the organism forward. **learning modality: kinesthetic**

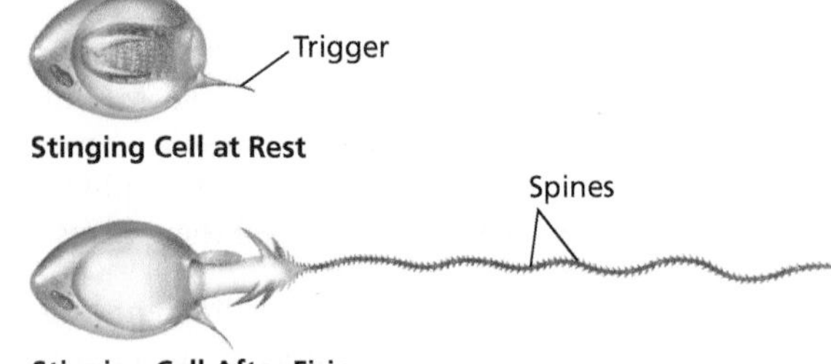

FIGURE 14
Cnidarian Attack!
A stinging cell fires when its trigger brushes against prey, such as a fish.

Obtaining Food Both polyps and medusas obtain food in the same way. Cnidarians use stinging cells to catch the animals they eat, which are called prey. You can see a stinging cell in Figure 14. The cell contains a threadlike structure, which has many sharp spines. When the stinging cell touches prey, this threadlike structure explodes out of the cell and into the prey. Some stinging cells also release venom into the prey. When the prey becomes helpless, the cnidarian uses its tentacles to pull the prey into its mouth. From there, the prey passes into a hollow central body cavity, where it is digested. Undigested food is expelled through the mouth.

Movement Unlike adult sponges, many cnidarians can move to escape danger and to obtain food. Some cnidarians have muscle-like tissues that allow them to move in different ways. Jellyfishes swim through the water, and hydras turn slow somersaults. Sea anemones stretch out, shrink down, bend slowly from side to side, and often move slowly from place to place. A cnidarian's movements are directed by nerve cells that are spread out like a basketball net. This nerve net helps a cnidarian respond quickly to danger and to nearby food.

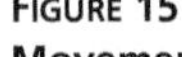

FIGURE 15
Movement of a Medusa
A medusa's nerve net signals the top part of the medusa's body to contract and relax. As the top of its body contracts, the medusa moves upward through the water.

Differentiated Instruction

Less Proficient Readers L1

Silent Consonants Students may have difficulty remembering that the *c* in *cnidarian* is silent. Write the word *cnidarian* on the board. Point out that the word begins with the letter *c*. Then say the word out loud. Call on volunteers to repeat the word. You might point out other words that begin with silent consonants, such as *pneumonia, knot, psalm, psychology, knuckle,* and *know.* **learning modality: verbal**

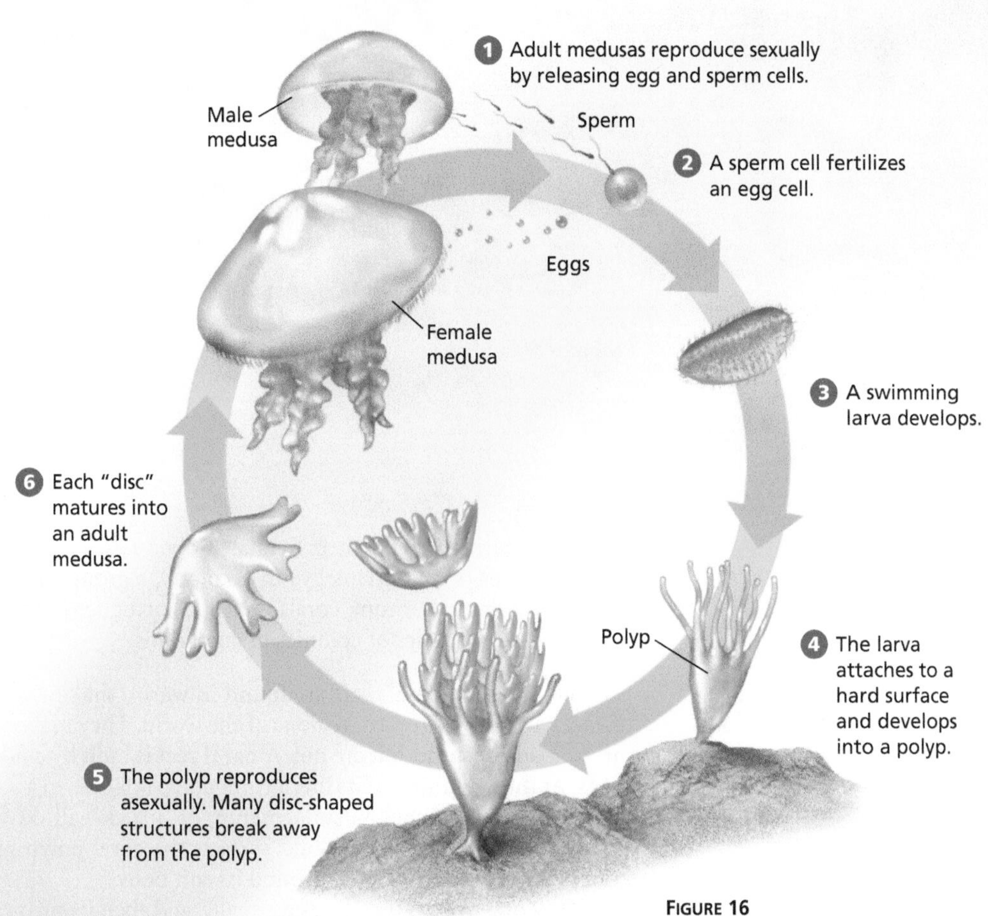

1 Adult medusas reproduce sexually by releasing egg and sperm cells.
Male medusa
Sperm
2 A sperm cell fertilizes an egg cell.
Eggs
Female medusa
3 A swimming larva develops.
6 Each "disc" matures into an adult medusa.
Polyp
4 The larva attaches to a hard surface and develops into a polyp.
5 The polyp reproduces asexually. Many disc-shaped structures break away from the polyp.

FIGURE 16
Life Cycle of a Jellyfish
The life cycle of a moon jelly has both a polyp and a medusa stage, and both asexual reproduction and sexual reproduction.
Interpreting Diagrams *Which form of the moon jelly (polyp or medusa) shows a form of asexual reproduction? Explain.*

Reproduction Cnidarians reproduce both asexually and sexually. For polyps such as hydras, corals, and sea anemones, budding is the most common form of asexual reproduction. Amazingly, some polyps just pull apart, forming two new polyps. Both kinds of asexual reproduction allow the numbers of polyps to increase rapidly in a short time.

Sexual reproduction in cnidarians occurs in a variety of ways. Some species of cnidarians have both sexes within one individual. In others, the sexes are separate individuals. Many cnidarians have life cycles, or a sequence of different stages of development. In Figure 16, you can see the life cycle of a moon jelly, which involves both asexual and sexual reproduction.

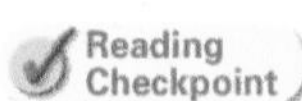
What are two examples of asexual reproduction seen in polyps?

Use Visuals: Figure 16 L1
Cnidarian Life Cycle

Focus Direct students' attention to Figure 16, the life cycle of a jellyfish.

Teach Pair students and have them read aloud the descriptions of the reproductive stages, starting with number one. Ask: **Which body form is reproducing sexually?** *(Medusa)* **Which is reproducing asexually?** *(Polyp)* **How are polyps produced?** *(Male medusas release sperm, which fertilize eggs of female medusas. The fertilized egg develops into a larva, which then develops into a polyp.)* Make sure students understand that polyps are produced sexually, but that they themselves reproduce asexually. The opposite is true for medusas, which are produced asexually but reproduce sexually.

Apply Compare reproduction in the moon jelly with reproduction in the hydra, which undergoes budding. Budding yields offspring that look like mini-adults projecting from the stalk of the parent. **learning modality: visual**

All in One Teaching Resources
- Transparency B8

Differentiated Instruction

Gifted and Talented L3
Comb Jellies Students might be interested in learning about comb jellies, or ctenophores. These organisms, like cnidarians, have a jellylike body that exhibits radial symmetry, but they are in a phylum, Ctenophora, of their own. Students can do library or Internet research to find out the structures, habitats, and other characteristics of these animals. When they have finished their research, students might present their findings in the form of an oral or written report accompanied by illustrations or photographs. **learning modality: verbal**

Monitor Progress L2

Skills Check Have students compare and contrast how jellyfish, sea anemones, and hydras move.

Answers
Figure 16 Polyp; disc-shaped structures break away and form new individuals.

 Budding, pulling apart

Life in a Colony

Teach Key Concepts

L2

Formation of a Coral Reef

Focus Discuss with students that a colony of settlers is a group of individuals living together in one place.

Teach Ask: **How is a colony of cnidarians similar to a colony of settlers?** *(A colony of cnidarians is a group of many individuals living together.)* **How is a colony like a single unit?** *(It moves and functions as one unit.)* Explain how the polyps in a Portuguese man-of-war colony perform specialized functions. Some capture and digest prey; others produce reproductive cells; some are swimming organs that act as floats, or air-filled sacs.

Apply Ask: **Why do you think this colonial organization is rare in animals?** *(Sample answer: Colonial organization requires that individual animals coordinate their activities to become part of a whole organism.)* **learning modality: logical/mathematical**

Discovery Channel School Video Field Trip

Sponges, Cnidarians, and Worms

Show the Video Field Trip to let students experience the world of the jellyfish.

FIGURE 17
Coral Reef
The massive reef surrounding this tropical island is made from the skeletal remains of the tiny cnidarians called coral (inset).

Life in a Colony

Many cnidarians spend their lives as individuals, but not all. Some species of cnidarians live in a **colony,** a group of many individual animals. Stony corals and the Portuguese man-of-war are two examples of colonies of cnidarians.

Stony Corals Coral reefs are found in warm, shallow ocean waters, mainly in tropical regions of the world. They may seem to be made of stone, but are not. A **coral reef** is built by cnidarians. At the beginning of its life, a coral polyp attaches to a solid surface. A broken shell, a sunken ship, or a rock will do just fine. After attaching to the solid surface, the coral polyp produces a hard, stony skeleton around its soft body.

The coral polyp reproduces asexually, and then its offspring reproduce asexually, too. Over time, that polyp may give rise to thousands more, each with a hard skeleton. When the polyps die, their skeletons remain behind. Over thousands of years, as live corals add their skeletons to those that have died, rocklike reefs grow up from the sea floor. The top layer of the reef is covered with hundreds of thousands of still-living coral polyps.

Coral reefs are home to more species of fishes and invertebrates than any other environment on Earth. Hundreds of sponge species live among the corals, constantly filtering water through their bodies. Worms burrow into the coral reef. Giant clams lie with their huge shells slightly open. Shrimp and crabs edge out of hiding places below the corals. At night, bright blue damselfish settle into pockets in the coral. At dawn and dusk, sea turtles, sea snakes, and sharks all visit the reef, hunting for prey. These living things interact in complex ways, creating a rich and beautiful environment.

FIGURE 18
Portuguese Man-of-War
The Portuguese man-of-war is a tightly coordinated colony of polyps and medusas.

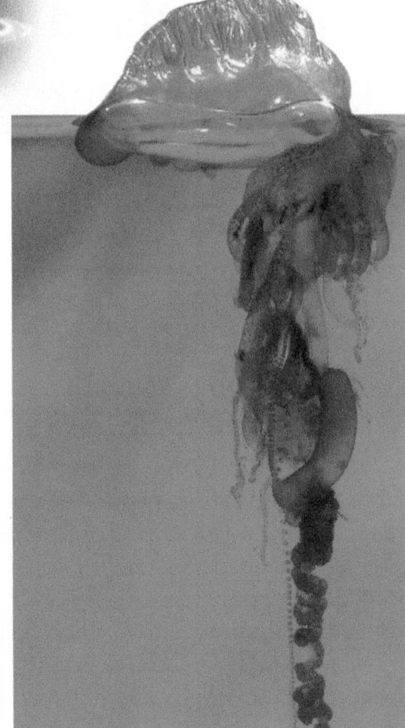

Portuguese Man-of-War Sometimes the association of individual animals in a colony is so tight that the colony acts like a single animal. The Portuguese man-of-war contains as many as 1,000 individuals that function together as one unit.

At the top of the Portuguese man-of-war is a gas-filled chamber that allows the colony to float on the surface of the ocean. Various polyps with different functions drift below. Some polyps catch prey for the colony with stinging cells. Others digest the prey. Still other polyps are adapted for reproduction.

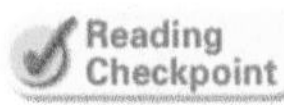
What are two examples of colonies of cnidarians?

Section 3 Assessment

Target Reading Skill Comparing and Contrasting Use your table to quiz a partner about how sponges and cnidarians trap food. How do their methods for trapping food differ?

Reviewing Key Concepts

1. a. Describing What are the characteristics of a sponge?
   b. Comparing and Contrasting How are the cells of a sponge alike? How are they different?
2. a. Identifying What is one type of cell that all cnidarians have?
   b. Sequencing What steps are involved in how a cnidarian obtains food?
   c. Inferring How might a cnidarian protect itself?
3. a. Identifying What is a coral reef?
   b. Summarizing How is a coral reef built?
   c. Making Judgments Why is it important to protect coral reefs?

Math Practice

4. Calculating a Rate A very large sponge can filter 1,500 liters of water in a day. How much water can it filter per hour?

Monitor Progress L2

Answer

Portuguese man-of-war and stony corals

Assess

Reviewing Key Concepts

1. a. Sponges are invertebrates that have no body symmetry and lack tissues and organs.
b. The cells of a sponge all surround a hollow central cavity. The cells have different structures for different functions. For example, collar cells have whiplike structures that beat back and forth to move water and food through the sponge. Jellylike cells digest food, carry away wastes, and form sperm or eggs.
2. a. Stinging cells **b.** The cnidarian's stinging cells capture the prey. Next the tentacles pull the prey to the cnidarian's mouth. Then, the prey goes into the central body cavity and is digested. **c.** A cnidarian might use its stinging cells to defend itself against other animals that might prey on it.
3. a. A coral reef is a stonelike structure in the ocean. **b.** It is built by the accumulation of many coral polyp skeletons. Its top layer is made of still-living polyps.
c. Coral reefs are rich with living things that interact in complex ways. Upsetting the balance on a reef could destroy it.

Reteach L1

Review reproduction in sponges. Use Figures 11 and 12 to identify the structures involved and the process of reproduction.

All in One Teaching Resources

- Section Summary: *Sponges and Cnidarians*
- Review and Reinforce: *Sponges and Cnidarians*
- Enrich: *Sponges and Cnidarians*

Lab zone Chapter Project

Keep Students on Track Give students time in class to study their animal and write down their observations. Suggest that students keep their observation records in a loose-leaf notebook so they can insert drawings and photographs. Review students' records on a regular basis. Be sure students include details of how the animal seems to be faring in its habitat. Check the health of the animals periodically.

4. 1,500 liters/24 hours = 62.5 liters/hour

Science and Society

Coral Reefs in Danger

Key Concept

Coral reefs provide homes and food sources for a large variety of sea life and are in danger of being destroyed by natural disasters and humans.

Build Background Knowledge

Review Life on A Coral Reef

Help students recall how coral reefs are formed. Ask: **What is the first stage in the formation of a coral reef?** *(A free-swimming coral larva attaches itself to a solid surface underwater and then produces a stony skeleton around its soft body.)* Ask: **How do coral reefs, such as the Great Barrier Reef, reach such enormous sizes?** *(The living coral polyps reproduce asexually and over time they produce thousands more. As organisms die they leave behind their skeletons, which form the structure of the reef.)* Explain that it is in the shelter of the reef that a large variety of sea life finds food and shelter.

Introduce the Debate

Explain to students that they will be debating the proposition that "Diving near coral reefs should be banned to protect the reefs from ecological damage."

Facilitate the Debate

- Separate the class into two groups: one to support the proposition, the other to oppose it. Have groups review and investigate the issue from their respective points of view.
- Encourage students in the pro-diving group to explore such ideas as education and environmental awareness as an alternative to banning diving. Encourage students in the other group to think realistically and offer alternatives for those affected by the diving ban.

Science and **Society**

Coral Reefs in Danger

Coral reefs off the coasts of many nations are in danger. Although coral reefs are as hard as rocks, the coral animals themselves are quite delicate. Recreational divers can damage the fragile reefs. Is it possible to protect the reefs while still allowing divers to explore them?

Diving supports local businesses

The Issues

What's the Harm in Diving?

More than 1.5 million recreational divers live in the United States. With so many divers it is hard to guarantee that no harm will occur to coral reefs. Divers can cause significant damage by standing on or even touching these fragile reefs. Harm to the reefs is even more likely to occur when divers collect coral for their own enjoyment or to sell for profit. You can see brightly colored coral from the sea in jewelry and in decorations.

Should Reefs Be Further Protected?

The United States government has passed laws making it illegal, under most circumstances, to remove coral from the sea. Because a few divers break these laws, some people want to ban diving altogether. However, many divers say it's unfair to ban diving just because of a few lawbreakers.

Many divers consider coral reefs the most exciting and beautiful places in the ocean to explore. As divers and other people visit and learn more about these delicate coral reefs, they increase others' awareness of them. Public awareness may be the best way to ensure that these rich environments are protected.

More Than a Diving Issue

Coral reefs are major tourist attractions that bring money and jobs to people in local communities. If diving were banned, local businesses would suffer significantly. Also, although divers can harm coral reefs, other human activities that result in ocean pollution, oil spills, and illegal fishing can also cause harm. In addition, natural events, such as tropical storms, changes in sea level, and changes in sea temperature, can also damage the fragile reefs.

24 ◆ B

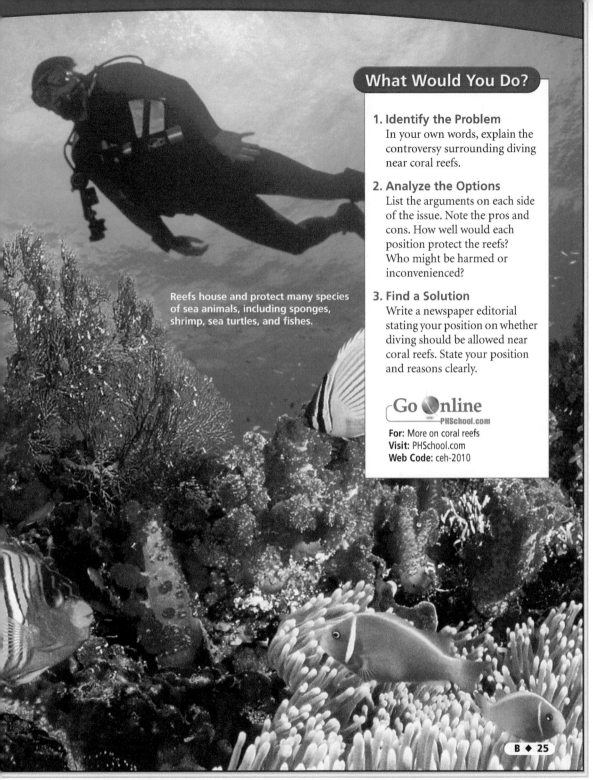

Reefs house and protect many species of sea animals, including sponges, shrimp, sea turtles, and fishes.

What Would You Do?

1. **Identify the Problem**
   In your own words, explain the controversy surrounding diving near coral reefs.
2. **Analyze the Options**
   List the arguments on each side of the issue. Note the pros and cons. How well would each position protect the reefs? Who might be harmed or inconvenienced?
3. **Find a Solution**
   Write a newspaper editorial stating your position on whether diving should be allowed near coral reefs. State your position and reasons clearly.

Go Online
PHSchool.com
For: More on coral reefs
Visit: PHSchool.com
Web Code: ceh-2010

What Would You Do?

1. The problem is that many coral reefs, which house and protect many species of sea life and protect coastlines from flooding, are endangered, damaged, or threatened with destruction. Recreational divers can cause damage to the reefs.
2. Students' responses should include alternative solutions. The various consequences of banning access to the reefs should be acknowledged and considered when forming solutions.
3. Students should be responsible for providing verifiable documentation to justify their opinions.

For: More on coral reefs
Visit: PHSchool.com
Web Code: ceh-2010

Students can research this issue online.

Background

Facts and Figures Coral reefs have extremely high levels of animal diversity—nowhere else in the ocean can you find so many kinds of fish and invertebrates. Like rain forests, coral reefs contain many plants and animals that produce potentially valuable chemicals. For this reason, it is important to protect the reefs.

Coral reefs are in danger from natural disasters and from humans. Natural forces, such as water that is too warm, can kill corals and produce a phenomenon called coral bleaching. Organisms that eat living corals, such as the crown-of-thorns sea star, can greatly damage reefs.

In addition to the destruction they cause when diving, people can harm reefs through ocean pollution, oil spills, fishing nets, and construction projects on islands near coral reefs.

Section 4 Worms

Objectives

After this lesson, students will be able to

B.1.4.1 Identify the three main phyla of worms.

B.1.4.2 Describe the characteristics of each worm phylum.

Target Reading Skill

Using Prior Knowledge Explain that using prior knowledge helps students connect what they already know to what they are about to read.

Answers

Possible answers:

What You Know

1. Worms are long and skinny.
2. Live in the ground, digest soil
3. Are slimy and wriggly

What You Learned

1. Worms have bilateral symmetry.
2. May be flat
3. Some live in water
4. May be parasites
5. Have a nervous system

All in One Teaching Resources

- Transparency B9

Preteach

Build Background Knowledge L1

Observations of Worms

Ask students if they have ever used worms as fishing bait or dug up worms in a garden. Encourage students to share any observations they have made about the appearance and behavior of worms. Then, ask: **What words would you use to describe worms?** *(Sample answer: Slimy, creepy, crawly)* Inform students that in this section, they will learn about the characteristics and nature of worms.

Section 4 Worms

Reading Preview

Key Concepts

- What are the three main phyla of worms?
- What are the main characteristics of each phylum of worms?

Key Terms

- parasite • host
- free-living organism
- scavenger • anus
- closed circulatory system

Target Reading Skill

Using Prior Knowledge Before you read, write what you know about worms in a graphic organizer like the one below. As you read, write what you learn.

What You Know
1. Worms are long and skinny. 2.

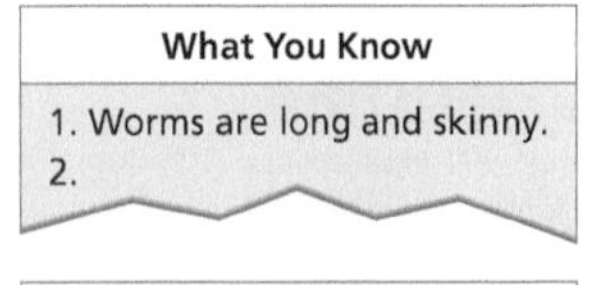

What You Learned
1. 2.

Lab zone Discover Activity

What Does a Flatworm Look Like?

1. Your teacher will give you a planarian, a kind of flatworm. Pick the worm up with the tip of a small paintbrush. Place it carefully in a container. Use a dropper to cover the planarian with spring water.
2. Observe the planarian with a hand lens for a few minutes. Describe how the planarian moves. Draw a picture of the planarian.
3. Return the planarian to your teacher, and wash your hands.

Think It Over

Observing How does a planarian differ from a sponge?

You might think that all worms are small, slimy, and wriggly. But many worms do not fit that description. Some worms are almost three meters long and are as thick as your arm. Others look like glowing, furry blobs. Worms may glide through water or climb around with paddle-like bristles. Still others are very small and live underwater in tubes cemented to rocks.

Characteristics of Worms

There are many kinds of worms, all with their own characteristics. **Biologists classify worms into three major phyla—flatworms, roundworms, and segmented worms.** Flatworms belong to the phylum Platyhelminthes (plat ee HEL minth eez); roundworms belong to the phylum Nematoda; segmented worms belong to the phylum Annelida.

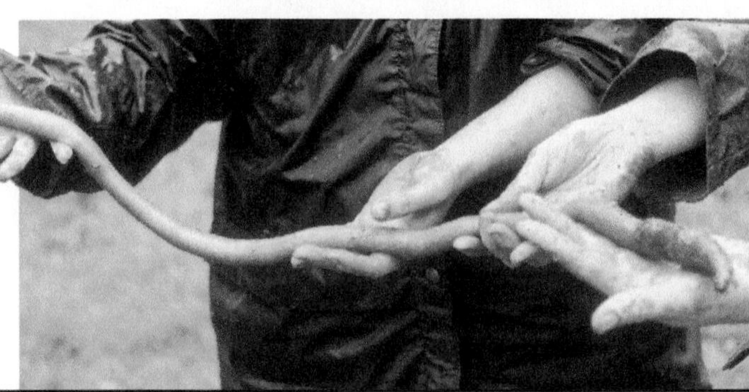

FIGURE 19
Giant Earthworm
A giant Gippsland earthworm can grow to be more than 1 meter long. It is one of approximately 1,000 earthworm species found in Australia.

Lab zone Discover Activity

Skills Focus Observing L1

Materials bottled water, hand lens, live planarian, plastic dropper, small paintbrush, small transparent container or petri dish

Time 15 minutes

Tips Ask students to discuss how the planarians behave. Have them sketch the planarian and make notes of what they see. Verify that students note the bilateral symmetry of planarians.

Expected Outcome Planarians should react visibly to being touched.

Think It Over Suggest students refer to Section 3. Planarians have bilateral symmetry and distinct head and tail ends. Sponges are asymmetrical and do not have head and tail ends.

FIGURE 20
Three Phyla of Worms
The three major phyla of worms are flatworms, roundworms, and segmented worms. Observing *How are the body shapes of these three types of worms similar?*

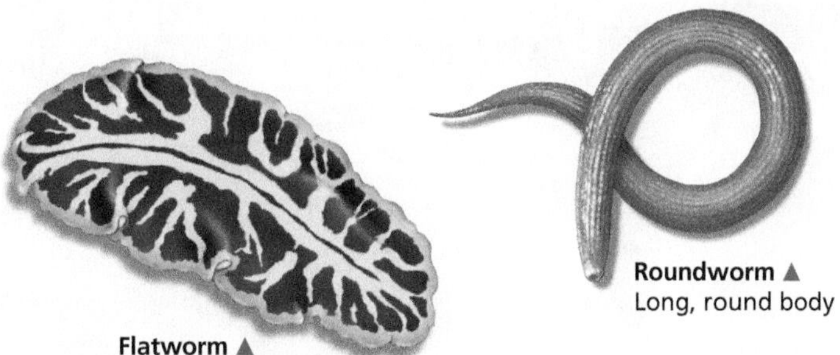

Flatworm ▲
Long, flat body

Roundworm ▲
Long, round body

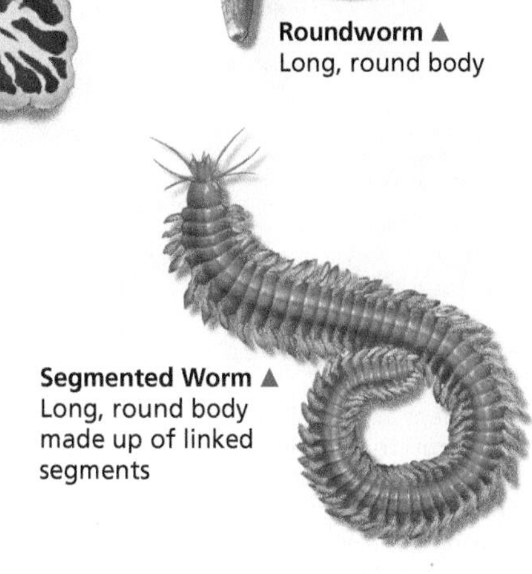

Segmented Worm ▲
Long, round body made up of linked segments

Body Structure All worms are invertebrates that have long, narrow bodies without legs. In Figure 20, you can compare the body shapes of three types of worms. Unlike sponges or cnidarians, worms have bilateral symmetry. Therefore, they have head and tail ends. In addition, they all have tissues, organs, and body systems.

Nervous System Worms are the simplest organisms with a brain, which is a knot of nerve tissue located in the head end. Because a worm's brain and some of its sense organs are located in its head end, the worm can detect objects, food, mates, and predators quickly. It can respond quickly, too. Sense organs that are sensitive to light, touch, and vibrations pick up information from the environment. The brain interprets that information and directs the animal's response. For example, if an earthworm on the surface of the ground senses the vibrations of a footstep, the worm will quickly return to its underground burrow.

Reproduction Both sexual and asexual reproduction are found in the worm phyla. In many species of worms, there are separate male and female animals, as in humans. In other species of worms, each individual has both male and female sex organs. A worm with both male and female sex organs does not usually fertilize its own eggs. Instead, two individuals mate and exchange sperm. Many worms reproduce asexually by methods such as breaking into pieces. In fact, if you cut some kinds of worms into several pieces, a whole new worm will grow from each piece.

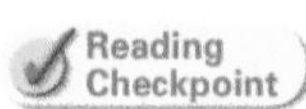

What type of symmetry do worms have?

Instruct

Characteristics of Worms

Teach Key Concepts L2

Shapes of Worms

Focus Have students note the shapes of the worms in Figure 20.

Teach Ask: **What distinguishes the three worms in the figure?** *(Shape and overall structure)* **What are the shapes and overall structure of the three worms?** *(Flat, round, segmented)* Point out that the terms *flatworm, roundworm,* and *segmented worm* describe major visible characteristics of the groups.

Apply Tell students that they may be familiar with the worm phyla, even though they may not realize it. Many students have observed planarians during school activities, or they may have a pet that has had worms (often tapeworms). Roundworms can often be seen in the soil as tiny, white objects. Finally, the familiar earthworm, which is segmented, is very common. **learning modality: visual**

Help Students Read L1

Outlining Have students outline the section using the red and blue heads. They can write supporting details below each head as they read.

Independent Practice L2

All in One Teaching Resources

- Guided Reading and Study Worksheet: *Worms*

Student Edition on Audio CD

Monitor Progress L2

Answer

Figure 20 Each worm has a long body without legs.

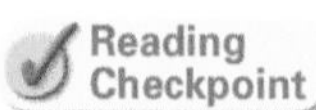

Bilateral symmetry

Flatworms

Teach Key Concepts

L2

Tapeworm Life Cycle

Focus Tell students that flatworms can be as long as 12 meters or so small they are almost microscopic.

Teach Discuss each stage in the tapeworm life cycle shown in Figure 22. Remind students that eating a rabbit is only one way a dog can become infected. Ask: **What are the parasite and the hosts in this picture?** *(Parasite: tapeworm; hosts: dog and rabbit)* Ask: **Why are the pictures arranged in a cycle?** *(To emphasize that the sequence of events is continuous)*

Apply Ask: **Why do you think the tapeworm must attach itself to the dog's digestive system?** *(Its body is adapted to absorbing digested food.)* **learning modality: visual**

For: More on worms
Visit: PHSchool.com
Web Code: ced-2014

Students can review worms in an online activity.

- Transparency B10

FIGURE 21
Planarian
Planarians are free-living flatworms that live in ponds, streams, and oceans.
Comparing and Contrasting
How does a free-living organism differ from a parasite?

Flatworms

As you'd expect from their name, flatworms are flat. They include such organisms as tapeworms, planarians, and flukes. Although tapeworms can grow to be 10 to 12 meters long, some other flatworms are almost too small to be seen. All flatworms share certain characteristics. **Flatworms are flat and as soft as jelly.**

Many flatworms are parasites. A **parasite** is an organism that lives inside or on another organism. The parasite takes its food from its **host,** the organism in or on which it lives. Parasites may rob their hosts of food and make them weak. They may injure the host's tissues or organs, but they rarely kill their host. All tapeworms and flukes are parasites.

In contrast, some flatworms are free-living. A **free-living organism** does not live in or on other organisms. Free-living flatworms may glide over the rocks in ponds, slide over damp soil, or swim slowly through the ocean like ruffled, brightly patterned leaves.

Planarians Planarians are free-living flatworms. Planarians are **scavengers**—they feed on dead or decaying material. But they are also predators and will attack any animal smaller than they are. A planarian feeds like a vacuum cleaner. The planarian glides onto its food and inserts a feeding tube into it. Digestive juices flow out of the planarian and into the food. These juices begin to break down the food while it is still outside the worm's body. Then the planarian sucks up the partly digested bits. Digestion is completed within a cavity inside the planarian. Undigested food exits through the feeding tube.

For: More on worms
Visit: PHSchool.com
Web Code: ced-2014

Differentiated Instruction

Gifted and Talented

L3

Reaction of Planarian to Light Provide students with planarians, flashlights, transparent plastic containers, bottled water, and dark paper or foil. Have them place a planarian in the dish and cover it with a few drops of water. Then, have them predict how the planarian will react to light and record their predictions. Have students cover half the container with paper or foil and shine the flashlight on the container. The planarians will probably move out of the light. **learning modality: visual**

If you look at the head of the planarian shown in Figure 21, you can see two dots. These dots are called eyespots. The eyespots can detect light but cannot see a detailed image as human eyes can. A planarian's head also has cells that pick up odors. Planarians rely mainly on smell, not light, to locate food.

Tapeworms Tapeworms are one kind of parasitic flatworm. A tapeworm's body is adapted to absorbing food from the host's digestive system. Some kinds of tapeworms can live in human hosts. Many tapeworms live in more than one host during their lifetime. You can see the life cycle of the dog tapeworm in Figure 22. Notice that this tapeworm has two different hosts—a dog and a rabbit.

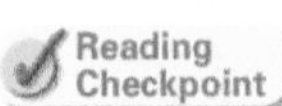

How does a scavenger obtain food?

FIGURE 22
Life Cycle of a Dog Tapeworm
The tapeworm is a parasite that lives in more than one host during its life cycle.

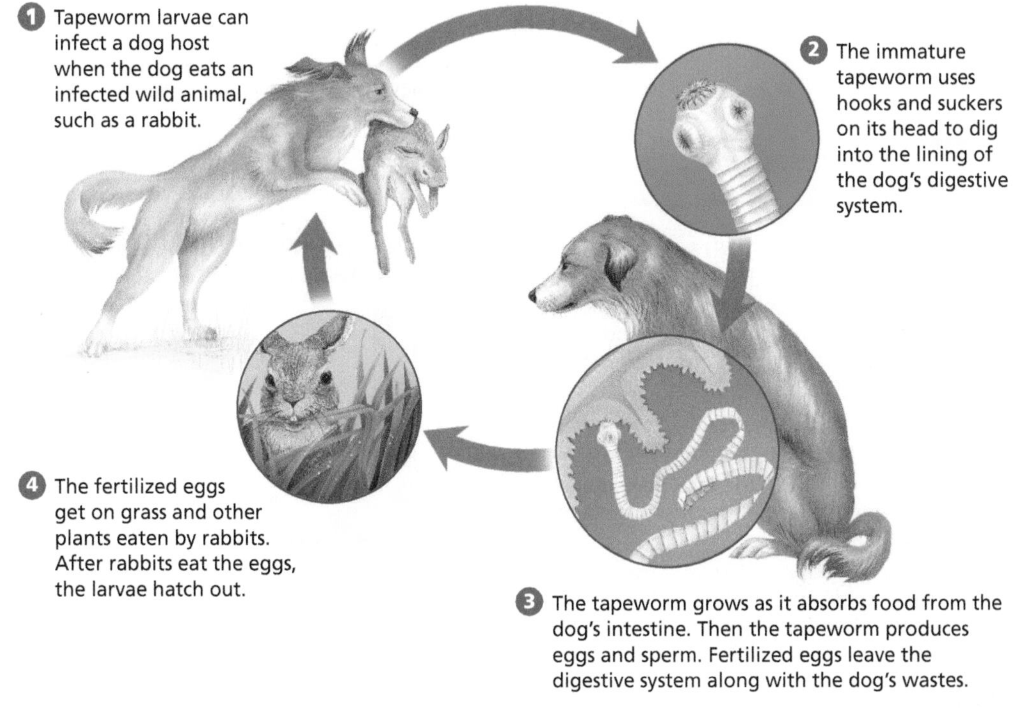

1 Tapeworm larvae can infect a dog host when the dog eats an infected wild animal, such as a rabbit.
2 The immature tapeworm uses hooks and suckers on its head to dig into the lining of the dog's digestive system.
3 The tapeworm grows as it absorbs food from the dog's intestine. Then the tapeworm produces eggs and sperm. Fertilized eggs leave the digestive system along with the dog's wastes.
4 The fertilized eggs get on grass and other plants eaten by rabbits. After rabbits eat the eggs, the larvae hatch out.

L3

Planarian Feeding Behavior

Materials bottled water, ground meat, hand lens, lettuce, live planarian, small plastic dish, soft paintbrush

Time 45 minutes

Focus Tell students they will observe planarians to draw conclusions about their food preferences.

Teach Withhold feeding for a day before the activity to make sure the planarians are hungry at the start of the activity. Have students pour water into the dish until the bottom is completely covered. Then, have them place a small piece of ground meat and a piece of lettuce in one side of the dish about 3 centimeters apart. Students can then use the paintbrush to place the planarian at the other side of the dish. Have students observe how long it takes a planarian to start moving and whether it moves toward the lettuce or the meat. *(Planarians are mainly carnivorous.)* If the planarians are slow to respond, place a dark cover over the dish to reduce ambient light. Leave the cover on for about 10 minutes. Then, remove it and observe any movement. Have students wash their hands after the activity.

Apply Ask: **How did the planarian locate the food?** *(It detected chemicals from the food.)* **Where are its sense organs located?** *(At the front end of its body)* **Is having sense organs at the front end related to the type of symmetry the planarian has?** *(Yes. Planarians are bilaterally symmetrical. Most bilaterally symmetrical animals have their sense organs at the front ends of their bodies.)* **learning modality: visual**

Monitor Progress
L2

Writing Ask students to list the distinguishing characteristics of flatworms. *(Bilateral symmetry; a brain; flat bodies; most are parasitic, but some are predators)*

Answers
Figure 21 A free-living organism does not live in or on other organisms and take food from these host organisms.

Scavengers feed on dead or decaying material.

Roundworms

Teach Key Concepts L2

Advancements in Roundworms

Focus Tell students that roundworms are different from flatworms in ways other than shape.

Teach Ask: **What feature do roundworms have that has not been observed in animals studied previously?** *(A complete digestive system, having both a mouth and an anus)*

Apply Ask: **What is the advantage of having a one-way digestive system?** *(It enables the animal's body to absorb a large amount of needed substances.)* **learning modality: verbal**

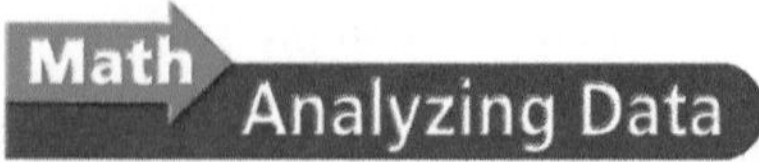

Skills Focus Interpreting graphs

Materials graph

Time 15 minutes

Tips Make sure students understand the relationship between the independent variable (soil depth) and dependent variable (number of worms).

Answers

1. in the first centimeter
2. about 87%
3. the deeper the soil, the fewer worms

Address Misconceptions L1

Ringworm Infection

Focus Tell students that ringworm infection is caused by a fungus, not a worm at all.

Teach Ringworm infection is a common skin infection in children. It is characterized by a round rash, often on the face. Make sure that students understand that fungi are in a different kingdom from roundworms.

Apply Pets, such as dogs and cats, may get ringworm, too. They will lose their fur at the site of the infection. **learning modality: verbal**

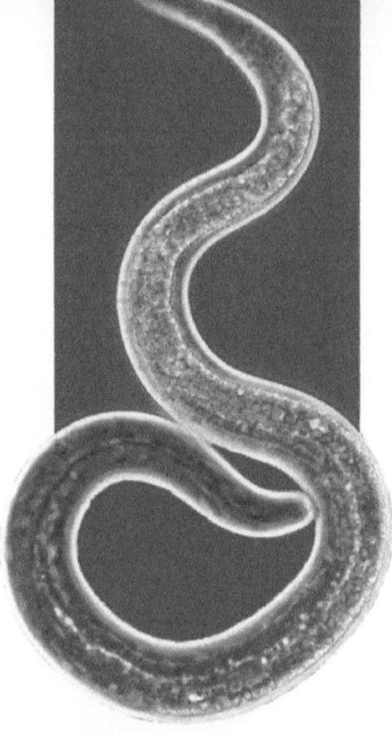

FIGURE 23
A Roundworm
The transparent body of this roundworm has been stained for better viewing under a microscope.

Roundworms

The next time you walk along a beach, consider that about a million roundworms live in each square meter of damp sand. Roundworms can live in nearly any moist environment—including forest soils, Antarctic sands, and pools of super-hot water. Most roundworms are tiny and difficult to see, but they may be the most abundant animals on Earth. Some species are free-living and some are parasites.

Unlike flatworms, roundworms have cylindrical bodies. They look like tiny strands of cooked spaghetti that are pointed at each end. **Unlike cnidarians or flatworms, roundworms have a digestive system that is like a tube, open at both ends.** Food travels in one direction through the roundworm's digestive system. Food enters at the animal's mouth, and wastes exit through an opening, called the **anus,** at the far end of the tube.

A one-way digestive system is efficient. It is something like an assembly line, with a different part of the digestive process happening at each place along the line. Digestion happens in orderly stages. First, food is broken down by digestive juices. Then the digested food is absorbed into the animal's body. Finally, wastes are eliminated. This type of digestive system enables the animal's body to absorb a large amount of the needed substances in foods.

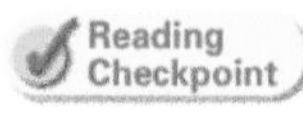

What is each opening at opposite ends of a roundworm's digestive tube called?

Math Analyzing Data

Roundworm Numbers

Biologists counted all the roundworms living in a plot of soil. Then they calculated the percentage that lives in different centimeter depths of soil. Their results are graphed to the right.

1. Reading Graphs Where in the soil was the largest percentage of roundworms found?
2. Calculating What is the total percentage of roundworms found in the first 3-cm depth of soil?
3. Drawing Conclusions What is the relationship between the depth of the soil and the abundance of roundworms in the soil?

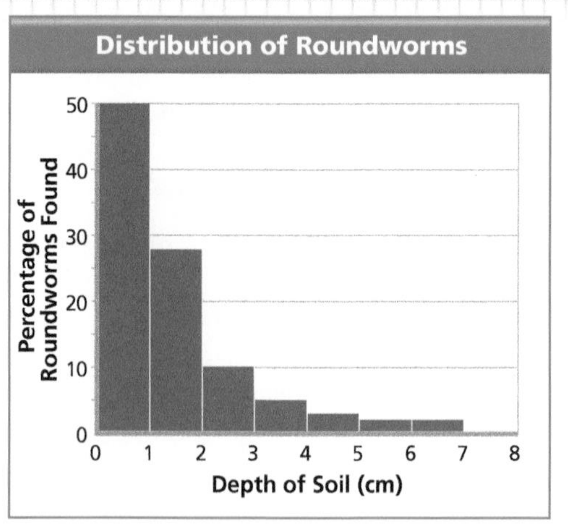

Differentiated Instruction

Special Needs L1

Digestive Systems Hold up two cardboard tubes, one open at both ends, the other sealed at one end. Ask: **Which digestive system(s) does each tube represent?** *(Closed—planarian; open—roundworm)* Fill the sealed tube with marbles. Pass marbles through the open tube. Stress that one advantage of two openings is that the animal can eat while digesting its food. **learning modality: kinesthetic**

Segmented Worms

If you have ever dug in a garden, you have probably seen earthworms wriggling through the moist soil. Earthworms are segmented worms. So are leeches and some sea-floor worms.

Body Structure When you look at an earthworm, you see a body made up of a series of rings separated by grooves, something like a vacuum cleaner hose. **Earthworms and other segmented worms have bodies made up of many linked sections called segments.** On the outside, the segments look nearly identical, as you can see in Figure 24. On the inside, some organs are repeated in most segments. For example, each segment has tubes that remove wastes. Other organs, however, such as the earthworm's reproductive organs, are found only in certain segments.

All segmented worms have a long string of nerve tissue called a nerve cord and a digestive tube that run the length of the worm's body. Like roundworms, segmented worms have a one-way digestive system with two openings.

Circulatory System Segmented worms have a closed circulatory system. In a **closed circulatory system,** blood moves only within a connected network of tubes called blood vessels. In contrast, some animals, such as snails and lobsters, have an open circulatory system in which blood leaves the blood vessels and sloshes around inside the body. In both cases the blood carries oxygen and food to cells. But a closed circulatory system can move blood around an animal's body much more quickly than an open circulatory system can.

FIGURE 24
Structure of an Earthworm
An earthworm's body is divided into more than 100 segments. Some organs are repeated in most of those segments. Other organs exist in only a few segments.
Interpreting Diagrams *Name an example of a body system that runs through all of the worm's segments.*

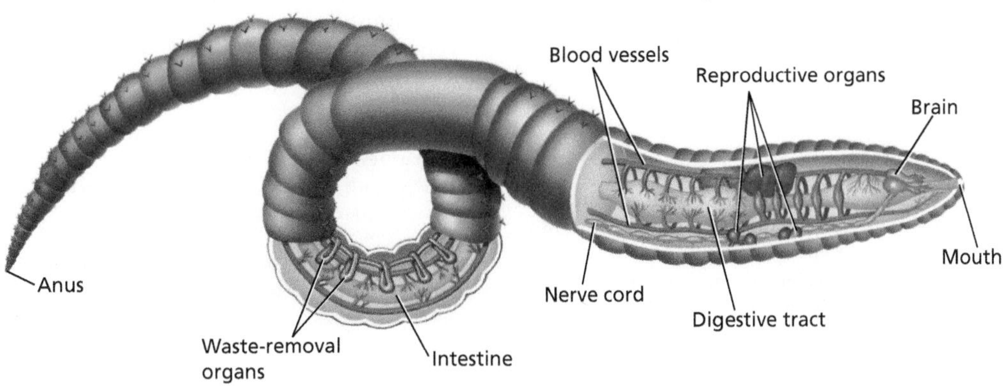

Segmented Worms

Teach Key Concepts

L2

Advancements in Segmented Worms

Focus Tell students that segmented worms show features not seen in roundworms.

Teach Ask: **What kind of circulatory system does an earthworm have?** *(Closed)* **Describe a closed circulatory system.** *(Blood moves within blood vessels.)*

Apply Ask: **What is the advantage of a closed circulatory system?** *(Blood can move throughout the body faster.)* **learning modality: verbal**

All in One Teaching Resources

- Transparency B11

L2

Earthworm Tunneling Behavior

Materials dark construction paper, earthworm, soil, transparent jar

Time 15 minutes per day for several days

Focus Tell students that earthworms break up and enrich the soil as they tunnel.

Teach Fill a jar with loose, moist soil and then add the earthworm. Wrap the jar with dark construction paper and keep the jar out of direct sunlight. That way the worms, which avoid light, may burrow along the outside wall of the jar. Have students note over several days the earthworm's location in the soil. Ask: **When the segments at the front end of the worm contract, do the segments at the back end contract at the same time?** *(No; segments contract independently.)*

Apply Raise earthworms in the classroom. Students will need to add a food source to the soil, such as vegetable waste or leaf litter. **learning modality: visual**

Monitor Progress

L2

Drawing Ask students to draw a flatworm, a roundworm, and a segmented worm. Have them label the main characteristics. Students can save their drawings in their portfolios.

Answers

Figure 24 Sample answers: Nervous system, digestive system, circulatory system

Mouth and anus

Monitor Progress L2

Answer

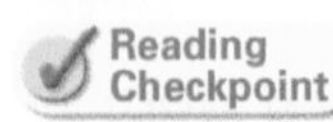 Earthworms obtain oxygen through moisture on their skin.

Assess

Reviewing Key Concepts

1. a. Flatworms (Platyhelminthes), roundworms (Nematoda), segmented worms (Annelida) **b.** The bodies of all worms have bilateral symmetry, tissues, organs, and body systems. They also have a brain. **c.** They use the sense organs of their nervous system to pick up information.
2. a. Flatworms are flat and have only one opening to their digestive system. Roundworms have cylindrical bodies with pointed ends and a digestive system with two openings. Segmented worms have segments, a digestive system with two openings, and a closed circulatory system. **b.** Sample answer: check to see if it's cylindrical with pointy ends and lacks segments.
c. Free-living flatworms have a digestive system with one opening. Parasitic flatworms absorb their food from the host's digestive system. Roundworms and segmented worms have a digestive system with two openings. Food travels in one direction, and digestion happens in orderly stages along the way.

Reteach L1

Revisit Figure 20 as you quiz students on the main characteristics that differentiate the three worm phyla.

All in One Teaching Resources

- Section Summary: *Worms*
- Review and Reinforce: *Worms*
- Enrich: *Worms*

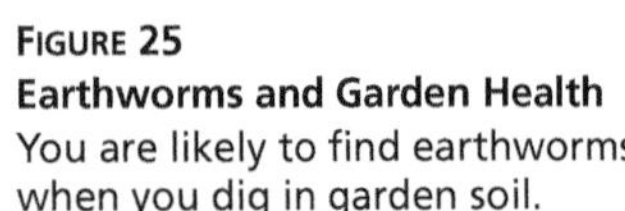

FIGURE 25
Earthworms and Garden Health
You are likely to find earthworms when you dig in garden soil.

Earthworms in the Environment Like many segmented worms, earthworms tunnel for a living. On damp nights or rainy days, they come up out of their burrows. They crawl on the surface of the ground, seeking leaves and other decaying matter that they will drag underground and eat. Staying in moist soil or damp air is important because this keeps the worm's skin moist. An earthworm obtains oxygen through moisture on its skin.

Did you know that earthworms are among the most helpful inhabitants of garden and farm soil? They benefit people by improving the soil in which plants grow. Earthworm tunnels loosen the soil, allowing air, water, and plant roots to move through it. Earthworm droppings make the soil more fertile.

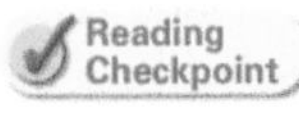 **Why must earthworms stay moist?**

Section 4 Assessment

 **Target Reading Skill** Using Prior Knowledge Review your graphic organizer about worms and revise it based on what you just learned in the section.

Reviewing Key Concepts

1. a. Listing What are the three main phyla of worms?
   b. Describing What are the common characteristics of the bodies of all worms?
   c. Explaining How do worms get information about their environments?
2. a. Reviewing What are the main differences among the three main phyla of worms?
   b. Classifying Suppose you use a microscope to look at a tiny worm. What characteristics would you look for to classify it?
   c. Comparing and Contrasting Compare and contrast the types of digestive systems found in worms.

Writing in Science

Interview Suppose that worms can talk, and that you are an editor for *Worm* magazine. You have been assigned to interview a tapeworm about its feeding habits. Write a transcript of your interview—your questions and the worm's answers.

Lab zone Chapter Project

Keep Students on Track Students should begin to analyze what they have learned about their animal and its habitat. Tell students that they should summarize their observations and decide what their observations tell them about their animal.

Writing in Science

Writing Mode Description

Scoring Rubric

4 Includes complete questions and accurate answers
3 Includes complete questions and accurate but incomplete answers
2 Includes complete questions, but incomplete and inaccurate answers
1 Includes incomplete and inaccurate questions and answers

Skills Lab

Earthworm Responses

Problem
Do earthworms prefer dry or moist conditions? Do they prefer light or dark conditions?

Skills Focus
observing, interpreting data

Materials
- plastic dropper • water • cardboard
- clock or watch • paper towels • flashlight
- 2 earthworms • storage container • tray

Procedure

1. Which environment do you think earthworms prefer—dry or moist? Record your hypothesis in your notebook.
2. Use the dropper to sprinkle water on the worms. Keep the worms moist at all times.
3. Fold a dry paper towel and place it on the bottom of one side of your tray. Fold a moistened paper towel and place it on the other side.
4. Moisten your hands. Then place the earthworms in the center of the tray. Make sure that half of each earthworm's body rests on the moist paper towel and half rests on the dry towel. Handle the worms gently.
5. Cover the tray with the piece of cardboard. After five minutes, remove the cardboard and observe whether the worms are on the moist or dry surface. Record your observations.
6. Repeat Steps 4 and 5.
7. Return the earthworms to their storage container. Moisten the earthworms with water.
8. Which do you think earthworms prefer—strong light or darkness? Record your hypothesis in your notebook.

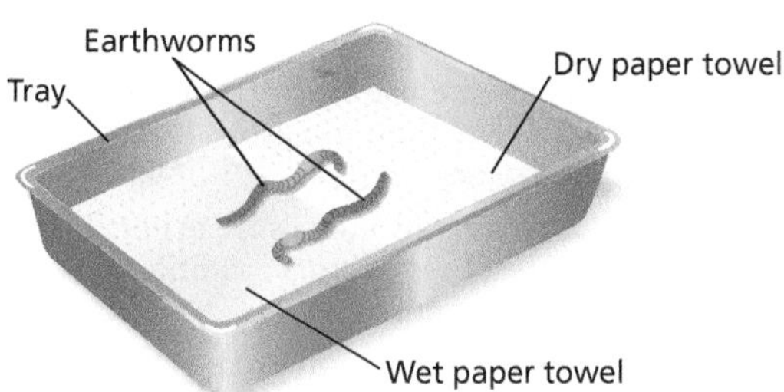

9. Cover the whole surface of the tray with a moistened paper towel.
10. Place the earthworms in the center of the tray. Cover half of the tray with cardboard. Shine a flashlight onto the other half.
11. After five minutes, note the locations of the worms. Record your observations.
12. Repeat Steps 10 and 11.
13. Moisten the earthworms and put them in the location designated by your teacher. Wash your hands after handling the worms.

Analyze and Conclude
1. Observing Which environment did the worms prefer—moist or dry? Bright or dark?
2. Interpreting Data Did the worms' behavior support your hypotheses?
3. Communicating Explain in a paragraph what knowledge or experiences helped you develop your hypotheses at the beginning of the experiments.

Design an Experiment
Do earthworms prefer a smooth or rough surface? Write your hypothesis. Then design an experiment to answer the question. *Obtain your teacher's permission before carrying out your investigation.*

Earthworm Responses L2

Prepare for Inquiry

Key Concept
Students test hypotheses regarding earthworm preferences for soil and light conditions.

Skills Objectives
After this lab, students will be able to
- observe earthworm behavior to determine soil condition and light preferences
- interpret data regarding earthworm preferences

Prep Time 20 minutes
Class Time 30 minutes

Advance Planning
You can get worms from a biological supply company, a bait shop, or loose garden soil.

Alternative Materials
Cake pans can be used for trays. Do not substitute tissues for paper towels; they are too absorbent and will not last.

Safety
Handle earthworms with care and keep them moist at all times. Return them to their container when finished.

All in One Teaching Resources
- Lab Worksheet: *Earthworm Responses*

Guide Inquiry

Invitation
Ask: **Think about the places you are likely to see an earthworm. Would these places be dry or moist?** *(Moist)* **Light or dark?** *(Dark)*

Introducing the Procedure
Have students review the diagram of the setup so they understand how to position the worms. Suggest that they conduct a trial one time before they collect data.

Troubleshooting the Experiment
Rough handling of worms can harm them and prevent them from moving. If a dry paper towel becomes damp, have students replace it.

Expected Outcome
The worms generally preferred the moist towel and the dark environment and moved toward them.

Analyze and Conclude
1. Moist, dark

2. Sample answer: Yes, the worms preferred moist, dark environments as hypothesized.

3. Paragraphs might explain that earthworms are usually found in dark, moist places in nature.

Extend Inquiry
Design an Experiment To test the hypothesis that earthworms prefer a rough surface, students might suggest using sandpaper on one side of a tray and smooth ceramic tile on the other. Remind students that they must control other variables, such as temperature on each side of the tray.

Study Guide

The BIG Idea

Have students read the answer to the Essential Question. Encourage them to evaluate and revise their own answers as needed.

Chapter 1 Study Guide

The BIG Idea **Structure and Function** The structures of animals' bodies enable them to obtain food and oxygen, keep internal conditions stable, move, and reproduce.

1 What Is an Animal?

Key Concepts

- The cells of most animals are organized into higher levels of structure, including tissues, organs, and systems.
- The major functions of animals are to obtain food and oxygen, keep internal conditions stable, move, and reproduce.
- Animals are classified according to how they are related to other animals. These relationships are determined by an animal's body structure, the way an animal develops, and its DNA.

Key Terms

• cell • tissue • organ • adaptation
• sexual reproduction • fertilization
• asexual reproduction • phylum • vertebrate
• invertebrate

2 Animal Symmetry

Key Concepts

- The balanced arrangement of parts, called symmetry, is characteristic of many animals.
- Depending on their symmetry, animals share some general characteristics.

Key Terms

bilateral symmetry
radial symmetry

3 Sponges and Cnidarians

Key Concepts

- Sponges are invertebrate animals that usually have no body symmetry and never have tissues or organs.
- Cnidarians use stinging cells to capture food and defend themselves.
- Coral reefs are home to more species of fishes and invertebrates than any other environment on Earth.

Key Terms

larva
cnidarian
polyp
medusa
colony
coral reef

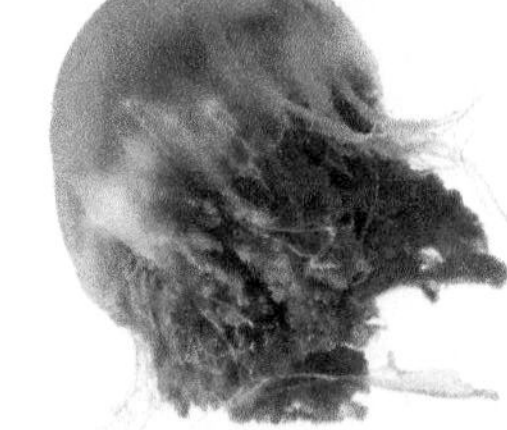

4 Worms

Key Concepts

- Biologists classify worms into three major phyla—flatworms, roundworms, and segmented worms.
- Flatworms are flat and soft as jelly.
- Unlike cnidarians or flatworms, roundworms have a digestive system that is like a tube, open at both ends.
- Earthworms and other segmented worms have bodies made up of many linked sections called segments.

Key Terms

• parasite • host • free-living organism
• scavenger • anus • closed circulatory system

Help Students Read

Building Vocabulary

Word Forms Students may have seen several of the vocabulary terms for this chapter used in different contexts. Help them to relate these familiar meanings to chapter content. For example, ask: **What is a scavenger hunt?** *(A game in which participants must find specific items, usually junk items, within a certain time limit)* **What is a scavenger?** *(An animal that feeds on refuse—that is, dead or decaying material; also, a person who is a scavenger is a junk collector)*

Words in Context Select Key Terms from the chapter. Have students write a sentence for each term that places the term in the correct context. Provide them with one example before they begin: *Cell: Sponges, cnidarians, flatworms, roundworms, and segmented worms are all animals and therefore are composed of many cells.*

Connecting Concepts

Concept Maps Help students develop one way to show how the information in this chapter is related. Have students brainstorm to identify the key concepts, key terms, details, and examples. Then write each one on a sticky note and attach it at random on chart paper or on the board.

Tell students that this concept map will be organized in hierarchical order and to begin at the top with the key concepts. Ask students these questions to guide them to categorize the information on the stickies: **What characteristics of animals can you observe directly? Indirectly? How are animals classified?** Prompt students by using connecting words or phrases, such as "composed of," "arranged by," and "are identified by," to indicate the basis for the organization of the map. The phrases should form a sentence between or among a set of concepts.

Answer

Accept logical presentations by students.

All in One Teaching Resources

- Key Terms Review: *Sponges, Cnidarians, and Worms*
- Connecting Concepts: *Sponges, Cnidarians, and Worms*

Review and Assessment

Go Online PHSchool.com
For: Self-Assessment
Visit: PHSchool.com
Web Code: cea-2010

Organizing Information

Sequencing Copy the cycle diagram about the life of a sponge onto a sheet of paper. Then complete it and add a title.

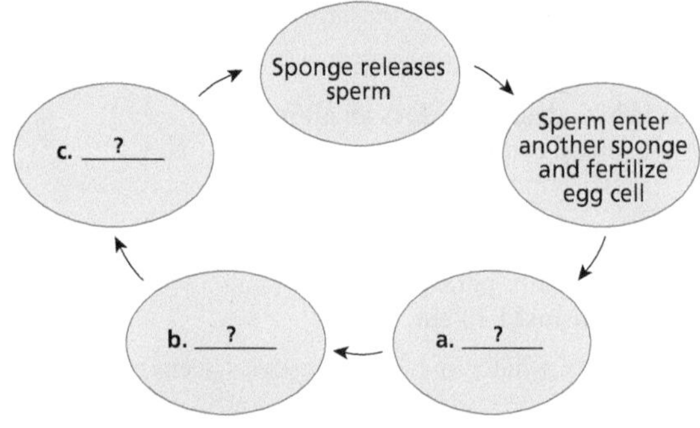

Reviewing Key Terms

Choose the letter of the best answer.

1. The highest level of organization in an animal is a(n)
   a. cell. **b.** tissue.
   c. organ. **d.** system.
2. An animal without a backbone is called a(n)
   a. vertebrate.
   b. invertebrate.
   c. larva.
   d. parasite.
3. An animal with many lines of symmetry
   a. has bilateral symmetry.
   b. has radial symmetry.
   c. has no symmetry.
   d. has a distinct head and tail end.
4. Which animal is a medusa?
   a. coral
   b. moon jelly
   c. planarian
   d. sea anemone
5. An organism that does not live in or on another organism is called a
   a. scavenger.
   b. parasite.
   c. free-living organism.
   d. host.

If the statement is true, write *true*. If it is false, change the underlined word or words to make the statement true.

6. A tissue is a group of <u>organs</u> that work together to perform a job.
7. Fishes have <u>bilateral symmetry</u>.
8. Budding is a form of <u>sexual reproduction</u>.
9. A <u>polyp</u> is an immature form of an animal that looks very different from the adult form.
10. Some tapeworms are <u>parasites</u> of dogs.

Writing in Science

Letter Suppose that you have just come back from a trip to a coral reef. Write a letter to a friend that compares corals and jellyfish. Be sure to explain how the two animals are alike and how they are different.

Sponges, Cnidarians, and Worms
Video Preview
Video Field Trip
▶ Video Assessment

For: Self-Assessment
Visit: PHSchool.com
Web Code: cea-2010

Students can take a practice test online that is automatically scored.

All in One Teaching Resources

- Transparency B12
- Chapter Test
- Performance Assessment Teacher Notes
- Performance Assessment Student Worksheet
- Performance Assessment Scoring Rubric

Review and Assessment

Organizing Information

a. Larva develops.
b. Water currents carry away larva.
c. Larva settles on a surface and develops into adult sponge.
Sample title: Life Cycle of a Sponge

Reviewing Key Terms

1. d **2.** b **3.** b **4.** b **5.** c
6. false; A tissue is a group of cells
7. true
8. false; Budding is a form of asexual reproduction.
9. false; A larva is an immature form of an animal that looks very different from the adult form.
10. true

Writing in Science

Writing Mode Description
Scoring Rubric
4 Includes detailed descriptions of sights, dangers and other adventures; descriptions are lively and fun to read.
3 Includes all criteria
2 Includes one or two criteria or only brief descriptions
1 Includes only one description and inaccurate information

Sponges, Cnidarians, and Worms

Show the Video Assessment to review chapter content and as a prompt for the writing assignment. Discussion question: **Describe two ways in which jellyfish move through the water.** *(They swim by expanding and contracting their bodies; they also float.)* **What is one possible function of bioluminescence in jellyfish?** *(To send signals to potential mates; to scare off predators)*

Checking Concepts

11. Tissues are made up of similar cells that work together to perform a specific job. Organs are made up of different types of tissues.

12. The functions of animals are obtaining food and oxygen, keeping internal conditions stable, moving, and reproducing.

13. Animals with bilateral symmetry have front ends and streamlined bodies. Thus, they can move quickly and efficiently. They have sense organs in their front ends that pick up information about what is in front of them, which helps them find food and avoid enemies.

14. A polyp is usually attached to a surface. Its mouth is at the top of its body. A medusa is free-swimming. Its mouth is at the bottom of its body. Both are radially symmetrical.

15. Humans are free-living organisms. They do not live in or on other organisms.

16. In a one-way digestive system, food enters at one end, is digested along the way, and wastes are expelled at the opposite end.

Thinking Critically

17. The title is misleading. The animals on Earth include both vertebrates and invertebrates; in fact 97% of Earth's animals are invertebrates.

18. Sea anemones have radial symmetry; sponges have no symmetry; fishes, humans, and butterflies have bilateral symmetry.

19. In a sponge, jellylike cells digest the food. In a planarian, digested juices that flow out onto the food begin digestion; digestion is continued in a cavity within the planarian; undigested material is expelled through the feeding tube. In a roundworm, digestion happens in orderly stages as food passes in one direction through the worm, from its mouth to its anus.

20. The plants' health might suffer because there will likely be less water, air, and nutrients available to the plants' roots. It might also be more difficult for plants' roots to move through the soil.

21. *B:* roundworm; *A:* sponge; *C:* cnidarian. Sponges have no symmetry and lack tissues and organs. Cnidarians have radial symmetry and stinging cells, and a mouth that opens into a central body cavity. Roundworms have bilateral symmetry, a digestive system with two openings, and long cylindrical bodies with pointed ends.

Review and Assessment

Checking Concepts

11. Explain the relationship among cells, tissues, and organs.
12. What are four key functions of animals?
13. What advantages does an animal with bilateral symmetry have over an animal with radial symmetry?
14. Compare and contrast a medusa and a polyp.
15. Are humans parasitic or free-living organisms? Explain.
16. Explain what a one-way digestive system is.

Thinking Critically

17. **Making Judgments** Suppose you check out a book from the library called *Earth's Animals.* You notice that all the animals in the book are vertebrates. Is this title a good one? Explain your reasoning.
18. **Classifying** Classify each of the following animals as having radial symmetry, bilateral symmetry, or no symmetry: sea anemones, sponges, fishes, humans, and butterflies.
19. **Comparing and Contrasting** Compare and contrast the ways in which a sponge, a planarian, and a roundworm digest their food.
20. **Relating Cause and Effect** If a disease killed off many of the earthworms in a garden, how might the plants growing in the soil be affected? Explain.
21. **Classifying** Which of the animals below is a roundworm? A sponge? A cnidarian? Describe the major characteristics of the members of these three phyla.

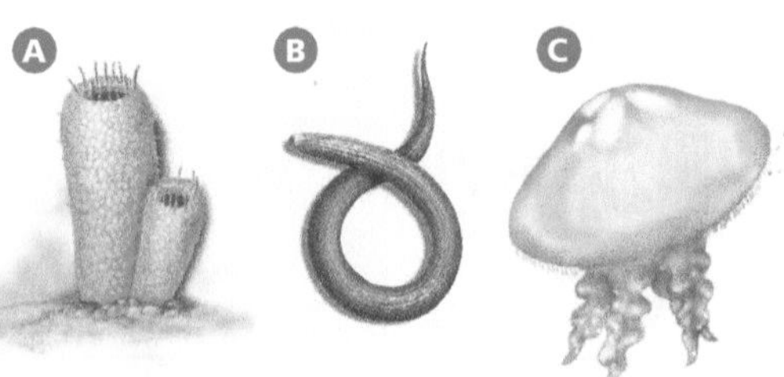

Math Practice

22. **Calculating a Rate** In 24 hours, 110 L of water pass through a sponge. What is the rate of water flow?

Applying Skills

Use the tables to answer Questions 23–25.

A scientist used a pesticide on one field and left a nearby field untreated. Next, she marked off five plots of equal size in each field. Then she dug up a cubic meter of soil beneath each plot and counted the earthworms in the soil. The tables below show her data.

Field With Pesticide

Plot	Worms per Cubic Meter
A	730
B	254
C	319
D	428
E	451

Untreated Field

Plot	Worms per Cubic Meter
F	901
G	620
H	811
I	576
J	704

23. **Controlling Variables** Identify the manipulated and responding variables in this experiment.
24. **Calculating** Calculate the average number of worms per cubic meter in the field treated with pesticide. Then do the same for the untreated field.
25. **Drawing Conclusions** How did this pesticide affect the number of worms?

Lab zone Chapter Project

Performance Assessment Write a summary explaining what you have learned about your animal. Describe its habitat, the food it eats, its behavior, and any surprising observations that you made. Then introduce your animal to your classmates and share what you have discovered.

Lab zone Chapter Project

L3

Performance Assessment Ask the students to write down the major characteristics of each animal as other students present their projects.

After all presentations have been made, have students evaluate their projects.

Students should decide what animals were best for the projects and the best methods for taking care of the animals. Help students resettle their animals humanely after completing their projects.

Standardized Test Prep

Test-Taking Tip

Sequencing Events

A test question may ask you to order a series of events. For example, you may be given several sequences and asked to determine which is correct, or identify which event comes before another. After you read the question, try to identify the correct sequence of events before you read the answer choices.

Sample Question

Which of the following best describes stages in the sexual life cycle of a sponge in the correct order?

A larva, fertilization, egg, adult
B adult, larva, egg, fertilization
C adult, bud, bud breaks free
D larva, adult, egg, fertilization

Answer

The correct answer is **D**. You can eliminate **C** because it uses terms that describe asexual reproduction. Of the remaining choices, **A** cannot be correct because eggs do not follow fertilization, but must be present before fertilization can occur. **B** cannot be correct because larvae cannot produce eggs.

Choose the letter of the best answer.

1. What is the correct sequence in which a stinging cell reacts to the touch of another organism?
A trigger brushes against prey, stinging cell fires, barbs snare prey
B barbs snare prey, stinging cell fires, barbs release prey
C prey is paralyzed, venom enters prey, stinging cell fires
D tentacles pull prey to mouth, prey is ingested, stinging cell fires

2. Which of the following is true of a one-way digestive system?
F It is found in all parasites.
G It has two openings.
H It has one opening.
J It is found in all parasites and has one opening.

3. Of the four animals shown below, which has the same symmetry as a jellyfish?

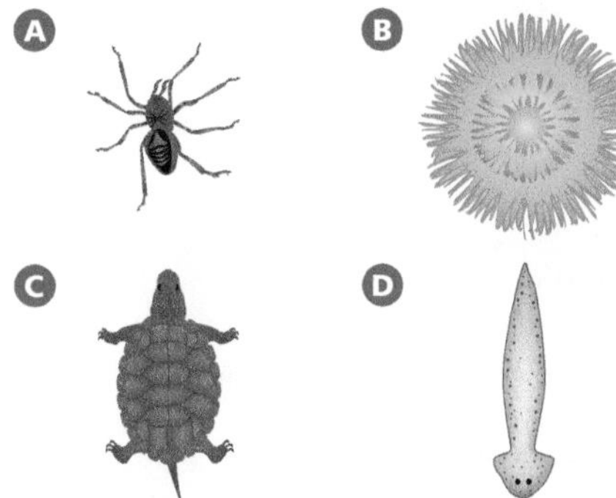

4. Imagine that the animals illustrated above are real and are resting on this page. Predict which of the animals would travel toward the top of the page if they began moving in a straight line.
F animals A and D
G animals A and B
H animals B and D
J animals A and C

5. The following terms can all be used to describe a tapeworm *except*
A parasite
B invertebrate
C flatworm
D medusa

Constructed Response

6. Compare and contrast the feeding process of a sponge with that of an earthworm. How are their feeding processes similar? How are they different?

Math Practice

22. 4.58 L/h

Applying Skills

23. The manipulated variable is whether the field is treated with the pesticide or not. The responding variable is the number of worms in the soil.

24. The average number of worms per cubic meter in the treated field is 436.4. The average number in the untreated field is 722.4.

25. The pesticide reduced the number of worms per cubic meter.

Standardized Test Prep

1. A **2.** G **3.** B **4.** J **5.** D

6. A sponge draws water in through its pores where collar cells strain tiny one-celled organisms from the water and jelly-like cells digest them. Wastes exit through the hole at its top. In contrast, food enters an earthworm's body through its mouth, enters its digestive system, and is digested along the way. Wastes leave the body through the anus.

The processes are similar in that there is a flow of food in one direction. For the sponge, the flow is from pores to central cavity, then out the large opening at the top; for the earthworm, it is from mouth to anus.

The BIG Idea

The Big Idea is the major scientific concept of the chapter. It is followed by the Essential Question. Read aloud the question to students. As students study the chapter, tell them to think about the Essential Question. Explain that they will discover the answer to the question as they read. The chapter Study Guide provides a sample answer.

Objectives

This project will give students an opportunity to investigate the metamorphosis of mealworms under a variety of different conditions (variables). After this Chapter Project, students will be able to

- observe how different conditions affect mealworm development
- design experiments to test the effect of an environmental variable on metamorphosis
- organize data in tables to record daily mealworm observations
- draw conclusions regarding the effect of the environmental change on metamorphosis

Skills Focus

Observing, designing, organizing data, drawing conclusions

Project Time Line 2 to 3 weeks

All in One Teaching Resources

- Chapter Project Teacher Notes
- Chapter Project Overview
- Chapter Project Worksheet 1
- Chapter Project Worksheet 2
- Chapter Project Scoring Rubric

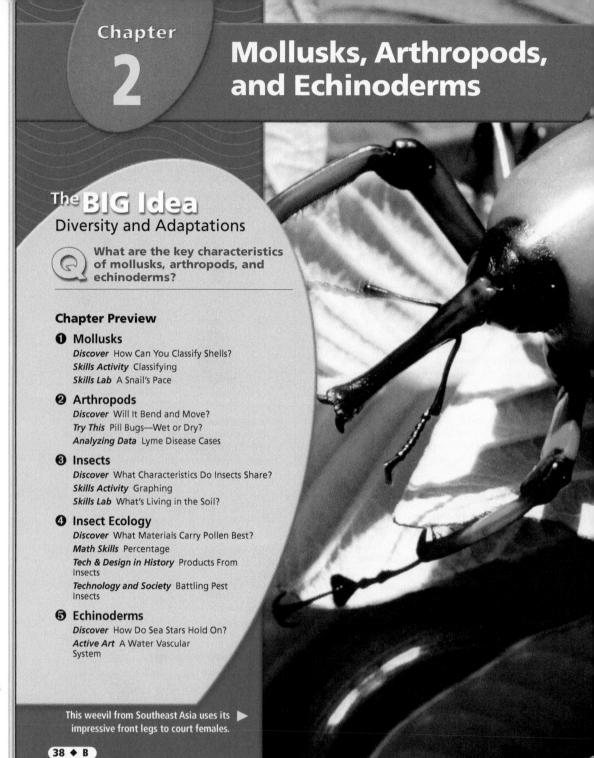

Chapter 2 Mollusks, Arthropods, and Echinoderms

The BIG Idea
Diversity and Adaptations

What are the key characteristics of mollusks, arthropods, and echinoderms?

Chapter Preview

This weevil from Southeast Asia uses its impressive front legs to court females.

Developing a Plan

Allow time for students to read the description of the project in their text. Then encourage discussions of the environmental factors that might affect metamorphosis, such as temperature, light, and type of food supplied. Students can work in small groups as a cooperative learning task. To ensure that every student will have ample opportunity to participate in designing an experiment, you may wish to limit groups to three students.

Possible Materials

- You can obtain mealworms from local pet stores. Make sure they are well fed and have a moisture source until the project launch day.
- Tell students to bring in plastic containers with lids, such as empty margarine tubs.
- Students can bring in corn meal, unprocessed bran, dry cereal or uncooked oatmeal for mealworm food. Slices of apple, potato, or carrot can be used as moisture sources. Students can use plastic spoons to transfer the cereal to the containers and to count the mealworms.

Chapter at a Glance

PRENTICE HALL TeacherEXPRESS™ Plan • Teach • Assess

 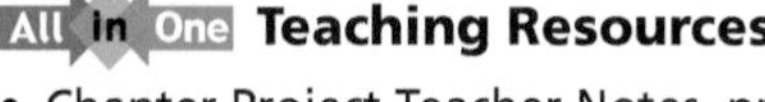

Chapter Project *Going Through Changes*

All in One Teaching Resources

- Chapter Project Teacher Notes, pp. 104–105
- Chapter Project Student Overview, pp. 106–107
- Chapter Project Student Worksheets, pp. 108–109
- Chapter Project Scoring Rubric, p. 110

Technology

Local Standards

Section 1 Mollusks

2–3 periods
1–1 1/2 blocks

B.2.1.1 Identify the main characteristics of mollusks.

B.2.1.2 Describe the major groups of mollusks and tell how they differ.

Section 2 Arthropods

3–4 periods
1 1/2–2 blocks

B.2.2.1 Identify four major groups of arthropods and the main characteristics of arthropods.

B.2.2.2 Describe how crustaceans, arachnids, and centipedes and millipedes differ.

Section 3 Insects

2–3 periods
1–1 1/2 blocks

B.2.3.1 Identify the main characteristics of insects.

B.2.3.2 Explain how insects are adapted to obtain food.

B.2.3.3 Name the two types of metamorphosis found in insects.

Section 4 Insect Ecology

2–3 periods
1–1 1/2 blocks

B.2.4.1 Explain why insects are important in food chains.

B.2.4.2 Name two other ways insects interact with their environments.

B.2.4.3 Describe some methods used to control pest insects.

Section 5 Echinoderms

1–2 periods
1/2–1 block

B.2.5.1 List the main characteristics of echinoderms.

B.2.5.2 Name the major groups of echinoderms.

Review and Assessment

All in One Teaching Resources

- Key Terms Review, p. 150
- Transparency B23
- Performance Assessment Teacher Notes, p. 159
- Performance Assessment Scoring Rubric, p. 160
- Performance Assessment Student Worksheet, p. 161
- Chapter Test, pp. 162–165

Video Assessment

Test Preparation

Test Preparation Blackline Masters

Chapter Activities Planner

For more activities

Student Edition	Inquiry	Time	Materials	Skills	Resources
Chapter Project, p. 39	Open-Ended	2 to 3 weeks	All in One **Teaching Resources** See p. 104	Observing, designing, organizing data, drawing conclusions	**Lab zone Easy Planner** All in One **Teaching Resources** Support pp. 104–105
Section 1					
Discover Activity, p. 40	Guided	20 minutes	Mollusk shells, such as those from clams, mussels, oysters, land and marine snails, and nautiluses	Inferring	**Lab zone Easy Planner**
Skills Activity, p. 43	Guided	10 minutes	None	Classifying	**Lab zone Easy Planner**
Skills Lab, p. 46	Guided	Prep: 30 minutes Class: 45 minutes	Freshwater snail, plastic petri dish, timer, spring water at three temperatures: cool (9–13°C); medium (18–22°C); warm (27–31°C), thermometer, 2 sheets graph paper, ruler	Interpreting data, predicting	**Lab zone Easy Planner** All in One **Teaching Resources** Skills Lab: *A Snail's Pace,* pp. 119–120
Section 2					
Discover Activity, p. 47	Directed	Prep: 5 minutes Class: 15 minutes	Sheets of heavy cardboard, about 30 × 45 cm; tape	Inferring	**Lab zone Easy Planner**
Try This Activity, p. 51	Directed	20 minutes	Shoe box, aluminum foil, paper towels, masking tape, live pill bugs, water	Interpreting data	**Lab zone Easy Planner**
Section 3					
Discover Activity, p. 55	Directed	Prep: 5 minutes Class: 15 minutes	Insect collection, hand lenses	Inferring	**Lab zone Easy Planner**
Skills Activity, p. 56	Guided	15 minutes	none	Graphing	**Lab zone Easy Planner**
Skills Lab, pp. 60–61	Guided	Prep: 45 minutes Class: 15 minutes on the first day, 45 minutes on the second day	2-liter plastic bottle, trowel, cheesecloth, gooseneck lamp, large, wide-mouthed jar, coarse steel wool, large scissors, large rubber band, hand lens, small jar, fresh sample of soil and leaf litter	Observing, classifying	**Lab zone Easy Planner** All in One **Teaching Resources** Skills Lab: *What's Living in the Soil?* pp. 135–137
Section 4					
Discover Activity, p. 62	Open-Ended	20 minutes	Flowers, cotton swab, pencil, other materials as selected	Inferring	**Lab zone Easy Planner**
Section 5					
Discover Activity, p. 70	Directed	5 minutes	Plastic dropper, water	Predicting	**Lab zone Easy Planner**

ABILITY LEVELS
L1 Basic to Average
L2 For All Students
L3 Average to Advanced

Section 1 Mollusks

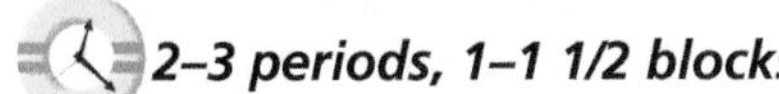
2–3 periods, 1–1 1/2 blocks

Objectives

B.2.1.1 Identify the main characteristics of mollusks.
B.2.1.2 Describe the major groups of mollusks and tell how they differ.

Local Standards

Key Terms

• mollusk • open circulatory system • gill • gastropod • herbivore
• carnivore • radula • bivalve • omnivore • cephalopod

Preteach

Build Background Knowledge

Ask students who are familiar with mollusks to share their knowledge.

Lab zone Discover Activity *How Can You Classify Shells?* L1

Targeted Print and Technology Resources

All in One Teaching Resources
L2 Reading Strategy Transparency B13: Comparing and Contrasting

PresentationExpress™ CD-ROM

Instruct

Characteristics of Mollusks Use pictures to show that all mollusks have the same basic body structures.

Snails and Slugs Use class discussion to help students identify the characteristics of gastropods.

Two-Shelled Mollusks Ask leading questions to identify the characteristics of bivalves.

Octopuses and Their Relatives Use photographs to teach the characteristics of cephalopods.

Lab zone Skills Lab *A Snail's Pace* L2

Targeted Print and Technology Resources

All in One Teaching Resources
L2 Guided Reading, pp. 113–116
L2 Transparency B14
L2 Skills Lab: *A Snail's Pace*, pp. 119–120

Lab Activity Video/DVD
Skills Lab: *A Snail's Pace*

Discovery Channel School
Video Field Trip

Student Edition on Audio CD

Assess

Section Assessment Questions

Have students use the information in their Comparing and Contrasting graphic organizers to help them answer the questions.

Reteach

Use a chart to compare different kinds of mollusks.

Targeted Print and Technology Resources

All in One Teaching Resources
• Section Summary, p. 112
L1 Review and Reinforce, p. 117
L3 Enrich, p. 118

Section 2 Arthropods

3–4 periods, 1 1/2–2 blocks

ABILITY LEVELS
- L1 Basic to Average
- L2 For All Students
- L3 Average to Advanced

Objectives

B.2.2.1 Identify four major groups of arthropods and the main characteristics of arthropods.

B.2.2.2 Describe how crustaceans, arachnids, and centipedes and millipedes differ.

Local Standards

Key Terms

• arthropod • exoskeleton • molting • antenna • crustacean • metamorphosis • arachnid • abdomen

Preteach

Build Background Knowledge

Question students about their experience with arthropods.

 *Will It Bend and Move?* L1

Targeted Print and Technology Resources

 **Teaching Resources**

L2 Reading Strategy Transparency B15: Asking Questions

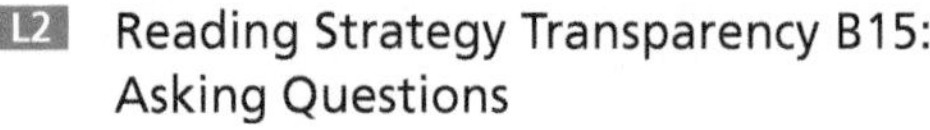

Instruct

Characteristics of Arthropods Use Figure 10 to compare the differences among the four major groups.

Crustaceans Have students use illustration callouts to identify characteristics of crustaceans.

Arachnids Use leading questions to discuss the characteristics of arachnids.

Centipedes and Millipedes Use simple sketches to illustrate characteristics of centipedes and millipedes.

Targeted Print and Technology Resources

All in One Teaching Resources

L2 Guided Reading, pp. 123–126

L2 Transparencies B16, B17

www.SciLinks.org Web Code: scn-0222

 **Student Edition on Audio CD**

Assess

Section Assessment Questions

Have students use their completed Asking Questions graphic organizers to answer the questions.

Reteach

Use a table to review characteristics of arthropod groups.

Targeted Print and Technology Resources

All in One Teaching Resources

- Section Summary, p. 122

L1 Review and Reinforce, p. 127

L3 Enrich, p. 128

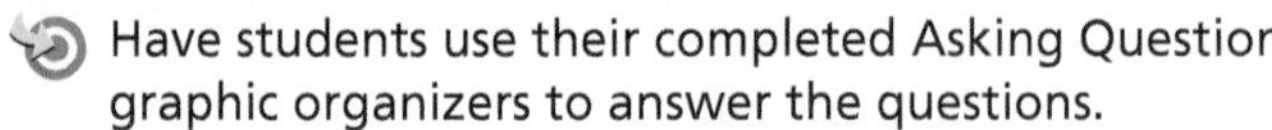

Section 3 Insects

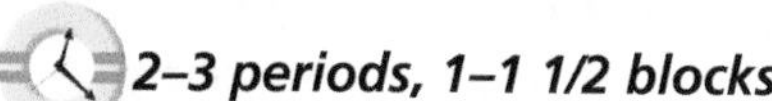
2–3 periods, 1–1 1/2 blocks

ABILITY LEVELS
- L1 Basic to Average
- L2 For All Students
- L3 Average to Advanced

Objectives

B.2.3.1 Identify the main characteristics of insects.
B.2.3.2 Explain how insects are adapted to obtain food.
B.2.3.3 Name the two types of metamorphosis found in insects.

Key Terms

• insect • thorax • complete metamorphosis • pupa • gradual metamorphosis
• nymph

Local Standards

Preteach

Build Background Knowledge

Ask students to describe insects they have observed.

Lab zone Discover Activity *What Characteristics Do Insects Share?* L1

Targeted Print and Technology Resources

All in One Teaching Resources
- L2 Reading Strategy Transparency B18: Sequencing

PresentationExpress™ CD-ROM

Instruct

Body Structure Use an illustration to discuss the three body sections of a grasshopper.

Obtaining Food Compare and contrast insects' mouthparts and discuss how they are adapted for a highly specific way of getting food.

Life Cycle Use illustrations to compare and contrast complete metamorphosis and gradual metamorphosis.

Lab zone Skills Lab *What's Living in the Soil?* L2

Targeted Print and Technology Resources

All in One Teaching Resources
- L2 Guided Reading, pp. 131–132
- L2 Transparencies B19, B20
- L2 Skills Lab: *What's Living in the Soil?* pp. 135–137

Lab Activity Video/DVD
Skills Lab: *What's Living in the Soil?*

PHSchool.com Web code: ced-2023

Student Edition on Audio CD

Assess

Section Assesment Questions

Have students use their completed Sequencing graphic organizers to answer the questions.

Reteach

Use an illustration to review the events in insect metamorphosis.

Targeted Print and Technology Resources

All in One Teaching Resources
- Section Summary, p. 130
- L1 Review and Reinforce, p. 133
- L3 Enrich, p. 134

Section 4 Insect Ecology

 *2–3 periods, 1–1 1/2 blocks*

ABILITY LEVELS
L1 Basic to Average
L2 For All Students
L3 Average to Advanced

Objectives

B.2.4.1 Explain why insects are important in food chains.
B.2.4.2 Name two other ways insects interact with their environments.
B.2.4.3 Describe some methods used to control pest insects.

Key Terms

• food chain • ecology • producer • consumer • decomposer • pollinator
• pesticide • biological control

Local Standards

Preteach

Build Background Knowledge

Ask questions to find out what students know about the roles of insects.

 *What Materials Carry Pollen Best?* L2

Targeted Print and Technology Resources

All in One Teaching Resources
L2 Reading Strategy: Building Vocabulary

PresentationExpress™ CD-ROM

Instruct

Insects and the Food Chain Describe the roles played by insects in food chains.

Other Interactions Use photographs to relate that some insects interact with their communities by carrying pollen or diseases.

Controlling Pests Discuss the benefits and costs of different types of insect pest control.

Targeted Print and Technology Resources

All in One Teaching Resources
L2 Guided Reading, pp. 140–141

www.SciLinks.org Web Code: scn-0224

PHSchool.com Web code: ceh-2020

Student Edition on Audio CD

Assess

Section Assessment Questions

Have students use their completed sentences to answer the questions.

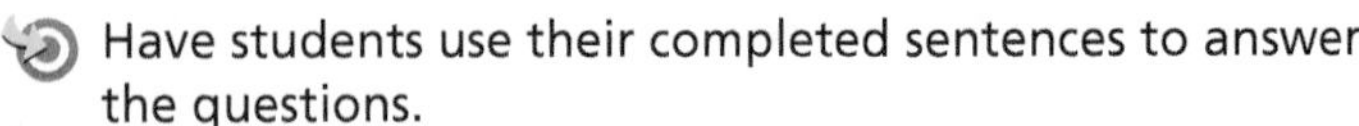

Reteach

List examples of beneficial insects and harmful insects.

Targeted Print and Technology Resources

All in One Teaching Resources
• Section Summary, p. 139
L1 Review and Reinforce, p. 142
L3 Enrich, p. 143

Section 5 Echinoderms

 *1–2 periods, 1/2–1 block*

ABILITY LEVELS
L1 Basic to Average
L2 For All Students
L3 Average to Advanced

Local Standards

Objectives

B.2.5.1 List the main characteristics of echinoderms.
B.2.5.2 Name the major groups of echinoderms.

Key Terms

• echinoderm • endoskeleton • water vascular system • tube feet

Preteach

Build Background Knowledge

Help students identify similarities among Echinoderms.

How Do Sea Stars Hold On? L1

Targeted Print and Technology Resources

Teaching Resources

L2 Reading Strategy Transparency B21: Previewing Visuals

PresentationExpress™ CD-ROM

Instruct

Characteristics of Echinoderms Use an illustration to discuss the distinctive characteristics of echinoderms.

Diversity of Echinoderms Compare photographs to identify the four major groups of echinoderms.

Targeted Print and Technology Resources

L2 Guided Reading, pp. 146–147
L2 Transparency B22

PHSchool.com Web Code: cep-2025

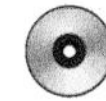

Student Edition on audio CD

Assess

Section Assessment Questions

Have students use their Previewing Visuals graphic organizers to answer the questions.

Reteach

Create a table to summarize the body structure, movement, and reproduction of echinoderms.

Targeted Print and Technology Resources

• Section Summary, p. 145
L1 Review and Reinforce, p. 148
L3 Enrich, p. 149

Chapter 2 Content Refresher

Go Online
NSTA-PD*i*LINKS
For: Professional development support
Visit: www.SciLinks.org/PDLinks
Web Code: scf-0220
Professional Development

Section 1 Mollusks

Open and Closed Circulatory Systems In open circulatory systems, a heart pumps blood into short blood vessels that empty into open spaces. In these low-pressure systems, the blood percolates along, delivering oxygen and nutrients and collecting wastes, until the cavities narrow into vessels that direct the blood back to the heart. In closed systems, blood remains within vessels, and all exchanges are carried out through the capillary walls. Blood pressure is generally much higher in closed systems.

The kind of system that an animal has relates generally to the oxygen demands of the animal. If the demands are low, the animal probably is sedentary or moves very slowly. For these animals, a low-pressure, more sluggish flow of blood is sufficient. If the oxygen demands are high, meaning that the animal is very active, the animal often has the oxygen-efficient, high-pressure, closed system. But there are important exceptions to these generalizations.

Most vertebrates are active animals. So, as you would expect, vertebrates have closed circulatory systems. There is no clear pattern in invertebrates. Many have open systems and are comparatively sluggish, but others with open systems, including insects, are quite active. Some slow-moving invertebrates, such as segmented worms, have closed systems.

Section 2 Arthropods

Lyme Disease Identified in 1975, the disease is named for the town of Lyme, Connecticut, where it was first observed. Lyme disease is caused by *Borrelia burgdorferi*, a spiral-shaped bacterium that is transmitted to the human bloodstream by the bite of a deer tick.

In humans, the disease begins with a circular rash in a bull's-eye pattern around the tick bite. If not treated in the early stage with antibiotics, the disease may go on to cause arthritic pain and neurological symptoms.

The disease cycle begins when a tick picks up the bacterium by biting an infected animal, often a white-tailed deer. Once infected, the adult tick lays eggs, which hatch and become larvae and then nymphs. Both the nymph stage and adult stage of the tick are likely to bite humans and transmit the disease, particularly during the summer months. Nymph stages of the deer tick are much smaller than the more familiar wood tick (commonly found on dogs and cats), making them difficult to spot.

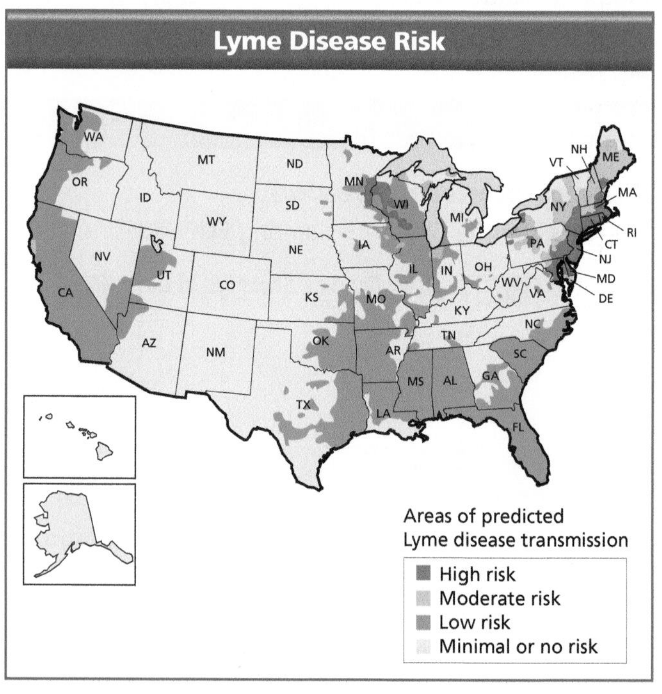

To reduce the likelihood of Lyme disease, persons who live in high-risk areas should take precautions before spending time in yards or in wooded areas with overgrown brush. Long-sleeved shirts, long pants, and high socks reduce the chance of tick bites. Tucking pants into socks or boot tops will reduce the chances of ticks reaching your skin. The risk of tick attachment can be reduced by using appropriate insecticides. Check all over your body for ticks after being outdoors. Use fine-tipped tweezers to promptly remove any attached ticks.

Address Misconceptions

Students may think that all spiders catch their prey in webs. This is false. For a strategy for overcoming this misconception, see **Address Misconceptions** in the section *Arthropods.*

Section 3 Insects

Mosquito-Borne Diseases Of all of the world's disease-carriers, mosquitoes transmit more serious human diseases than any other. Because female mosquitoes require a blood meal before laying their eggs, mosquitoes are common transmitters of bloodborne diseases.

Mosquitoes in the genus *Anopheles* are the sole carriers of malaria. Malaria is caused by a single-celled parasite, the protozoan *Plasmodium*. The mosquito picks up the parasite when biting an infected person. The parasite reproduces inside the mosquito, producing infective cells that pass into the human bloodstream during the mosquito's next bite. Mosquitoes also carry the microorganisms that cause filariasis, encephalitis, yellow fever, dengue, and West Nile encephalitis.

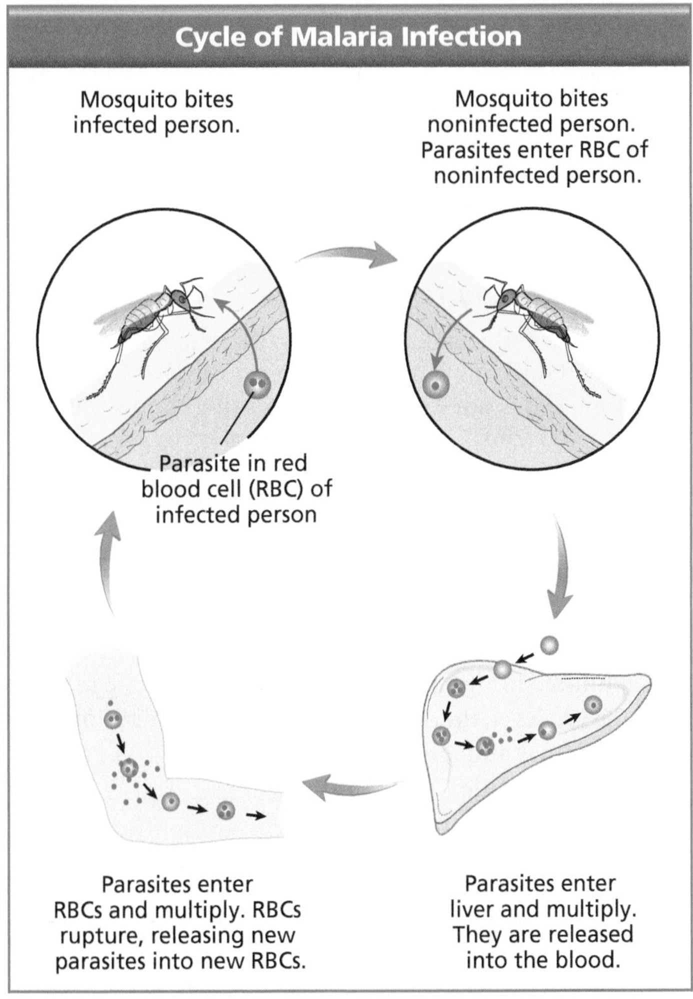
Cycle of Malaria Infection
Mosquito bites infected person.
Mosquito bites noninfected person. Parasites enter RBC of noninfected person.
Parasite in red blood cell (RBC) of infected person
Parasites enter RBCs and multiply. RBCs rupture, releasing new parasites into new RBCs.
Parasites enter liver and multiply. They are released into the blood.

Mosquito control efforts involve community-wide measures, such as draining swamps, marshes, and stagnant water where mosquitoes breed, and the use of insecticides. Window screens and mosquito netting are widely used to protect sleeping individuals from mosquitoes, which are active mainly at night.

Section 4 Insect Ecology

Food Chains and Food Webs A food chain is a series of events in which one organism eats another and obtains energy. Food chains are generally diagrammed as shown in the illustration, with an arrow running from each organism that is eaten to the organism that eats it. The sun is the source of energy in almost all food chains.

The first organism in a food chain is always a producer, such as a plant or photosynthetic microorganism. In the food chain in the illustration, algae are the producers. The other organisms in this particular food chain, such as the zooplankton that eat the algae and the small fish that eat the zooplankton, are consumers. Energy from the sun flows in one direction, indicated by the arrows, to the producer, to the first consumer, and so forth.

In most environments, feeding relationships are much more complex than those diagrammed in food chains. Different food chains usually intersect with one another. For example, the small fish, which in the illustration are eaten by squid, may also be eaten by larger fishes and birds. Scientists use the term *food web* to describe these complex feeding relationships.

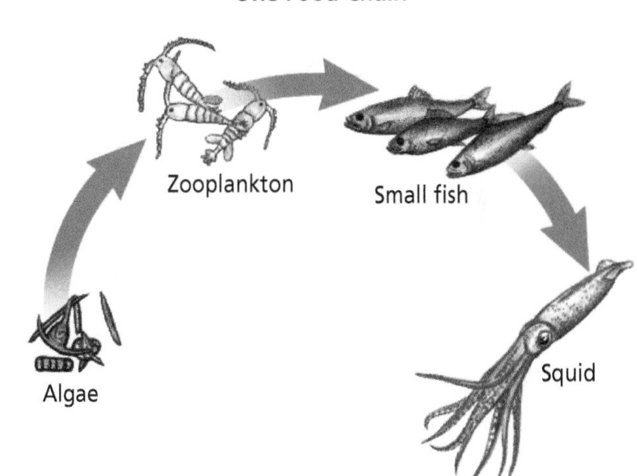
One Food Chain
Zooplankton
Small fish
Algae
Squid

Section 5 Echinoderms

The Water Vascular System An echinoderm's water vascular system is involved in more than movement. The fluid in the water vascular system is the main medium through which needed materials and wastes travel throughout the echinoderm's body. Oxygen passes from water into the echinoderm's body through the tube feet, which have thin walls. The tube feet also pass nitrogenous wastes, mainly in the form of ammonia, into the water that surrounds the echinoderm.

Crown-of-Thorns Sea Star As one of the largest and most venomous sea stars, the crown-of-thorns sea star, *Acanthaster planci,* can reach 50 cm in diameter. It has 10 to 20 arms covered with toxic spines. At about six months of age, the crown-of-thorns sea star begins to eat coral. Although they don't look edible, coral reefs are actually the home of coral polyps, the living invertebrates that produce the colorful corals. After the coral polyps are eaten, the white coral skeleton is left behind.

A healthy coral reef can support small populations of crown-of-thorns sea stars for many years. But when sea stars are present in large numbers, they can kill most of the living coral within an entire section of the reef. When this occurs, a reef can take 10 years or more to recover its coral population.

Help Students Read

Outline

Understanding Text Structure

Strategy Help students focus on the text and not simply skim it. Outlining is a good strategy to apply to an entire section, if it is not excessively long, using the headings as major divisions. Outlining is best applied to sections in which the headings are parallel, and in which there are main headings and subheadings. Before you begin, choose a section for students to read and outline.

Example

1. Before students read, have them preview the section's title and headings. Demonstrate and display how to make a skeleton outline for the section. Have students list the section title at the top level, the main headings as major divisions, and the subheadings at the next level.

2. I. Section Title
  A. Main Heading
    1. Subheading
      a. detail
      b. detail
      c. detail

3. Have students copy the skeleton outline as they read, filling in details under each main heading and subheading of the outline.

4. Advise students not to outline sections that focus on the details of cycles or processes. Students can better represent these by diagrams and flowcharts rather than outlining.

5. After reading, have students review the entire section and their outlines to make sure they have included all vocabulary definitions and Key Concepts as main ideas or details under the appropriate levels of their outlines.

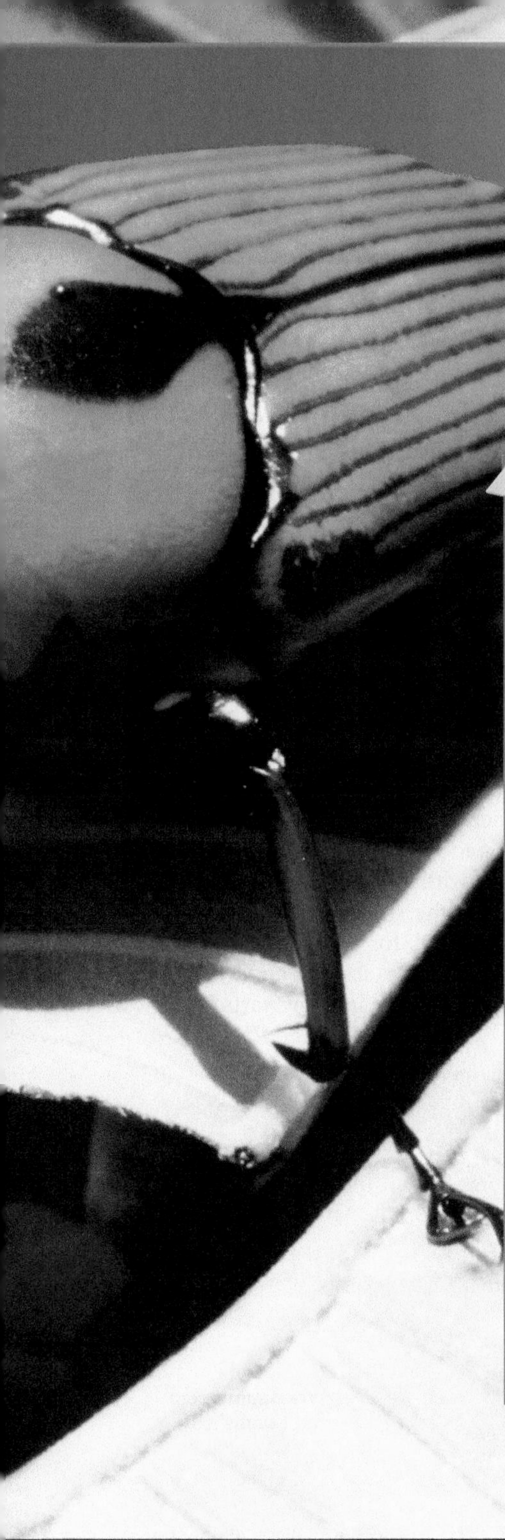

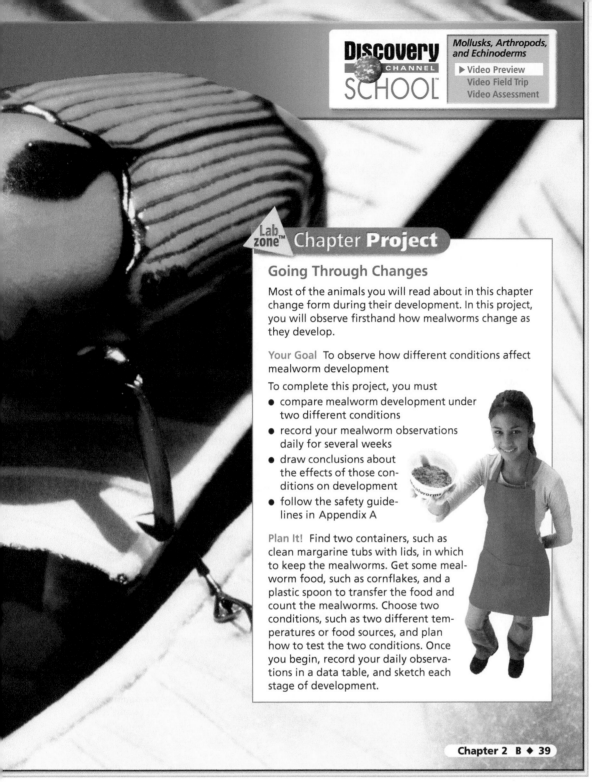

Chapter Project

Going Through Changes

Most of the animals you will read about in this chapter change form during their development. In this project, you will observe firsthand how mealworms change as they develop.

Your Goal To observe how different conditions affect mealworm development

To complete this project, you must

- compare mealworm development under two different conditions
- record your mealworm observations daily for several weeks
- draw conclusions about the effects of those conditions on development
- follow the safety guidelines in Appendix A

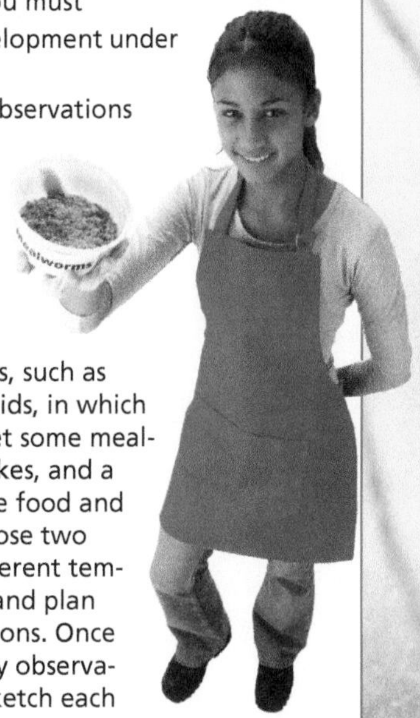

Plan It! Find two containers, such as clean margarine tubs with lids, in which to keep the mealworms. Get some mealworm food, such as cornflakes, and a plastic spoon to transfer the food and count the mealworms. Choose two conditions, such as two different temperatures or food sources, and plan how to test the two conditions. Once you begin, record your daily observations in a data table, and sketch each stage of development.

Mollusks

Show the Video Preview to introduce the Chapter Project and overview the chapter content. Discussion question: **In what ways do squids use their tentacles?** *(For movement and to capture prey)*

Possible Shortcuts

- Acquire mealworms in advance of the project. The larval stage of mealworms lasts for 10 weeks. However, mealworms obtained from a pet store are probably partly through the larval period. Larger larvae are generally older.
- If necessary for scheduling purposes, keep the mealworms at a warm temperature to accelerate development or a cold temperature to delay development.

Launching the Project

To introduce the project, ask: **Have any of you seen a caterpillar turn into a butterfly?** *(Answers may vary.)* **What are the major differences and similarities between caterpillars and butterflies?** *(Sample answer: differences—wings; similarities—legs)* Tell students the mealworms will turn into beetles. Reassure them that the beetles will not fly out when the lid of the container is removed.

Performance Assessment

The Chapter Project Scoring Rubric will help you evaluate how well students complete the Chapter Project. You may want to share the scoring rubric with your students so they are clear about what will be expected of them. Students will be assessed on

- how well they describe the two conditions that they are comparing
- how well they identify and observe the larval, pupal, and adult stages of mealworm development
- how clearly the data sheets show the number of larvae, pupae, and adults in their samples
- how correctly the graphs show the numbers of mealworm larvae, pupae, and adult beetles

Section 1 Mollusks

Objectives

After completing the lesson, students will be able to

B.2.1.1 Identify the main characteristics of mollusks.

B.2.1.2 Describe the major groups of mollusks and tell how they differ.

Target Reading Skill

Comparing and Contrasting Explain that comparing and contrasting information shows how ideas, facts, and events are similar and different. The results of the comparison can have importance.

Answer

Possible answers: Gastropods—use radula to tear through plant or animal tissues; creep along on a broad foot. Bivalves—filter feed; float or swim. Cephalopods—use tentacles to capture prey, crush prey in beaks, use radula to scrape and cut flesh; swim by jet propulsion.

All in One Teaching Resources

- Transparency B13

Preteach

Build Background Knowledge L2

Experience With Mollusks

Ask: **Have you ever eaten a mollusk?** If students don't know what a mollusk is, ask if they have eaten clams, squid, or snails. Then inform them that all of these animals are mollusks. **Where could you find mollusks in nature?** *(Answers will vary, but may include oceans, bays, ponds, rivers, streams, or moist areas in forests.)*

Section 1 Mollusks

Reading Preview

Key Concepts

- What are the main characteristics of mollusks?
- What are the major groups of mollusks and how do they differ?

Key Terms

- mollusk
- open circulatory system
- gill
- gastropod
- herbivore
- carnivore
- radula
- bivalve
- omnivore
- cephalopod

Target Reading Skill

Comparing and Contrasting When you compare and contrast things, you explain how they are alike and different. As you read, compare and contrast three groups of mollusks by completing a table like the one below.

Characteristics of Mollusks

Type of Mollusk	How They Obtain Food	How They Move
Gastropod		
Bivalve		
Cephalopod		

Lab zone Discover Activity

How Can You Classify Shells?

1. Your teacher will give you an assortment of shells.
2. Examine each shell carefully. Look at the shape and color of the shells and feel their inner and outer surfaces.
3. Classify the shells into groups based on the characteristics you observe.

Think It Over

Inferring How might it help an animal to have a shell? How might it be a disadvantage?

From the shells of clams, Native Americans in the Northeast once carved purple and white beads called wampum. They wove these beads into belts with complex designs that often had special, solemn significance. A wampum belt might record a group's history. When warring groups made peace, they exchanged weavings made of wampum. Iroquois women would honor a new chief with gifts of wampum strings.

The soft bodies inside the shells used to make wampum were a major source of food for Native Americans. Today, clams and similar animals, such as scallops and oysters, are still valuable sources of food for people in many parts of the world.

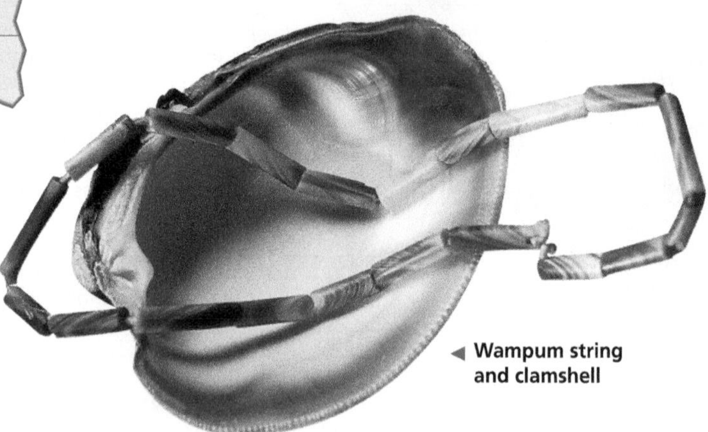

◀ Wampum string and clamshell

Lab zone Discover Activity

Skills Focus Inferring L1

Materials mollusk shells, such as those from clams, mussels, oysters, land and marine snails, and nautiluses

Time 20 minutes

Tips Place the shells at the stations around the room. Group students at each station. Help students develop a set of characteristics to use for grouping the shells. Be sure that students write down the characteristics they used to group the shells.

Expected Outcome Students should become aware of the wide diversity of shells.

Think It Over The shell might help the animal by protecting the animal from predators and supporting its body; it also might be cumbersome and slow down the animal's movements.

Characteristics of Mollusks

Clams, oysters, and scallops are all mollusks (phylum Mollusca). Snails and squids are mollusks, too. **Mollusks** are invertebrates with soft, unsegmented bodies that are often protected by a hard outer shell. **In addition to a soft body often covered by a shell, a mollusk has a thin layer of tissue called a mantle that covers its internal organs, and an organ called a foot.** In many mollusks, the mantle produces the hard shell. Depending on the type of mollusk, the foot has different functions—crawling, digging, or catching prey.

Body Structure Like segmented worms, mollusks have bilateral symmetry and a digestive system with two openings. However, unlike segmented worms, the body parts of mollusks are not usually repeated. Instead, the internal organs are located together in one area, as shown in Figure 1.

Circulatory System Most groups of mollusks have an **open circulatory system,** in which the blood is not always inside blood vessels. The heart pumps blood into a short vessel that opens into the body spaces containing the internal organs. The blood sloshes over the organs and returns eventually to the heart.

Obtaining Oxygen Most mollusks that live in water have **gills,** organs that remove oxygen from the water. The gills have tiny, hairlike structures called cilia and a rich supply of blood vessels. The cilia move back and forth, making water flow over the gills. The gills remove the oxygen from the water and the oxygen moves into the blood. At the same time, carbon dioxide, a waste gas, moves out of the blood and into the water.

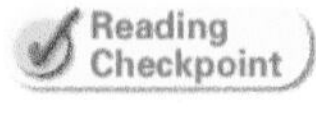

Which organs of a mollusk obtain oxygen from water?

FIGURE 1

Comparing Mollusks

Although they don't look much alike at first, a snail, a clam, and a squid have the same basic body structures.

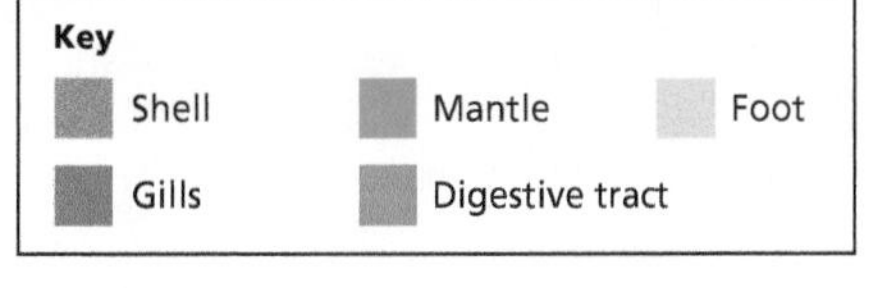

Snail

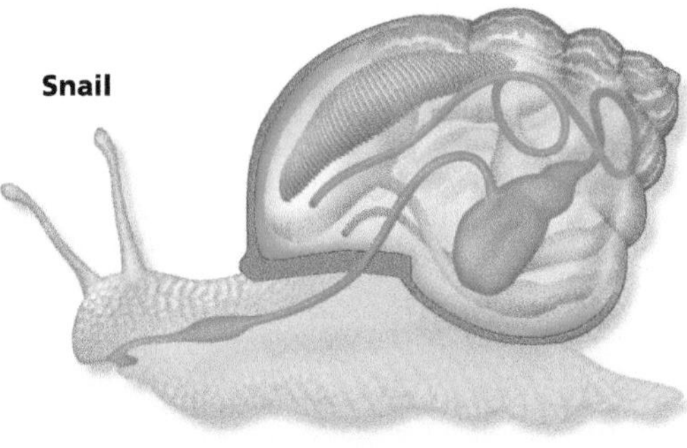

Clam

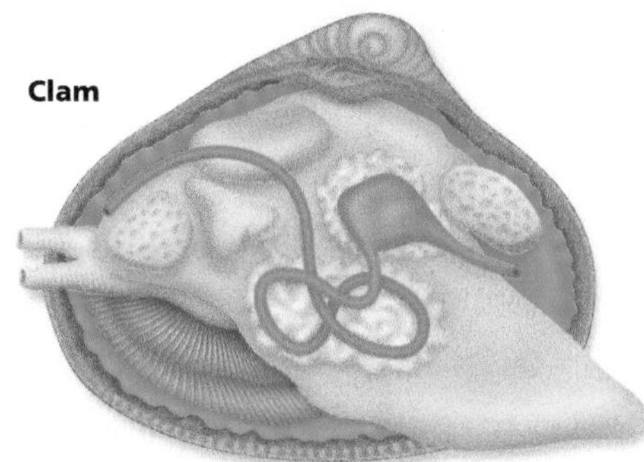

Squid

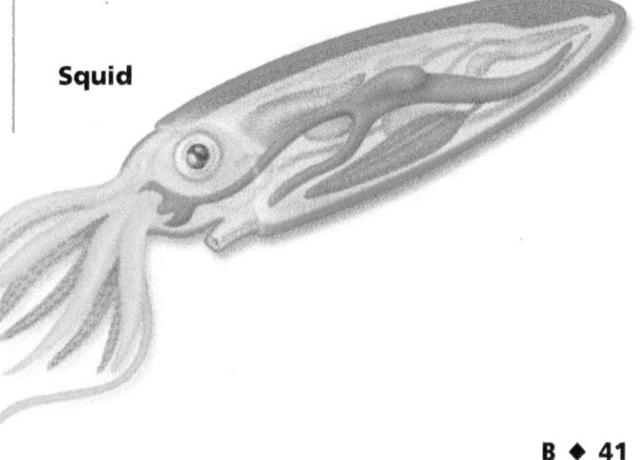

Instruct

Characteristics of Mollusks

Teach Key Concepts L2

Definition of a Mollusk

Focus Remind students that all mollusks, no matter how different they look, share common features.

Teach Have students study the three illustrations in Figure 1. Ask: **What do these three mollusks have in common?** *(Each of them has a mantle, a foot, a digestive tract, a shell, and gills.)* **What is a mantle?** *(A thin layer of tissue that covers the internal organs of mollusks)* **What is a foot?** *(A muscular structure adapted for crawling, digging, or catching prey)* **What gas exchange takes place in the gills?** *Oxygen passes into the blood and carbon dioxide moves out of the blood.)* Discuss with students additional key characteristics of mollusks: internal organs located within the mantle cavity and an open circulatory system.

Apply Ask: **If you found a new animal in the ocean, what features would you look for to determine whether it is a mollusk?** *(Bilateral symmetry, soft body, mantle, foot, open circulatory system)* **Why don't you find mollusks in hot dry areas?** *(Soft bodies would dry out, gills only function in water or in damp environments.)* **learning modality: logical/mathematical**

All in One Teaching Resources

- Transparency B14

Independent Practice L2

All in One Teaching Resources

- Guided Reading and Study Worksheet: *Mollusks*

Student Edition on Audio CD

Differentiated Instruction

English Learners/Beginning L1

Vocabulary: Science Glossary

Pronounce and define aloud the following Key Terms for students: *mollusk, open circulatory system, gill.* Suggest that they start a personal glossary of vocabulary terms, with each term and its definition in English on one side of an index card and in the student's primary language on the other side. **learning modality: verbal**

English Learners/Intermediate L2

Vocabulary: Science Glossary Students can expand on the activity for Beginning students by adding the other Key Terms in this section. Have students write sentences that use each of these words. Give students an opportunity to practice pronunciation by calling on individuals to read their sentences aloud. **learning modality: verbal**

Monitor Progress L2

Drawing Have students make a simple drawing of a mollusk. Label the major characteristics. Have students place their drawings in their portfolios.

Answer

Gills obtain oxygen from water.

Snails and Slugs

Teach Key Concepts L2

Characteristics of Gastropods

Focus Tell students that gastropods are mollusks that have a single external shell or no shell at all. Gastropods also have a unique feeding structure called a radula.

Teach Ask: **What characteristics do snails and slugs have that cause them to be classified as gastropods?** *(They have a radula; they creep along using their broad feet; those with shells have a single external shell)* **How does a gastropod eat?** *(A gastropod uses a radula, a flexible ribbon of tiny teeth, to scrape up food and move it into the digestive tract.)* **How do gastropods vary?** *(Presence and absence of shell, type of shell, type of foot, complexity of nervous system)*

Apply Ask: **How do the characteristics that enable the organism to obtain food differ between gastropods that are herbivores and gastropods that are carnivores?** *(The radulas of herbivores are designed to scrape off plant material. Some carnivores use their radulas to drill into the shells and then scrape the flesh.)* **learning modality: logical/mathematical**

L2

Studying Snails

Materials aquarium, live snails

Time 20 minutes

Focus Tell students that people put snails in fish tanks to eat the algae.

Teach Ask students to study the snails but not touch them or bang the aquarium. Ask: **What features can you identify?** *(Students can probably identify the shell, foot, and mouth.)* Have students study the foot of snails crawling up the side of the tank. Help students observe the foot moving and the slime trails left behind.

Apply Ask: **How would you describe the way in which the snails feed on algae in the tank?** *(They use their radulas to scrape up algae growing on the side of the tank.)* **learning modality: visual**

FIGURE 2
Gastropods
Although the land snail has a shell and the sea slug does not, both are gastropods.

Snails and Slugs

Biologists classify mollusks into groups based on their physical characteristics. These characteristics include the presence of a shell, the type of shell, the type of foot, and the type of nervous system. **The three major groups of mollusks are gastropods, bivalves, and cephalopods.**

The **gastropods** are the largest group of mollusks. They include snails and slugs, like the ones shown in Figure 2, and live nearly everywhere on Earth. They live in oceans, on rocky shores, in fresh water, and on land. **Gastropods have a single external shell or no shell at all.**

Obtaining Food Like all organisms, gastropods need food. Some gastropods are **herbivores,** animals that eat only plants. Some are scavengers that eat decaying material. Still others are **carnivores,** animals that eat only other animals.

But no matter what they eat, gastropods use an organ called a **radula** (RAJ oo luh), a flexible ribbon of tiny teeth, to obtain food. Herbivores use the radula like sandpaper to tear through plant tissues. Carnivores use their radulas in different ways. For example, a gastropod called an oyster drill uses its radula to bore a hole through an oyster's shell. Then it scrapes up the oyster's soft body tissues.

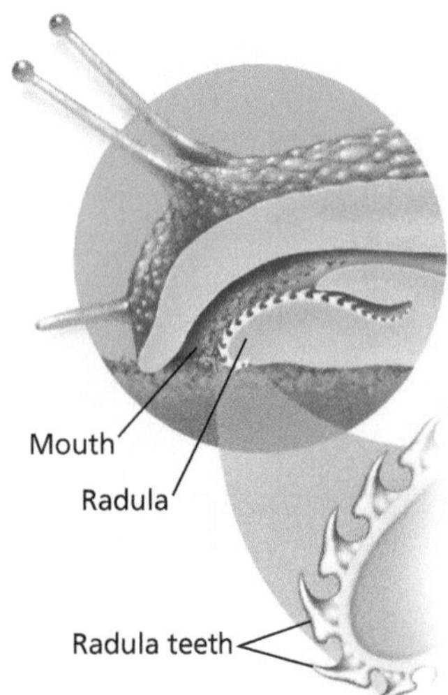

FIGURE 3
The Radula of a Snail
A snail has a food-gathering organ called a radula, which tears and scrapes up food.

Movement A gastropod usually moves by creeping along on a broad foot. The foot may ooze a carpet of slippery mucus, which you may have seen if you've ever watched a snail move. The mucus makes it easier for the gastropod to move.

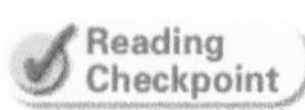

What is the function of a radula?

Two-Shelled Mollusks

A second group of mollusks, **bivalves,** includes oysters, clams, scallops, and mussels. **Bivalves are mollusks that have two shells held together by hinges and strong muscles.** They are found in all kinds of watery environments.

Obtaining Food Like gastropods, bivalves need food. But unlike gastropods, bivalves do not have radulas. Instead, most are filter feeders that strain tiny organisms from water. Bivalves capture food as water flows over their gills. Food particles stick to mucus that covers the gills. The cilia on the gills then move the food particles into the bivalve's mouth. Most bivalves are **omnivores,** animals that eat both plants and animals.

Movement Like gastropods, bivalves don't move quickly. The larvae of most bivalves float or swim through the water. But the adults stay in one place or use their foot to move very slowly. For example, oysters and mussels attach themselves to rocks or other underwater surfaces. Clams, in contrast, move. Look at Figure 4 to see how a clam digs into mud.

Protection Sometimes an object such as a grain of sand gets stuck between a bivalve's mantle and shell. The object irritates the soft mantle. Just as you might put smooth tape around rough bicycle handlebars to protect your hands, the bivalve's mantle produces a smooth, pearly coat to cover the irritating object. Sometimes a pearl forms eventually around the object. Some oysters make beautiful pearls that are used in jewelry.

Lab zone Skills Activity

Classifying

While wading in a stream, you step on a small animal with a hard covering. As you examine the animal, you discover that it has a soft body inside its shell. It may be a mollusk. What characteristics would you look for to classify the animal into a group of mollusks?

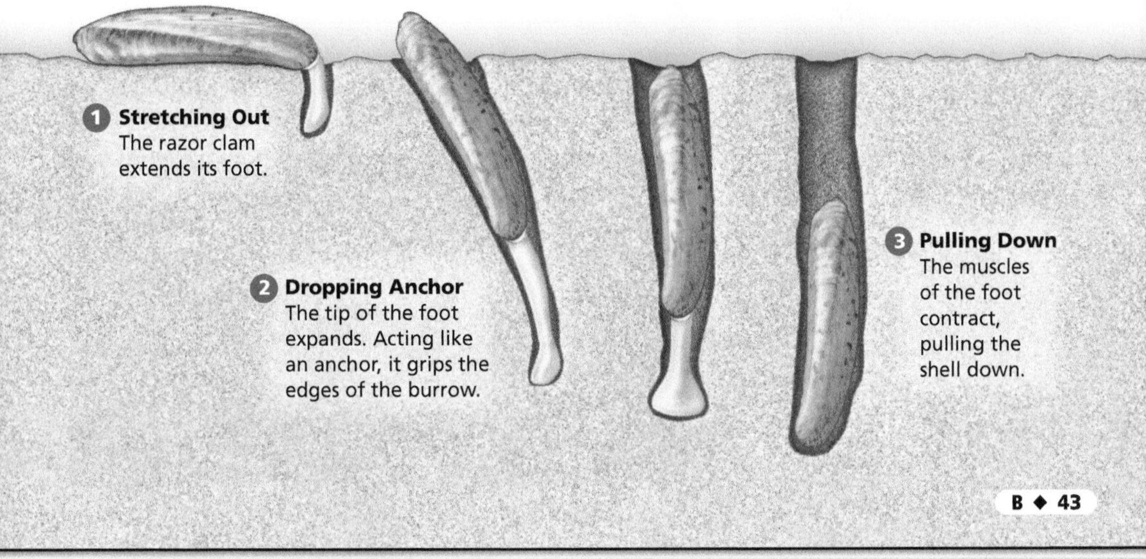

1 Stretching Out
The razor clam extends its foot.
2 Dropping Anchor
The tip of the foot expands. Acting like an anchor, it grips the edges of the burrow.
3 Pulling Down
The muscles of the foot contract, pulling the shell down.

FIGURE 4
How a Clam Digs
A razor clam digs into the mud by changing the shape of its foot.
Predicting *How might the clam use its foot to move back up?*

Two-Shelled Mollusks

Teach Key Concepts L2

Bivalves

Focus Ask: **What is the meaning of the prefix bi- in bicycle?** *(Two)* Tell students that two-shelled mollusks are called bivalves.

Teach Explain to students that bivalves have two shells held together by hinges and strong muscles. Ask: **How do pearls form?** *(If sand or grit lodges between a bivalve's mantle and shell, the mantle produces a smooth pearly cover to coat the sand or grit.)* **How do bivalves obtain food?** *(They are filter feeders; they strain tiny plants and animals from water.)*

Apply Ask: **How do gastropods colonize new habitats if they can barely move?** *(The larvae swim away after they hatch. If they settle in a suitable habitat, they will survive until they are adults.)* **learning modality: logical/mathematical**

Lab zone Skills Activity

Skills Focus Classifying L1

Materials none

Time 10 minutes

Tips You may want to ask students to look at Figure 1 once again to see the three different kinds of mollusks.

Expected Outcome The following characteristics would help students determine the major group of mollusks to which the animal belongs: single shell or double shell, presence or absence of a radula, and presence or absence of tentacles.

Extend Ask: **Do you think the mollusk you stepped on could be a slug?** *(No, because a slug does not have an external shell.)* **learning modality: verbal**

Monitor Progress L2

Oral Presentation Ask students to give a brief presentation explaining how bivalves can move.

Answers

Figure 4 Possible answer: A clam could use its foot to move back to the surface by extending the foot from the shell and pushing against the mud up to the surface.

A radula is used to obtain food.

Octopuses and Their Relatives

Teach Key Concepts L2

Characteristics of Cephalopods

Focus Have students look at Figure 5. Ask: **What is the first thing you notice when you look at the octopus?** *(Most students will answer that they notice the tentacles first.)*

Teach Ask: **Which characteristics enable cephalopods to catch prey?** *(Tentacles for snaring prey, suckers that sense food, large eyes, jet propulsion.)* **How does a complex nervous system enable cephalopods to capture prey?** *(It allows them to process information that they sense with their tentacles and see with their eyes; it may help them learn and remember strategies for catching prey.)*

Apply Give students this fictional scenario: A zoo octopus is given a glass screw-top jar containing a fish. The octopus opens the jar. Describe how the characteristics of cephalopods made this possible. *(Cephalopods have flexible tentacles that can grasp and manipulate objects. They have relatively large brains and can learn how to solve puzzles, such as opening the closed jar.)* **learning modality: logical/mathematical**

L2

Jet Propulsion in Cephalopods

Materials aquarium or sink, balloon, water
Time 10 minutes

Focus Ask: **How is the ability to swim fast helpful to cephalopods?** *(It helps cephalopods pursue and capture prey. It also helps them escape from danger.)*

Teach To demonstrate how cephalopods move using jet propulsion, fill the balloon with water. Pinch the neck to keep water from squirting out. Immerse the balloon in an aquarium or sink. Ask: **What will happen when I release the balloon?** *(It will shoot through the water.)* Release the balloon. Students will observe the balloon shooting through the water.

Apply Ask students to compare the movement of the octopus with the movement of a balloon. *(Just as the balloon squeezes water out through the opening, cephalopods squeeze out water from their mantle.)* **learning modality: visual**

Octopuses and Their Relatives

Octopuses and squids are **cephalopods** (SEF uh luh pahdz). So are nautiluses and cuttlefishes. **A cephalopod is an ocean-dwelling mollusk whose foot is adapted to form tentacles around its mouth.** Unlike bivalves, not all cephalopods have shells. For example, nautiluses have an external shell, squids and cuttlefish have a small shell within the body, and octopuses have no shells. Cephalopods are the only mollusks with a closed circulatory system.

Obtaining Food Cephalopods are carnivores. A cephalopod captures prey using its muscular tentacles. Then it crushes the prey in a beak and scrapes and cuts the flesh with its radula.

A cephalopod's tentacles contain sensitive suckers, which you can see on the octopus in Figure 5. The suckers receive sensations of taste as well as touch. A cephalopod doesn't have to touch something to taste it because the suckers respond to chemicals in the water. For example, when an octopus feels beneath a rock, its tentacles may find a crab by taste before touching it.

FIGURE 5
Three Cephalopods
A nautilus, an octopus, and a squid are all cephalopods. In cephalopods, the foot is adapted to form tentacles.
Drawing Conclusions *Why is cephalopod, which is Greek for "head foot," a good name for members of this group?*

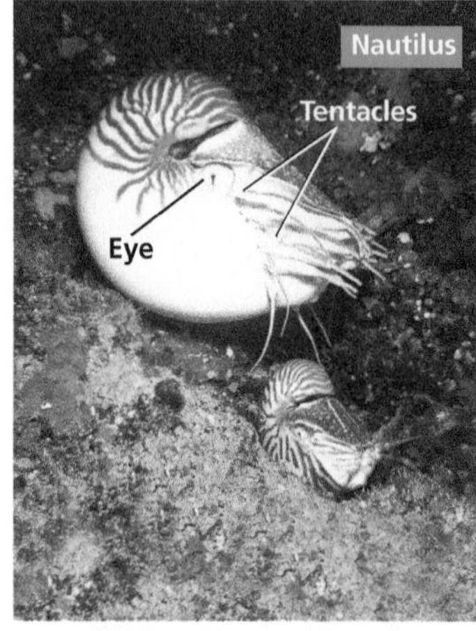

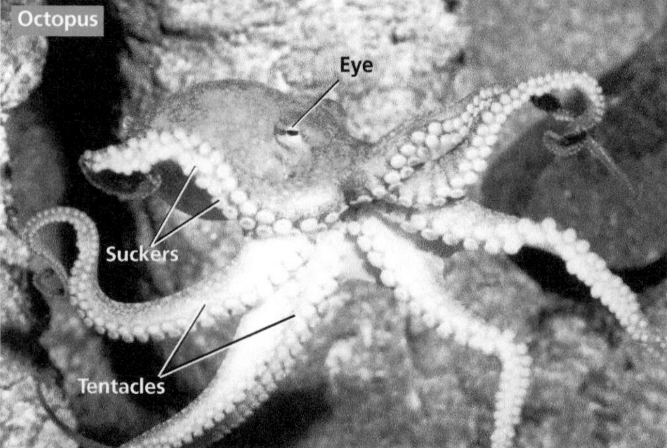

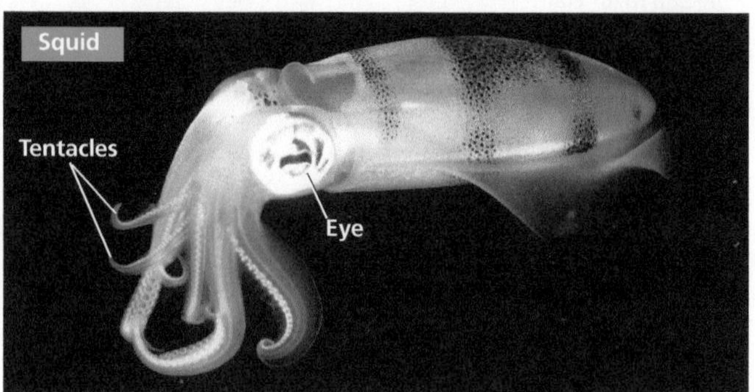

Nervous System Cephalopods have large eyes and excellent vision. They also have the most complex nervous system of any invertebrate. Cephalopods have large brains and can remember things they have learned. For example, in captivity, octopuses can learn when to expect deliveries of food. Some even figure out how to escape from their tanks.

FIGURE 6
An Escaping Octopus
This octopus has figured out how to escape from a jar through a tiny hole in the lid.

Movement Cephalopods swim by jet propulsion. They squeeze a current of water out of the mantle cavity and through a tube. Then, like rockets, they shoot off in the opposite direction. By turning the tube around, they can reverse direction.

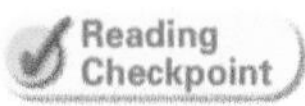
What does the foot of a cephalopod look like?

Section 1 Assessment

Target Reading Skill Comparing and Contrasting Use the information in your table about mollusks to help you answer Question 2 below.

Reviewing Key Concepts

1. a. Listing List the characteristics of a mollusk.
   b. Explaining How is a mollusk's mantle related to its shell?
   c. Predicting What would happen to a mollusk if the cilia on its gills did not work? Explain.
2. a. Identifying What are three groups of mollusks?
   b. Classifying What are the characteristics of the three groups of mollusks?
   c. Comparing and Contrasting How are the foot structures of a snail, a clam, and an octopus similar? How are they different?

Lab zone At-Home Activity

Edible Mollusks Visit a local supermarket with a family member and identify any mollusks that are being sold as food. Be sure to look in places other than the fish counter, such as the canned-foods section. Discuss the parts of the mollusks that are used for food and the parts that are not edible.

Lab zone At-Home Activity

Edible Mollusks L2 Ask students which mollusks they expect to find. *(Snails, oysters, clams, squid, canned clams, smoked oysters)* Suggest students visit a seafood store with a larger variety of seafood.

Mollusks

Show students the Video Field Trip to help them understand the adaptations of octopuses that make octopuses well suited to their habitat. Discussion question: **How do octopuses move quickly through the water?** *(They are able to move about by jet propulsion.)*

Monitor Progress L2

Answers

Figure 5 Because the tentacles (modified foot) extend from the head

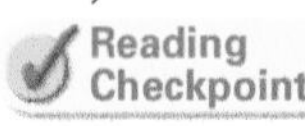
The foot is adapted into tentacles.

Assess

Reviewing Key Concepts

1. a. A mollusk is an invertebrate with a soft unsegmented body usually protected by a shell. A mollusk has a mantle that covers its internal organs, and a mollusk has a foot. **b.** The mantle produces the hard shell in mollusks that have a shell. **c.** Without working cilia, water would not flow over the gills, and the mollusk then might become oxygen-deprived.

2. a. The three groups of mollusks are gastropods, bivalves, and cephalopods. **b.** Gastropods have no shell or one shell and use a radula to obtain food. Bivalves have two shells. Cephalopods have a foot adapted to form tentacles. **c.** In a snail and a clam the food is used for movement; in a cephalopod it is adapted as tentacles and used for capturing prey.

Reteach L1

Have student groups make a chart comparing the different kinds of mollusks.

Performance Assessment L2

Writing Have each student explain, in his or her own words, why snails, slugs, clams, and squids are all classified as mollusks.

All in One Teaching Resources

- Section Summary: *Mollusks*
- Review and Reinforce: *Mollusks*
- Enrich: *Mollusks*

A Snail's Pace

Prepare for Inquiry

Key Concept
The activity of some animals can be affected by the temperature of their environment.

Skills Objectives
After this lab, students will be able to
- interpret data on how a snail's activity changes as temperature changes
- predict snail activity at higher temperatures

Prep Time 30 minutes
Class Time 45 minutes

Advance Planning
Place the snails in a small aquarium of pond water. Aerate the aquarium if the snails will be kept more than a few days. For the lab, use the most active snails. For safety reasons, prepare the cool, medium, and warm water yourself.

Safety   
- Students should be very careful with the thermometers. Make sure they do not let them roll off a table top.
- Remind students to treat snails gently and disturb them as little as possible.

All in One Teaching Resources
- Lab Worksheet: *A Snail's Pace*

Guide Inquiry

Introduce the Procedure
Have students read through the entire activity, and then ask: **What is the purpose of this activity?** *(To compare the distance a snail moves in water of different temperatures)* **Why do you draw four circles on the graph paper?** *(One is to place under the petri dish with the snail so that students can observe how the snail moves; each of the others is for recording the snail's movement in different temperatures.)*

Troubleshooting the Experiment
Do not allow students to tap the petri dish to get the snail moving. Remind students not to leave the snails out of the water for very long.

Expected Outcome
Snails usually move more slowly in colder water than in warmer water.

Lab zone Skills Lab

A Snail's Pace

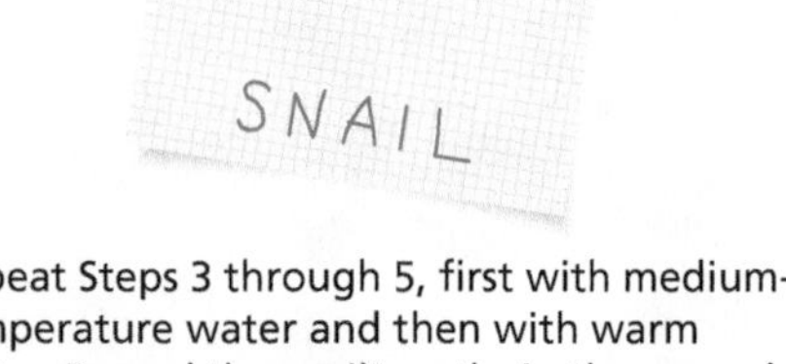

Problem
How do changes in the temperature of the environment affect the activity level of a snail?

Skills Focus
interpreting data, predicting

Materials
- freshwater snail
- thermometer
- ruler
- plastic petri dish
- graph paper, 2 sheets
- timer
- spring water at three temperatures: cool (9–13°C); medium (18–22°C); warm (27–31°C)

Procedure    
1. Create a data table for recording the water temperatures and the distance the snail travels at each temperature.
2. On one sheet of graph paper labeled *Snail,* trace a circle using the base of an empty petri dish. Divide and label the circle as shown in the illustration. On a second sheet of graph paper labeled *Data,* draw three more circles like the one in the illustration.
3. Place the petri dish over the circle on the Snail page, fill it with cool water, and record the water temperature. Then place the snail in the water just above the "S" in the circle. Handle the snail gently.
4. For five minutes, observe the snail. Record its movements by drawing a line that shows its path in the first circle on the Data page.
5. Find the distance the snail moved by measuring the line you drew. You may need to measure all the parts of the line and add them together. Record the distance in your data table.
6. Repeat Steps 3 through 5, first with medium-temperature water and then with warm water. Record the snail's paths in the second circle and third circle on the Data page.
7. Return the snail to your teacher when you are done. Wash your hands thoroughly.
8. For each temperature, compute the class average for distance traveled.

Analyze and Conclude
1. Graphing Make a bar graph showing the class average for each temperature.
2. Interpreting Data How does a snail's activity level change as temperature increases?
3. Predicting Do you think the pattern you found would continue at higher temperatures? Explain.
4. Communicating Write an e-mail to a friend describing how you conducted your experiment, any problems you ran into, and your results. Did your results help answer the question posed at the beginning of the lab? Explain your results to your friend.

Design an Experiment
Design an experiment to measure how different kinds of natural surfaces beneath the snail affect its rate of movement. Obtain three surface materials, such as fine sand, medium-grain gravel, and coarse gravel. Explain how you would modify the procedure. *Obtain your teacher's permission before carrying out your investigation.*

46 ◆ B

Analyze and Conclude
1. Answers will vary. Plot temperature on the *x*-axis and the distance moved on the *y*-axis.

2. Snails move more in warmer water.

3. No. Although snails move more in warmer water, hot water will kill them.

4. Answers will vary. Student responses should accurately describe their experiment and whether or not its results answered the question posed at the beginning of the lab.

Extend the Inquiry

Design an Experiment Advise students to ensure that all surface materials are thoroughly rinsed with pond water and allowed to settle before beginning their experiments.

Section 2 Arthropods

Reading Preview

Key Concepts

- What are the four major groups of arthropods and what are their characteristics?
- How do crustaceans, arachnids, and centipedes and millipedes differ?

Key Terms

- arthropod • exoskeleton
- molting • antenna
- crustacean • metamorphosis
- arachnid • abdomen

Target Reading Skill

Asking Questions Before you read, preview the red headings. In a graphic organizer like the one below, ask a *what* or a *how* question for each heading. As you read, write the answers to your questions.

Characteristics of Arthropods

Question	Answer
What is an arthropod?	

Lab zone Discover Activity

Will It Bend and Move?

1. Have a partner roll a piece of cardboard around your arm to form a tube that covers your elbow. Your partner should put three pieces of tape around the tube to hold it closed—one at each end and one in the middle.
2. With the tube in place, try to write your name on a piece of paper. Then try to scratch your head.
3. Keep the tube on your arm for 10 minutes. Observe how the tube affects your ability to do things.

Think It Over

Inferring Insects and many other animals have rigid skeletons on the outside of their bodies. Why do their skeletons need joints?

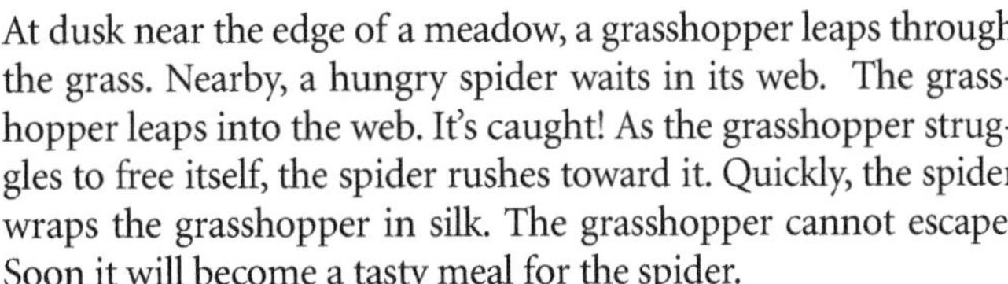

At dusk near the edge of a meadow, a grasshopper leaps through the grass. Nearby, a hungry spider waits in its web. The grasshopper leaps into the web. It's caught! As the grasshopper struggles to free itself, the spider rushes toward it. Quickly, the spider wraps the grasshopper in silk. The grasshopper cannot escape. Soon it will become a tasty meal for the spider.

The spider and grasshopper are both **arthropods,** or members of the arthropod phylum (phylum Arthropoda). Animals such as crabs, lobsters, centipedes, and scorpions are also arthropods.

FIGURE 7
A Spider at Work
This spider wraps its prey, a grasshopper, in silk. Both animals are arthropods.

Lab zone Discover Activity

Skills Focus Inferring L1

Materials sheets of heavy cardboard, about 30 × 45 cm, tape

Prep Time 5 minutes

Class Time 15 minutes

Tips Use cardboard that is flexible enough to roll into a tube and tape that is strong enough to stay attached when students attempt to bend their elbows. Students whose partners already have an arm wrapped in cardboard will need assistance when putting on their own tubes.

Expected Outcome Students will find that restricting their joints makes it impossible for them to bend their elbows.

Think It Over Joints in skeletons allow movement.

Section 2 Arthropods

Objectives

After completing the lesson, students will be able to

B.2.2.1 Identify four major groups of arthropods and the main characteristics of arthropods.

B.2.2.2 Describe how crustaceans, arachnids, and centipedes and millipedes differ.

Target Reading Skill

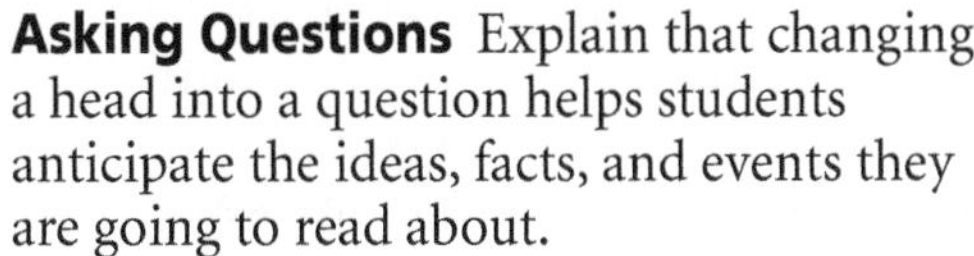

Asking Questions Explain that changing a head into a question helps students anticipate the ideas, facts, and events they are going to read about.

Answers

Possible questions and answers are these: **What is an arthropod?** *(Invertebrate that has an external skeleton, a segmented body, and jointed appendages)* **What is a crustacean?** *(Arthropod with two or three body sections, five or more pairs of legs, and two pairs of antennae)* **What is an arachnid?** *(Arthropod with two body sections, four pairs of legs, and no antennae)* **What are centipedes and millipedes?** *(Arthropods with two body sections and numerous pairs of legs)*

All in One Teaching Resources

- Transparency B15

Preteach

Build Background Knowledge L2

Experience with Arthropods

Ask students to name examples of insects and spiders they have seen. Ask: **Who has ever seen scorpions, crabs, crayfish, or lobsters?** *(Answers will vary depending on students' experiences.)* Ask volunteers to describe these animals. Use leading questions to prompt students to mention the external shells and jointed limbs of these animals. Tell students that the features they described are characteristics of arthropods.

Instruct

Characteristics of Arthropods

Teach Key Concepts L2

Key Traits of Arthropods

Focus Tell students that arthropods share certain similarities with mollusks, but also have other different and unique characteristics.

Teach Ask: **What are three features of arthropods?** *(Exoskeleton, segmented body, jointed appendages)* **What are the advantages of having an exoskeleton?** *(It protects the body, prevents water loss, and provides support.)* ***What are the disadvantages of having an exoskeleton?*** *(Its rigidity limits movement and growth.)*

Apply Ask: **What features compensate for the limitations of the exoskeleton?** *(Segmented bodies and jointed appendages enable movement. Molting enables growth.)* Point out that despite the exoskeleton's limitations, arthropods are the most successful and diverse animals in the world. **learning modality: logical/mathematical**

Help Students Read L1

Summarize Summarizing the information presented in the text will help students to focus on main ideas and remember what they read. Have students read about the main characteristics of arthropods. Ask them to summarize the information by restating the main ideas in their own words.

Independent Practice L2

All in One Teaching Resources

- Guided Reading and Study Worksheet: *Arthropods*

Student Edition on Audio CD

FIGURE 8
Arthropod Characteristics
This Sally lightfoot crab shows the tough exoskeleton, the segmented body, and the jointed appendages that are characteristic of arthropods.

Characteristics of Arthropods

Arthropods are classified into four major groups. **The major groups of arthropods are crustaceans, arachnids, centipedes and millipedes, and insects.** All arthropods share certain characteristics. **Arthropods are invertebrates that have an external skeleton, a segmented body, and jointed attachments called appendages.** Wings, mouthparts, and legs are all appendages. Jointed appendages are such a distinctive characteristic that arthropods are named for it. *Arthros* means "joint" in Greek, and *podos* means "foot" or "leg."

Arthropods share some characteristics with many other animals, too. They have bilateral symmetry, an open circulatory system, and a digestive system with two openings. In addition, most arthropods reproduce sexually.

Outer Skeleton If you were an arthropod, you would have a waterproof covering. This waxy covering is called an **exoskeleton,** or outer skeleton. It protects the animal and helps prevent evaporation of water. Water animals are surrounded by water, but land animals need a way to keep from drying out. Arthropods may have been the first animals to live on land. Their exoskeletons probably enabled them to do this because they keep the arthropods from drying out.

As an arthropod grows larger, its exoskeleton cannot expand. The growing arthropod is trapped within its exoskeleton, like a knight in armor that is too small. Arthropods solve this problem by occasionally shedding their exoskeletons and growing new ones that are larger. The process of shedding an outgrown exoskeleton is called **molting.** After an arthropod has molted, its new skeleton is soft for a time. During that time, the arthropod has less protection from danger than it does after its new skeleton has hardened.

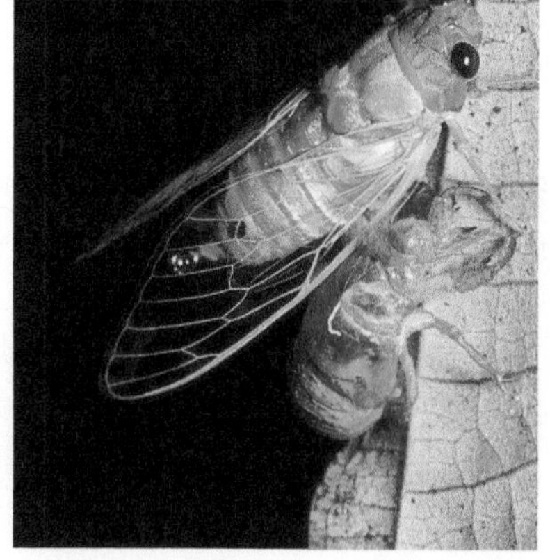

FIGURE 9
A Molting Cicada
This cicada has just molted. You can see its old exoskeleton hanging on the leaf just below it.
Applying Concepts *Why must arthropods molt?*

Comparisons of the Largest Arthropod Groups				
Characteristic	Crustaceans	Arachnids	Centipedes and Millipedes	Insects
Number of body sections	2 or 3	2	2	3
Pairs of legs	5 or more	4	Many	3
Pairs of antennae	2	None	1	1

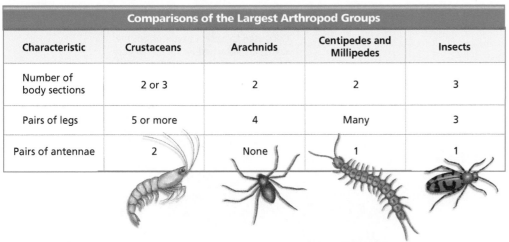

FIGURE 10
Members of the largest arthropod groups differ in several characteristics. **Interpreting Tables** *Which group of arthropods has no antennae?*

Segmented Body The bodies of arthropods are segmented. A segmented body plan is easiest to see in centipedes and millipedes, which have bodies made up of many identical-looking segments. In fact, their bodies look something like the bodies of earthworms. You can also see segments on the tails of shrimp and lobsters. In some groups of arthropods, several body segments become joined into distinct sections. An arthropod may have up to three sections—a head, a midsection, and a hind section.

Jointed Appendages Just as your fingers are appendages attached to your palms, many arthropods have jointed appendages attached to their bodies. The joints in the appendages give the animal flexibility and enable it to move. If you did the Discover activity, you saw how important joints are for allowing movement. Arthropod appendages tend to be highly specialized tools used for moving, obtaining food, reproducing, and sensing the environment. For example, arthropods use legs to walk and wings to fly. In addition, most arthropods have appendages called antennae (singular *antenna*). An **antenna** is an appendage attached to the head that contains sense organs.

Diversity Scientists have identified more species of arthropods—over one million—than all other species of animals combined! There are probably many others that have not yet been discovered. Look at Figure 10 to compare some characteristics of the four major groups of arthropods.

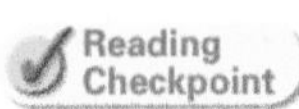

What does an antenna do?

For: Links on arthropods
Visit: www.SciLinks.org
Web Code: scn-0222

L2

Examining Arthropods

Materials fresh or frozen whole crab leg; whole shrimp with head from supermarket

Time 20 minutes

Focus Review with students the major characteristics of arthropods.

Teach Encourage students to handle the specimens and flex the legs. Ask them to count the legs and antennae and identify the body segments.

Apply Have students compare the exoskeletons of the shrimp and crab. Ask: **Which is the more flexible?** *(Shrimp)* **Which is stronger?** *(Crab)* **learning modality: kinesthetic**

Use Visuals: Figure 10

L2

Comparisons of Arthropod Groups

Focus Remind students that all arthropods have exoskeletons, segmented bodies, and jointed appendages.

Teach Ask: **Which group has the largest number of antennae?** *(Crustaceans)*

Apply Ask: **How could you determine whether an unfamiliar arthropod is an arachnid?** *(An arachnid has four pairs of legs and no antennae.)* **learning modality: visual**

All in One Teaching Resources
- Transparency B16

For: Links on arthropods
Visit: www.SciLinks.org
Web Code: scn-0222

Download a worksheet that will guide students' review of Internet resources on arthropods.

Monitor Progress

L2

Writing Have students write the following words: *exoskeleton, segmented bodies, appendages.* Ask them to write a sentence describing what they have learned about each characteristic.

Answers

Figure 9 Arthropods must molt in order to grow.

Figure 10 Arachnids

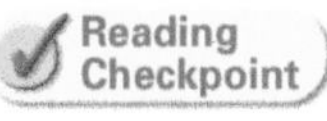

An antenna senses the environment.

Differentiated Instruction

Less Proficient Readers L1

Identifying Prefixes To help students remember the meaning of *exoskeleton*, point out that the words *external* and *exoskeleton* both begin with the prefix *ex-*. Explain that *ex-* and *exo-* may mean "outside." Ask students to think of other words that start with these prefixes. *(Possible answers:* exit, expedition*)* **learning modality: verbal**

Crustaceans

Teach Key Concepts L2

Key Traits of Crustaceans

Focus Tell students that a unique feature of crustaceans is the large number of specialized appendages.

Teach Have students observe Figure 11. Point out specific features such as the segmented abdomen, the different types of antennae, and the walking legs and chelipeds. Have volunteers read aloud the callouts. Ask: **How are the walking legs different from the chelipeds?** *(The chelipeds are larger and have pincers.)* **What are they used for?** *(Capturing food and defense)* **How do the many different specialized appendages help crustaceans?** *(The large number of specialized appendages enables crustaceans to carry out highly specific tasks, such as catching prey or manipulating food.)* **What are some ways crustaceans obtain food?** *(Many are scavengers; others are predators. Krill are herbivores.)*

Apply Remind students that most crustaceans are aquatic. Ask: **What characteristics enable crustaceans to live in the water?** *(Swimmerets, gills for obtaining oxygen, larvae that swim)* **learning modality: verbal**

All in One Teaching Resources

- Transparency B17

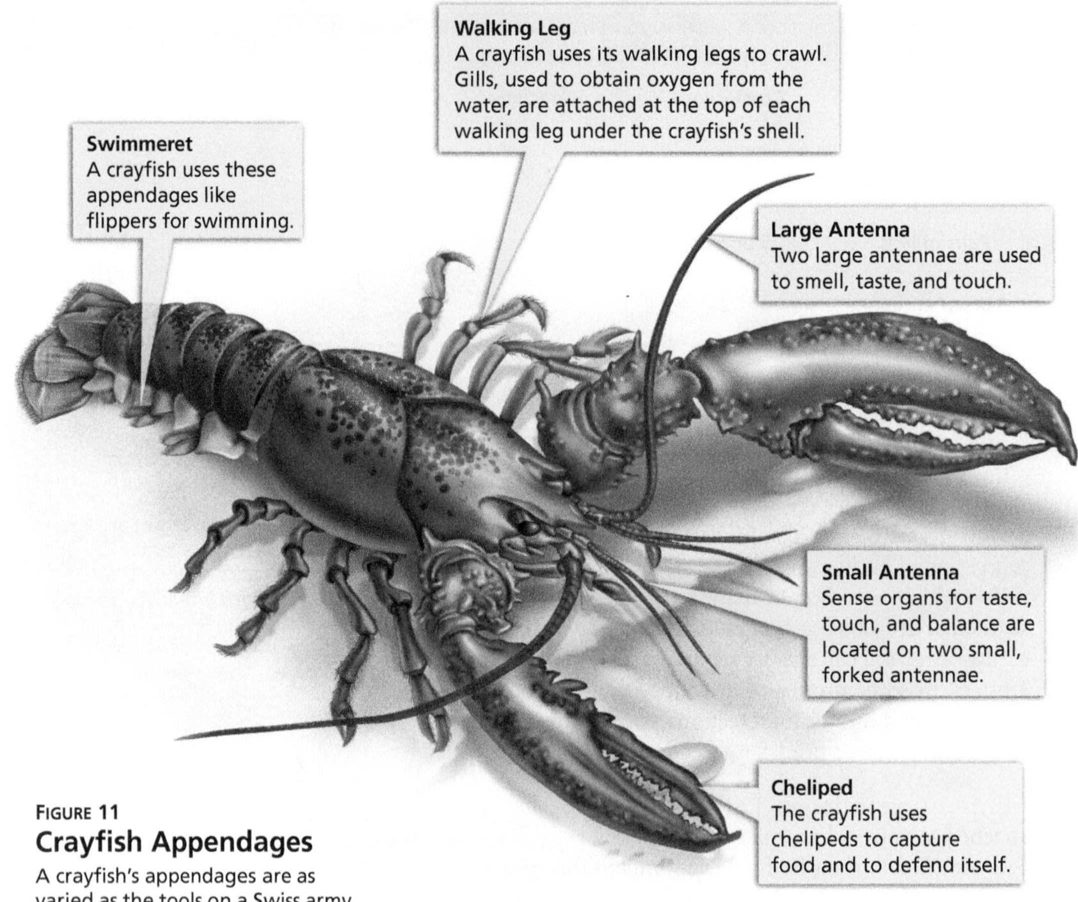

Walking Leg
A crayfish uses its walking legs to crawl. Gills, used to obtain oxygen from the water, are attached at the top of each walking leg under the crayfish's shell.
Swimmeret
A crayfish uses these appendages like flippers for swimming.
Large Antenna
Two large antennae are used to smell, taste, and touch.
Small Antenna
Sense organs for taste, touch, and balance are located on two small, forked antennae.
Cheliped
The crayfish uses chelipeds to capture food and to defend itself.

FIGURE 11
Crayfish Appendages
A crayfish's appendages are as varied as the tools on a Swiss army knife. The appendages are adapted for different functions.
Interpreting Diagrams *What functions do the chelipeds serve?*

Crustaceans

If you've ever eaten shrimp cocktail or crab cakes, you've dined on **crustaceans** (krus TAY shunz). Crayfish and lobsters are other familiar crustaceans. Crustaceans thrive in freshwater lakes and rivers, and even in puddles that last a long time. You can find them in the deepest parts of oceans and along coastlines. A few, like the pill bug, live in damp places on land.

Body Structure Crustaceans share certain characteristics. **A crustacean is an arthropod that has two or three body sections, five or more pairs of legs, and two pairs of antennae.** Each crustacean body segment has a pair of legs or another type of appendage attached to it. The various types of appendages function differently, as you can see in Figure 11.

50 ◆ B

Differentiated Instruction

Less Proficient Readers L1

Answering Questions Select a passage from the text, such as *Obtaining Oxygen and Food.* Read the passage aloud to students as they follow along in their books. After reading, ask some questions about the passage. If they don't know the answers, challenge them to find them in the passage. **learning modality: verbal**

Gifted and Talented L3

Researching Specialized Appendages Have students research and summarize the specialized appendages found in crayfish. *(One or more pairs of the following: antennules, antennae, mandibles, maxillae, maxillipeds, chelipeds, walking legs, swimmerets, and uropods)* **learning modality: verbal**

The appendages attached to the head of a crayfish include two pairs of antennae that are used for smelling, tasting, touching, and keeping balance. The crayfish uses most of its leg appendages for walking. However, it uses its first pair of legs, called chelipeds, for obtaining food and defending itself.

Obtaining Oxygen and Food Because crustaceans live in watery environments, most have gills to obtain oxygen. The gills are located beneath the shell of a crustacean. Water containing oxygen reaches the gills as a crustacean moves along in its environment.

Crustaceans obtain food in many ways. Some are scavengers that eat dead plants and animals. Others are predators, eating animals they have killed. The pistol shrimp is a predator with an appendage that moves with such force that it stuns its prey. Krill, which are shrimplike crustaceans that live in cold ocean waters, are herbivores that eat plantlike microorganisms. In turn, krill are eaten by predators such as fishes, penguins, seals, and even great blue whales, the world's largest animals.

Life Cycle Most crustaceans, such as crabs, barnacles, and shrimp, begin their lives as microscopic, swimming larvae. The bodies of these larvae do not resemble those of adults. Crustacean larvae develop into adults by **metamorphosis** (met uh MAWR fuh sis), a process in which an animal's body undergoes dramatic changes in form during its life cycle.

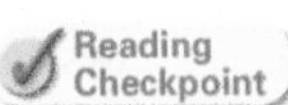
What organs does a crustacean use to obtain oxygen?

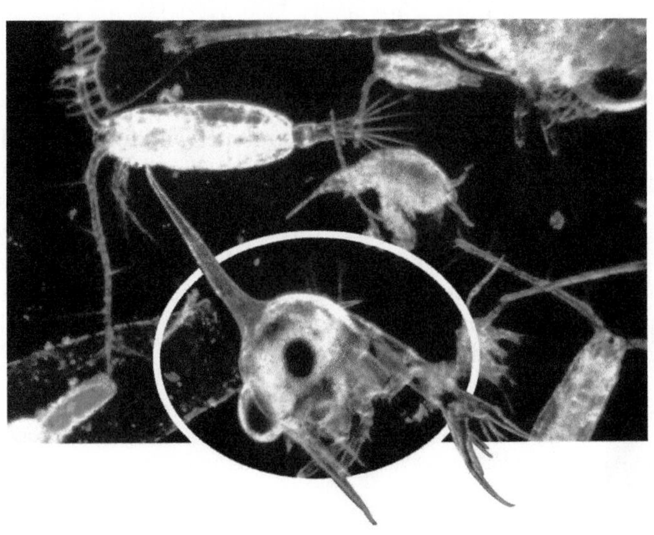

FIGURE 12
Crab Larva
This larva of a crab floats in the ocean with other microscopic animals.

Lab zone Try This **Activity**

Pill Bugs—Wet or Dry?

1. Line a box with aluminum foil. Tape down two paper towels side by side in the box. Tape a strip of masking tape between the two towels. Moisten one of the paper towels. Keep the other towel dry.

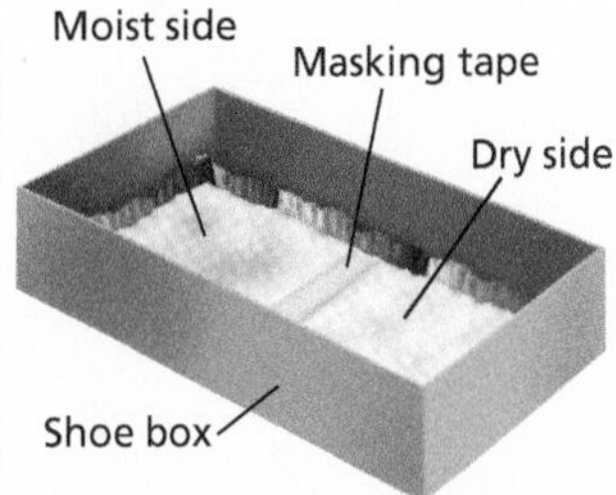

2. Put ten pill bugs on the masking tape. Then put a lid on the box.
3. After 5 minutes, lift the lid and count the pill bugs on the dry towel, the moist towel, and the masking tape. Record your results in a data table.
4. Repeat Steps 2 and 3 two more times. Then average the results of the three trials. Wash your hands after handling the pill bugs.

Interpreting Data Do pill bugs prefer a moist or a dry environment?

Lab zone Teacher **Demo** L2

Describing a Lobster

Materials a preserved lobster

Focus Tell students that lobsters are closely related to crayfish.

Teach Have students refer to Figure 11. Ask them to identify and count as many appendages on the lobster as they can. *(Four pairs of walking legs, one pair of chelipeds, two pairs of antennae, five pairs of swimmerets, mouth parts)* Ask: **How many body sections does the lobster have?** *(Two)*

Apply Ask: **Based on its appendages, where do you think lobsters live? Why?** *(Walking legs indicate they live on the ocean bottom.)* **How do they obtain their food?** *(They capture prey with their chelipeds.)* **learning modality: visual**

Lab zone Try This **Activity**

Skills Focus Interpreting data L2

Materials shoe box, aluminum foil, paper towels, masking tape, live pill bugs, water

Time 20 minutes

Tips Group students. Repeat steps 2 and 3 two more times, and then average the results of the three trials. During the first trial, have students design their data table. During the second and third trials, have them reread the text information on crustaceans.

Expected Outcome The pill bugs will prefer the moist environment. **learning modality: logical/mathematical**

Monitor Progress L2

Drawing Ask students to draw a new species of crustacean. Have them label all the features that make it an arthropod and a crustacean. Students can save their drawings in their portfolios. Portfolio

Answers

Figure 11 Chelipeds are used to capture food and for defense.

 A crustacean uses gills to obtain oxygen.

Arachnids

Teach Key Concepts L2

Recognizing Four Kinds of Arachnids

Focus Point out to students that arachnids are abundant everywhere we live and that most escape our notice.

Teach Ask: **What is an example of an arachnid?** *(Answers will vary, but most students will mention spiders first.)* **How does a spider differ from a mite?** *(Spiders are predators; mites are parasites.)* Have students study the picture of the deer tick, and then ask: **What disease is spread by deer ticks?** *(Lyme disease)* After students look at Figure 15, ask: **Where would you most likely find a scorpion during the day?** *(Hiding in a cool place, such as under a rock)*

Apply Ask: **What are some ways arachnids defend themselves?** *(A spider has fangs through which it injects venom into its prey. A scorpion has a spinelike stinger at the end of its abdomen.)* **learning modality: verbal**

Address Misconceptions L1

Spiders

Focus Many students believe that all spiders catch their prey in webs and that all spiders' bites are extremely dangerous to people.

Teach Help students understand that many commonly held beliefs about spiders are false. Ask: **How do spiders catch their prey?** *(Some spiders use webs, but others chase or trap their prey.)* **Are most spiders' bites extremely dangerous to people?** *(Spiders rarely bite people, and most spider bites are uncomfortable but not dangerous.)*

Apply Tell students that two kinds of spiders that may inflict bites that require medical care are the brown recluse and the black widow. **learning modality: logical/ mathematical**

FIGURE 13
Red Knee Tarantula
This red knee tarantula lives in an underground burrow. The spider uses fangs to inject venom into its prey.

Arachnids

Spiders, mites, ticks, and scorpions are the **arachnids** (uh RAK nidz) that people most often meet. **Arachnids are arthropods with two body sections, four pairs of legs, and no antennae.** Their first body section is a combined head and midsection. The hind section, called the **abdomen,** is the other section. The abdomen contains the reproductive organs and part of the digestive system.

Spiders Spiders are probably the most familiar, most feared, and most fascinating kind of arachnid. All spiders are predators, and most of them eat insects. Some, such as tarantulas and wolf spiders, run down their prey. Others, such as golden garden spiders, spin sticky webs to trap their prey.

Spiders have hollow fangs through which they inject venom into their prey. Spider venom turns the tissues of the prey into mush. Later the spider uses its fangs like drinking straws, and sucks in the food. In spite of what some people might think, spiders rarely bite people. When spiders do bite, their bites are often painful but not life-threatening. However, the bite of a brown recluse or a black widow may require hospital care.

FIGURE 14
Dust Mite
This microscopic dust mite feeds on dead skin and hair shed by humans. Classifying *Would you describe the mite as a carnivore, scavenger, or filter feeder? Why?*

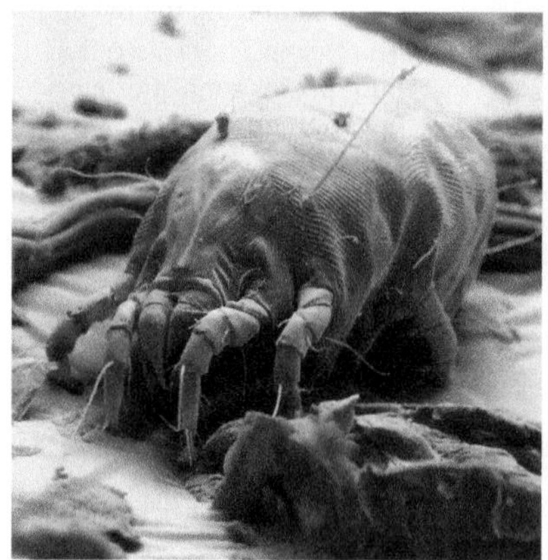

Mites If chiggers have ever given you an itchy rash, you've had an unpleasant encounter with tiny arachnids called mites. Chiggers and many other mites are parasites. Ear mites, for example, give dogs and cats itchy ears. Mites are everywhere. Even the cleanest houses have microscopic dust mites. If you are allergic to dust, you may actually be allergic to the exoskeletons of dust mites. In addition to living in dry areas, mites also live in fresh water and in the ocean.

What kind of arachnid is a chigger?

FIGURE 15
Scorpion
A scorpion is a carnivore that injects venom from a stinger at the end of its abdomen.

Scorpions Scorpions live mainly in hot climates, and are usually active at night. During the day, scorpions hide in cool places—under rocks and logs, or in holes in the ground, for example. At the end of its abdomen, a scorpion has a spinelike stinger. The scorpion uses the stinger to inject venom into its prey, which is usually a spider or an insect.

Ticks Ticks are parasites that live on the outside of a host animal's body. Nearly every kind of land animal has a species of tick that sucks its blood. Some ticks that attack humans can carry diseases. Lyme disease, for example, is spread by the bite of an infected deer tick. You can see an enlarged deer tick to the right. In reality, a deer tick is just a few millimeters long.

◀ Deer tick

Math Analyzing Data

Lyme Disease Cases

The graph shows the numbers of cases of Lyme disease by age group reported by Connecticut during one year. Use the graph to answer the questions.

1. **Reading Graphs** What variable is plotted on the *y*-axis? What does the first bar tell you?
2. **Interpreting Data** Which age group is least at risk for Lyme disease? Explain.
3. **Interpreting Data** Which two age groups are most at risk?
4. **Calculating** Suppose a particular school in Connecticut has 1,000 students ranging in age from 10 to 19. About how many of these students would you expect to get Lyme disease per year?

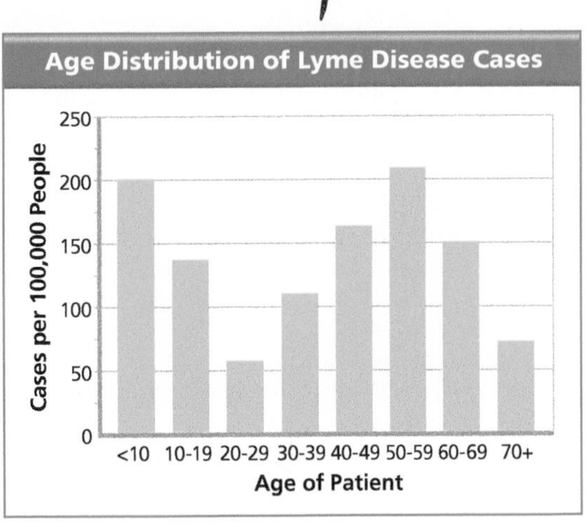

Math Skill Interpreting Data

Focus Point out to students that a bar graph is used to compare data.

Teach Ask: **What does the *x* -axis show?** *(Age of the patients)* **What does the *y* -axis show?** *(Cases per 100,000 people)* **What do the bars represent?** *(Number of people in each category)*

Answers

1. Cases per 100,000 people; the first bar shows that for every 100,000 children under the age of ten, 200 had Lyme disease.
2. 20–29 year-olds; just over 50 per 100,000 people were infected
3. Children under 10 and people between the ages of 50 and 59
4. One or two students

Differentiated Instruction

English Learners/Beginning L1
Comprehension: Modified Cloze Write some simple sentences on the board that require the terms *arthropod, arachnid,* and *abdomen.* For example: "A group of animals called _____ includes crustaceans, _____, centipedes and millipedes, and insects." "The second body section of an arachnid is called the _____." Complete one or two sentences as a model, then fill in the blanks together. **learning modality: verbal**

English Learners/Intermediate L2
Comprehension: Modified Cloze Use the same sentences described for Beginning students, but fill in incorrect terms. Have students work in pairs to determine the correct answers. **learning modality: verbal**

Monitor Progress L2

Writing Have each student choose a group of arachnids and list its characteristics.

Answers

Figure 14 The dust mite is a scavenger; it eats dead skin and hair from humans.

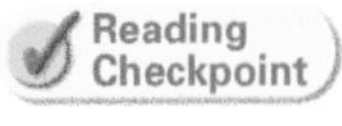

A mite

Centipedes and Millipedes

Teach Key Concepts L2

Centipede and Millipede Characteristics

Focus Tell students that centipedes and millipedes search for food in dark, moist places, such as under logs and stones.

Teach Draw two lines of connected circles on the blackboard. Tell students that the circles represent body segments. Ask: **How many pairs of legs should I draw on each segment to make it a centipede?** *(One)* **How many for a millipede?** *(Two)*

Apply Ask: **How does the way millipedes get energy differ from that of a centipede?** *(Centipedes are carnivores that eat other animals; millipedes are scavengers that eat decayed leaves.)* **learning modality: visual**

FIGURE 16
Centipede and Millipede
Both centipedes and millipedes have many pairs of legs.
Interpreting Photographs *How many pairs of legs does each segment of the centipede have?*

Centipedes and Millipedes

Centipedes and millipedes are arthropods with two body sections and many pairs of legs. The two body sections are a head with one pair of antennae, and a long abdomen with many segments. Centipedes have one pair of legs attached to each segment. Some centipedes have more than 100 segments. In fact, the word *centipede* means "hundred feet." Centipedes are swift predators that inject venom into their prey.

Millipedes, which may have more than 80 segments, have two pairs of legs on each segment—more legs than any other arthropod. Though *millipede* means "thousand feet," they don't have quite that many legs. Most millipedes are scavengers that graze on partly decayed leaves. When they are disturbed, millipedes can curl up into a ball, protected by their tough exoskeleton. Some will also squirt an awful-smelling liquid at a potential predator.

Monitor Progress L2

Answer
Figure 16 One pair

Section 2 Assessment

Target Reading Skill Asking Questions Use the answers to the questions you wrote about the headings to help you answer the questions below.

Reviewing Key Concepts

1. a. Naming What are the major groups of arthropods?
   b. Summarizing How are all arthropods alike?
   c. Applying Concepts Some restaurants serve soft-shelled crab. What do you think happened to the crab just before it was caught?
2. a. Identifying What are the characteristics of a crustacean?
   b. Reviewing Describe the body structure of an arachnid.
   c. Comparing and Contrasting How are centipedes and millipedes alike? How are they different?

Writing in Science

Observation Write about an arthropod that you have observed. Describe details about its physical appearance, its movements, and any other behaviors that you observed.

Assess

Reviewing Key Concepts

1. a. Crustaceans, arachnids, centipedes and millipedes, and insects **b.** All arthropods are invertebrates with an exoskeleton, segmented body, and jointed appendages. **c.** It had just molted.

2. a. Crustaceans are arthropods with two or three body sections, five or more pairs of legs, and two pairs of antennae. **b.** An arachnid has two body sections, four pairs of legs, and no antennae. **c.** Centipedes and millipedes both have two body sections and many pairs of legs. A centipede has one pair of legs on each segment of its abdomen, while a millipede has two legs per segment.

Reteach L1

Use Figure 10 to review the characteristics of each arthropod group.

All in One Teaching Resources

- Section Summary: *Arthropods*
- Review and Reinforce: *Arthropods*
- Enrich: *Arthropods*

Lab zone Chapter Project

Keep Students on Track Ensure that students observe mealworms daily, recording how many mealworms in each group are wormlike larvae, how many have formed motionless pupae, and how many, if any, have become adult insects. Ensure each mealworm container has food and a source of moisture.

Writing in Science

Writing Mode Description

Scoring Rubric

4 Includes complete descriptions, and is written in an engaging tone
3 Includes complete, accurate description of the organism
2 Includes accurate but brief description
1 Includes incomplete or inaccurate descriptions

Section 3

Insects

Reading Preview

Key Concepts

- What are the main characteristics of insects?
- What is one way insects are adapted to obtain particular types of food?
- What are two types of metamorphosis that insects undergo?

Key Terms

- insect • thorax
- complete metamorphosis
- pupa
- gradual metamorphosis
- nymph

Target Reading Skill

Sequencing A sequence is the order in which a series of events or steps in a process occurs. As you read, make a cycle diagram that shows the steps in the complete metamorphosis of an insect. Write each step in a separate circle.

Complete Metamorphosis

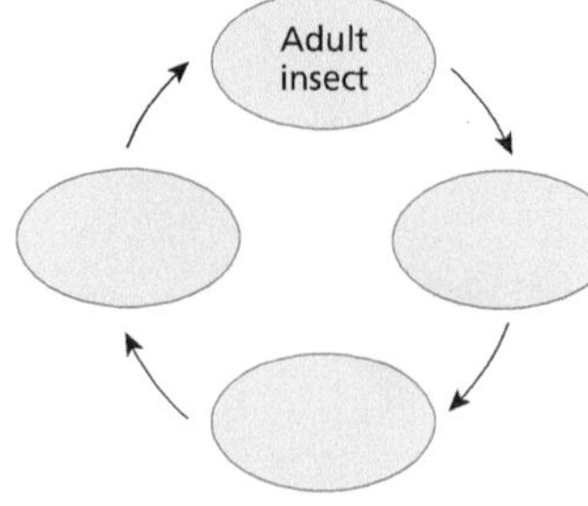

Lab zone Discover Activity

What Characteristics Do Insects Share?

1. Your teacher will give you a collection of insects. Observe the insects carefully.
2. Note the physical characteristics of each insect's body covering. Count the number of body sections.
3. Count the number of legs, wings, and antennae on each insect. Then return the insects to your teacher and wash your hands.

Think It Over

Inferring Compare the legs and the wings of two different species of insect. How is each insect adapted to move?

What do you do if you want to avoid being noticed? You keep perfectly quiet and you don't do anything that will attract attention. You might even wear clothes that help you to blend into the environment—a tactic called camouflage. The thorn insect is a master of camouflage. Not only does it look like a thorn, but it acts like one, too, staying quite still unless a predator like a bird comes too close. Then it springs away to safety.

Other kinds of insects have different camouflage tactics. For example, some caterpillars look like bird droppings, and others look and act like twigs. Plant hoppers may gather in clusters that look like yellow blossoms. And many kinds of moths resemble dead leaves.

Thorn insect ▶

Section 3

Insects

Objectives

After completing the lesson, students will be able to

B.2.3.1 Identify the main characteristics of insects.

B.2.3.2 Explain how insects are adapted to obtain food.

B.2.3.3 Name the two types of metamorphosis found in insects.

Target Reading Skill

Sequencing Explain that sequencing shows the steps in a process. A process is easier to remember when you put each step in a separate box in the order in which it occurs.

Answers

Adult, egg, larva, pupa

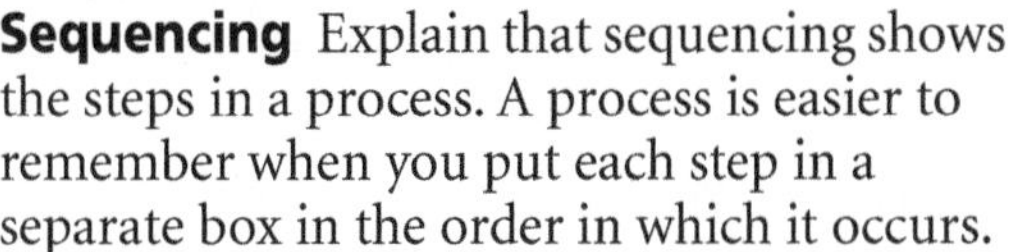

All in One Teaching Resources

- Transparency B18

Preteach

Build Background Knowledge L2

Insect Structure and Behavior

Ask students to describe insects they have observed. Ask: **What do they have in common?** *(Sample answers: Antennae, six legs, hard outer covering)* Tell students that they will learn the characteristics insects share in this section.

Lab zone Discover Activity

Skills Focus Inferring L1

Materials hand lenses, insect collection

Prep Time 5 minutes

Class Time 15 minutes

Tips Facilitate careful observation of the specimens by asking students to describe one or two insects that they find particularly interesting. Ask students to point out several characteristics that the insects have in common.

Expected Outcome Students should observe that all the insects have the same number of legs *(six)* and body sections *(three)*.

Think It Over Encourage students to compare insects that are very different. *(Answers may vary. Sample: A grasshopper and a dragonfly both have six legs and two pairs of wings. The grasshopper has large hind legs that it uses to jump. The dragonfly has large flat wings that it uses to fly.)*

Instruct

Body Structure

Teach Key Concepts L2

Characteristics of Arthropod

Focus Direct students' attention to Figure 17. Have them read the callouts.

Teach Ask: **What structures are visible on the head of this grasshopper?** *(Simple eyes, compound eyes, antennae)* **How do the functions of the simple eye and compound eye differ?** *(Compound eyes are keen at seeing movement; simple eyes can distinguish between light and dark.)* **What important parts of an insect are attached to the thorax?** *(Legs and wings)*

Apply Ask: **Why are insects classified as arthropods?** *(They have body segments, jointed appendages, and an exoskeleton.)* **learning modality: verbal**

All in One Teaching Resources

- Transparency B19

L1

Identifying External Parts of the Grasshopper

Materials sealable plastic bags or small clear plastic container containing grasshoppers or crickets from a pet or bait shop; hand lenses

Time 10 minutes

Focus Review the parts of a grasshopper.

Teach Let students examine the insects, without opening the bags or containers, with and without a hand lens and note the varying structures, particularly the three distinct body sections. You may wish to use dead insects, or insects that have been refrigerated to slow activity. In either case, remind students to handle the bags containing the insects gently. Cricket structures will be similar to those found in a grasshopper. Have students compare what they see with the grasshopper shown in Figure 17.

Apply Ask: **How are jointed appendages essential for the grasshopper's survival?** *(Jointed appendages enable the grasshopper to move to seek food and to jump to evade predators.)* **learning modality: visual**

Lab zone Skills Activity

Graphing

Use the data to make a circle graph that shows the percentage of total insect species in each group. (See the Skills Handbook.)

Insect Groups

Group	Number of Species
Ants, bees, and wasps	115,000
Beetles and weevils	350,000
Butterflies and moths	178,000
Flies and mosquitoes	110,000
Other insect groups	147,000

Body Structure

Moths are **insects,** as are caterpillers, plant hoppers, dragonflies, cockroaches, and bees. You can identify insects, like other arthropods, by counting their body sections and legs. **Insects are arthropods with three body sections, six legs, one pair of antennae, and usually one or two pairs of wings.** The three body sections are the head, thorax, and abdomen, as you can see in Figure 17.

Head Most of an insect's sense organs, such as the eyes and antennae, are located on the head. Insects usually have two large compound eyes. These eyes contain many lenses, which are structures that focus light to form images. Compound eyes are especially keen at seeing movement. Most insects also have small simple eyes that can distinguish between light and darkness.

Thorax An insect's midsection, or **thorax,** is the section to which wings and legs are attached. Most species of insects can fly once they are adults. Insects are the only invertebrates that can fly. By flying, insects can travel long distances to find mates, food, and new places to live. Being able to fly also enables insects to escape from many predators.

Abdomen Inside the abdomen are many of the insect's internal organs. Small holes on the outside of the abdomen lead to a system of tubes inside the insect. These tubes allow air, which contains oxygen, to enter the body. The oxygen in the air travels directly to the insect's cells.

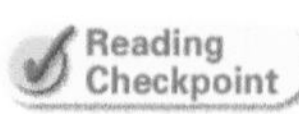

What are the three sections of an insect's body?

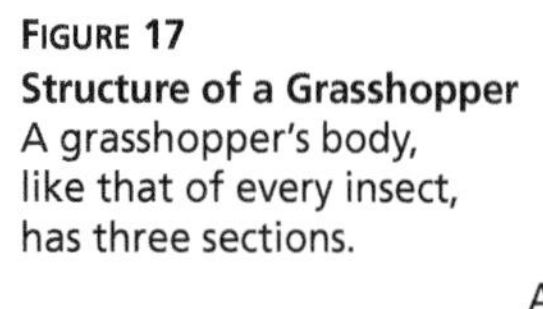

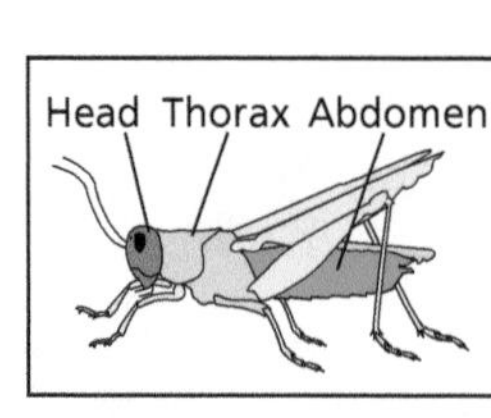

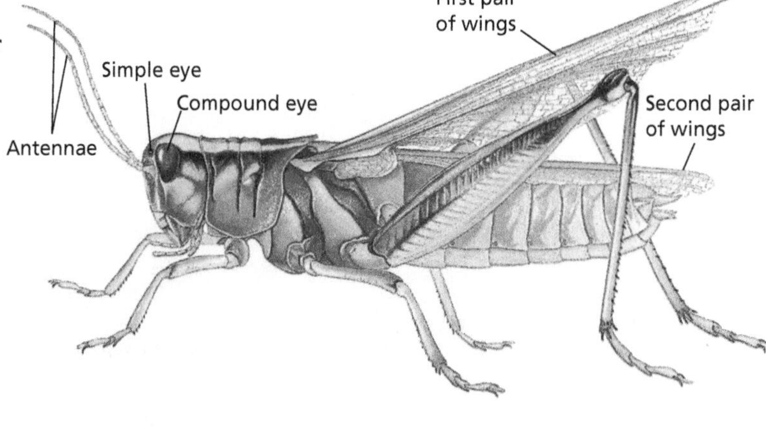

FIGURE 17
Structure of a Grasshopper
A grasshopper's body, like that of every insect, has three sections.

Lab zone Skills Activity

Skills Focus Graphing L3

Materials none

Time 15 minutes

Tips Review the method for constructing a circle graph by calculating one section of the graph with students. First, note the total number of insects *(900,000)*. Calculate the ratio of ants, bees, and wasps to the total number of insects: 115,000/900,000 = 0.13, or 13%. Find the angle measure of the section: $360° \times 0.13 = 47°$. Sketch this section inside a circle using a protractor to measure the central angle.

Expected Outcome Ants, bees wasps: 13%; Beetles and weevils: 39%; Butterflies and moths: 20%; Flies and mosquitoes: 12%; Other: 16% **learning modality: logical/mathematical**

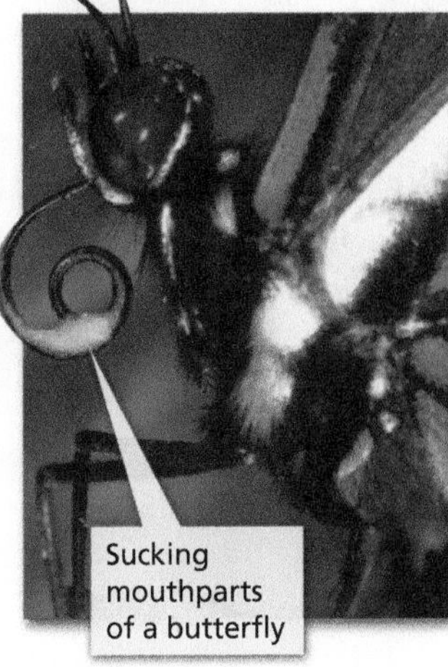

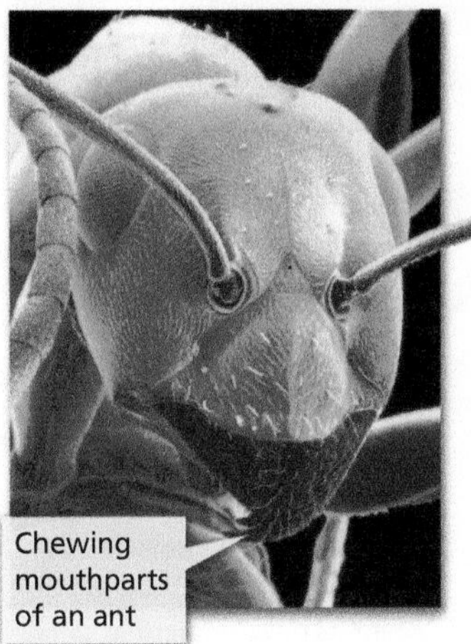

FIGURE 18
Diversity of Mouthparts
The mouthparts of this fly, butterfly, and wood ant are very different in their structure.
Inferring *Could a butterfly eat an ant's food? Explain.*

Obtaining Food

The rule seems to be this: If it is living, or if it once was living, some kind of insect will eat it. You probably know that many insects eat parts of plants, such as leaves or nectar. But insects also eat products that are made from plants, such as paper. If you open a very old book, watch for book lice. These tiny insects live in old books, chewing crooked tunnels through the pages.

Insects may feed on animals, too. Some, like fleas and mosquitoes, feed on the blood of living animals. Others, like dung beetles, feed on animal droppings. Still others, like burying beetles, feed on the decaying bodies of dead animals.

An insect's mouthparts are adapted for a highly specific way of getting food. You can see some of these adaptations in Figure 18. Some flies have a sponge-like mouthpart that they use to lap up decaying flesh. A butterfly's mouthparts are shaped like a coiled tube, which can be uncoiled and used like a drinking straw to suck up nectar from flowers. Most ants have sharp-edged mouthparts that can cut through seeds, wood, and other foods.

Reading Checkpoint **How does a butterfly obtain food?**

Life Cycle

Insects begin life as tiny, hard-shelled, fertilized eggs. After they hatch, insects begin a process of metamorphosis that eventually produces an adult insect. **Each insect species undergoes either complete metamorphosis or gradual metamorphosis.**

For: More on insect metamorphosis
Visit: PHSchool.com
Web Code: ced-2023

Obtaining Food

Teach Key Concepts L2

Diet and Mouthpart Adaptations

Focus Tell students that one reason insects are so successful is that they have adapted to eating a huge variety of things.

Teach Explain that insect mouthparts are highly adapted to suit the diet of each species. Emphasize that insects eat many different kinds of materials, yet most insect species have fairly narrow food requirements. Ask: **What does a grasshopper eat?** *(leaves)* **What does a female mosquito eat?** *(blood)*

Apply Ask students to describe examples they have seen of insects eating different things. *(Possible answers: Aphids on house plants, hornets eating fruit, grasshoppers eating grass)* **learning modality: verbal**

For: More on insect metamorphosis
Visit: PHSchool.com
Web Code: ced-2023

Students can review metamorphosis in an online activity.

Differentiated Instruction

Special Needs L1

Communicating Partner special needs students with more able students. Have them write the names of structures found on insects on separate index cards. On the other side of each card, tell them to write the function of each structure. Then have them separate the cards into three piles representing the body sections where they belong. **learning modality: kinesthetic**

Gifted and Talented L3

Researching Mosquitoes Have students research the biting apparatus of mosquitoes. Have students prepare a brief summary and drawing describing how mosquitoes are able to bite and withdraw blood without the victim's knowledge. **learning modality: logical/mathematical**

Monitor Progress L3

Oral Presentation Call on individual students to name one insect body part and tell its function.

Answers

Figure 18 No; the butterfly's mouthparts are not adapted to cut through seeds, wood, and other foods.

Reading Checkpoint Head, thorax, abdomen

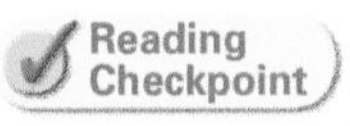
Reading Checkpoint A butterfly sucks up nectar from flowers using its tube-shaped mouthpart.

Life Cycle

Teach Key Concepts L2

Two Kinds of Metamorphosis

Focus Remind students that in order to grow, insects must shed their exoskeleton (molt) and grow a new one. Tell students that every insect species undergoes either complete metamorphosis or gradual metamorphosis.

Teach Have students study Figure 19 and read the description of each type of metamorphosis. Discuss each stage and its characteristics. Ask: **How do insects change when they undergo complete metamorphosis?** *(After hatching, they spend time as a larva, then become an immobile pupa, and then become an adult.)* **How does a firefly's metamorphosis differ from a grasshopper's metamorphosis?** *(A firefly goes through four distinct stages. A grasshopper changes form gradually.)* **When does a grasshopper acquire wings?** *(After the final molt.)* **At what stage do fireflies reproduce?** *(Adult)*

Apply Ask: **Which stage does a moth cocoon represent?** *(Pupa)* **learning modality: logical/mathematical**

All in One Teaching Resources

- Transparency B20

Help Students Read L1

Outlining Refer to the Content Refresher, which provides guidelines for using an outline. Have students create an outline of the information in this section. Outlines should use the head structures used in the section. Major headings are shown in red, and subheads are shown in blue.

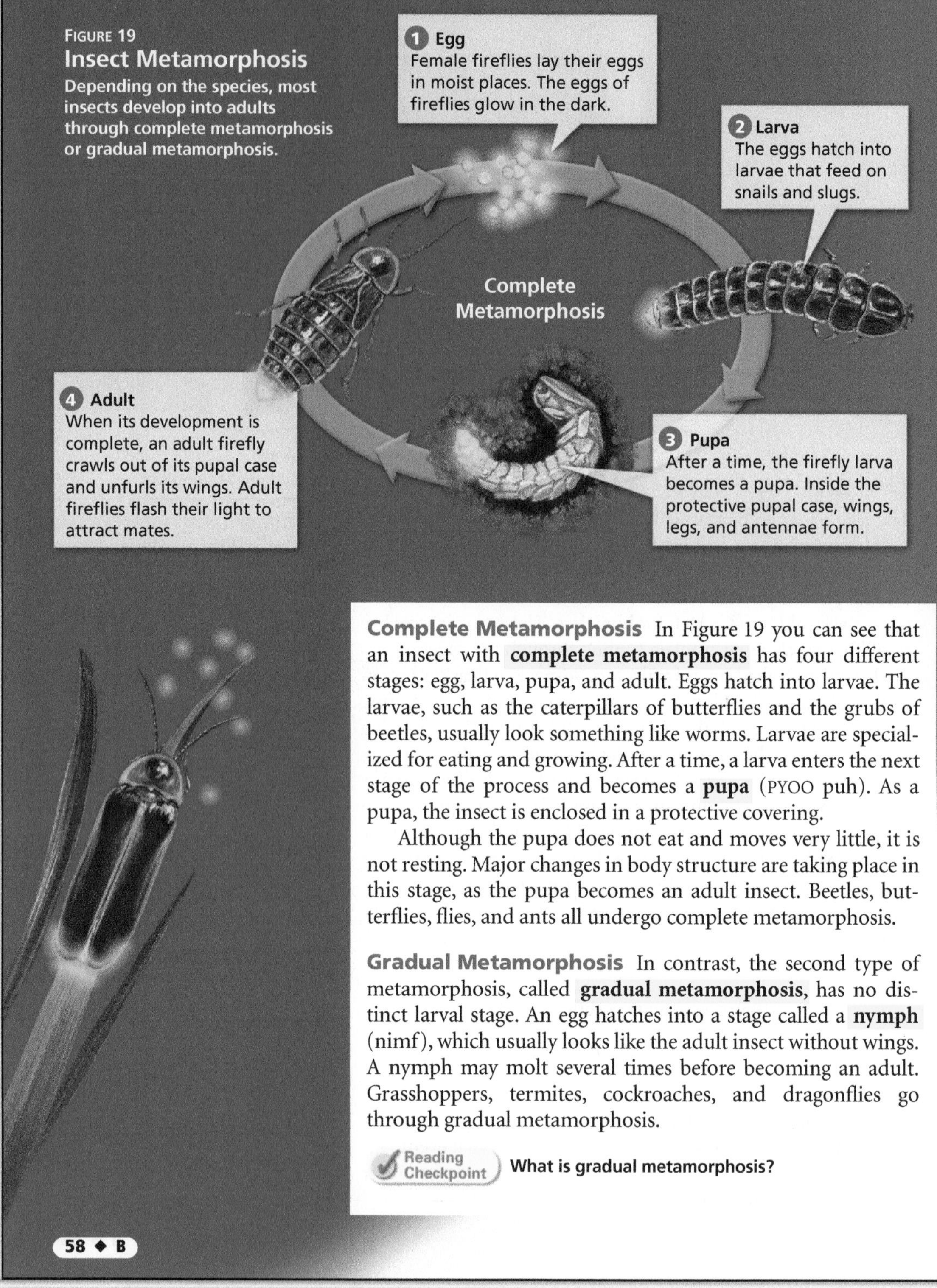
FIGURE 19
Insect Metamorphosis
Depending on the species, most insects develop into adults through complete metamorphosis or gradual metamorphosis.

1 Egg
Female fireflies lay their eggs in moist places. The eggs of fireflies glow in the dark.
2 Larva
The eggs hatch into larvae that feed on snails and slugs.
Complete Metamorphosis
3 Pupa
After a time, the firefly larva becomes a pupa. Inside the protective pupal case, wings, legs, and antennae form.
4 Adult
When its development is complete, an adult firefly crawls out of its pupal case and unfurls its wings. Adult fireflies flash their light to attract mates.

Complete Metamorphosis In Figure 19 you can see that an insect with **complete metamorphosis** has four different stages: egg, larva, pupa, and adult. Eggs hatch into larvae. The larvae, such as the caterpillars of butterflies and the grubs of beetles, usually look something like worms. Larvae are specialized for eating and growing. After a time, a larva enters the next stage of the process and becomes a **pupa** (PYOO puh). As a pupa, the insect is enclosed in a protective covering.

Although the pupa does not eat and moves very little, it is not resting. Major changes in body structure are taking place in this stage, as the pupa becomes an adult insect. Beetles, butterflies, flies, and ants all undergo complete metamorphosis.

Gradual Metamorphosis In contrast, the second type of metamorphosis, called **gradual metamorphosis**, has no distinct larval stage. An egg hatches into a stage called a **nymph** (nimf), which usually looks like the adult insect without wings. A nymph may molt several times before becoming an adult. Grasshoppers, termites, cockroaches, and dragonflies go through gradual metamorphosis.

Reading Checkpoint **What is gradual metamorphosis?**

58 ◆ B

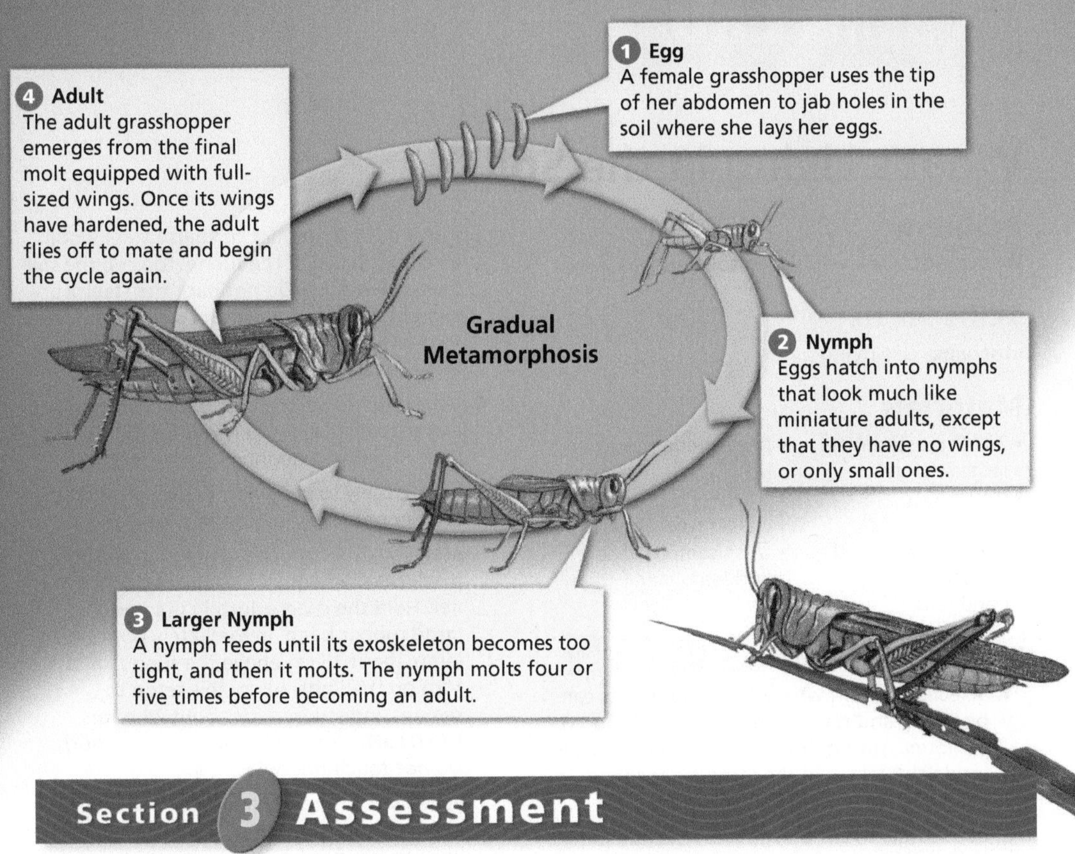

1 Egg
A female grasshopper uses the tip of her abdomen to jab holes in the soil where she lays her eggs.
4 Adult
The adult grasshopper emerges from the final molt equipped with full-sized wings. Once its wings have hardened, the adult flies off to mate and begin the cycle again.
Gradual Metamorphosis
2 Nymph
Eggs hatch into nymphs that look much like miniature adults, except that they have no wings, or only small ones.
3 Larger Nymph
A nymph feeds until its exoskeleton becomes too tight, and then it molts. The nymph molts four or five times before becoming an adult.

Section 3 Assessment

Target Reading Skill Sequencing Refer to your cycle diagram about complete metamorphosis as you answer Question 3.

Reviewing Key Concepts

1. a. Identifying What characteristics do insects share?
   b. Interpreting Diagrams Look at Figure 17. To which body section are a grasshopper's wings attached?
   c. Making Generalizations Suppose the adaptation of wings was suddenly lost in all insects. Predict what would happen to the number and diversity of insects.
2. a. Naming Name a type of insect that has chewing mouthparts.
   b. Reviewing What are three ways that the mouthparts of insects are adapted for obtaining food?
3. a. Listing List the stages of gradual metamorphosis and the stages of complete metamorphosis.
   b. Interpreting Diagrams Look at Figure 19. How are complete metamorphosis and gradual metamorphosis different?
   c. Applying Concepts Why is a nymph more likely than a larva to eat the same food as its parents?

Lab zone At-Home Activity

Bug Hunt Walk with a family member in your backyard or neighborhood. Search the undersides of leaves, under woodchips or rocks, and other likely places for insects. Show your family member what distinguishes an insect from other kinds of arthropods.

Lab zone At-Home Activity

Bug Hunt L2 Encourage students to keep a record of their search, including drawings or photographs of the insects they discover.

Monitor Progress L2

Answer

Reading Checkpoint A type of metamorphosis with no distinct larval stage

Assess

Reviewing Key Concepts

1. a. Three body sections; six legs; one pair of antennae; usually wings **b.** Thorax **c.** Their number and diversity would decline because wings enable insects to live in many unique habitats that would be otherwise inaccessible.
2. a. Answers may vary. Sample: ant, grasshopper. **b.** Some flies have sponge-like mouthparts that are used to lap up decaying flesh; most ants have mouthparts that can cut through seeds, wood, and other foods. Butterflies have a tubelike mouthpart that can be uncoiled and used to suck nectar.
3. a. Gradual: egg, nymph, adult; complete: egg, larva, pupa, adult **b.** Complete metamorphosis consists of four very different stages; in gradual metamorphosis, a nymph looks very much like an adult. **c.** A nymph resembles an adult insect, so it would have similar food preferences and the abilities to eat the same food.

Reteach L1

Use Figure 19 to review the events in insect metamorphosis. Ask students to work with a partner. Students explain one form of metamorphosis (complete or gradual) to their partners, and then switch roles.

Performance Assessment L2

Writing Have students explain how complete metamorphosis reduces competition for food among members of the same species. (Different stages—larva and adult—often eat different kinds of food, which reduces competition within the species.)

All in One Teaching Resources

- Section Summary: *Insects*
- Review and Reinforce: *Insects*
- Enrich: *Insects*

What's Living in the Soil?

L2

Prepare for Inquiry

Key Concept

Soil and leaf litter make up a miniature environment that contains a variety of organisms.

Skills Objectives

After this lab, students will be able to

- observe soil, leaf litter, and the organisms they contain
- classify organisms into phyla based on key distinguishing characteristics

Prep Time 45 minutes

Class Time 15 minutes on the first day, 45 minutes on the second day

Advance Planning

Try the lab in advance to ensure that there are enough organisms present. Three or four days before the lab, go to two different sites. Try to select sites that are moist but not too wet. Collect leaf litter and the first inch or so of soil in buckets. Keep the buckets covered to keep contents moist. Set up the lamp and jars, and test a soil sample from each site. If you do not obtain enough organisms, collect more material from another site.

Safety

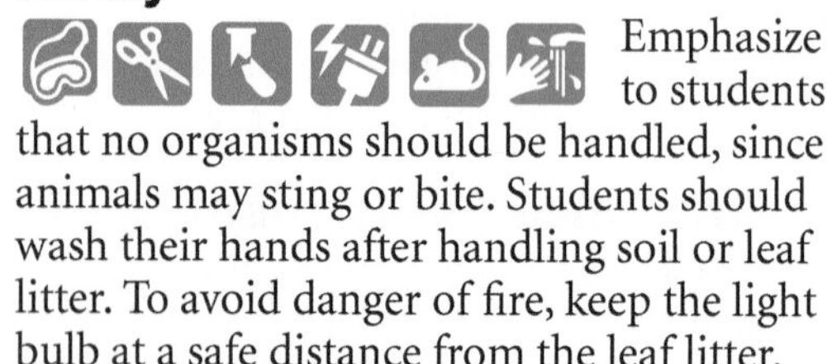

Emphasize to students that no organisms should be handled, since animals may sting or bite. Students should wash their hands after handling soil or leaf litter. To avoid danger of fire, keep the light bulb at a safe distance from the leaf litter.

All in One Teaching Resources

- Lab Worksheet: *What's Living in the Soil?*

Guide Inquiry

Invitation

Have students think about how many animals might be present in soil. Ask: **What advantage do you think living in the soil gives some animals?** *(Moist environment, decaying organic matter for food, protection from predators)* Invite students to write predictions about the number and kind of organisms they will see in a few scoops of soil.

Lab zone Skills Lab

What's Living in the Soil?

Problem

What kinds of animals live in soil and leaf litter?

Skills Focus

observing, classifying

Materials

- 2-liter plastic bottle
- large scissors
- trowel
- cheesecloth
- large rubber band
- gooseneck lamp
- hand lens
- large, wide-mouthed jar
- small jar
- coarse steel wool
- fresh sample of soil and leaf litter

Procedure    

1. Select a location where your equipment can be set up and remain undisturbed for about 24 hours. At that location, place the small jar inside the center of the large jar as shown in the photograph on page 61.
2. Use scissors to cut a large plastic bottle in half. **CAUTION:** *Cut in a direction away from yourself and others.* Turn the top half of the bottle upside down to serve as a funnel.
3. Insert a small amount of coarse steel wool into the mouth of the funnel to keep the soil from falling out. Do not pack the steel wool too tightly. Leave spaces for small organisms to crawl through. Place the funnel into the large jar as shown in the photograph.
4. Using the trowel, fill the funnel with soil and surface leaf litter. When you finish, wash your hands thoroughly.
5. Look closely to see whether the soil and litter are dry or wet. Record your observation.
6. Make a cover for your sample by placing a piece of cheesecloth over the top of the funnel. Hold the cheesecloth in place with a large rubber band. Immediately position a lamp about 15 cm above the funnel, and turn on the light. Allow this setup to remain undisturbed for about 24 hours. **CAUTION:** *Hot light bulbs can cause burns. Do not touch the bulb.*
7. When you are ready to make your observations, turn off the lamp. Leave the funnel and jar in place while making your observations. Use a hand lens to examine each organism in the jar. **CAUTION:** *Do not touch any of the organisms.*
8. Use a data table like the one shown to sketch each type of organism and to record other observations. Be sure to include evidence that will help you classify the organisms. (*Hint:* Remember that some animals may be at different stages of metamorphosis.)
9. Examine the soil and leaf litter, and record whether this material is dry or wet.
10. When you are finished, follow your teacher's directions about returning the organisms to the soil. Wash your hands with soap.

Data Table				
Sketch of Organism	Number Found	Size	Important Characteristics	Probable Phylum

Analyze and Conclude

1. **Observing** Describe the conditions of the soil environment at the beginning and end of the lab. What caused the change?
2. **Classifying** What types of animals did you collect in the small jar? What characteristics did you use to identify each type of animal? Which types of animals were the most common?
3. **Developing Hypotheses** Why do you think the animals moved down the funnel away from the soil?
4. **Inferring** Using what you have learned about arthropods and other animals, make an inference about the role that each animal you collected plays in the environment.
5. **Communicating** Develop a field guide that categorizes and describes the types of animals you found in your soil sample. Include sketches and brief descriptions of the animals.

Design an Experiment

What kinds of organisms might live in other soil types—for example, soil at the edge of a pond, dry sandy soil, or commercially prepared potting soil? Design an experiment to answer this question.

Extend Inquiry

Design an Experiment To find out which types of organisms live in other types of soil, students can repeat the lab with other soil types.

Introducing the Procedure

Tell students not to disturb the funnel once they have placed soil and leaf litter in it. If they do, soil may run into the collection jar. Warn students only to observe the animals, not to handle them, since some might bite or sting. Students should find that millipedes and other small animals are best viewed with a hand lens. The types and numbers of soil organisms found will vary in different regions of the country. Help students familiarize themselves with the animals they might find.

Troubleshooting the Experiment

If students have trouble classifying the organisms, have them list the features of worms and arthropods. Features include the presence or absence of legs and wings, and the number of pairs of legs. Certain times of the year are better than others for finding a greater variety and abundance of organisms. If students find only a few organisms, tell them not to be discouraged. The scarcity of organisms may be seasonal.

Expected Outcome

Several kinds of organisms may be present, and distinguishing among them may be difficult. Have students count the number of pairs of legs, number of body segments, and, if possible, observe how the organism moves.

Analyze and Conclude

1. At first, the soil was damp and clumped together. At the end of the lab, it was dry and loose. The heat from the lamp dried out the soil.

2. Answers will vary. Students should refer to the animals listed in their data tables. These will most likely be worms and arthropods.

3. The animals moved away from the heat and drying soil.

4. Answers will vary. Sample: Some animals, such as worms and insects, are important as decomposers. Some, such as pseudoscorpions and spiders, are carnivores.

5. Answers will vary. Student field guides should accurately categorize and describe the types of animals that they found in their sample.

Section 4

Insect Ecology

Objectives

After completing this lesson, students will be able to

B.2.4.1 Explain why insects are important in food chains.

B.2.4.2 Name two other ways insects interact with their environments.

B.2.4.3 Describe some methods used to control pest insects.

Target Reading Skill

Building Vocabulary Explain that using a new word in a sentence helps students understand its meaning.

Answer

Call on volunteers to read their sentences aloud. Make sure that students have come up with original sentences.

Preteach

Build Background Knowledge L1

Insects—Good or Bad?

Help students to think about the many roles played by insects in their community. Ask: **What are some insects you see at least once a week?** *(Answers will vary depending on the season and your region. Examples: mosquitoes, bees, flies, cockroaches, spiders, moths, butterflies, ants, scorpions)* **Are these insects helpful or harmful?** *(Accept all responses without comment at this time.)* Encourage students to recognize that even insect pests, although annoying, play an important ecological role and should not necessarily be labeled as "bad."

Section 4

Integrating Environmental Science

Insect Ecology

Reading Preview

Key Concepts

- Why are insects important in food chains?
- What are two other ways insects interact with their environments?
- What are some ways used to control insect pests?

Key Terms

- food chain
- ecology
- producer
- consumer
- decomposer
- pollinator
- pesticide
- biological control

Target Reading Skill

Building Vocabulary Using a word in a sentence helps you think about how best to explain the word. After you read the section, reread the paragraphs that contain definitions of Key Terms. Use all the information you have learned to write a meaningful sentence using the Key Term.

Lab zone Discover Activity

What Materials Carry Pollen Best?

1. Use an eraser to transfer some pollen between two flowers your teacher gives you.
2. Next, use a cotton swab to do the same. Did the eraser or cotton swab transfer pollen better?

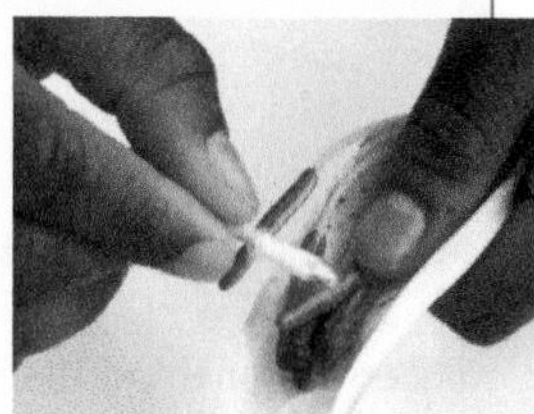

Think It Over

Inferring How might its ability to transfer pollen between flowers affect an insect's role in the environment?

In a meadow, a caterpillar munches the leaves of a plant. Later that day, a bird eats the caterpillar. Years later, after the bird has died, a beetle eats the dead bird. The plant, caterpillar, bird, and beetle are all part of one food chain. A **food chain** is a series of events in which one organism eats another and obtains energy. The study of food chains and other ways that organisms interact with their environment is called **ecology.**

Insects and the Food Chain

A food chain starts with a **producer**—an organism that makes its own food. Most producers, such as grass and other plants, use energy from sunlight to make their food. In a food chain, producers are food for consumers. A **consumer** is an organism that obtains energy by eating other organisms. Some consumers, like caterpillars, eat producers, and some eat other consumers. Decomposers, such as carrion beetles, also play a role in food chains. A **decomposer** breaks down the wastes and dead bodies of other organisms. In a food chain insects may play the roles of consumer and decomposer. In addition, some insects are prey for other consumers.

Lab zone Discover Activity

Skills Focus Inferring L2

Materials flowers, cotton swabs, pencil, other materials as selected

Time 20 minutes

Tips Pre-select the test materials to save time. Use large flowers with plenty of pollen. Tell the students to handle the flowers gently. Advise students with strong allergies to pollen to observe a classmate transfer the pollen rather than do it themselves. Have all students wash their hands afterwards.

Expected Outcome Materials with a textured surface will hold pollen best.

Think It Over The insects will help plants reproduce. Many plants have adaptations to attract good pollinators.

Insects as Consumers of Plants The roles of insects in a food chain are shown in Figure 20. **Insects play key roles in food chains because of the many different ways that they obtain food and then become food for other animals.**

Many insects are consumers of plants. Perhaps you have tried growing tomato plants and seen how fat green caterpillars ate up the leaves. In fact, insects eat about 20 percent of the crops grown for humans. Insects eat most species of wild plants, too. Some insects eat the leaves of plants, while others eat the sap, bark, roots, and other parts of plants.

Insects as Prey Insects play another role in food chains—they are prey for many animals. That is, other consumers eat insects. Many fishes and birds eat insects to survive. For example, the main source of food for trout and bass is insects. Indeed, that's why people use lures called "flies" to catch fishes like these. The lures look like the mayflies and stoneflies these fishes normally eat. Some species of birds feed their young, called chicks, only insects. And the chicks are big eaters! A single swallow chick, for example, may consume about 200,000 insects before it leaves the nest.

Math Skills

Percentage

A percentage is a ratio that compares a number to 100. If 25 percent of 900,000 insect species eat other insects, how many insect-eating species are there? Set up a proportion and solve it.

$$\frac{\text{Insect-eating species}}{\text{900,000 insect species}} = \frac{25\%}{100\%}$$

$$\text{Insect-eating species} = 225{,}000$$

Practice Problem A swallow chick eats 200,000 insects. If 12 percent of the insects are beetles, how many beetles does it eat?

FIGURE 20
Insects in a Food Chain
In a food chain, some insects are consumers of plants. Some insects are prey for other consumers. Other insects are decomposers.

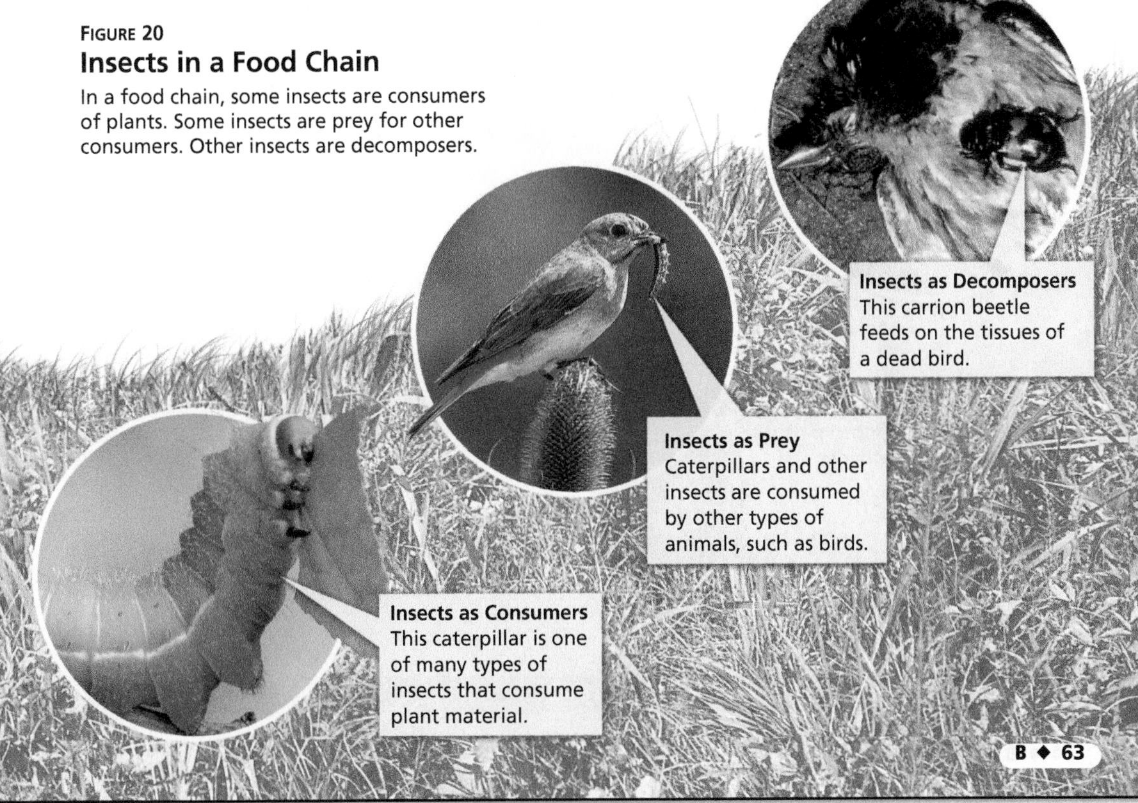

Insects as Decomposers
This carrion beetle feeds on the tissues of a dead bird.
Insects as Prey
Caterpillars and other insects are consumed by other types of animals, such as birds.
Insects as Consumers
This caterpillar is one of many types of insects that consume plant material.

Instruct

Insects and the Food Chain

Teach Key Concepts L2

Many Roles of Insects

Focus Remind students how insects fill many different roles.

Teach Make a different column on the chalkboard for each of the four roles discussed in this section. Ask: **What are the three roles that insects play in food chains?** *(They are consumers that eat plants and other insects. They are food for other animals. They are decomposers.)* **What insects are major consumers of plants?** *(Answers will vary. Examples: Caterpillars, grasshoppers)* **What kinds of animals eat insects?** *(Birds, fishes)* **How can insects serve as decomposers?** *(They eat wastes and dead organisms.)* **What kinds of insects are eaten by humans?** *(grasshoppers, beetles, ants, crickets, cicadas)*

Apply Ask: **What would happen if the insects that are decomposers vanished?** *(Wastes and dead organisms would accumulate; nutrients could not be recycled.)* **learning modality: logical/mathematical**

Independent Practice

All in One Teaching Resources

- Guided Reading and Study Worksheet: *Insect Ecology*

Student Edition on Audio CD

Math Skills

Percentage Remind students that 25% is equal to 0.25.

Answer
Practice problem
p beetles/200,000 insects = 12%/100%
$p = 24{,}000$

Differentiated Instruction

Less Proficient Readers L1

Classifying Examples Have students use sketches, photographs, and short captions to create a poster for each of the three insect roles discussed in this section. Tell students to use ideas from the headings and illustrations in the chapter. **learning modality: visual**

Gifted and Talented L3

Researching Fishing Lures Have students do research to learn about fly-fishing lures that are made to mimic aquatic insects. Ask students to describe how anglers select lures to match the insect species that are currently hatching. **learning modality: logical/mathematical**

Monitor Progress L2

Oral Presentation Ask students to define three important roles that insects play in food chains.

For: Links on insects
Visit: www.SciLinks.org
Web Code: scn-0224

Download a worksheet that will guide students' review of Internet resources on insects.

• Tech & Design in History •

Focus Tell students that people have been using products from insects for thousands of years.

Teach Ask: **What time span does the time line cover?** *(From 100 B.C. until 2000, or 2100 years)* **When did humans first spin silk from silkworms?** *(More than 4,000 years ago)* **How have scientists used the light-producing chemicals from fireflies?** *(To study genes and diseases)* **What is cochineal?** *(A red dye extracted from a tiny cactus-eating insect)*

For: Links on insects
Visit: www.SciLinks.org
Web Code: scn-0224

Insects as Decomposers In a food chain some insects play the role of decomposers by breaking down the wastes and bodies of dead organisms. For example, in some tropical food chains, termites may break down up to one third of the dead wood, leaves, and grass produced there every year. In other food chains, flies and dung beetles break down animal droppings, called manure. By doing this, the buildup of manure from large animals is prevented.

The substances that insect decomposers break down enrich the soil. In addition, insect decomposers may burrow and nest in the ground. By doing so, these insects expose soil to oxygen from the air and mix up the nutrients in the soil.

• Tech & Design in History •

Products From Insects

Over the last few thousand years, insects have supplied humans with some important products.

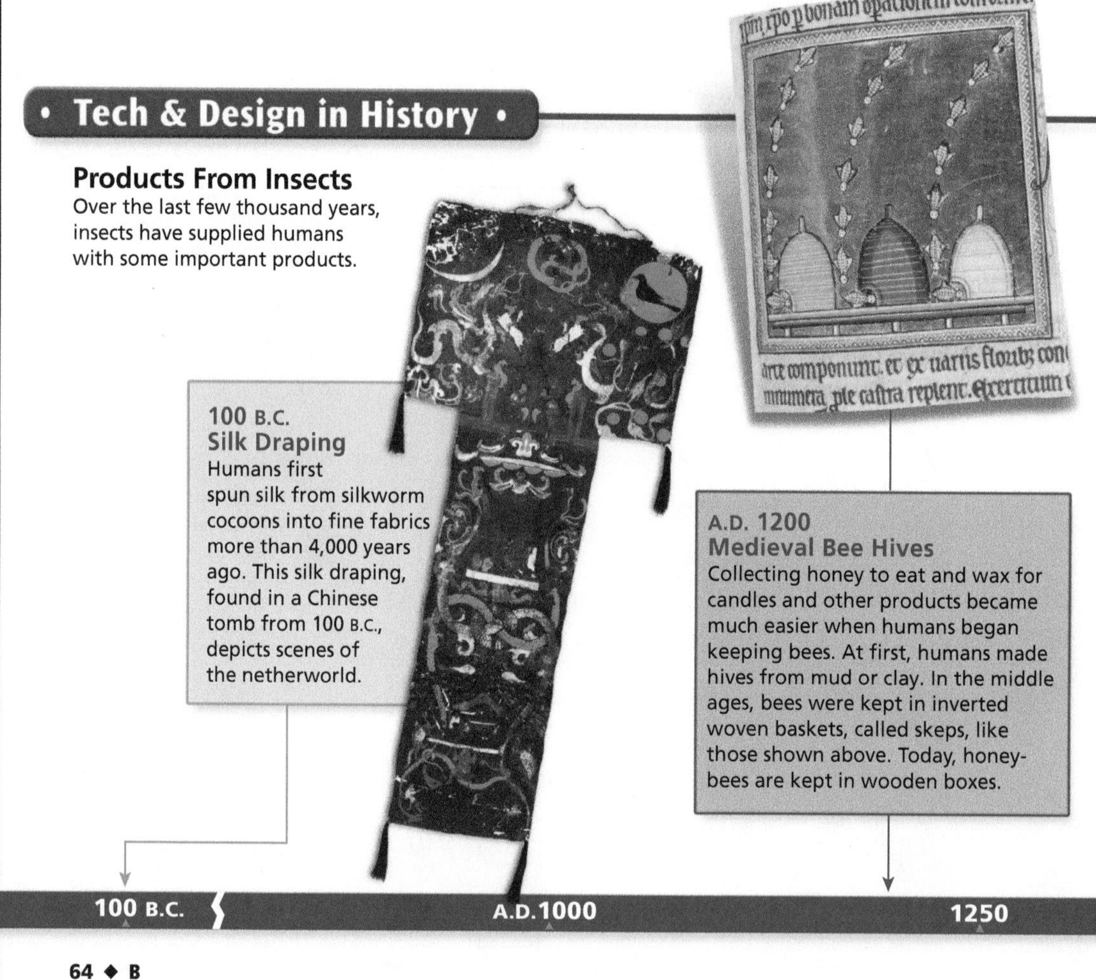

100 B.C.
Silk Draping
Humans first spun silk from silkworm cocoons into fine fabrics more than 4,000 years ago. This silk draping, found in a Chinese tomb from 100 B.C., depicts scenes of the netherworld.

A.D. 1200
Medieval Bee Hives
Collecting honey to eat and wax for candles and other products became much easier when humans began keeping bees. At first, humans made hives from mud or clay. In the middle ages, bees were kept in inverted woven baskets, called skeps, like those shown above. Today, honeybees are kept in wooden boxes.

Insects as Food for Humans Did you know that insects were an important source of nutrition for prehistoric humans? Even today, insects are collected and eaten by people in many parts of the world. In some Mexican villages, dried grasshoppers are ground up and mixed with flour to make tortillas. In other parts of the world, the larvae of certain species of beetles are roasted over an open fire. Ants, crickets, and cicadas are just a few of the other types of insects eaten by humans.

Maybe you are thinking, "Yuck! I'd never eat an insect." Even if you'd never allow an insect on your dinner plate, you are likely to have used the products of insects in other aspects of your daily life. You can see some of the major uses of insect products through history in the timeline below.

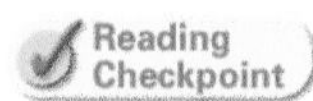

What is an animal that breaks down wastes and dead organisms called?

Writing in Science

Research and Write

Research one of the products described in the timeline below. Then write an advertisement for the product. Include information about the species of insect used to develop the product, and details about how the product is made.

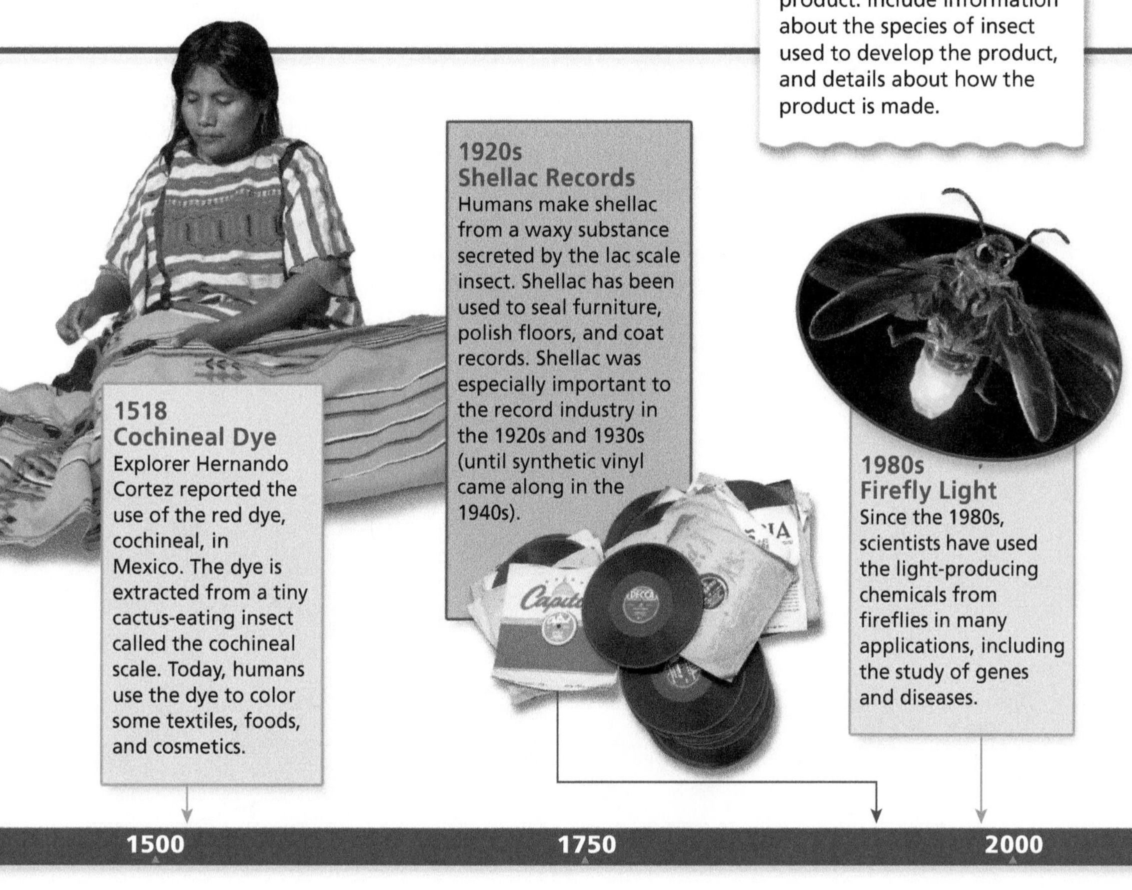

1518
Cochineal Dye
Explorer Hernando Cortez reported the use of the red dye, cochineal, in Mexico. The dye is extracted from a tiny cactus-eating insect called the cochineal scale. Today, humans use the dye to color some textiles, foods, and cosmetics.
1920s
Shellac Records
Humans make shellac from a waxy substance secreted by the lac scale insect. Shellac has been used to seal furniture, polish floors, and coat records. Shellac was especially important to the record industry in the 1920s and 1930s (until synthetic vinyl came along in the 1940s).
1980s
Firefly Light
Since the 1980s, scientists have used the light-producing chemicals from fireflies in many applications, including the study of genes and diseases.
1500
1750
2000

Writing in Science

Writing Mode Persuasive

Scoring Rubric

4 Includes accurate, detailed information about the insect species and the product

3 Includes accurate and complete information

2 Includes accurate but incomplete information

1 Includes inaccurate information

Help Students Read L2

Summarizing Summarizing the information presented in the text will help students to focus on main ideas and remember what they have read. Have students read the text and summarize the paragraphs by restating the main ideas in their own words.

Differentiated Instruction

Gifted and Talented L3

Creating Displays Have students research and collect photographs of insects that are eaten by humans. Have students mount the photos on the correct country of a world map drawn on a poster board. Have students include the insect's name, the name of the country in which the insect is part of people's diet, and a short caption describing how the insects are eaten. (You may wish to show students *Man Eating Bugs: The Art and Science of Eating Insects* by Peter Menzel and Faith D'Aluisio if this book is available in your school media center.) **learning modality: visual**

Monitor Progress L2

Drawing Have students make drawings to visually summarize the roles that insects play in food chains. Students can save their drawings in their portfolios.

Answer

 Decomposer

Other Interactions

Teach Key Concepts L2

Helpful and Harmful Insect Roles

Focus Ask: **Do you think bees are helpful or harmful?** *(Students might respond that they are helpful because they carry pollen from one plant to another or that they are harmful because they can sting.)*

Teach Have students preview Figure 21. Ask: **What does a bee look like after it has visited a flower?** *(The bee looks like it is covered with dust.)* **What is the dust-like substance on the bee?** *(pollen)* **Why are pollinators critical to many plants?** *(By carrying pollen between plants, they enable plants to reproduce.)* Direct attention to Figure 22, and point out that the mosquito is piercing its host. Ask: **Why are some species of mosquitoes considered harmful?** *(Mosquitoes can spread disease since disease organisms may travel from a mosquito to its prey when the mosquito pierces its victim.)*

Apply Ask: **How do bees benefit by visiting flowers?** *(They take nectar and some pollen back to the hive.)* **How do flowers benefit from the visits of the bees?** *(They are able to produce fruits and seeds.)* **learning modality: visual**

Controlling Pests

Teach Key Concepts L2

Insect Pest Control

Focus Ask students if they are familiar with ways of controlling insect pests. Ask volunteers to describe their experiences.

Teach Ask: **What are some ways to kill pest insects other than using pesticides?** *(Traps, natural predators of the pest)*

Apply Ask: **What is the benefit of using biological control?** *(Biological control targets a specific pest.)* **learning modality: verbal**

FIGURE 21
A Bee as a Pollinator
This bee is getting dusted with yellow pollen as it drinks nectar from the flower. **Observing** *On which of the bee's structures can you observe pollen grains?*

Other Interactions

Besides eating and being eaten, insects interact in other ways with the living things in their environments. **Two ways insects interact with other living things are by moving pollen among plants and by spreading disease-causing organisms.**

Pollen Carriers Have you ever seen a bee crawling into a flower on a warm summer day? Have you wondered what it is doing? The bee is helping itself to the plant's nectar and pollen, which are food for bees. But plants also need to share their pollen with other plants. Pollen contains cells that become sperm cells, allowing plants to reproduce. When the bee crawls into a flower to obtain its food, it gets dusted with pollen, as shown in Figure 21. Then, as the bee enters the next flower, some of the pollen on its body is left in the second flower. An animal that carries pollen among plants is called a **pollinator.** Bees are pollinators, and so are many beetles and flies. Without pollinators, some plants cannot reproduce.

Disease Carriers Not all interactions between insects and other living things have happy endings. While some insects transfer pollen, others spread diseases to both plants and animals, including humans. Insects that spread diseases include some mosquitoes and fleas. These insects often have sucking mouthparts that pierce the skin of their prey, providing an opening for the disease-causing organisms to enter. Diseases that are carried by insects include malaria, which is spread by mosquitoes. Malaria causes high fevers and can be treated with medicines today.

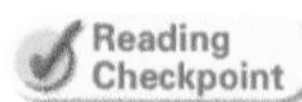

What is a pollinator?

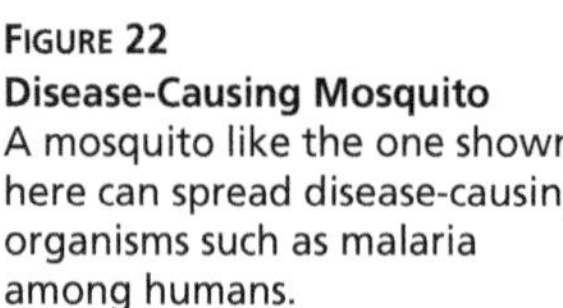

FIGURE 22
Disease-Causing Mosquito
A mosquito like the one shown here can spread disease-causing organisms such as malaria among humans.

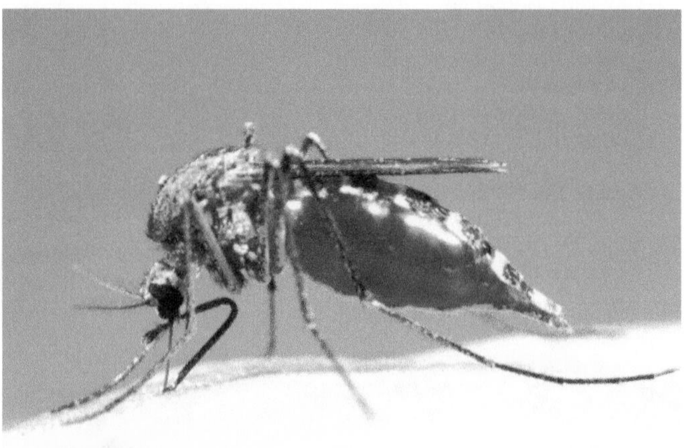

Controlling Pests

Some insects are harmful, even though they don't spread diseases. Harmful insects are called pests. **To try to control pests, people use chemicals, traps, and living things, including other insects.** Chemicals that kill pests are called **pesticides.** However, pesticides also kill pollinators, such as bees, and can harm other animals.

What are the alternatives to pesticides? Biologists are using their knowledge of insect ecology to develop new pest controls. One such control is a trap that attracts mosquitoes in a way similar to how humans attract mosquitoes. Another control is to surround crops with wild plants that are bad-tasting or even poisonous to the harmful insect.

People may prefer to use biological controls. A **biological control** is a natural predator or disease released into an area to fight a harmful insect. For example, ladybugs, which eat other insects, have been introduced to some areas where crops grow to control aphids. Aphids are tiny insects that damage plants by sucking plant sap.

FIGURE 23
Biological Control
Ladybugs are used as biological control agents against aphids. Here, one ladybug consumes its prey.

Reading Checkpoint What is a chemical intended to kill pest insects called?

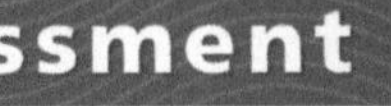

Section 4 Assessment

Target Reading Skill Building Vocabulary Use your sentences to help answer the questions.

Reviewing Key Concepts

1. a. Defining What is a food chain?
   b. Interpreting Photographs What three roles do insects play in the food chain shown in Figure 20?
2. a. Reviewing Besides their role in food chains, what are two other ways insects interact with their environment?
   b. Summarizing What effect do pollinators have on their environment?
   c. Predicting What would a world without pollinators be like?
3. a. Reviewing How can insect pests be controlled?
   b. Comparing and Contrasting How are the effects of using biological controls similar to the effects of using pesticides? How are they different?
   c. Applying Concepts Some insect species are harmful only in areas of the world where they do not normally live but have been accidentally released. Why might this be?

Math Practice

4. Percentage Suppose 33 percent of the 50 tons of wood produced in one year by a forest is consumed by termites and other insects. How many tons do the insects eat?

Monitor Progress L2

Answers

Figure 21 Legs, abdomen, thorax, head, antennae, and wings

Reading Checkpoint A pollinator is an insect or other animal that carries pollen among plants.

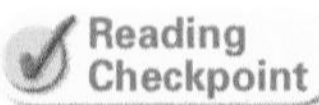

Reading Checkpoint A chemical that kills pest insects is called a pesticide.

Assess

Reviewing Key Concepts

1. a. A series of events in which one organism eats another and obtains energy
b. Consumers, prey, decomposers
2. a. Two other ways insects interact are as pollinators and disease-carriers.
b. Pollinators enable plants to reproduce.
c. There would be a sharp decline in the number of plants, which would cause a decline in the number of herbivores. That decline would result in fewer carnivores and decomposers.
3. a. Insect pests may be controlled with chemicals, traps, or living things (such as natural predators). **b.** Alike: Both can kill harmful insects. Different: Pesticides may kill or harm other types of animals, too. **c.** In their native countries, these insects have natural predators that control their population size.

Reteach L1

As a class, list examples of beneficial insects and harmful insects.

Performance Assessment L2

Oral Presentation Ask students to create brief oral presentations summarizing the roles of insects in food chains.

All in One Teaching Resources

- Section Summary: *Insect Ecology*
- Review and Reinforce: *Insect Ecology*
- Enrich: *Insect Ecology*

Lab zone Chapter Project

Keep Students on Track Verify that students' data are being collected on time and appear reasonable. Check students' sketches. Tell students they must be able to identify the stages of mealworm development from their sketches.

Math Practice

Math Skill Percentage

Answer

4. 16.5 tons

Technology and Society

Battling Pest Insects

Key Concepts

The use of pesticides has advantages and disadvantages.

Build Background Knowledge

Recalling Information About Insects

Review with students the concepts they learned in this chapter that apply to this feature content. Ask: **What is an exoskeleton?** *(A tough, waterproof, outer covering that protects the animal and helps prevent evaporation of water from the animal's body)* **What are the stages of an insect's life cycle?** *(Depending on the species, the insect can undergo complete metamorphosis—egg, larva, pupa, adult—or incomplete metamorphosis—egg, nymph, adult.) Point out that each year insects (not just adults, but larvae and nymphs, too) cause millions of dollars of damage to crops, buildings, and other materials. Ask:* **What are some examples of insect damage you are familiar with?** *(Sample answers: damage to lawns, shrubs, trees, fruit; holes in clothing)*

Introduce the Debate

Direct student's attention to the picture of the boll weevil. Point out that the boll weevil is the most serious cotton pest in North America. Tell students that it is estimated that between 3,000,000 and 5,000,000 bales of cotton are destroyed annually by this insect. Ask students what impact they think this damage has on cotton farmers and consumers. Lead students to understand the economic consequences of insect damage.

Technology and Society • Tech & Design •

Battling Pest Insects

It's hard to believe that insects can cause much harm. But some species, such as the cotton boll weevil, can devastate crops. Boll weevils eat cotton bolls, the part of the plant that produces cotton fibers. Other insects, such as some mosquitoes, spread diseases. To control insect pests, people often use pesticides—chemicals or substances that kill insects or alter their life processes.

How Pesticides Work
Pesticides kill insects in a variety of ways. People may select one or more pesticides to attack a particular pest.

What Are Pesticides?

Since ancient times, people have used substances such as sulfur to kill pests. In the 1900s, people began developing new chemicals to battle harmful insects. Today, most pesticides used in the United States are synthetic—made by people in laboratories. On average, it takes about 15 years and about 20 million dollars to develop a new pesticide. That time includes obtaining approval from the Environmental Protection Agency, which oversees pesticide use. Once on the market, pesticides can work to kill insects in a variety of ways. They might attack the physical, chemical, or biological processes of the pests.

Attack the Gut
Pesticides that contain certain bacteria and viruses can attack the gut lining, killing the insect.

Paralyze the Nervous System
Pesticides that interfere with signals in the brain can cause convulsions, paralysis, and death.

Boll weevil on a cotton boll

68 ◆ B

Background

Facts and Figures Adult boll weevils emerge in spring, and each female deposits between 100 and 300 eggs in cotton buds or fruit, called bolls. A female will not deposit eggs in cotton bolls that have already been visited by another female unless most of the cotton bolls are already infested.

Larvae live within the cotton boll, where they destroy the seeds and the surrounding cotton fibers. Because larvae do not leave the cotton boll, pesticides are useless at killing larvae. Because an egg develops into an adult in just two or three weeks, as many as ten generations can develop in a single year.

Programs to control boll weevil infestations include cleaning up areas where they hibernate, diversifying crops (mixing other crops in with the cotton crop), developing early maturing varieties of cotton, and early planting.

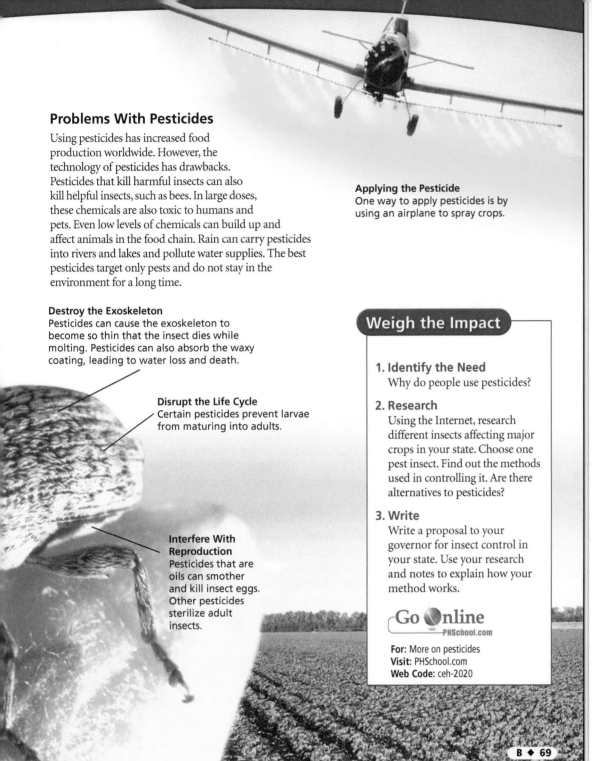

Problems With Pesticides

Using pesticides has increased food production worldwide. However, the technology of pesticides has drawbacks. Pesticides that kill harmful insects can also kill helpful insects, such as bees. In large doses, these chemicals are also toxic to humans and pets. Even low levels of chemicals can build up and affect animals in the food chain. Rain can carry pesticides into rivers and lakes and pollute water supplies. The best pesticides target only pests and do not stay in the environment for a long time.

Applying the Pesticide
One way to apply pesticides is by using an airplane to spray crops.

Destroy the Exoskeleton
Pesticides can cause the exoskeleton to become so thin that the insect dies while molting. Pesticides can also absorb the waxy coating, leading to water loss and death.

Disrupt the Life Cycle
Certain pesticides prevent larvae from maturing into adults.

Interfere With Reproduction
Pesticides that are oils can smother and kill insect eggs. Other pesticides sterilize adult insects.

Weigh the Impact

1. Identify the Need
Why do people use pesticides?

2. Research
Using the Internet, research different insects affecting major crops in your state. Choose one pest insect. Find out the methods used in controlling it. Are there alternatives to pesticides?

3. Write
Write a proposal to your governor for insect control in your state. Use your research and notes to explain how your method works.

Go Online
PHSchool.com

For: More on pesticides
Visit: PHSchool.com
Web Code: ceh-2020

Facilitate the Debate

- Have students read the feature and do the research in Weigh the Impact individually or in pairs as a homework assignment. The next day discuss these questions: What are the advantages of pesticides? What are the disadvantages? How might some of the disadvantages be reduced or eliminated? What other types of insect control might be used in place of the pesticides? What are the disadvantages of those methods?
- Organize the class into group according to the pest insects students have chosen. Have group members work together to write a proposal.
- Have one member of each groups present his or her group's proposal to the class. Allow time for students to respond to each proposal.

Weigh the Impact

1. People need pesticides to kill harmful insects and thereby reduce insect damage.
2. Students research will depend on individual state crops. If your state does not grow major crops, consider having students find information about several states in your area of the country.
3. Remind students to provide clear reasons for their proposals.

For: More on pesticides
Visit: PHSchool.com
Web Code: ceh-2020

Students can research this issue online.

Objectives

After completing this lesson, students will be able to

B.2.5.1 List the main characteristics of echinoderms.

B.2.5.2 Name the major groups of echinoderms.

Target Reading Skill

Previewing Visuals Explain that previewing visuals helps students focus their thinking before reading by giving them something specific to look for as they read.

Answers

Possible student questions and answers are these: **What are tube feet?** *(Tiny structures that stick out from the underside of an echinoderm and act like suction cups)* **How does a sea star eat?** *(It captures food with tube feet and envelops it with its stomach.)* **How does a sea star reproduce?** *(By external fertilization)*

All in One Teaching Resources

- Transparency B21

Preteach

Build Background Knowledge

L2

Echinoderm Symmetry

Have students examine the figures in this section. Ask: **What do the animals in these figures have in common?** *(Radial symmetry)*

Section 5 Echinoderms

Reading Preview

Key Concepts

- What are the main characteristics of echinoderms?
- What are the major groups of echinoderms?

Key Terms

- echinoderm
- endoskeleton
- water vascular system
- tube feet

Target Reading Skill

Previewing Visuals When you preview, you look ahead at the material to be read. Preview Figure 24. Then write two questions that you have about the diagram in a graphic organizer like the one below. As you read, answer your questions.

Water Vascular System

Q. What are tube feet?
A.
Q.

Lab zone Discover Activity

How Do Sea Stars Hold On?

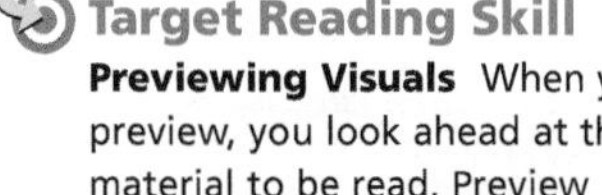

1. Use a plastic dropper and water to model how a sea star moves and clings to surfaces. Fill the dropper with water, and then squeeze out most of the water.
2. Squeeze the last drop of water onto the inside of your arm. Then, while squeezing the bulb, touch the tip of the dropper into the water drop. With the dropper tip against your skin, release the bulb.
3. Hold the dropper by the tube and lift it slowly, paying attention to what happens to your skin.

Think It Over

Predicting Besides moving and clinging to surfaces, what might sea stars use their suction structures for?

While exploring a rocky beach one day, you see what looks like a dill pickle at the bottom of a tide pool. You think it might be a plant or a rock covered with green slime. But as you look more closely, the pickle begins to crawl very slowly. This amazing creature is a sea cucumber, a relative of sea stars.

Characteristics of Echinoderms

Sea cucumbers, sea stars, sea urchins, and sand dollars are all **echinoderms** (ee KY noh durmz), members of the phylum Echinodermata. **Echinoderms are invertebrates with an internal skeleton and a system of fluid-filled tubes called a water vascular system.** All echinoderms live in salt water.

Body Structure The skin of most echinoderms is stretched over an internal skeleton, or **endoskeleton,** made of hardened plates. These plates give the animal a bumpy texture. Adult echinoderms have a unique kind of radial symmetry in which the body parts, usually in multiples of five, are arranged like spokes on a wheel.

Lab zone Discover Activity

L1

Skills Focus Predicting

Materials plastic dropper, water

Time 5 minutes

Tips If students have trouble creating suction against their arm, have them practice the activity without using water. Tell them to squeeze the bulb, press the dropper tip against their skin, and then release the bulb. After a few tries, have them try the activity again with a drop of water.

Expected Outcome The droppers will briefly attach to the students' skins.

Think It Over Sea stars might use their suction structures to pry open mollusk shells.

Movement The internal system of fluid-filled tubes in echinoderms is called the **water vascular system.** You can see a sea star's water vascular system in Figure 24. Portions of the tubes in this system can contract, or squeeze together, forcing water into structures called **tube feet.** This process is something like how you move water around in a water balloon by squeezing different parts of the balloon.

The tube feet stick out from the echinoderm's sides or underside. The ends of tube feet are sticky. When filled with water, they act like small, sticky suction cups. The stickiness and suction enable the tube feet to grip the surface beneath the echinoderm. Most echinoderms use their tube feet to move along slowly and to capture food.

Reproduction and Life Cycle Almost all echinoderms are either male or female. Eggs are usually fertilized in the water, after a female releases her eggs and a male releases his sperm. The fertilized eggs develop into tiny, swimming larvae that look very different from the adults. The larvae eventually undergo metamorphosis and become adult echinoderms.

Reading Checkpoint **What are the functions of an echinoderm's tube feet?**

Go Online active art

For: Water Vascular System activity
Visit: PHSchool.com
Web Code: cep-2025

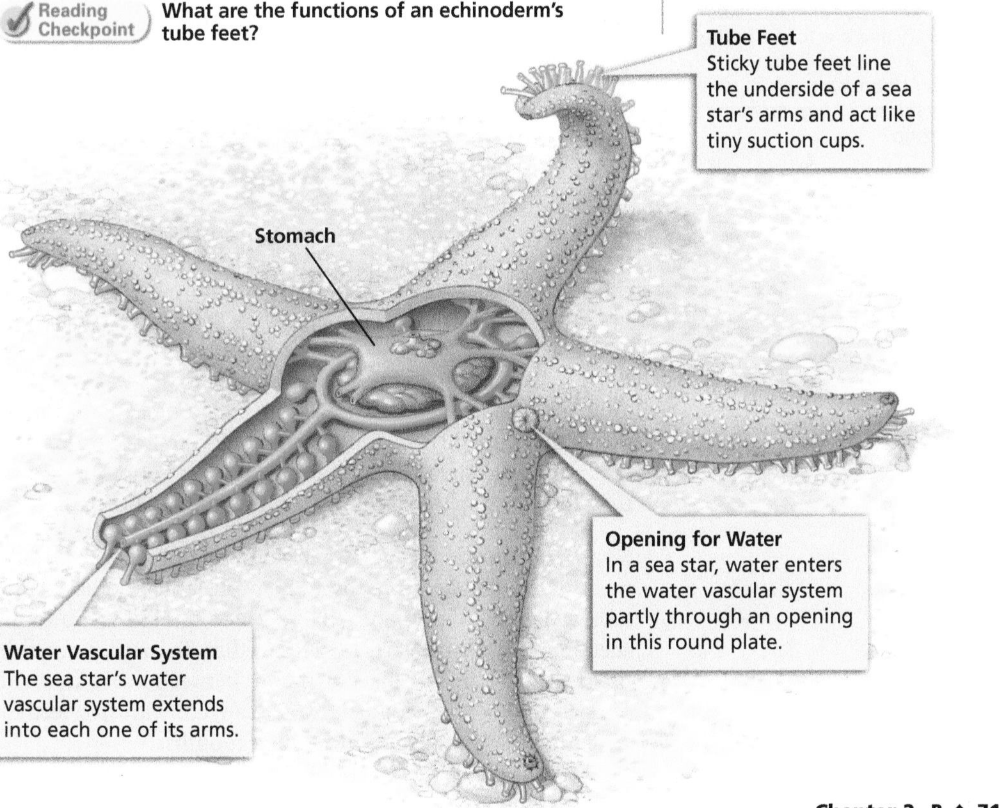
Tube Feet
Sticky tube feet line the underside of a sea star's arms and act like tiny suction cups.
Stomach
Opening for Water
In a sea star, water enters the water vascular system partly through an opening in this round plate.
Water Vascular System
The sea star's water vascular system extends into each one of its arms.

FIGURE 24
A Water Vascular System
Echinoderms, such as this sea star, have a water vascular system that helps them move and catch food.
Interpreting Diagrams *Where does water enter the water vascular system?*

Instruct

Characteristics of Echinoderms

Teach Key Concepts L2

Radially Symmetrical Invertebrates

Focus Tell students that echinoderms live on the sea floor at all depths throughout the ocean.

Teach Have students study Figure 24. Point out the animal's bumpy surface. **What forms these bumps?** *(The internal skeleton)* **Which structures enable the sea star to move?** *(The water vascular system and tube feet)* **Do sea stars ever swim?** *(Only during the larval phase)*

Apply **Why do you think there are no echinoderms that live on land?** *(The water vascular system would not function on land.)* **learning modality: logical/mathematical**

All in One **Teaching Resources**

- Transparency B22

Help Students Read L1

Build Vocabulary: Word-Part Analysis

Tell students that the prefix *exo-* means "out" and the prefix *endo-* means "in." Have students relate this to the meanings of the terms *exoskeleton* and *endoskeleton*. Ask: **What is an exoskeleton?** *(An outer skeleton)* **What is an endoskeleton?** *(An internal skeleton)*

For: Water Vascular System activity
Visit: PHSchool.com
Web Code: cep-2025

Students explore the water vascular system of a sea star.

Differentiated Instruction

English Learners/Beginning L1

Vocabulary: Science Glossary
Pronounce and define the following terms for students: echinoderm, endoskeleton, water vascular system, tube feet. Give students the opportunity to practice the pronunciation, and then have them locate the water vascular system and tube feet in Figure 24. Have students write their own definitions of the terms in their science glossaries. **learning modality: visual**

English Learners/Intermediate L2

Vocabulary: Science Glossary Students can expand on the Beginning activity by adding other vocabulary or unfamiliar terms in this section. Students can write a sentence that uses each term. **learning modality: visual**

Monitor Progress L2

Answers

Figure 24 Through an opening in a round plate near the center of the body

Reading Checkpoint An echinoderm's tube feet grip the surface beneath the echinoderm and enable it to move and to capture food.

Diversity of Echinoderms

Teach Key Concepts L2

Major Groups of Echinoderms

Focus Ask: **Have you ever observed echinoderms while visiting a zoo or a marine aquarium or while scuba diving?** *(Have student volunteers describe the characteristics of the animals they observed.)*

Teach Have students study the four major groups of echinoderms shown in Figure 25. Point out that the animals look very different. Ask: **Why are these animals grouped together?** *(They share similar internal features.)* **What common feature do these echinoderms have for movement?** *(Tube feet)*

Apply Ask students to compare how the four groups of echinoderms acquire their food. *(Sea stars pry open their prey using their tube feet. Brittle stars use their arms to catch food. Sea urchins scrape algae with teeth-like structures. Sea cucumbers use tentacles to sweep food into their mouths.)* **learning modality: logical/mathematical**

◄ Sea star eating a clam

▲ Brittle stars slithering on the ocean floor

FIGURE 25
Diversity of Echinoderms
Echinoderms are diverse in their appearance, but all have radial symmetry and are found in the ocean. **Interpreting Photographs** *Why is echinoderm, which means "spiny skinned," a good name for this group?*

Diversity of Echinoderms

There are four major groups of echinoderms: sea stars, brittle stars, sea urchins, and sea cucumbers. The members of these groups share many characteristics, but look quite different. They also have different ways of feeding and moving.

Sea Stars Sea stars are predators that eat mollusks, crabs, and even other echinoderms. Sea stars use their tube feet to move across the ocean bottom. They also use their tube feet to capture prey. A sea star will grasp a clam with all five arms. Then it pulls on the tightly closed shells with its tube feet. When the shells open, the sea star forces its stomach out through its mouth and into the opening between the clam's shells. Digestive chemicals break down the clam's tissues, and the sea star sucks in the partially digested body of its prey.

Brittle Stars Unlike a sea star's arms, a brittle star's arms are long and slender, with flexible joints. The tube feet, which have no suction cups, are used for catching food but not for moving. Instead, brittle stars slither along the ocean bottom by waving their long arms in a snakelike motion against the ocean floor.

Sea Urchins Unlike sea stars and brittle stars, sea urchins have no arms. Moveable spines cover and protect their bodies, so they look something like a pincushion. These spines cover a central shell that is made of plates joined together. To move, sea urchins use bands of tube feet that extend out between the spines. They scrape and cut their food, such as seaweed, with five teethlike structures that they project from their mouths.

▲ Sea urchins eating seaweed

▲ Sea cucumber crawling on the ocean floor

Sea Cucumbers As you might expect from their name, sea cucumbers look a little bit like the cucumbers you eat. These animals can be red, brown, blue, or green. Underneath their leather-like skin, their bodies are soft, flexible, and muscular. Sea cucumbers have rows of tube feet on their underside, enabling them to crawl slowly along the ocean floor where they live. At one end of a sea cucumber is a mouth surrounded by tentacles. The sea cucumber, which is a filter feeder, can lengthen its tentacles to sweep food toward its mouth.

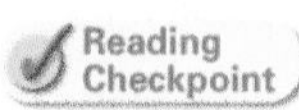 **How does a sea cucumber move?**

Section 5 Assessment

 **Target Reading Skill** Previewing Visuals Refer to your questions and answers about Figure 24 to help you answer Question 1 below.

Reviewing Key Concepts

1. a. Reviewing What characteristics do echinoderms have?
   b. Summarizing How does an echinoderm use its tube feet to grip a surface?
   c. Inferring Why is movement using tube feet slow?
2. a. Identifying Identify the four major groups of echinoderms.
   b. Comparing and Contrasting Compare and contrast how sea stars and sea urchins feed.
   c. Predicting Would a sea star be able to eat clams without using its tube feet? Explain.

Writing in Science

Comparison Paragraph In a paragraph, compare and contrast how sea stars, brittle stars, and sea urchins move.

Monitor Progress L2

Answers

Figure 25 The surface of the skin of an echinoderm is bumpy or spiny.

Reading Checkpoint Sea cucumbers move by crawling slowly along the ocean floor using their tube feet.

Assess

Reviewing Key Concepts

1. a. Echinoderms are invertebrates that have an internal skeleton and a water vascular system. **b.** Tube feet are sticky at the ends; when filled with water, they act like suction cups. **c.** Tube feet operate by suction. Each time the animal moves, it must pull its feet up by releasing the suction, and then put them down again. Because this process is slow, tube feet are adapted to slow movement.

2. a. Sea stars, brittle stars, sea urchins, sea cucumbers **b.** Sea stars use their tube feet to open mollusks and then insert their stomach into the mollusk and digest the mollusk tissues; sea urchins scrape and cut food, using teeth-like structures. **c.** Without tube feet, sea stars would not be able to pry open animals protected by hard shells.

Reteach L1

As a class, describe the four major groups of echinoderms.

Performance Assessment L2

Skills Check Ask students to create a table summarizing the body structure, movement, and reproduction of echinoderms.

All in One Teaching Resources

- Section Summary: *Echinoderms*
- Review and Reinforce: *Echinoderms*
- Enrich: *Echinoderms*

Lab zone Chapter Project

Keep Students on Track When one half of a student's mealworms have reached the adult stage, have the student write a simple summary of his or her observations. To draw conclusions, students can make a bar graph comparing the numbers of mealworms in different stages of development under the two conditions. Tell students their conclusions must be based on data they have collected.

Writing in Science

Writing Mode Comparison

Scoring Rubric

4 Includes complete, accurate comparisons and many details
3 Includes complete, accurate comparisons but few details
2 Includes accurate comparisons; no details
1 Includes inaccurate or incomplete comparisons

Study Guide

The BIG Idea

Have students read the answer to the Essential Question. Encourage them to evaluate and revise their own answers as needed.

Help Students Read

Developing Vocabulary

Definition Mapping Explain that using vocabulary strategies such as definition mapping and vocabulary quick-write help students define Key Concept words. Ask students to make definition maps for the Key Terms in this chapter. The Key Term is used in the center of the map. Branches include a definition of the Key Term, adjectives that describe it, and examples.

Vocabulary Quick-Write Write a group of related vocabulary terms on the board. Discuss the definitions of the terms. Ask students to write a paragraph that includes each of the terms.

Connecting Concepts

Concept Maps Help students develop one way to show how the information in this chapter is related. Mollusks, arthropods, and echinoderms are major groups of invertebrate animals. Have students brainstorm to identify the Key Concepts, Key Terms, details, and examples. Then write each one on a sticky note and attach it at random on chart paper on the board.
Tell students that this concept map will be organized in hierarchical order and to begin at the top with the Key Concepts. Ask students these questions to guide them to categorize the information on the stickies: **What are three groups of invertebrates? What are some characteristics of each group?** Prompt students by using connecting words or phrases, such as "move by," "have bodies with," and "include" to indicate the basis for the organization of the map. The phrases should form a sentence between or among a set of concepts.

Answer Accept logical presentations by students.

Chapter 2 Study Guide

The BIG Idea **Diversity and Adaptations** Each group of invertebrates has distinctive characteristics, such as a mantle, an exoskeleton, or a water vascular system.

1 Mollusks

Key Concepts

- In addition to a soft body often covered by a shell, a mollusk has a thin layer of tissue called a mantle that covers its internal organs, and an organ called a foot.
- Gastropods are mollusks that have a single external shell or no shell at all.
- Bivalves are mollusks that have two shells held together by hinges and strong muscles.
- A cephalopod is an ocean-dwelling mollusk whose foot is adapted to form tentacles around its mouth.

Key Terms

• mollusk • open circulatory system • gill
• gastropod • herbivore • carnivore • radula
• bivalve • omnivore • cephalopod

2 Arthropods

Key Concepts

- The major groups of arthropods are crustaceans, arachnids, centipedes and millipedes, and insects.
- Arthropods are invertebrates that have an external skeleton, a segmented body, and jointed attachments called appendages.
- A crustacean is an arthropod that has two or three body sections, five or more pairs of legs, and two pairs of antennae.
- Arachnids are arthropods with two body sections, four pairs of legs, and no antennae.
- Centipedes and millipedes are arthropods with two body sections and many pairs of legs.

Key Terms

arthropod, antenna, arachnid, exoskeleton, crustacean, abdomen, molting, metamorphosis

3 Insects

Key Concepts

- Insects are arthropods with three body sections, six legs, one pair of antennae, and usually one or two pairs of wings.
- An insect's mouthparts are adapted for a highly specific way of getting food.
- Each insect species undergoes either complete metamorphosis or gradual metamorphosis.

Key Terms

• insect • thorax • complete metamorphosis
• pupa • gradual metamorphosis • nymph

4 Insect Ecology

Key Concepts

- Insects play key roles in food chains because of the many different ways that they obtain food and then become food for other animals.
- Two ways insects interact with other living things are by moving pollen among plants and by spreading disease-causing organisms.
- To try to control pests, people use chemicals, traps, and living things, including other insects.

Key Terms

• food chain • ecology • producer
• consumer • decomposer • pollinator
• pesticide • biological control

5 Echinoderms

Key Concepts

- Echinoderms are invertebrates with an internal skeleton and a system of fluid-filled tubes called a water vascular system.
- There are four major groups of echinoderms: sea stars, brittle stars, sea urchins, and sea cucumbers.

Key Terms

echinoderm, water vascular system, endoskeleton, tube feet

All in One Teaching Resources

- Key Terms Review: *Mollusks, Arthropods, and Echinoderms*
- Connecting Concepts: *Mollusks, Arthropods, and Echinoderms*

Review and Assessment

Go Online PHSchool.com
For: Self-Assessment
Visit: PHSchool.com
Web Code: cea-2020

Organizing Information

Concept Mapping Copy the concept map about the classification of arthropods onto a sheet of paper. Then complete it and add a title. (For more on Concept Mapping, see the Skills Handbook.)

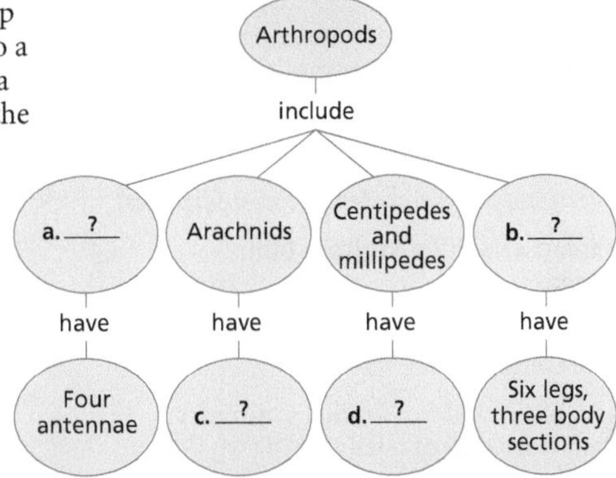

Reviewing Key Terms

Choose the letter of the best answer.

1. An animal that eats other animals is a(n)
   a. carnivore. **b.** omnivore.
   c. filter feeder. **d.** herbivore.
2. Mollusks with two shells are known as
   a. cephalopods. **b.** gastropods.
   c. bivalves. **d.** sea stars.
3. An arthropod's antennae are located on its
   a. head. **b.** thorax.
   c. abdomen. **d.** mantle.
4. To obtain oxygen from their environments, mollusks and crustaceans use which organ?
   a. radula **b.** lungs
   c. gills **d.** legs
5. The shedding of an outgrown exoskeleton is called
   a. complete metamorphosis.
   b. incomplete metamorphosis.
   c. molting.
   d. reproduction.
6. At which stage of development would an insect be enclosed in a cocoon?
   a. egg **b.** larva
   c. pupa **d.** adult
7. One example of a biological control is
   a. catching pest insects in traps.
   b. making and selling honey by raising bees in hives.
   c. killing pest insects with pesticides.
   d. introducing a pest insect's natural predator.
8. An echinoderm has
   a. a radula.
   b. tube feet.
   c. antennae.
   d. an exoskeleton.

Writing in Science

News Report As a television reporter, you are covering a story about a giant squid that has washed up on the local beach. Write a short news story describing the discovery. Be sure to describe how scientists classified the animal as a squid.

Mollusks, Arthropods, and Echinoderms
Video Preview
Video Field Trip
▶ Video Assessment

For: Self-Assessment
Visit: PHSchool.com
Web Code: cea-2020

Students can take an online practice test that is automatically scored.

All in One Teaching Resources

- Transparency B23
- Chapter Test
- Performance Assessment Teacher Notes
- Performance Assessment Student Worksheet
- Performance Assessment Scoring Rubric

***ExamView®* Computer Test Bank CD-ROM**

Review and Assessment

Organizing Information

a. Crustaceans
b. Insects
c. Eight legs, two body segments, no antennae
d. Highly segmented body, one or two pairs of legs on each segment, two antennae
Sample title: Arthropod Groups

Reviewing Key Terms

1. a **2.** c **3.** a **4.** c **5.** c **6.** c
7. d **8.** b

Writing in Science

Writing Mode Description

Scoring Rubric

4 Includes a description of the discovery of the squid and details of how it was identified in an interesting and engaging manner
3 Includes a description of the discovery of the squid and details of how it was identified
2 Includes a description of the discovery of the squid but few details of how it was identified
1 Includes a description of the discovery of the squid but lacks accurate details of how it was identified

Mollusks

Show the Video Assessment to review chapter content and as a prompt for the writing assignment. Discussion questions: **List two differences between squids and octopuses.** *(Squids have an internal shell; octopuses do not; squids have ten tentacles, but octopuses have only eight.)* **What is one advantage of octopuses not having hard shells?** *(They can squeeze into small places to hide from predators.)*

Checking Concepts

9. A snail uses its radula like a tongue to scrape up food and in some cases to bore holes in hard-shelled prey.

10. Cephalopods have a complex nervous system; they have large brains and they can learn and remember things.

11. Antennae can smell, taste, touch, and balance; legs walk; swimmerets function in swimming; chelipeds catch food and defend crayfish.

12. Centipedes have one pair of legs on each segment behind their head, while millipedes have two. Centipedes are carnivores, while millipedes are scavengers.

13. Unlike other arthropods, all insects have three body sections, six legs, and one pair of antennae. In addition, most have wings.

14. Answers may vary. Sample: Some insects destroy the food supply of humans (crops); some spread serious diseases, such as malaria.

15. An echinoderm's radial symmetry is a five-part symmetry, while a jellyfish's symmetry is not five-part.

Thinking Critically

16. Alike: Bivalves and cephalopods have a mantle covering internal organs; have soft bodies; live in water. Different: Bivalves have two outer shells, but many cephalopods have an internal shell or no shell; a cephalopod's foot is adapted to form tentacles; cephalopods move by jet propulsion, while bivalves move slowly using a foot; cephalopods have complex nervous systems, but bivalves do not.

17. Arthropods; A-crustacean, B-arachnid; number of antennae and legs

18. The cub looks similar to the adult lion from the time it is born. It grows larger, but does not change its form.

19. He might conclude that the dung beetles, which are decomposers, are improving the quality of the soil the grass is growing in by recycling the nutrients in the dung back into the soil.

20. Any argument presented by students is acceptable as long as it is supported by facts.

21. Both animals secrete juices that begin to digest the food before it enters the body.

Math Practice

22. 40,500

Review and Assessment

Checking Concepts

9. Explain how a snail uses its radula.
10. How is a cephalopod's nervous system different from that of other mollusks?
11. Describe four things that a crayfish can do with its appendages.
12. How are centipedes different from millipedes?
13. How are insects different from other arthropods?
14. Identify two reasons why insects sometimes must be controlled.
15. How is an echinoderm's radial symmetry different from that of a jellyfish?

Thinking Critically

16. **Comparing and Contrasting** Compare and contrast bivalves and cephalopods.
17. **Classifying** Which phylum does each of the animals below belong to? Explain your answer.

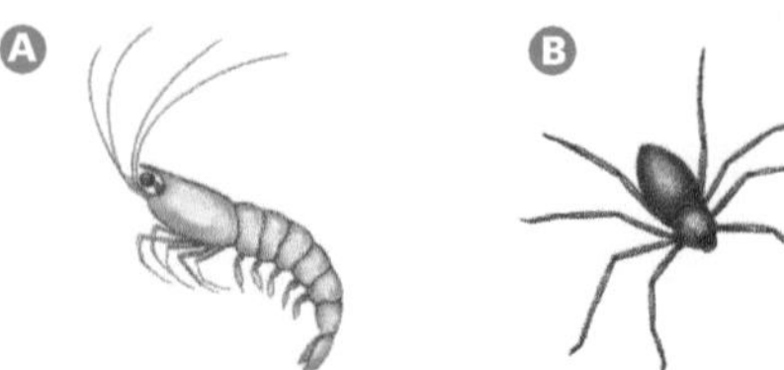

18. **Applying Concepts** Explain why the development of a lion, which grows larger as it changes from a tiny cub to a 90 kg adult, is not metamorphosis.
19. **Drawing Conclusions** A rancher imports dung beetles from Africa to help control manure build-up from cattle. Later, he observes that the pastures are producing more grass for the cattle to eat. What conclusion could the rancher draw about the dung beetles?
20. **Making Judgments** Do you think pesticides should be used to kill insect pests? Explain.
21. **Comparing and Contrasting** How is a spider's method of obtaining food similar to that of a sea star? How is it different?

Math Practice

22. **Percentage** Of approximately 150,000 species of mollusks, 27 percent are gastropods. About how many species of gastropods are there?

Applying Skills

Use the data table to answer Questions 23–25.

The following data appeared in a book on insects.

Flight Characteristics

Type of Insect	Wing Beats (per second)	Flight Speed (kilometers per hour)
Hummingbird moth	85	17.8
Bumblebee	250	10.3
Housefly	190	7.1

23. **Graphing** Use the data to make two bar graphs: one showing the three insect wing-beat rates and another showing the flight speeds.
24. **Interpreting Data** Which of the three insects has the highest wing-beat rate? Which insect flies the fastest?
25. **Drawing Conclusions** Based on the data, is there a relationship between the rate at which an insect beats its wings and the speed at which it flies? Explain. What factors besides wing-beat rate might affect flight speed?

Lab zone Chapter Project

Performance Assessment Prepare a display to show how you set up your experiment and what your results were. Construct and display graphs to show the data you collected. Include pictures of the mealworms in each stage of development. Write your conclusion of how the experimental conditions affected the growth and development of the mealworms. Also suggest some possible explanations for your results.

Lab zone Chapter Project L3

Performance Assessment Remind students to include illustrations of their setup, data, graph, and results. They must also include diagrams of the larvae, pupae, and adults, with arrows between these diagrams to illustrate the sequence of complete metamorphosis. Consider grouping students according to the variable they tested. Direct each group to discuss their results. Have them combine their data, create a graph to display the data, and then summarize their results. Instruct each group to present its graph and results to the rest of the class.

Reflect and Record Ask students to discuss their conclusions. Encourage discussion of why metamorphosis was or was not affected by the variables they tested.

Standardized Test Prep

Test-Taking Tip

Interpreting Graphs

Before you answer a question about a line graph, read all of its labels. The labels on the axes tell you what variables are being compared. On the graph below, the variables are temperature and the number of cricket chirps (sounds).

Relationship of Temperature and Cricket Chirps

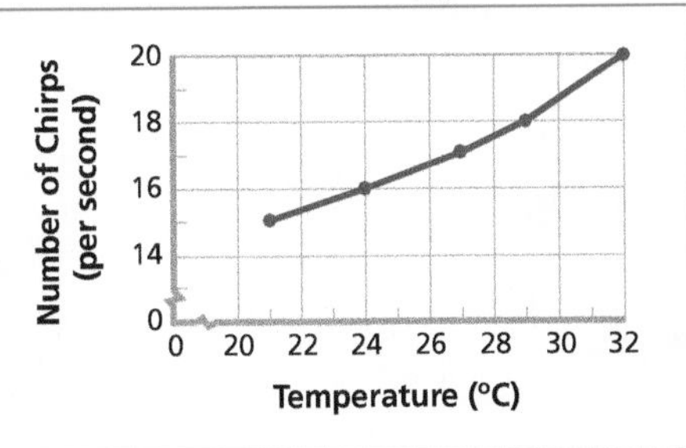

Sample Question

How is the number of cricket chirps related to temperature?

A The number of chirps increases as the temperature decreases.
B The number of chirps stays the same as the temperature increases.
C The number of chirps increases as the temperature increases.
D The graph does not show a relationship.

Answer

The correct answer is **C**. The plotted line reveals that as the temperature increases, the number of chirps also increases. Therefore, **A, B,** and **D** can not be correct.

Choose the letter of the best answer.

1. An animal that has a soft, unsegmented body surrounded by a hard outer shell is most likely
A an earthworm.
B a cnidarian.
C a mollusk.
D an arthropod.

2. Which animal feature most likely evolved as an adaptation to provide direct protection from a predator's attack?
F a snail's radula
G a sea urchin's spines
H a crayfish's antennae
J an insect's thorax

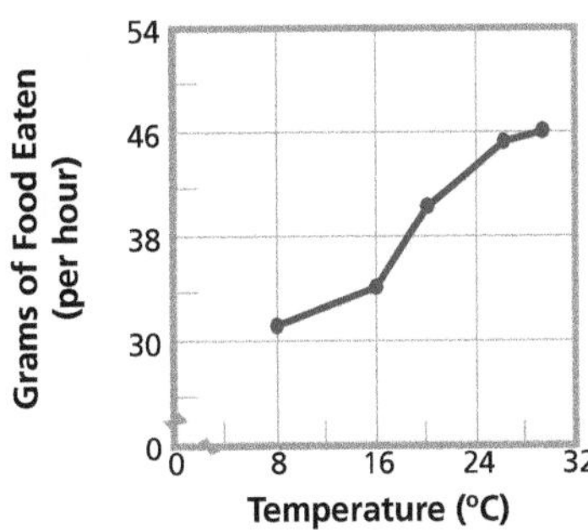

3. Examine the information in the graph above. Which is the best title for the graph?
A Effect of Caterpillar Feeding Rate on Temperature
B Caterpillar Behavior and Temperature
C Respiration Rate and Temperature
D Relationship of Temperature and Caterpillar Feeding Rate

4. What is the most reasonable prediction for what the feeding rate would be at 32°C?
F 60 g/hr
G 46 g/hr
H 40 g/hr
J 0 g/hr

Constructed Response

5. In a certain small country, mosquitoes are very common. The mosquitoes spread a disease that is deadly to humans. The government decides to spray the entire country with a pesticide that will kill all mosquitoes and other flying insects as well. How is this action likely to affect the food chain?

Standardized Test Prep

1. C **2.** G **3.** D **4.** G

Constructed Response

5. The action will disrupt the food chain by eliminating flying insects that act as consumers, decomposers, and prey for other animals.

Applying Skills

23.

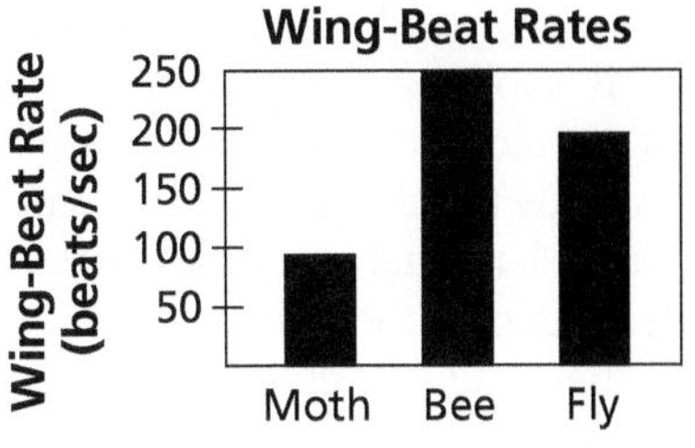

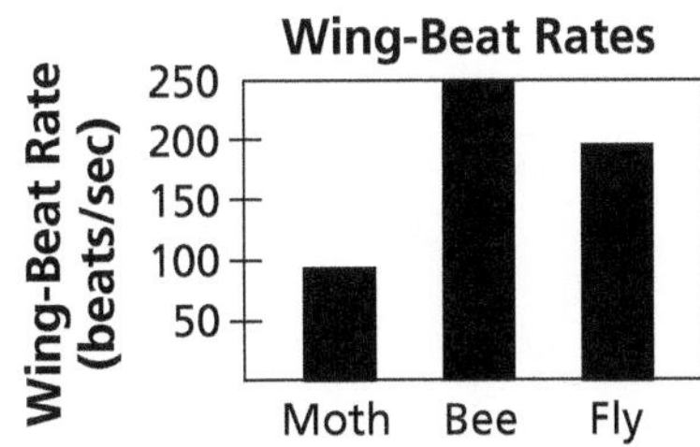

24. The bumblebee has the highest wing-beat rate. The hummingbird moth flies the fastest.

25. There is no trend in the data to support any relationship between wing-beat rate and flight speed. Other factors that affect flight speed might include mass and shape of the insect and the shape of the insect's wings.

The BIG Idea

The Big Idea is the major scientific concept of the chapter. It is followed by the Essential Question. Read aloud the question to students. As students study the chapter, tell them to think about the Essential Question. Explain that they will discover the answer to the question as they read. The chapter Study Guide provides a sample answer.

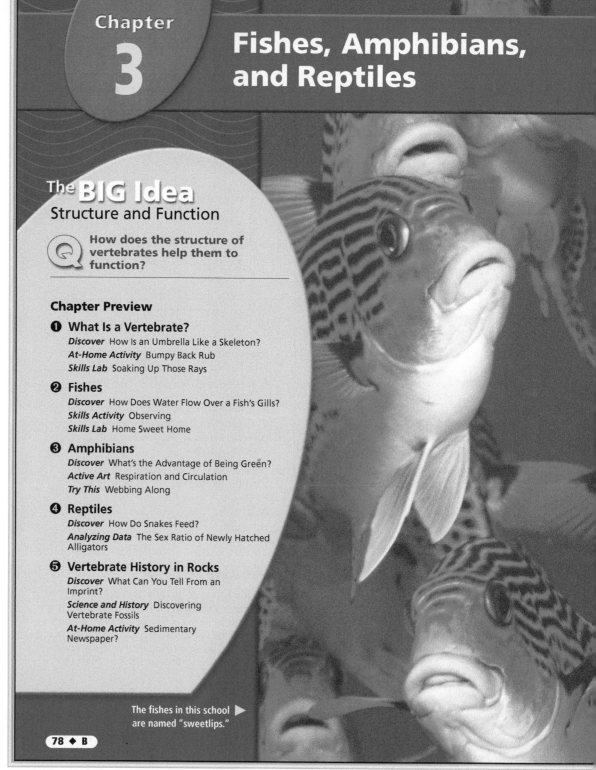

Chapter 3 Fishes, Amphibians, and Reptiles

The BIG Idea

Structure and Function

How does the structure of vertebrates help them to function?

Chapter Preview

The fishes in this school ▶ are named "sweetlips."

L3

Objectives

This project will allow students to investigate and model how adaptations enable animals to survive in their environments. Students will select one adaptation to model in a reptile, an amphibian, and a fish. After this Chapter Project, students will be able to

- make models of adaptations that perform similar functions in three different kinds of organisms
- compare and contrast the adaptations of the three organisms
- communicate their findings about the adaptations that they model to their classmates

Skills Focus

Making models, comparing and contrasting, communicating

Project Time Line 3 to 4 weeks

All in One Teaching Resources

- Chapter Project Teacher Notes
- Chapter Project Overview
- Chapter Project Worksheet 1
- Chapter Project Worksheet 2
- Chapter Project Scoring Rubric

Developing a Plan

Each pair or group of students will review the chapter and other references.Then select an adaptation to model. As students complete each chapter section, they should begin to construct a model of one type of organism they studied in the section. Students can work on projects at home as well as at school.

Possible Materials

Provide a wide variety of materials from which students can choose. Have students bring any extra materials they might have at home for others in the class to use. Some possibilities are listed below. Encourage students to suggest and use other materials as well.

- For model building, include toothpicks, pipe cleaners, Styrofoam®, cardboard, construction paper, chicken wire, balsa wood, balloons, modeling clay, papier

Chapter at a Glance

PRENTICE HALL

 Chapter **Project** *Animal Adaptations*

All in One Teaching Resources
- Chapter Project Teacher Notes, pp. 174–175
- Chapter Project Student Overview, pp. 176–177
- Chapter Project Student Worksheets, pp. 178–179
- Chapter Project Scoring Rubric, p. 180

Technology

Video Preview

Local Standards

Section 1 What Is a Vertebrate?

1–2 periods
1/2–1 block

B.3.1.1 Name the characteristics that chordates share.
B.3.1.2 Describe the main characteristic shared by all vertebrates.
B.3.1.3 Describe how vertebrates differ in the way they control body temperature.

Section 2 Fishes

2–3 periods
1–1 1/2 blocks

B.3.2.1 Name the main characteristics of fishes.
B.3.2.2 Name the major groups of fishes and describe how they differ.

Section 3 Amphibians

1–2 periods
1/2–1 block

B.3.3.1 Describe amphibian characteristics.
B.3.3.2 Examine how adult amphibians are adapted for life on land.

Section 4 Reptiles

3–4 periods
1 1/2–2 blocks

B.3.4.1 Identify adaptations that allow reptiles to live on land.
B.3.4.2 Contrast the characteristics of each of the three main groups of reptiles.
B.3.4.3 Describe one adaptation that helped dinosaurs survive before they became extinct.

Video Field Trip

Section 5 Vertebrate History in Rocks

1–2 periods
1/2–1 block

B.3.5.1 Identify the kind of rock in which fossils are frequently found.
B.3.5.2 Describe what scientists can learn from studying fossils.

Review and Assessment

All in One Teaching Resources
- Key Terms Review, p. 220
- Transparency B34
- Performance Assessment Teacher Notes, p. 229
- Performance Assessment Scoring Rubric, p. 230
- Performance Assessment Student Worksheet, p. 231
- Chapter Test, pp. 232–235

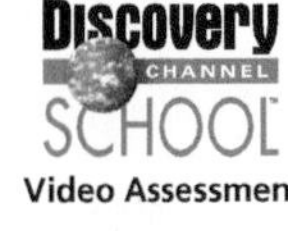
Video Assessment

Test Preparation

Test Preparation Blackline Masters

Chapter Activities Planner

For more activities

Student Edition	Inquiry	Time	Materials	Skills	Resources
Chapter Project, p. 79	Open-Ended	3–4 weeks	**All in One Teaching Resources** See p. 174	Making models, comparing and contrasting, communicating	**Lab zone Easy Planner** **All in One Teaching Resources** Support pp. 174–175
Section 1					
Discover Activity, p. 80	Directed	15 minutes	Umbrella	Inferring	**Lab zone Easy Planner**
Skills Lab, pp. 84–85	Directed	30 minutes	Paper, pencil	Interpreting data, predicting	**Lab zone Easy Planner** **Lab Activity Video** **All in One Teaching Resources** Skills Lab: *Soaking Up Those Rays,* pp. 188–189
Section 2					
Discover Activity, p. 86	Guided	10 minutes	Several live fish, each one in an aquarium or fishbowl	Observing	**Lab zone Easy Planner**
Skills Activity, p. 91	Guided	50 minutes	Preserved fish, goggles, dissecting tray, blunt probe, hand lens, rubber glove	Observing	**Lab zone Easy Planner**
Skills Lab, p. 93	Directed	Prep: 30 minutes Class: 10 minutes per day for two weeks	Gravel, guppy food, thermometer, aquarium filter, rectangular aquarium tank (15 to 20 liters) with cover, metric ruler, dip net, water plants, aquarium heater, guppies, tap water, snails	Observing, making models	**Lab zone Easy Planner** **Lab Activity Video** **All in One Teaching Resources** Skills Lab: *Home Sweet Home,* pp. 197–198
Section 3					
Discover Activity, p. 94	Guided	10 minutes	Dried yellow and green peas; paper cup; green construction paper, approximately 1 m × 1 m; clock or watch with second hand	Inferring	**Lab zone Easy Planner**
Try This Activity, p. 97	Guided	15 minutes	Plastic bags, heavy rubber bands, pail of water or sink	Making models	**Lab zone Easy Planner**
Section 4					
Discover Activity, p. 99	Directed	10 minutes	sock with ribbed cuff, grapefruit, strong rubber band	Inferring	**Lab zone Easy Planner**
Section 5					
Discover Activity, p. 107	Directed	15 minutes	Modeling clay; paper; small objects of various textures and degrees of rigidity	Observing	**Lab zone Easy Planner**

ABILITY LEVELS KEY
- L1 Basic to Average
- L2 For All Students
- L3 Average to Advanced

Section 1 What Is a Vertebrate?

1–2 periods, 1/2–1 block

Objectives

B.3.1.1 Name the characteristics that chordates share.
B.3.1.2 Describe the main characteristic shared by all vertebrates.
B.3.1.3 Explain how vertebrates differ in the way they control body temperature.

Local Standards

Key Terms

• chordate • notochord • vertebra • ectotherm • endotherm

Preteach

Build Background Knowledge

Ask leading questions to discuss what students know about vertebrates and invertebrates.

Lab zone Discover Activity *How Is an Umbrella Like a Skeleton?* L1

Targeted Print and Technology Resources

All in One **Teaching Resources**

L2 Reading Strategy: Building Vocabulary

PresentationExpress™ CD-ROM

Instruct

Characteristics of Chordates Identify characteristics of animals in the phylum Chordata.

Characteristics of Vertebrates Use a photograph to illustrate the function of the backbone and other features of vertebrate endoskeletons.

Keeping Conditions Stable Contrast the two groups of vertebrates, ectotherms and endotherms, by how they control body temperature.

Lab zone Skills Lab *Soaking Up Those Rays* L2

Targeted Print and Technology Resources

All in One **Teaching Resources**

L2 Guided Reading, pp. 183–185
L2 Skills Lab: *Soaking Up Those Rays*, pp. 188–189

Lab Activity Video/DVD
Skills Lab: *Soaking Up Those Rays*

www.SciLinks.org Web Code: scn-0231

Student Edition on Audio CD

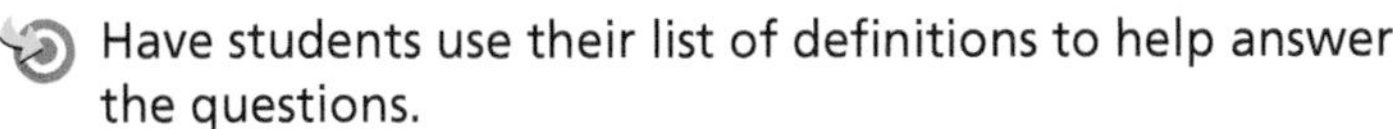

Assess

Section Assessment Questions

Have students use their list of definitions to help answer the questions.

Reteach

List characteristics of vertebrates.

Targeted Print and Technology Resources

All in One **Teaching Resources**

- Section Summary, p. 182
- L1 Review and Reinforce, p. 186
- L3 Enrich, p. 187

Section 2 Fishes

 *2–3 periods, 1–1 1/2 blocks*

ABILITY LEVELS KEY
L1 Basic to Average
L2 For All Students
L3 Average to Advanced

Objectives

B.3.2.1 Name the main characteristics of fishes.
B.3.2.2 Name the major groups of fishes and describe how they differ.

Key Terms

• fish • cartilage • swim bladder

Local Standards

Preteach

Build Background Knowledge

Draw on students' experiences with fishes to discuss fish characteristics they have observed.

How Does Water Flow Over a Fish's Gills? L1

Targeted Print and Technology Resources

L2 Reading Strategy Transparency B24: Previewing Visuals

Instruct

Characteristics of Fishes Define *fish* and discuss body systems of fishes.

Jawless Fishes Identify traits that distinguish jawless fishes from other fish groups.

Cartilaginous Fishes Describe how cartilaginous fishes obtain food and oxygen.

Bony Fishes Use a diagram to identify features of bony fishes and explain the functions of those features.

Home Sweet Home L2

Targeted Print and Technology Resources

All in One Teaching Resources

L2 Guided Reading, pp. 192–194
L2 Transparencies B25, B26
L2 Skills Lab: *Home Sweet Home*, pp. 197–198

Lab Activity Video/DVD
Skills Lab: *Home Sweet Home*

Student Edition on Audio CD

Assess

Section Assessment Questions

Have students use their Previewing Visuals graphic organizers to help answer the questions.

Reteach

Draw a table on the board to direct a class discussion comparing and contrasting the three groups of fishes.

Targeted Print and Technology Resources

All in One Teaching Resources

• Section Summary, p. 191
L1 Review and Reinforce, p. 195
L3 Enrich, p. 196

Section 3 Amphibians

 *1–2 periods, 1/2–1 block*

ABILITY LEVELS KEY
L1 Basic to Average
L2 For All Students
L3 Average to Advanced

Objectives

B.3.3.1 Describe amphibian characteristics.
B.3.3.2 Examine how adult amphibians are adapted for life on land.

Local Standards

Key Terms

• amphibian • tadpole • lung • atrium • ventricle • habitat

Preteach

Build Background Knowledge

Students share any knowledge they have of characteristics of animals that live part of their life on land and part in the water.

What's the Advantage of Being Green? L1

Targeted Print and Technology Resources

All in One Teaching Resources

L2 Reading Strategy Transparency B27: Sequencing

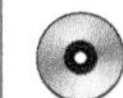 **PresentationExpress™ CD-ROM**

Instruct

What Is an Amphibian? Identify traits shared by amphibians and use a diagram to trace the life cycle of a frog.

Living on Land Compare and contrast the adaptations of amphibians for life in water and on land.

Targeted Print and Technology Resources

All in One Teaching Resources

L2 Guided Reading, pp. 201–203
L2 Transparencies B28, B29

PHSchool.com Web Code: ced-2033

PHSchool.com Web Code: cep-2032

Student Edition on Audio CD

Assess

Section Assessment Questions

Have students use their cycle diagram to help answer the questions.

Reteach

Call on students to give one characteristic of amphibians and tell how the characteristic helps the species survive in its environment.

Targeted Print and Technology Resources

All in One Teaching Resources

• Section Summary, p. 200
L1 Review and Reinforce, p. 204
L3 Enrich, p. 205

ABILITY LEVELS KEY
L1 Basic to Average
L2 For All Students
L3 Average to Advanced

Section 4 Reptiles

3-4 periods, 1 1/2–2 blocks

Objectives

B.3.4.1 Identify adaptations that allow reptiles to live on land.

B.3.4.2 Contrast the characteristics of each of the three main groups of reptiles.

B.3.4.3 Describe one adaptation that helped dinosaurs survive before they became extinct.

Key Terms

• reptile • kidney • urine • amniotic egg

Local Standards

Preteach

Build Background Knowledge

Brainstorm characteristics of snakes.

Lab zone Discover Activity *How Do Snakes Feed?* L1

Targeted Print and Technology Resources

All in One **Teaching Resources**

L2 Reading Strategy Transparency B30: Identifying Main Ideas

PresentationExpress™ CD-ROM

Instruct

Adaptations for Life on Land Identify and describe adaptations that help reptiles survive on land.

Lizards and Snakes Compare and contrast characteristics and adaptations of lizards and snakes.

Alligators and Crocodiles Discuss traits that make crocodiles and alligators successful predators.

Turtles Define *turtle* and describe physical features and feeding habits of land and aquatic turtles.

Extinct Reptiles—The Dinosaurs Contrast characteristics of dinosaurs and modern reptiles.

Targeted Print and Technology Resources

All in One **Teaching Resources**

L2 Guided Reading, pp. 208–211

L2 Transparency B31

PHSchool.com Web Code: ced-2034

Discovery Channel School Video Field Trip

Student Edition on Audio CD

Assess

Section Assessment Questions

Have students use their Identifying Main Ideas graphic organizer to help answer the questions.

Reteach

Call on students to describe the features of one of the three groups of reptiles.

Targeted Print and Technology Resources

All in One **Teaching Resources**

• Section Summary, p. 207

L1 Review and Reinforce, p. 212

L3 Enrich, p. 213

ABILITY LEVELS KEY
L1 Basic to Average
L2 For All Students
L3 Average to Advanced

Section 5 Vertebrate History in Rocks

1–2 periods, 1/2–1 block

Objectives

B.3.5.1 Identify the kind of rock in which fossils are frequently found.
B.3.5.2 Describe what scientists can learn from studying fossils.

Key Terms

• fossil • sedimentary rock • paleontologist

Local Standards

Preteach

Build Background Knowledge

Use fossil-bearing rocks to elicit student observations and inferences about fossilized organisms.

What Can You Tell From an Imprint? L1

Targeted Print and Technology Resources

All in One **Teaching Resources**

L2 Reading Strategy Transparency B32: Asking Questions

Instruct

What Are Fossils? Describe how fossils form in sedimentary rock.

Interpretation of Fossils Use diagrams to show how paleontologists use fossils to understand how animals are related.

Targeted Print and Technology Resources

All in One **Teaching Resources**

L2 Guided Reading, pp. 216–217
L2 Transparency B33

www.SciLinks.org Web Code: scn-0235

Assess

Section Assessment Questions

Have students use their Asking Questions graphic organizers to answer the questions.

Reteach

Use a sketch of layers of sedimentary rock to place vertebrate fossils in their correct order.

Targeted Print and Technology Resources

All in One **Teaching Resources**

• Section Summary, p. 215
L1 Review and Reinforce, p. 218
L3 Enrich, p. 219

Chapter 3 Content Refresher

Go Online
NSTA-PD LINKS
For: Professional development support
Visit: www.SciLinks.org/PDLinks
Web Code: scf-0230
Professional Development

Section 1 What Is a Vertebrate?

Keeping the Heat Endotherms are vertebrates—birds and mammals—that maintain steady body temperatures regardless of the environmental temperatures. This adaptation allows these animals to take advantage of many different habitats and to function throughout the seasons. In contrast, the body temperatures of ectotherms—reptiles, amphibians, and fishes—are greatly affected by the temperature of their surroundings. Both the reptile and the human (represented by a hand) shown in the diagram below are in an environment with a temperature around 85°F. Notice that the human maintains its temperature.

Endotherms and Ectotherms

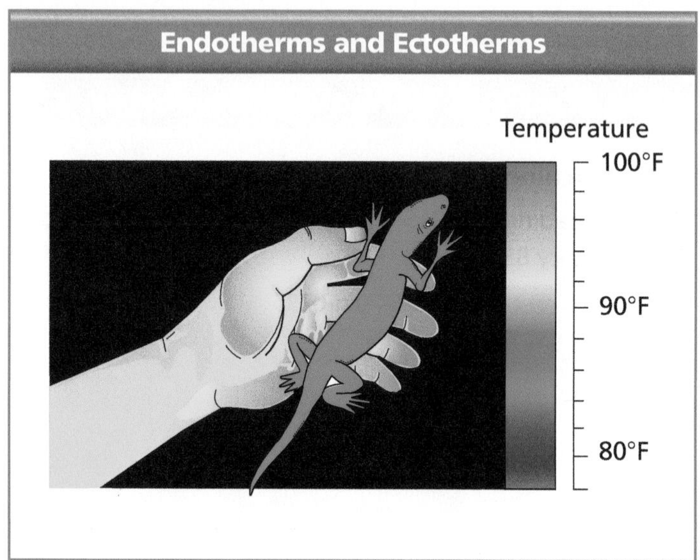

Endotherms use a lot of energy to maintain their body temperatures. The energy allows them to cool themselves in hot environments and to generate heat in cold environments. The metabolic rate—the rate by which an animal generates energy—for a resting endotherm is about six times greater than the metabolic rate of a resting ectotherm that is the same size. Endotherms must eat more food than ectotherms to generate energy. For example, a snake might eat a small mammal only once every several days, yet a shrew—a tiny, insect-eating mammal—eats constantly when it is awake.

Endotherms do not depend entirely on generating energy to maintain internal temperatures, and ectotherms are not completely at the mercy of environmental temperatures. Endotherms and ectotherms both move between warm and cool areas to regulate body temperatures; some lizards that alternate basking in the sun with moving to shade have been shown to maintain nearly constant body temperatures with this behavior. Endotherms also have skin, fur, and feathers that prevent heat loss; some, particularly birds and whales, migrate when environmental conditions become too demanding.

All vertebrates, whether they are ectotherms or endotherms, need to maintain their body temperatures within a relatively narrow range. One reason is that an animal's enzymes function only within a narrow temperature range. Enzymes are proteins that speed up chemical reactions within cells. For example, enzymes help break food molecules into simpler substances, releasing energy in the process. Without the enzymes, such reactions could take a long time or not happen at all. With the enzymes, they take place in seconds. However, because enzymes are delicate chemicals, a substantial change in body temperature inactivates or destroys them. If an animal's body temperature is too high or too low, enzyme activity stops and the body will not function properly.

Section 2 Fishes

Hunting and Avoiding Being Eaten Fishes have adaptations for hunting prey and for avoiding predators. The lateral line system of fishes, a sensory organ uniquely suited to aquatic habitats, is an example. The lateral line system detects both vibrations in the water and changes in the water pressure. This information is then converted into nerve impulses. Scientists believe that fishes use the sensory information provided by the lateral line to determine the threat of an approaching predator as well as to locate prey.

Sharks and some bony fishes possess a modified version of the pressure-sensitive lateral line system, called the ampullae of Lorenzini, which allows the fish to detect electrical charges and fields in the water. Humans and most other animals emit an electrical field when in seawater. This field is altered if an organism is wounded or injured. This change in the electrical field can be detected by fishes with this sensory adaptation, thus targeting the injured organism as potential prey.

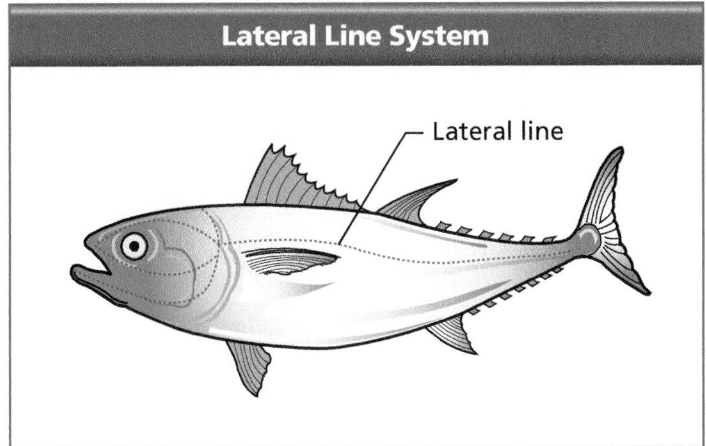

Beyond physiological adaptations, some fishes exhibit behaviors that reduce their vulnerability to predators. One such behavior is schooling. Scientists think that an individual fish that lives within a group of fishes has a better chance of survival than a lone fish when a predator approaches. Predators are believed to be confused by the fish school, and less likely to single out any particular individual prey.

Section 3 Amphibians

Mysterious Declines Declines of frog populations in the United States are particularly dramatic in the Rocky Mountains, California, the Southwest, and Puerto Rico. But these areas are not the only ones with populations in trouble, as physical deformities have been documented for almost 60 species across 44 states. In some areas, as much as 60 percent of the local frog species show deformities. Common deformities include extra eyes or limbs, missing eyes, missing or malformed limbs, and malformed faces.

Scientists have been unable to isolate a single source of harm to the world's frogs. Many researchers suspect that there is more than one destructive process at work, and that this combination is especially damaging. In addition to environmental contamination and loss of habitat, other suspected culprits are UV radiation, parasites, and disease. Populations affected are found in urban, crowded areas where habitat has been recently destroyed, as well as in areas seemingly unaffected by humans, such as national parks.

Address Misconceptions

Students may think that someone who touches a toad will get warts. Anyone who has held a toad knows that this is not true, although toads can secrete irritating substances through their skin. For more explanation of this misconception, see the section entitled *Amphibians.*

Section 4 Reptiles

The Pain and Danger of Venom Of the 2,300 snake species found on Earth, only 300 species are venomous. Although this is a small percentage of the total snake population, about 30,000 to 40,000 people worldwide die each year from snake bites. The greatest number of deaths occurs in Southeast Asia. Fewer than 100 people in the United States die each year from snake bites.

Snake venom is actually toxic saliva. Venom, which immobilizes a snake's prey, can be one of two types. Neurotoxic venoms attack a victim's central nervous system, and hemotoxic venoms attack the circulatory system and the muscle tissue.

Poisonous snakes can sometimes be distinguished from nonpoisonous snakes by differences in physical characteristics. Poisonous snakes usually have pupils that are vertically elliptical, like a cat's, and facial pits between the nostril and the eye, whereas nonpoisonous snakes generally have round pupils and no facial pits.

Nonvenomous Snakes	Venomous Snakes
Round pupils; No sensing pit	Elliptical pupils; Sensing pit
Head slightly wider than neck	Head much wider than neck
Double row of scales on the underside of the tail	Single scales on the underside of the tail

Section 5 Vertebrate History in Rocks

Preserved Animal History Some animal fossils are fossilized body parts or structures, such as bones, claws, teeth, and eggs. Other fossils are traces of animals—footprints, toothmarks, nests, dung, burrows, and so on. There are different forms of fossils: mold fossils preserve impressions, or negative images of an organism; cast fossils occur when a mold fossil is filled in; true-form fossils are the actual animals or parts of the animals; and trace fossils preserve evidence of animals' movements and behaviors, such as walking.

Animals or plants are turned into fossils by several very different processes. Sometimes animals are preserved unaltered, such as an intact insect trapped in amber, which is fossilized tree sap. Most bone and wood fossils are petrified, which means that original tissues were slowly replaced with rocklike minerals. Another means of fossilization is carbonization, which leaves only carbon behind.

Fossils in History Aristotle realized that fossils were evidence of past life, but he thought the organisms had grown in the rocks. During medieval times, from about A.D. 500 to 1500, people dismissed fossils as simply odd mineral formations that resembled living things by chance.

Leonardo da Vinci was one of the first scholars to understand how fossils were formed. He noticed that certain fossils not only looked like the live animal but were also buried in the rock in lifelike positions.

It was not until the late eighteenth century, when the English engineer William Smith recognized that certain fossils are limited to particular layers in Earth's crust, that paleontology became the study of the development of organisms over time.

Help Students Read

Previewing Visuals

Setting a Purpose Before Reading Through Visual Images

Strategy To show students why graphics and tables should be previewed prior to reading, explain that the preview helps a reader anticipate what the text will be about. Have students examine all the section graphics. Ask students to predict what the material in that section will be about, based on their observations.

Example

Select a section of the chapter, such as the section on fishes, or a single topic, such as *Characteristics of Fishes*. Instruct students to preview the material presented in the graphics. Discuss the ideas displayed in the graphics and ask students to predict what the text will be about.

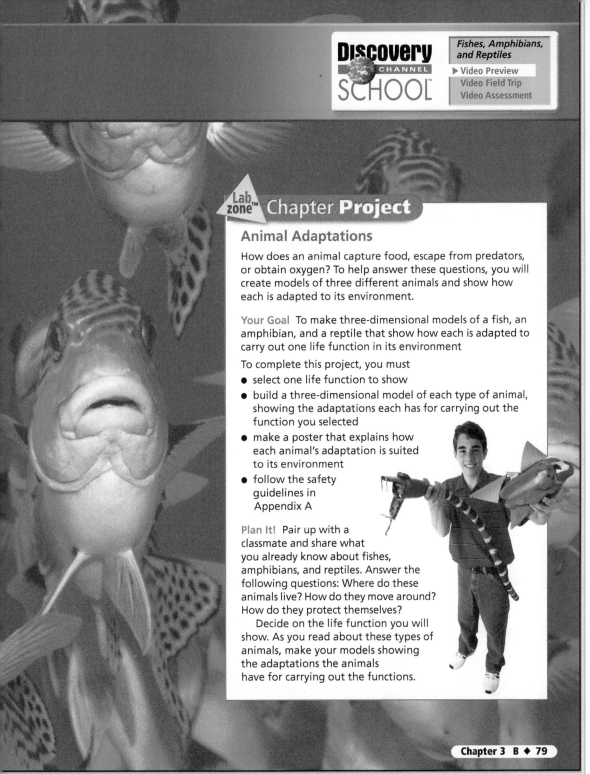

Lab zone™ Chapter Project

Animal Adaptations

How does an animal capture food, escape from predators, or obtain oxygen? To help answer these questions, you will create models of three different animals and show how each is adapted to its environment.

Your Goal To make three-dimensional models of a fish, an amphibian, and a reptile that show how each is adapted to carry out one life function in its environment

To complete this project, you must

- select one life function to show
- build a three-dimensional model of each type of animal, showing the adaptations each has for carrying out the function you selected
- make a poster that explains how each animal's adaptation is suited to its environment
- follow the safety guidelines in Appendix A

Plan It! Pair up with a classmate and share what you already know about fishes, amphibians, and reptiles. Answer the following questions: Where do these animals live? How do they move around? How do they protect themselves?

Decide on the life function you will show. As you read about these types of animals, make your models showing the adaptations the animals have for carrying out the functions.

maché, glue, tape, scissors, paints, markers, and other decorating materials.

- For information about organisms, students can consult magazines and picture books.

Launching the Project

Students should read the project description and the Chapter Project Overview in Teaching Resources. Allow students to work in groups of three or four. Encourage them to skim through the chapter, books, and magazines to consider the ways fishes, amphibians, and reptiles are different, and then discuss characteristics that allow the three types of vertebrates to move, feed, and protect themselves. Suggest that students choose adaptations that differ in at least two of the three organisms. Before they construct each of their models, students should sketch the design and plan for needed materials. Where appropriate, suggest that students model only a part of the organisms, such as the mouths if they are modeling feeding behaviors. Pass out copies of the Chapter Project Worksheets in Teaching Resources for students to review.

Fishes, Amphibians, and Reptiles

Show the Video Preview to introduce the Chapter Project and overview the chapter content. Discussion question: **List three functions of reptile scales.** *(Three functions are preventing evaporation of water, helping forward motion, and camouflage.)*

Performance Assessment

The Chapter Project Scoring Rubric will help you evaluate how well students complete the Chapter Project. You may wish to share the scoring rubric with your students so they are clear about what will be expected of them. Students will be assessed on

- the thoroughness of their research into the adaptation that they model, and the appropriateness and accuracy of their sketches
- the size, proportion, and accuracy of their models
- the clarity and thoroughness of their posters
- the thoroughness and organization of their presentations

Section 1

What Is a Vertebrate?

Objectives

After completing the lesson, students will be able to

B.3.1.1 Name the characteristics that chordates share.

B.3.1.2 Describe the main characteristic shared by all vertebrates.

B.3.1.3 Describe how vertebrates differ in the way they control body temperature.

Target Reading Skill

Building Vocabulary Explain that knowing the definitions of Key Concept words helps students understand what they read.

Answer

Call on volunteers to read their definitions aloud. Make sure that students have explained the definitions in their own words.

Preteach

Build Background Knowledge

L2

Comparing Vertebrates and Invertebrates

Help students recall what they know about vertebrates and invertebrates. Then ask a volunteer to list on the board all the kinds of vertebrates and invertebrates the students see in a single day. Once the lists are completed, have students compare and contrast several obvious ways vertebrates and invertebrates are similar and ways they are different.

Section 1

What Is a Vertebrate?

Reading Preview

Key Concepts

- What characterisics do chordates share?
- What characteristic do all vertebrates have?
- How do vertebrates differ in the way they control body temperature?

Key Terms

- chordate
- notochord
- vertebra
- ectotherm
- endotherm

Target Reading Skill

Building Vocabulary A definition states the meaning of a word or phrase by telling about its most important feature or function. After you read the section, reread the paragraphs that contain definitions of Key Terms. Use all the information you have learned to write a definition of each Key Term in your own words.

Lab zone Discover Activity

How Is an Umbrella Like a Skeleton?

1. Open an umbrella. Turn it upside down and examine how it is made.
2. Now close the umbrella and watch how the braces and ribs collapse.
3. Think of what would happen if you removed the ribs from the umbrella and then tried to use it during a rainstorm.

Think It Over

Inferring What is the function of the ribs of an umbrella? How are the ribs of the umbrella similar to the bones in your skeleton? How are they different?

Look backward in time, into an ocean 530 million years ago. There you see a strange-looking creature—a jawless fish—that is about as long as your index finger. The creature is swimming with a side-to-side motion, like a flag flapping in the wind. Its tail fin is broad and flat. Tiny armorlike plates cover its small body. Its eyes are set wide apart. If you could see inside the animal, you would notice that it has a backbone. You are looking at one of the earliest vertebrates at home in an ancient sea.

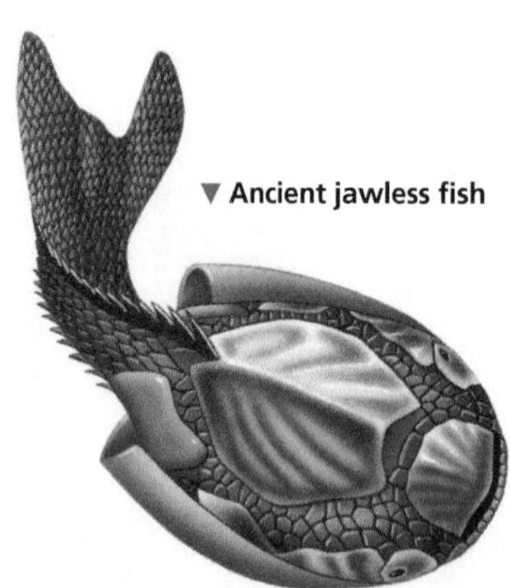

▼ Ancient jawless fish

Characteristics of Chordates

Vertebrates like the ancient jawless fish are a subgroup in the phylum Chordata. All members of this phylum are called **chordates** (KAWR dayts). Most chordates, including fishes, amphibians, such as frogs, and reptiles, such as snakes, are vertebrates. So are birds and mammals. But a few chordates are invertebrates. **At some point in their lives, chordates will have a notochord, a nerve cord that runs down their back, and pouches in their throat area.**

Notochord The phylum name Chordata comes from the **notochord,** a flexible rod that supports a chordate's back. Some chordates, like the lancelet shown in Figure 1, have notochords all their lives. In contrast, in vertebrates, part or all of the notochord is replaced by a backbone.

Discover Activity

Skills Focus Inferring L1

Materials umbrella

Time 15 minutes

Tips To avoid injuries, make sure students are standing in an open area away from others when they open the umbrellas.

Expected Outcome An umbrella without its ribs loses its support and cannot function.

Think It Over The umbrella's ribs provide support to the umbrella and give it shape, just as human bones support and give shape to the body. The ribs of an umbrella are different from human bones in that they are near the surface, rather than deep within the body and covered by soft tissue.

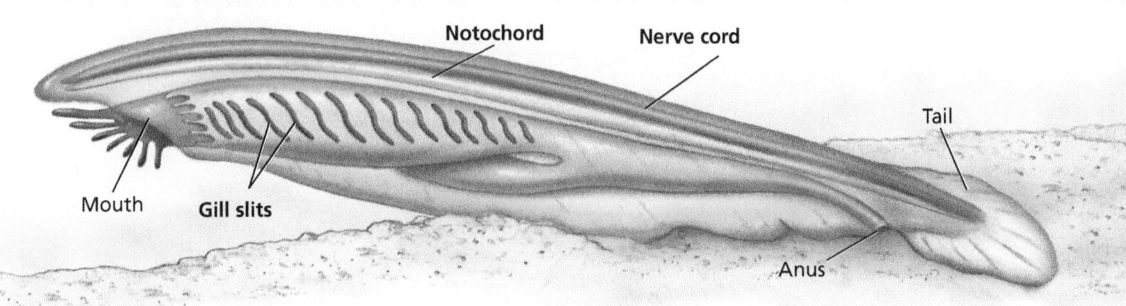

FIGURE 1
Characteristics of a Lancelet
This lancelet shows the characteristics of a chordate: a notochord that helps support its body, a nerve cord down its back, and gill slits that develop from pouches.

Nerve Cord in Back In addition to having a notochord, all chordates have a nerve cord that runs down their back. Your spinal cord is such a nerve cord. The nerve cord is the connection between the brain and the nerves, on which messages travel back and forth. Many other groups of animals—arthropods and segmented worms, for example—have nerve cords, but their nerve cords do not run down their backs.

Pouches in Throat Area At some point in their lives, chordates have pouches in their throat area. In some chordates, such as fishes and the lancelet shown in Figure 1, grooves between these pouches become slits called gill slits. In many vertebrates, including humans, the pouches disappear before birth.

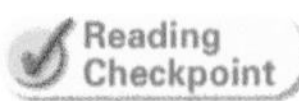

What is a notochord?

Characteristics of Vertebrates

Most chordates are vertebrates. In addition to the characteristics shared by all chordates, vertebrates share certain other characteristics. **A vertebrate has a backbone that is part of an internal skeleton.** This endoskeleton supports the body and allows it to move.

Backbone A vertebrate's backbone, which is also called a spine, runs down the center of its back. You can see in Figure 2 that the backbone is formed by many similar bones called **vertebrae** (singular *vertebra*). The vertebrae are lined up in a row like beads on a string. Joints, or movable connections between the vertebrae, give the spine flexibility. You can bend over and tie your shoes because your backbone has flexibility. Each vertebra has a hole in it that allows the spinal cord to pass through it. The spinal cord fits into the vertebrae like fingers fit into rings.

FIGURE 2
The Backbone of a Lizard
The backbone of this gila monster has flexibility. **Predicting** *Could the backbone bend if the vertebrae did not have joints?*

Differentiated Instruction

English Learners/Beginning L1
Vocabulary: Science Glossary Suggest that students start a personal glossary of vocabulary terms, with each term and its definition in English on one side of an index card and in the student's primary language on the other side. Use the index cards as flash cards for reviewing important terms. **learning modality: verbal**

English Learners/Beginning L2
Vocabulary: Link to Visual To reinforce word meanings, have students find graphics that illustrate the Key Terms. Figures that illustrate the section's Key Terms include Figure 1 for *chordate* and *notochord*, Figures 2 and 3 for *vertebrae*, and Figure 4 for *endotherm* and *ectotherm*. **learning modality: visual**

Instruct

Characteristics of Chordates

Teach Key Concepts L2
Identifying the Notochord

Focus Remind students that the notochord is firm yet flexible.

Teach Ask: **What are the five vertebrate groups?** *(Fishes, amphibians, reptiles, birds, and mammals)*

Apply Ask: **Why is it important for the notochord to be both firm and flexible?** *(The notochord supports the animal but allows it to move.)* **learning modality: verbal**

Characteristics of Vertebrates

Teach Key Concepts L2
Investigating Vertebrate Advantages

Focus Have students study Figure 3.

Teach Ask: **From head to tail, what benefits does the endoskeleton offer?** *(Skull protects brain; ribs protect heart, lungs, and other organs; muscles attach to bones; arm and leg bones adapted for a variety of movement; whole skeleton gives body shape.)* Point to parts of the skeleton as students reply.

Apply Ask: **How does an endoskeleton differ from an arthropod exoskeleton?** *(Endoskeleton provides internal support and grows as the animal grows.)* **learning modality: visual**

Independent Practice L2
All in One Teaching Resources
- Guided Reading and Study Worksheet: *What Is a Vertebrate?*

Student Edition on Audio CD

Monitor Progress L2

Drawing Provide students with unlabeled diagrams of vertebrate skeletons. Ask them to label the skull, backbone, and ribs.

Answers

Figure 2 No. If the vertebrae were fused, the backbone would be too stiff to bend.

Reading Checkpoint A notochord is a flexible rod that supports a chordate's back during part or all of its life.

Keeping Conditions Stable

Teach Key Concepts

L2

Comparing Endotherms and Ectotherms

Focus Tell students that vertebrates differ in the way they control body temperature.

Teach Write two headings on the board, *Endotherms* and *Ectotherms*. Read aloud facts about each and ask students to assign each fact to its correct heading. *(Endotherms: birds and mammals; produces internal heat; stable body temperatures; have fur or feathers, sweat glands. Ectotherms: fishes, reptiles, and amphibians; do not produce internal heat; body temperatures change with environmental temperatures.)*

Apply Ask: **How can an ectotherm change its body temperature?** *(It can seek sun or shade.)* **learning modality: logical/mathematical**

For: Links on vertebrates
Visit: www.SciLinks.org
Web Code: scn-0231

Download a worksheet that will guide students' review of Internet resources on vertebrates.

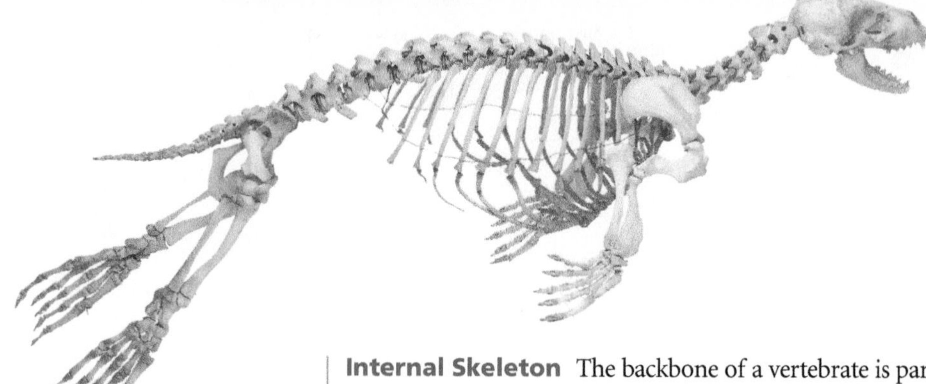

FIGURE 3
The Skeleton of a Seal
This seal's skeleton has adaptations for swimming. Long, flat bones support the flippers. The flat skull helps the seal move smoothly through the water.

Internal Skeleton The backbone of a vertebrate is part of its endoskeleton. This endoskeleton protects the internal organs of the body, helps give the body shape, and gives muscles a place to attach. In addition to the backbone, a vertebrate's endoskeleton includes the skull and ribs. The skull protects the brain. The ribs attach to the vertebrae and protect the heart, lungs, and other internal organs. Many vertebrates, like the seal shown in Figure 3, also have arm and leg bones adapted for movement.

A vertebrate's endoskeleton has several characteristics. Unlike an arthropod's exoskeleton, an endoskeleton doesn't need to be replaced as the animal grows. It also forms an internal frame that supports the body against the downward pull of gravity, while allowing easy movement. Because of these characteristics, vertebrates can grow bigger than animals with exoskeletons or no skeletons at all.

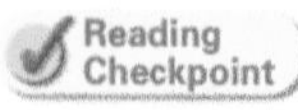

What does an endoskeleton protect?

Keeping Conditions Stable

One characteristic that differs among the major groups of vertebrates is the way they control their body temperature. **The body temperature of most fishes, amphibians, and reptiles is close to the temperature of their environment. In contrast, birds and mammals have a stable body temperature that is often warmer than their environment.**

Ectotherms Fishes, amphibians, and reptiles are ectotherms. An **ectotherm** is an animal whose body does not produce much internal heat. Its body temperature changes depending on the temperature of its environment. For example, when a turtle is lying on a sunny riverbank, it has a higher body temperature than when it is swimming in a cool river. Ectotherms are sometimes called "coldblooded." This term is misleading because their blood is often quite warm.

For: Links on vertebrates
Visit: www.SciLinks.org
Web Code: scn-0231

Woma python ▶

▼ Emperor penguins

Endotherms In contrast to a turtle, a beaver would have the same body temperature whether it is in cool water or on warm land. The beaver is an example of an **endotherm**—an animal whose body regulates its own temperature by controlling the internal heat it produces. An endotherm's body temperature usually does not change much, even when the temperature of its environment changes. Birds and mammals, such as beavers, are endotherms.

Endotherms also have other adaptations, such as sweat glands and fur or feathers, for maintaining their body temperature. On hot days, some endotherms sweat. As the sweat evaporates, the animal is cooled. On cool days, fur or feathers keep endotherms warm. Because endotherms can keep their body temperatures stable, they can live in a greater variety of environments than ectotherms can.

FIGURE 4
Temperature Regulation
On a cool, sunny morning, a woma python raises its body temperature by basking in the sun. In contrast, an emperor penguin stays warm by producing internal heat.
Inferring *Which animal is an endotherm?*

Section 1 Assessment

Target Reading Skill Building Vocabulary Use your definitions to help answer the questions.

Reviewing Key Concepts

1. a. Listing List three characteristics of chordates.
   b. Comparing and Contrasting In chordates, how does the notochord of a vertebrate differ from that of an invertebrate?
   c. Explaining An earthworm has a nerve cord that runs along its body. Is an earthworm a chordate? Explain.
2. a. Identifying What characteristic do only vertebrates have?
   b. Describing Describe a backbone.
   c. Relating Cause and Effect What gives a backbone flexibility?
3. a. Summarizing What is the difference between an ectotherm and an endotherm?
   b. Making Generalizations Would an ectotherm or an endotherm be more active on a cold night? Explain your answer.

Lab zone At-Home Activity

Bumpy Back Rub Have members of your family feel the tops of the vertebrae running down the center of their backs. Then have them feel the hard skull beneath the skin on their foreheads. Tell them about the functions of the backbone and skull.

Lab zone At-Home Activity

Bumpy Back Rub L1 Review the various benefits of the backbone and skull for the students to share with family members: protection of the brain and the spinal cord, flexibility, support, muscle attachment, and growth. Remind them that joints between vertebrae give the spine flexibility, and that the ribs attach to the vertebrae and protect the heart, lungs, and other organs.

Monitor Progress L2

Oral Presentation Call on students to explain the differences between ectotherms and endotherms.

Answers

Figure 4 The penguin

Reading Checkpoint The endoskeleton protects the brain, heart, lungs, and other internal organs.

Assess

Reviewing Key Concepts

1. a. notochord, nerve cord down their back, pouches in throat area **b.** In a vertebrate, the notochord is replaced by a backbone, whereas invertebrate chordates have notochords their whole lives. **c.** No. An earthworm's nerve cord does not run down its back, and an earthworm does not have a notochord or pouches in the throat area.
2. a. Backbone **b.** A backbone runs down the center of the back and is made of many similar bones called vertebrae. **c.** The joints between the vertebrae give the backbone flexibility.
3. a. An ectotherm does not produce much internal heat and its body temperature changes with that of the environment. An endotherm regulates its body temperature by controlling the internal heat it produces.
b. Endotherms; their constantly high body temperatures allow them to remain active when environmental temperatures are cool. Ectotherms would slow down because their body temperatures would drop.

Reteach L1

As a class, list characteristics of vertebrates.

Performance Assessment L2

Drawing Have students sketch simple human skeletons and label the skull, ribs, backbone, vertebrae, and spinal cord. Then ask them to title their sketches "An Endotherm" or "An Ectotherm." Students can save their drawings in their portfolios.

Portfolio

All in One Teaching Resources

- Section Summary: *What Is a Vertebrate?*
- Review and Reinforce: *What Is a Vertebrate?*
- Enrich: *What Is a Vertebrate?*

Lab zone **Skills Lab** L2

Soaking Up Those Rays

Prepare for Inquiry

Key Concept
The temperature of ectotherms changes as the animals approach or avoid heat sources in their environment.

Skills Objectives
After this lab, students will be able to
- interpret data associated with an ectotherm
- make predictions for endotherms

Class Time 30 minutes

All in One Teaching Resources
- Lab Worksheet: *Soaking Up Those Rays*

Guide Inquiry

Invitation
Heat flows from a warmer object to a cooler object. Challenge students to consider whether this rule applies to living organisms. Ask: **What do you notice if you lean against a car parked in the sun?** *(The part of my body touching the car starts to get warm.)*

Introducing the Procedure
As needed, help individual students understand the significance of each type of information in the illustration.

Troubleshooting the Experiment
Students may have trouble relating to Celsius temperatures. Students can convert a few key temperatures in the diagram into degrees Fahrenheit. This may make it easier for them to understand the lizard's behavior. Students can check each other's work.

Expected Outcome
Through their behavior, lizards can maintain their body temperature within a range that is more limited than the temperature range in the environment.

Lab zone **Skills Lab**

Soaking Up Those Rays

Problem
How do some lizards control their body temperatures in the extreme heat of a desert?

Skills Focus
interpreting data, predicting

Materials
- paper
- pencil

Procedure
1. The data below were collected by scientists studying how lizards control their body temperature. Examine the data.
2. Copy the data table into your notebook.
3. Organize the data in the diagrams by filling in the table, putting the appropriate information in each column. Begin by writing a brief description of each type of lizard behavior.
4. Complete the data table using the information in the diagrams.

Analyze and Conclude
1. **Interpreting Data** Describe how the lizard's body temperature changed between 6 A.M. and 9 P.M.
2. **Inferring** What are three sources of heat that caused the lizard's body temperature to rise during the day?
3. **Interpreting Data** During the hottest part of the day, what were the air and ground temperatures? Why do you think the lizard's temperature remained below 40°C?
4. **Predicting** Predict what the lizard's body temperature would have been from 9 P.M. to 6 A.M. Explain your prediction.
5. **Predicting** Predict what would happen to your own body temperature if you spent a brief period outdoors in the desert at noon. Predict what your temperature would be if you spent time in a burrow at 7 P.M. Explain your predictions.

6 A.M.–7 A.M.
Emerging from burrow
Air temperature **20°C**
Ground temperature **28°C**
Body temperature **25°C**

7 A.M.–9 A.M.
Basking (lying on ground in sun)
Air temperature **27°C**
Ground temperature **29°C**
Body temperature **32.6°C**

9 A.M.–12 NOON
Active (moving about)
Air temperature **27°C**
Ground temperature **30.8°C**
Body temperature **36.6°C**

Data Table					
Activity	Description of Activity	Time of Day	Air Temperature (°C)	Ground Temperature (°C)	Body Temperature (°C)
1. Emerging					
2. Basking					
3. Active					
4. Retreat					
5. Stilting					
6. Retreat					

6. **Drawing Conclusions** Based on what you learned from the data, explain why it is misleading to say that an ectotherm is a "cold-blooded" animal.
7. **Communicating** Write a paragraph explaining why it is helpful to organize data in a data table before you try to interpret the data.

More to Explore

Make a bar graph of the temperature data. Explain what the graph shows you. How does this graph help you interpret the data about how lizards control their body temperature in the extreme heat of a desert?

12 NOON–2:30 P.M.
Retreat to burrow
Air temperature **40.3°C**
Ground temperature **53.8°C**
Body temperature **39.5°C**

2:30 P.M.–6 P.M.
Stilting (belly off ground)
Air temperature **34.2°C**
Ground temperature **47.4°C**
Body temperature **39.5°C**

6 P.M.–9 P.M.
Retreat to burrow
Air temperature **25°C**
Ground temperature **26°C**
Body temperature **25°C**

Sample Data Table				
Description of Activity	Time	Air Temp. °C	Ground Temp. °C	Body Temp. °C
Leaves burrow	6–7 A.M.	20	28	25
Rests on surface	7–9	27	29	32.6
Moves around	9–12	27	30.8	36.6
Enters burrow	12–12:30 P.M.	40.3	53.8	39.5
Belly away from surface, tail over head	2:30–6	34.2	47.4	39.5
Enters burrow	6	25	26	25

Analyze and Conclude

1. The lizard's body temperature varied from a low of 25°C to a high of 39.5°C. By 9 P.M. it had dropped back down to 25°C.

2. The sun's rays, the surrounding air, and surface rocks. Note: In some periods, the air was cooler than the lizard's body temperature and so served to cool it.

3. Air temperature = 40.3°C, ground temperature = 53.8°C. The lizard remained cooler by staying in its burrow, which was in the shade and cooler than the ground temperature.

4. Accept all reasonable answers. Students may say that the body temperature will probably remain about 25°C, since the burrow tends to have a stable temperature.

5. Our body temperatures at both times would remain relatively constant, since human body temperature is controlled by its own internal controls.

6. "Coldblooded" implies that an animal's body temperature is cold. The lizard's temperature gets as high as 39°C, which is hotter than 100°F.

7. Sample answer: Organizing data in a table allows us to list all the data in the same place and makes data easier to compare. In this lab, the data table lets us quickly see temperature changes that happened over the course of the day. The table also makes comparing the temperatures at different times of the day easier.

Extend Inquiry

More to Explore On the bar graph, the temperature is plotted on the *y*-axis; the time of the day on the *x*-axis. The graph of ground temperature shows that the rocks are cool in the morning, become hot at noon, and remain hot until evening. Lizards keep their bodies off the rocks after the rocks become hot. They either retreat, as they did from 12–2:30 P.M., or show stilting behavior. Stilting keeps their bodies away from the heat of the rocks.

Objectives

After completing the lesson, students will be able to

B.3.2.1 Name the main characteristics of fishes.

B.3.2.2 Name the major groups of fishes and describe how they differ.

Target Reading Skill

Previewing Visuals Explain that looking at the visuals before they read helps students activate prior knowledge and predict what they are about to read.

Answers

Possible student questions and answers include: **What is a swim bladder?** *(A swim bladder is an internal, gas-filled sac that helps stabilize the fish at different depths in the water.)* **What is the function of the tail fin?** *(It helps provide the power for swimming.)*

All in One Teaching Resources

- Transparency B24

Preteach

Build Background Knowledge

L2

Recalling Fish Characteristics

Ask students to describe characteristics of fishes they have observed. Ask questions such as: **What did the skin look like? What did the scales feel like? Where were the fins located?**

Section 2 Fishes

Reading Preview

Key Concepts

- What are the characteristics of most fishes?
- What are the major groups of fishes and how do they differ?

Key Terms

- fish
- cartilage
- swim bladder

Target Reading Skill

Previewing Visuals Before you read, preview Figure 12. Then write two questions that you have about the diagram in a graphic organizer like the one below. As you read, answer your questions.

Structure of a Fish

Q. What is a swim bladder?
A.
Q.

Lab zone Discover Activity

How Does Water Flow Over a Fish's Gills?

1. Closely observe a fish in an aquarium for a few minutes. Note how frequently the fish opens its mouth.
2. Notice the flaps on each side of the fish's head behind its eyes. Observe how the flaps open and close.
3. Observe the movements of the mouth and the flaps at the same time. Note any relationship between the movements of these two structures.

Think It Over

Observing What do the flaps on the sides of the fish do when the fish opens its mouth? What role do you think these two structures play in a fish's life?

In the warm waters of a coral reef, a large spotted fish called a graysby hovers in the water, barely moving. A smaller striped fish called a goby swims up to the graysby. Then, like a vacuum cleaner moving over a rug, the goby swims slowly over the larger fish, eating dead skin and tiny parasites. The goby even cleans inside the graysby's mouth and gills. Both fishes benefit from this cleaning. The graysby gets rid of unwanted materials, and the goby gets a meal.

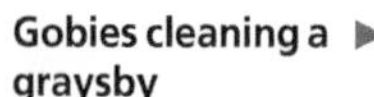

Gobies cleaning a graysby ►

Lab zone Discover Activity

Skills Focus Observing L1

Materials several live fish, each one in an aquarium or fishbowl

Time 10 minutes

Tips Use a larger fish, such as a goldfish, whose gill movements can be easily observed.

Expected Outcome Students should observe that when the fish opens its mouth, its gill flaps also open.

Think It Over The mouth and the gill flaps open at the same time. The mouth enables water to enter the fish and pass over the gills, which take in oxygen from the water. The flaps open to enable the water to leave.

Extend Ask students to count the number of times the gill flaps open per minute. Direct them to work in pairs and compare their results with those of the other groups.

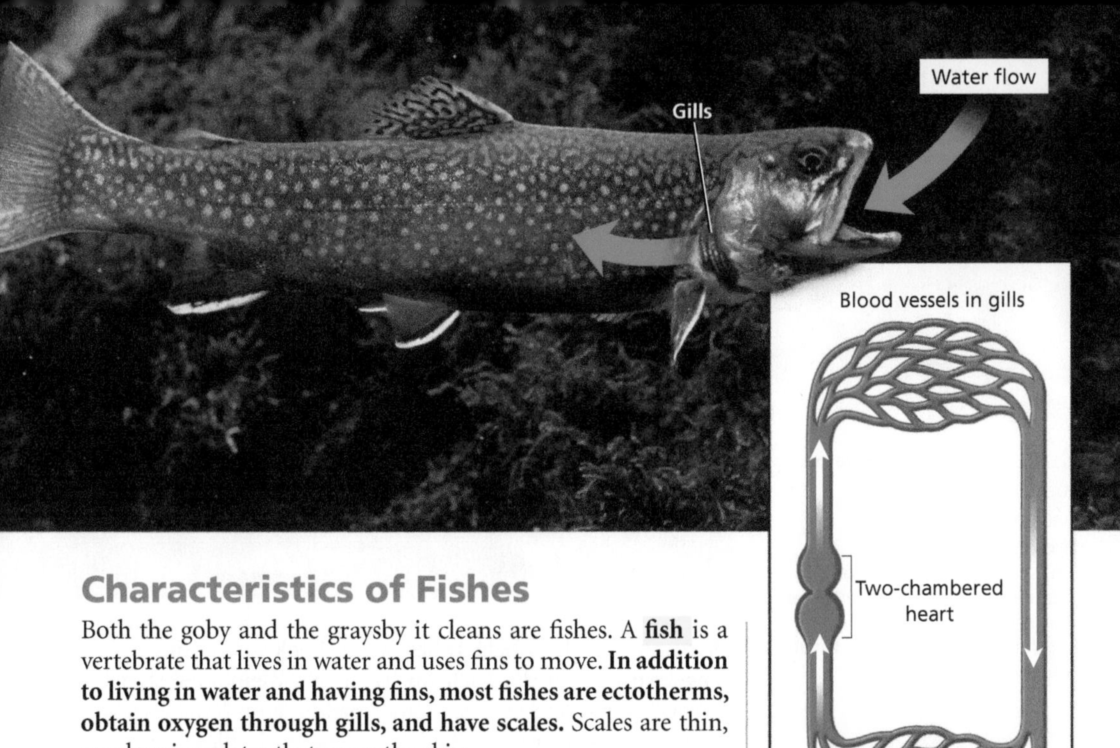

Characteristics of Fishes

Both the goby and the graysby it cleans are fishes. A **fish** is a vertebrate that lives in water and uses fins to move. **In addition to living in water and having fins, most fishes are ectotherms, obtain oxygen through gills, and have scales.** Scales are thin, overlapping plates that cover the skin.

Fishes make up the largest group of vertebrates. Nearly half of all vertebrate species are fishes. In addition, fishes have been on Earth longer than any other kind of vertebrate.

Obtaining Oxygen Fishes get their oxygen from water. As a fish swims, it opens its mouth and takes a gulp of water, as you observed if you did the Discover Activity. The water, which contains oxygen, moves through openings in the fish's throat region that lead to the gills. Gills, which look like tiny feathers, have many blood vessels within them. As water flows over the gills, oxygen moves from the water into the fish's blood. At the same time, carbon dioxide, a waste product, moves out of the blood and into the water. After flowing over the gills, the water flows out of the fish through slits beneath the gills.

Circulatory System From the gills, the blood travels throughout the fish's body, supplying the body cells with oxygen. Like all vertebrates, fishes have a closed circulatory system. The heart of a fish has two chambers, or inner spaces. The heart of a fish pumps blood in one loop—from the heart to the gills, from the gills to the rest of the body, and back to the heart. You can trace this path in Figure 5.

FIGURE 5
Respiration and Circulation
Water flows into the mouth of this fish and then over its gills. Oxygen moves into the blood and is delivered to the cells of the fish.
Interpreting Diagrams *Where does oxygen get into the blood of a fish?*

Instruct

Characteristics of Fishes

Teach Key Concepts L2

Describing Fish Characteristics

Focus Tell students that fishes have specific characteristics that allow them to circulate blood, obtain oxygen and food, move about, reproduce, and avoid predators.

Teach Help students form a general characterization of fishes. Ask: **Are fishes ectotherms or endotherms?** *(Ectotherms)* **How do fishes obtain oxygen?** *(They extract it from water, moving it into their bloodstream as water moves across their gills.)*

Apply Ask: **What characteristics do fishes share with all other vertebrates?** *(A backbone/notochord, closed circulatory system, gill slits, nerve chord along the back)* **learning modality: verbal**

All in One Teaching Resources
- Transparency B25

Independent Practice L2

All in One Teaching Resources
- Guided Reading and Study Worksheet: *Fishes*

Student Edition on Audio CD

Monitor Progress L2

Answer

Figure 5 As water flows over the gills, oxygen moves from the water into fishes' blood.

Teach Key Concepts

L2

Evaluating Reproduction Strategies

Focus Challenge students to make inferences about the advantages and disadvantages of external and internal fertilization in fishes.

Teach List on the chalkboard the advantages and disadvantages of each kind of fertilization. *(External fertilization: advantage—less energy expended by parent(s); disadvantage—lower survival rate. Internal fertilization: advantage—higher survival rate; disadvantage—more energy expended by parent(s))*

Apply Ask: **Why do you think more eggs are fertilized with external fertilization?** *(Because the survival rate is low; predators eat eggs and young receive no care.)* **learning modality: logical/mathematical**

Help Students Read

L1

Previewing Visuals Before students read, have them study Figures 5 and 6 and read the captions. Call on student volunteers to predict topics that the text will cover. *(How fishes obtain and use oxygen, details of the fish circulatory system, how fish swim)* Have students read the text, and then together discuss how accurately students predicted the text topics using only the figures.

▲ Skeleton

FIGURE 6
Fins of an Angelfish
The skeleton of a fish shows that the fins have bony support. The fins of this angelfish act like paddles as the fish moves through the water.

Movement Fins help fishes swim. Look at the fins on the angelfish in Figure 6. Each fin has a thin membrane stretched across bony supports. Like a canoe paddle, a fin provides a large surface to push against the water. The push allows for faster movement through the water. If you have ever swum wearing a pair of swim fins, you probably noticed how fast you moved through the water. Most of the movements of fishes are related to obtaining food, but some are related to reproduction.

Reproduction Most fishes have external fertilization. In external fertilization, the eggs are fertilized outside the female's body. The male hovers close to the female and spreads a cloud of sperm cells over the eggs she releases. The young develop outside the female's body.

In contrast, some fishes, such as sharks and guppies, have internal fertilization. In internal fertilization, eggs are fertilized inside the female's body. The young develop inside her body. When they are mature enough to live on their own, she gives birth to them.

Reading Checkpoint **What is the structure of a fin?**

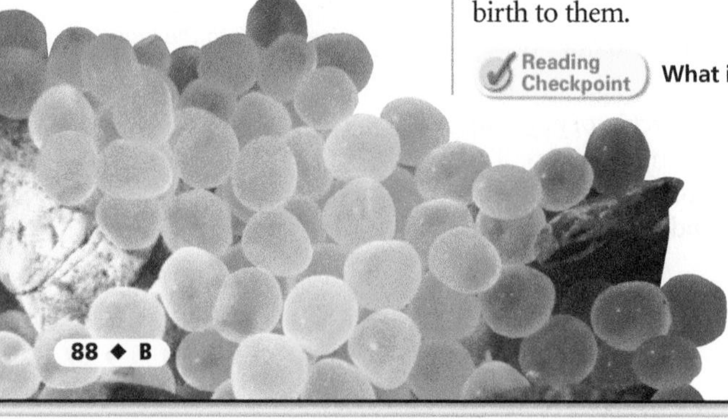

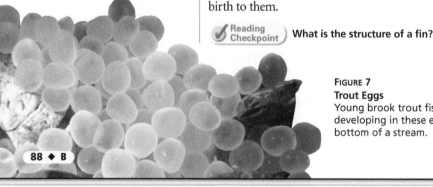

FIGURE 7
Trout Eggs
Young brook trout fish are developing in these eggs on the bottom of a stream.

Nervous System The nervous system and sense organs of fishes help them find food and avoid predators. Most fishes can see much better in water than you can. Keen senses of touch, smell, and taste also help fishes capture food. Some fishes have taste organs in unusual places. For example, the catfish shown in Figure 8 tastes with its whiskers.

Jawless Fishes

Fishes have lived on Earth longer than any other kind of vertebrate. Fishes are organized into three main groups based on the structures of their mouths and the types of skeletons they have. **The major groups of fishes are jawless fishes, cartilaginous fishes, and bony fishes.**

Jawless fishes are unlike other fishes in that they have no jaws and no scales. Jaws are hinged bony structures that allow animals to open and close their mouths. Instead of jaws, jawless fishes have mouths containing structures for scraping, stabbing, and sucking their food. Their skeletons are made of **cartilage,** a tissue that is more flexible than bone.

Hagfishes and lampreys are the only kinds of jawless fishes that exist today. Hagfishes look like large, slimy worms. They crawl into the bodies of dead or dying fishes and use their rough tongues to scrape decaying tissues. Many lampreys are parasites of other fishes. They attach their mouths to healthy fishes and then suck in the tissues and blood of their victims. If you look at the lamprey's mouth in Figure 9, you can probably imagine the damage it can do.

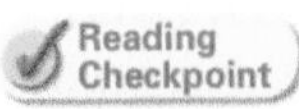

What material makes up the skeleton of a jawless fish?

FIGURE 8
A Catfish
The whiskers of a catfish have many taste buds. To find food, the catfish drags its whiskers along muddy lake or river bottoms.

FIGURE 9
A Lamprey
Lampreys have eel-shaped bodies. They use sharp teeth and suction-cup mouths to feed on other fishes. Classifying *To which group of fishes do lampreys belong?*

Jawless Fishes

Teach Key Concepts L2

Examining a Jawless Mouth

Focus Review with students the location of the jaw on a fish.

Teach Direct students to locate the mouth of the jawless fish in Figure 9. Have them describe the mouth. *(Round, filled with many sharp teeth, and so on.)* Ask: **Does the lamprey's mouth look like the mouths of fishes that you are familiar with?** *(Students will probably say no.)* Inform students that the lamprey feeds by attaching to a living fish, gnawing a hole in the fish's side, and eating the fluids that leak out. Ask: **What do the teethlike structures do?** *(Help the lamprey stay attached to its host)*

Apply Ask: **What is the feeding classification if an animal gains its nutrients by attaching itself to and feeding on the tissues of another organism?** *(A parasite)* **learning modality: visual**

Help Students Read L1

Comparing and Contrasting As students read the section, have them compare and contrast photos and captions for Figures 9 and 11. Ask students to describe the differences in how lampreys and sharks feed.

Monitor Progress L2

Writing Ask students to write a few paragraphs that describe an hour in a fish's life. Paragraphs should include how a fish hunts for food and eludes predators. Encourage students to focus on how the fish uses its highly developed sense organs. Students can save their paragraphs in their portfolios. Portfolio

Answers

Figure 9 The jawless fishes

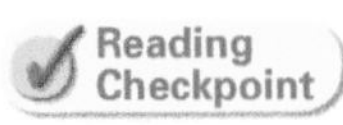

A fin has a thin membrane stretched over bony supports.

Cartilage

Differentiated Instruction

Gifted and Talented L3

Comparing Fish Movement Provide books or online sources on fish movement. Have students choose two fishes with very different physical features *(Example: Shark and catfish)*, and then make simple cardboard models of the body shape and fin shape for both. **learning modality: kinesthetic**

Special Needs L1

Comparing Fish Movement Allow students needing extra instruction on fish movement to work with those completing the Gifted and Talented exercise above. Students should read through the text's description of fish movement, and manipulate the models to visualize how fish move. **learning modality: kinesthetic**

Cartilaginous Fishes

Teach Key Concepts L2

Describing Cartilaginous Fishes

Focus Review the meaning of *cartilage.*

Teach Ask: **Name the cartilaginous fishes.** *(Sharks, skates, and rays)* **Which of their body parts are made of cartilage?** *(Jaws, scales, and skeletons)*

Apply Ask: **Do most cartilaginous fishes obtain the same types of food?** *(Yes, they are carnivores.)* **Do they all have the same patterns of moving and feeding?** *(No; sharks swim constantly and eat almost anything; skates and rays are less active and hunt small animals on the ocean floor.)* **learning modality: verbal**

L2

Comparing Bone and Cartilage

Materials partial skeleton from a whole, cooked chicken breast

Time 15 minutes

Focus Have students directly compare the properties of bone and cartilage.

Teach Allow students to work in small groups. Before removing the skeleton from the breast, cut the cartilage away from the meat to be sure it remains with the skeleton. Give a skeleton to each group and direct students to distinguish between the bones and the cartilage. Tell them that the cartilage in the chicken breast is bluish-white and the bone is brown. Urge students to attempt to bend and twist both cartilage and bone. Circulate among groups to be sure students can distinguish between bone and cartilage. Have students wash their hands afterwards. Ask: **Which is more flexible, bone or cartilage?** *(Cartilage)* **Which is more likely to break than to bend?** *(Bone)*

Extend Ask: **Why is it beneficial to have a skeleton made out of both bone and cartilage?** *(Bone is stronger and provides support; cartilage gives flexibility.)* **learning modality: kinesthetic**

FIGURE 10
Blue-Spotted Ray
This ray is a cartilaginous fish that lives on the ocean floor.

Cartilaginous Fishes

Sharks, rays, and skates are cartilaginous (kahr tuh LAJ uh nuhs) fishes. **The cartilaginous fishes have jaws and scales, and skeletons made of cartilage.** The pointed, toothlike scales that cover their bodies give their skin a texture that is rougher than sandpaper.

Obtaining Oxygen Most sharks cannot pump water over their gills. Instead, they rely on swimming or currents to keep water moving across their gills. For example, when sharks sleep, they position themselves in currents that send water over their gills.

Rays and skates are not as active as sharks. They spend a lot of time partially buried in the sand of the ocean floor. During this time, they take in water through small holes located behind their eyes. Water leaves through gill openings on their undersides.

Obtaining Food Cartilaginous fishes are usually carnivores. Rays and skates hunt on the ocean floor, crushing mollusks, crustaceans, and small fishes with their teeth. Sharks will attack and eat nearly anything that smells like food. They can smell and taste even a tiny amount of blood—as little as one drop in 115 liters of water! Although sharks have a keen sense of smell their eyesight is poor. Because they see poorly, sometimes they swallow strange objects. Indeed, one shark was found to have a raincoat and an automobile license plate in its stomach.

The mouth of a shark contains jagged teeth arranged in rows. Most sharks use only the first couple of rows for feeding. The remaining rows are replacements. If a shark loses a front-row tooth, a tooth behind it moves up to replace it.

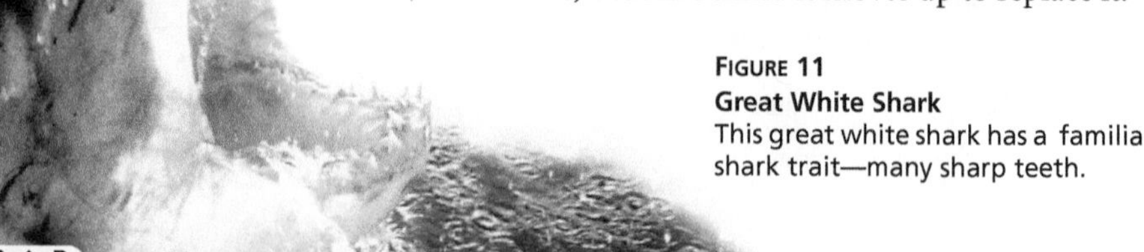

FIGURE 11
Great White Shark
This great white shark has a familiar shark trait—many sharp teeth.

Differentiated Instruction

English Learners/Intermediate L2
Vocabulary: Word Analysis Write the word *cartilaginous* on the board. Explain that the word is an adjective formed from the noun *cartilage,* and that English has many words formed in this way. Find other examples in the text of an adjective and noun sharing the same root. *(symmetry—symmetrical; parasite—parasitic; nerve—nervous)* **learning modality: verbal**

English Learners/Beginning L1
Vocabulary: Use Visuals Use Figure 12 to help beginning students understand section concepts. Point to each structure in the diagram and say its name. Then have beginning students work with those who are more fluent in English to understand the function of each structure. **learning modality: visual**

FIGURE 12
Structure of a Bony Fish
This yellow perch has the characteristics of a bony fish. **Interpreting Diagrams** *What are the functions of fins?*

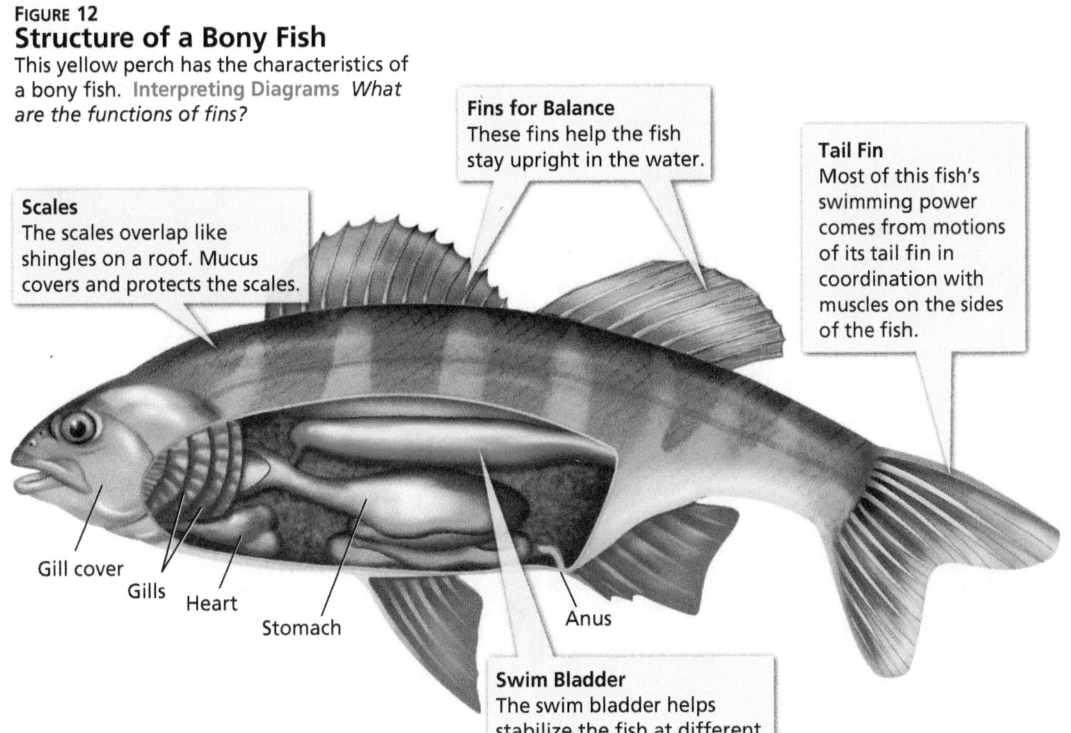

Fins for Balance
These fins help the fish stay upright in the water.
Tail Fin
Most of this fish's swimming power comes from motions of its tail fin in coordination with muscles on the sides of the fish.
Scales
The scales overlap like shingles on a roof. Mucus covers and protects the scales.
Gill cover
Gills
Heart
Stomach
Anus
Swim Bladder
The swim bladder helps stabilize the fish at different depths in the water.

Bony Fishes

Most familiar kinds of fishes, such as trout, tuna, and goldfishes, are bony fishes. **A bony fish has jaws, scales, a pocket on each side of the head that holds the gills, and a skeleton made of hard bones.** Each gill pocket is covered by a flap that opens to release water.

The major structures of a bony fish are shown in Figure 12. Notice that a bony fish has an organ called a **swim bladder,** which is an internal, gas-filled sac that helps the fish stay stable at different depths in the water. Gas levels in the swim bladder are adjusted after the fish reaches its desired depth. By adjusting these levels, the fish can stay at a depth without using a lot of energy.

Bony fishes make up about 95 percent of all fish species. They live in both salt water and fresh water. Some live in the dark depths of the ocean. Others thrive in light-filled waters, such as those around coral reefs. Figure 13 on the next page shows some of the great variety of bony fishes.

Reading Checkpoint **Which organ helps a bony fish maintain its position in the water?**

Lab zone Skills Activity

Observing

Put on your goggles and disposable gloves. Place a preserved fish on newspaper on your desk and examine it closely. Note its size and shape, and the number and locations of its fins. Lift the gill cover and observe the gills with a hand lens. Use your observations to make a diagram of the fish. Wash your hands when you are finished.

Bony Fishes

Teach Key Concepts L2

Evaluating Bony Fish Characteristics

Focus Tell students that bony fishes have skeletons made of bone.

Teach Direct students to Figure 12. Discuss as a class the function of each structure shown. Ask students to think of how the structures described in the figure accomplish that function. For example, ask: **How does the tail fin help the perch move through the water?** *(The tail fin provides a large surface to push against the water, propelling the fish.)*

Apply Assign students to work in pairs to continue discussing the means by which structures carry out their functions. Have students describe for the class how they think each structure works. *(Descriptions will vary but should relate directly to Figure 12 descriptions.)* **learning modality: visual**

All in One Teaching Resources

- Transparency B26

Lab zone Skills Activity

Skills Focus Observing L2

Materials preserved fish, goggles, dissecting tray, blunt probe, hand lens, rubber gloves

Time 50 minutes

Tips CAUTION: *Provide gloves to all students. Students should wash their hands after handling the fish.* Help students see the connection between the mouth and gill slits by letting them pass the end of the probe into the fish's mouth and out through the gill openings.

Extend Have students closely examine the feathery structure of the gills. Ask: **How is the structure of the gills related to their function?** *(The feathery structure provides more surface area for absorbing oxygen.)*

Monitor Progress L2

Skills Check Have students infer what would happen to a shark in still water if the shark could not move. *(The shark would die, because it could not obtain oxygen.)*

Answers

Figure 12 Fins help a fish maintain its balance and power its swimming.

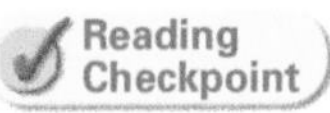
Reading Checkpoint The swim bladder

Assess

Reviewing Key Concepts

1. a. Vertebrates; live in water; move using fins; most are ectotherms; obtain oxygen through gills, and have scales **b.** Fishes have gills for obtaining oxygen. As water is moved across the gills, oxygen in the water moves into the gills' many blood cells. **c.** The goldfish would not be able to obtain oxygen from water because water enters through the mouth before passing over the gills.
2. a. Jawless, cartilaginous, and bony fishes **b.** Cartilaginous fishes. **c.** Hagfishes use their rough tongues to scrape away decaying tissues from the bodies of dead or dying fishes; sharks directly attack their living prey, using mouths with many rows of jagged teeth.

Reteach L1

Draw a table on the board to direct a class discussion comparing and contrasting the three groups of fishes.

Performance Assessment L2

Concept Mapping Have each student draw a concept map to show the three main types of fishes described in this section, their characteristics, and examples.

All in One Teaching Resources

- Section Summary: *Fishes*
- Review and Reinforce: *Fishes*
- Enrich: *Fishes*

FIGURE 13
Diversity of Bony Fishes
These photographs show just a few species of bony fishes.

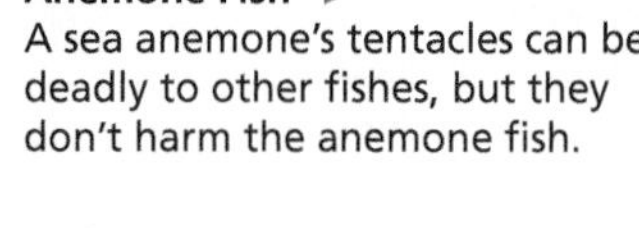

Anemone Fish ▶ A sea anemone's tentacles can be deadly to other fishes, but they don't harm the anemone fish.

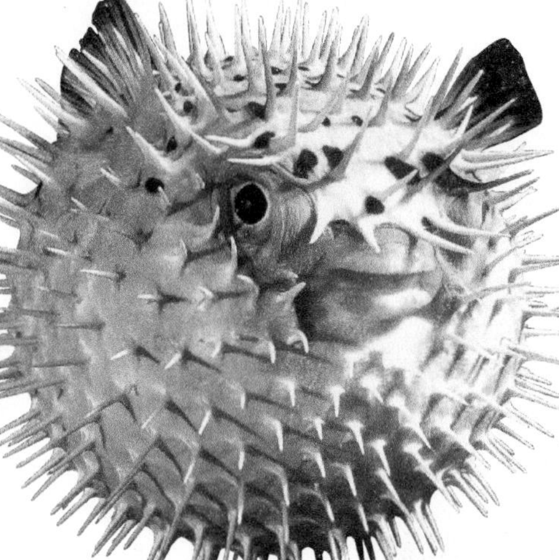

Balloonfish ▶ When threatened, a balloonfish swallows large amounts of water or air to make itself into a spiny ball.

◀ **Sea Dragon** The leafy sea dragon is well camouflaged in weedy bays and lagoons.

▼ **Sockeye Salmon** Sockeye salmon are Pacific Ocean fishes that migrate from ocean to inland lakes to reproduce.

Section 2 Assessment

Target Reading Skill Previewing Visuals Use the information in your graphic organizer about the structure of a fish to quiz a partner.

Reviewing Key Concepts

1. a. Reviewing What are the main characteristics of fishes?
b. Explaining Why do fishes have gills?
c. Applying Concepts What would happen to a goldfish that could not open its mouth? Explain.
2. a. Identifying What are three major groups of fishes?
b. Classifying Into which group of fishes would you classify a fish with jaws and a skeleton made of cartilage?
c. Comparing and Contrasting How do sharks and hagfishes obtain food?

Writing in Science

Wanted Poster Design a "Wanted" poster for a lamprey. Present the lamprey as a "criminal of the ocean." Include the lamprey's physical characteristics, feeding habits, and any other details that will allow people to track down this fish.

Lab zone Chapter Project

Keep Students on Track Review and approve students' adaptation and fish choices. Make sure that the adaptation they have chosen is easily modeled for the fish and for an amphibian and a reptile. Help students locate reference sources and materials.

Writing in Science

Writing Mode Description
Scoring Rubric
4 Includes an exceptional number of details in a neat, creative format
3 Includes an acceptable number of details; appealing display
2 Lacks some important details; adequate display
1 Includes few details; disorganized and inadequate display

Lab zone **Skills Lab**

Home Sweet Home

Problem

What features does an aquarium need for fish to survive in it?

Skills Focus

observing, making models

Materials

- gravel • metric ruler • guppies • snails
- guppy food • dip net
- tap water • thermometer • water plants
- aquarium filter • aquarium heater
- rectangular aquarium tank (15 to 20 liters) with cover

Procedure

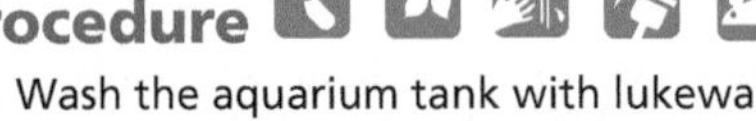

1. Wash the aquarium tank with lukewarm water—do not use soap. Then place it on a flat surface in indirect sunlight.
2. Rinse the gravel and spread it over the bottom of the tank to a depth of about 3 cm.
3. Fill the tank about two-thirds full with tap water. Position several water plants in the tank by gently pushing their roots into the gravel. Wash your hands after handling the plants.
4. Add more water until the level is about 5 cm from the top.
5. Place the filter in the water and turn it on. Insert an aquarium heater into the tank and turn it on. Set the temperature to 25°C. **CAUTION:** *Do not touch electrical equipment with wet hands.*
6. Allow the water to "age" by letting it stand for two days. Aging allows the chlorine to evaporate.
7. When the water has aged and is at the proper temperature, add guppies and snails to the tank. Include one guppy and one snail for each 4 liters of water. Cover the aquarium. Wash your hands after handling the animals.
8. Observe the aquarium every day for two weeks. Feed the guppies a small amount of food daily. Look for evidence that the fishes and snails have adapted to their new environment. Also look for the ways they carry out their life activities, such as feeding and respiration. Record your observations.
9. Use a dip net to keep the gravel layer clean and to remove any dead plants or animals.

Analyze and Conclude

1. Observing How does the aquarium meet the following needs of the organisms living in it: (a) oxygen supply, (b) proper temperature, and (c) food?
2. Inferring What happens to the oxygen that the fishes take in from the water in this aquarium? How is that oxygen replaced?
3. Making Models How is an aquarium like a guppy's natural environment? How is it different?
4. Communicating Write an e-mail to a friend or relative in which you summarize the record you made during the two weeks you observed the aquarium.

Design an Experiment

Write a one-page procedure for adding a second kind of fish to the aquarium. Include a list of questions that you would need to have answered before you could carry out your plan successfully. (Success would be marked by both types of fishes surviving together in the tank.) *Obtain your teacher's permission before carrying out your investigation.*

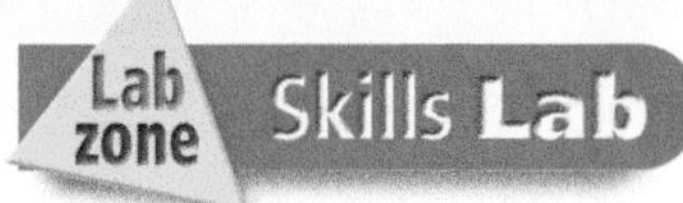

Home Sweet Home L2

Prepare for Inquiry

Key Concept

Organisms need habitats that meet certain requirements in order to survive.

Skills Objectives

After this lab, students will be able to
- make a model habitat
- observe organisms in the model habitat

Prep Time 30 minutes
Class Time 10 minutes per day for two weeks

Advance Planning

- Provide sufficient clean water for all the groups. Chlorine may be removed by letting the water stand for 2–3 days or by treating it with a special chemical available at pet stores.
- Make sure other supplies are thoroughly clean. Do not use soap.

Safety

Students should be careful carrying the glass aquariums and should not move the aquarium once it is filled with water. **CAUTION:** *Students should make sure the area around the tank is dry and that their hands are dry before they plug in the electrical equipment.* Review the safety guidelines in Appendix A.

All in One **Teaching Resources**
- Lab Worksheet: *Home Sweet Home*

Guide the Inquiry

Invitation

Help students focus on the Key Concept by asking: **What is a key factor in an organism's survival?** *(An organism's habitat must meet its requirements for survival.)*

Introducing the Procedure

- Invite students to observe a functioning aquarium and to read over the procedure and materials list for this lab. Ask: **What habitat conditions will you establish for an aquarium?** *(Water temperature, food availability, plant cover)*

Expected Outcome

After a day or two, if the animals have adapted, the snails should be moving about the tank feeding. The fish should be swimming normally and feeding.

Analyze and Conclude

1. a. By air entering through the filter and oxygen from plants **b.** From the heater or sunlight **c.** By the plants and by the students.
2. The oxygen is used by the fish. Plants release oxygen.
3. In an aquarium, ideal conditions are maintained artificially. In nature, animals have to locate their own food and avoid predators.
4. E-mails should summarize observations and conclusions.

Extend Inquiry

Design an Experiment Questions might include: *Will the new fish prey on or be eaten by the guppies? Is there enough space?*

Section 3 Amphibians

Objectives

After completing the lesson, students will be able to

B.3.3.1 Describe amphibian characteristics.

B.3.3.2 Examine how adult amphibians are adapted for life on land.

Target Reading Skill

Sequencing Explain that organizing information from beginning to end helps students understand a step-by-step process.

Answers

Adult frog; Fertilized eggs; Tadpole hatches; Hind legs develop; Front legs develop; Tail is absorbed.

All in One Teaching Resources

- Transparency B27

Preteach

Build Background Knowledge L2

Identifying Amphibian Characteristics

Have students describe any animals they know of that live part of their life on land and part in the water *(Frogs, salamanders)*. Then ask: **What characteristics allow these animals to live on land and in water?** *(Ability to change/undergo metamorphosis; body structures that allow movement, feeding, and breathing on land or in water).*

Section 3 Amphibians

Reading Preview

Key Concepts

- What are the main characteristics of amphibians?
- What are some adaptations of adult amphibians for living on land?

Key Terms

- amphibian
- tadpole
- lung
- atrium
- ventricle
- habitat

Target Reading Skill

Sequencing As you read, make a cycle diagram like the one below that shows the different stages of a frog's metamorphosis during its life cycle. Write each step of the process in a separate circle.

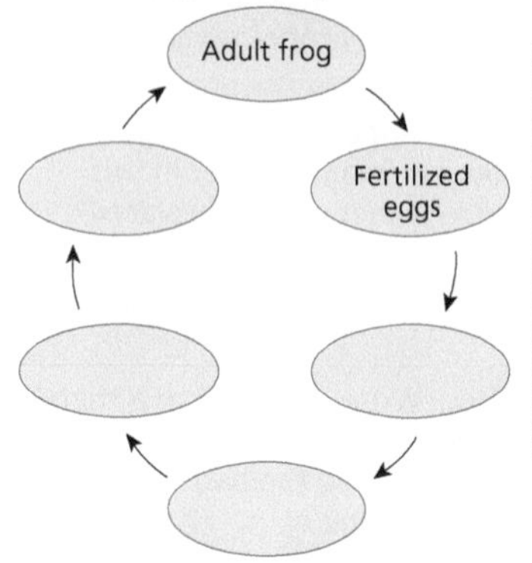

Lab zone Discover Activity

What's the Advantage of Being Green?

1. Count out 20 dried yellow peas and 20 green ones. Mix them up in a paper cup.
2. Cover your eyes. Have your partner gently scatter the peas onto a large sheet of green paper.
3. Uncover your eyes. Have your partner keep time while you pick up as many peas, one at a time, as you can find in 15 seconds.
4. When 15 seconds are up, count how many peas of each color you picked up.
5. Repeat Steps 2 through 4, but this time you scatter the peas and keep time while your partner picks up the peas.
6. Compare your results with those of your partner and your classmates.

Think It Over

Inferring Many frogs are green, as are their environments. What advantage does a frog have in being green?

What's that sound coming from the pond? Even 1 kilometer away you can hear the shrill calls of frogs called spring peepers on this damp spring night. By the time you reach the pond, the calls are ear-splitting. You might think that the frogs must be huge to make such a loud sound. But each frog is smaller than the first joint of your thumb! In the beam of your flashlight, you see the puffed-up throats of the males, vibrating with each call. Female peepers bound across roads and swim across streams to mate with the noisy males.

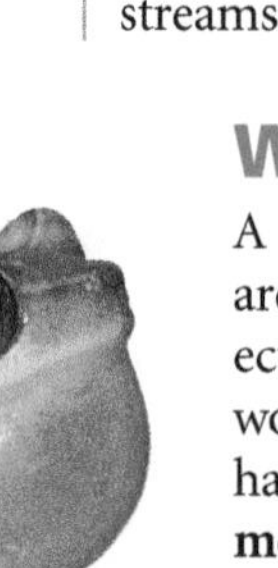

Spring peeper ▶

What Is an Amphibian?

A frog is one kind of amphibian; toads and salamanders are other kinds. An **amphibian** is a vertebrate that is ectothermic and spends its early life in water. Indeed, the word *amphibian* means "double life," and amphibians have exactly that. **After beginning their lives in water, most amphibians spend their adulthood on land, returning to water to reproduce.**

Lab zone Discover Activity

Skills Focus Inferring L1

Materials dried yellow and green peas; paper cup; green construction paper, approximately 1 m × 1 m; clock or watch with second hand

Time 10 minutes

Tips To intensify the camouflage effect, make sure that the green background closely matches the color of the green peas.

Expected Outcome Students should pick up more yellow peas than green peas from the green background.

Think It Over Being a color that blends in with the environment makes frogs harder for predators to see and thus more likely to survive and reproduce. **learning modality: visual**

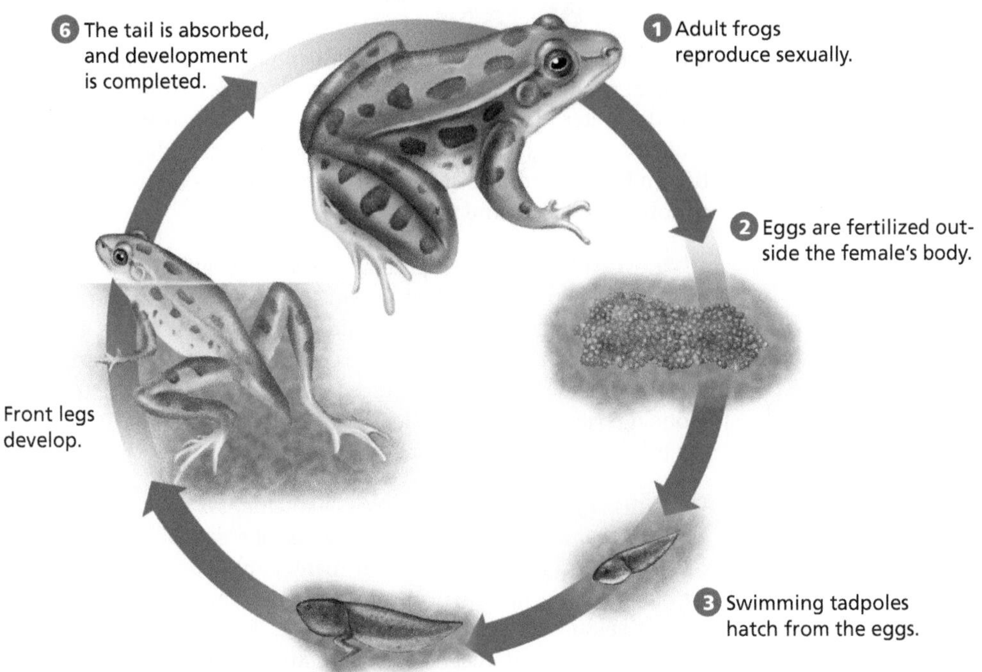
6 The tail is absorbed, and development is completed.
1 Adult frogs reproduce sexually.
2 Eggs are fertilized outside the female's body.
5 Front legs develop.
3 Swimming tadpoles hatch from the eggs.
4 Hind legs develop.

FIGURE 14
Life Cycle of a Frog
During its metamorphosis from tadpole to adult, a frogs body undergoes a series of dramatic changes. **Applying Concepts** *How do these changes prepare a frog for living on land?*

Groups of Amphibians The two major groups of amphibians are salamanders and frogs and toads. You can distinguish between the groups by the presence of a tail in the adults. Salamanders keep their tails in adulthood, while almost all frogs and toads do not.

Reproduction and Development Amphibians have a life cycle that suits the "double lives" they lead. Eggs are fertilized internally in most salamanders and externally in most frogs and toads. Fertilized eggs develop in water. After a few days, larvae wriggle out of a jelly that coats the eggs and begin a free-swimming, fishlike life.

The larvae of most amphibians grow and eventually undergo metamorphosis. You can trace the process of frog metamorphosis in Figure 14. The larva of a frog or a toad is called a **tadpole.**

Unlike tadpoles, the larvae of salamanders look like adults. Most salamander larvae undergo a metamorphosis in which they lose their gills. However, the changes are not as dramatic as those that happen during a frog or toad's metamorphosis.

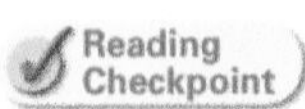
What is a frog larva called?

For: More on the frog life cycle
Visit: PHSchool.com
Web Code: ced-2033

Instruct

What Is an Amphibian?

Teach Key Concepts L2

Exploring Amphibian Development

Focus Tell students that, during their life cycles, amphibians live both on land and in water.

Teach Direct students to Figure 14. Have students trace the stages of development, stating at least one difference between each stage *(Front legs develop, tail disappears, and so on).*

Apply Ask: **Why is water essential for amphibian life?** *(Amphibian eggs are laid and hatched in water; larvae live in water; adults must stay moist to absorb oxygen through their skin.)* **learning modality: visual**

All in One **Teaching Resources**
- Transparency B28

Independent Practice L2

All in One **Teaching Resources**
- Guided Reading and Study Worksheet: *Amphibians*

Student Edition on Audio CD

For: More on the frog life cycle
Visit: PHSchool.com
Web Code: ced-2033

Students can review the frog life cycle in an online activity.

Differentiated Instruction

English Learners/Beginning L1

Use Visuals Point to each part of the cycle in Figure 14, saying the most important terms, e.g., *adult frog, eggs.* Help students understand that the diagram shows a sequence. Then have students write, in their first language, a description of what happens in each part of the cycle. **learning modality: visual**

English Learners/Intermediate L2

Use Visuals Have students extend the beginning activity. After they have written the descriptions in their first language, students can write words and phrases in English that describe each stage. **learning modality: visual**

Monitor Progress L2

Answers

Figure 14 Developing legs and losing the tail allows frogs to move on land.

A tadpole

Living on Land

Teach Key Concepts L2

Comparing Amphibian Adaptations

Focus Ask students to describe some differences between adult frogs and tadpoles.

Teach Write two headings on the board, *Larvae* and *Adults*. Then read characteristics of each aloud. Have students discuss which heading is appropriate for each characteristic. *(Example: Larvae—herbivores, swim, obtain oxygen through gills, have one-loop circulatory system; adults—carnivores, crawl/leap, breathe through lungs, have two-loop circulatory system)*

Apply Ask: **How does acquiring lungs change the life of amphibians?** *(They are able to leave the water, breathe air, and live on land.)* **learning modality: logical/mathematical**

All in One Teaching Resources

- Transparency B29

Address Misconceptions L1

Toads Do Not Cause Warts

Focus Explain that the belief that someone who touches a toad will get warts is merely a superstition.

Teach Ask: **Can you think of any reason why this superstition came about?** *(Toads' skin is bumpy and looks "warty." People assumed that toads' "warts" were contagious.)*

Apply Explain further that although toad skin will not cause warts, it does sometimes secrete substances that can severely irritate skin. Ask: **What adaptation would these secretions offer?** *(Irritation would discourage predators.)* **learning modality: logical/mathematical**

For: Respiration and Circulation activity
Visit: PHSchool.com
Web Code: cep-2032

Students compare and contrast the circulatory systems found in fishes, typical adult amphibians, and birds.

Living on Land

Once an amphibian becomes an adult and moves onto land, its survival needs change. It must now get its oxygen from the air, not the water. Fins no longer help it move. **The respiratory and circulatory systems of adult amphibians are adapted for life on land. In addition, adult amphibians have adaptations for obtaining food and moving.**

Obtaining Oxygen Amphibian larvae use gills to obtain oxygen from the water they live in. During metamorphosis, most amphibians lose their gills and develop lungs. **Lungs** are organs of air-breathing vertebrates in which oxygen gas and carbon dioxide gas are exchanged between the air and the blood. Oxygen and carbon dioxide are also exchanged through the thin, moist skins of adult amphibians.

Circulatory System A tadpole's circulatory system has a single loop and a heart with two chambers, like that of a fish. In contrast, the circulatory system of many adult amphibians has two loops and a heart with three chambers. You can trace the path of blood through an amphibian in Figure 15. The two upper chambers of the heart, called **atria** (singular *atrium*), receive blood. One atrium receives oxygen-rich blood from the lungs, and the other receives oxygen-poor blood from the rest of the body. From the atria, blood moves into the lower chamber, the **ventricle,** which pumps blood out to the lungs and body. Oxygen-rich and oxygen-poor blood mix in the ventricle.

Go Online active art

For: Respiration and Circulation activity
Visit: PHSchool.com
Web Code: cep-2032

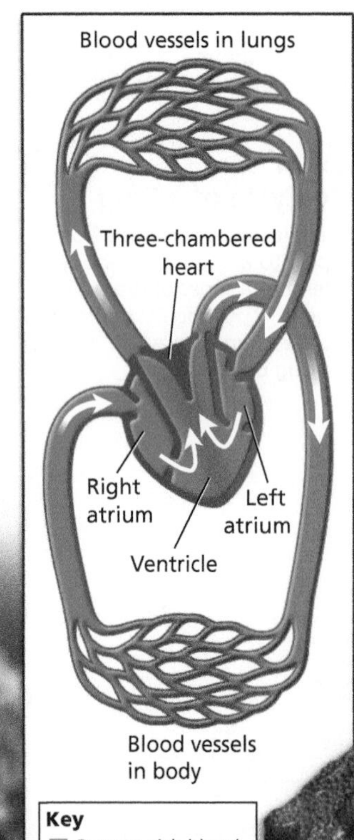

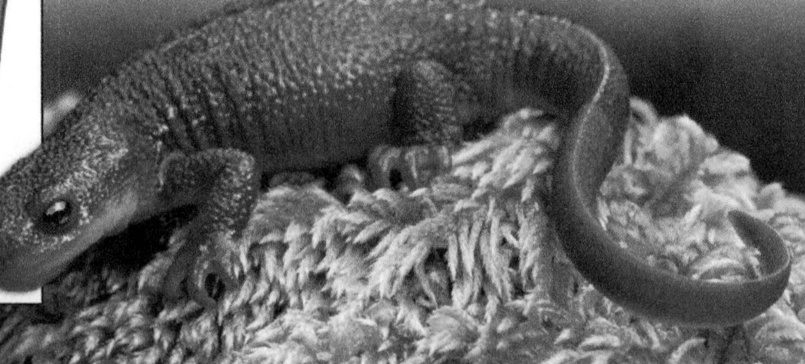

FIGURE 15
Respiration and Circulation
This adult salamander has lungs and a double-loop circulatory system. **Interpreting Diagrams** *What kind of blood is in the ventricle?*

96 ◆ B

FIGURE 16
Adaptations for Movement
Some frogs have sticky pads on their toes for climbing. Others have webbed feet for swimming.

Sticky pads on the toes of this tree-dwelling frog give it a secure foothold as it climbs.

The webbed hind feet of this African clawed frog help it swim through water.

Obtaining Food Although most tadpoles are herbivores, most adult salamanders, frogs, and toads are carnivores that feed on small animals. Frogs and toads usually wait for their prey to come close. But salamanders, unlike frogs and toads, actively stalk and ambush their prey.

Frogs and toads have camouflage that helps them obtain food. Most frogs and toads are brownish-green, making them hard to see in their environment. In the Discover Activity, you learned that it is hard to see something green against a green background.

Movement A vertebrate that lives on land needs a strong skeleton to support its body against the pull of gravity. In addition, a land animal needs some way of moving. Fins work in water, but they don't work on land. Most adult amphibians have strong skeletons and muscular limbs adapted for moving on land.

Salamanders usually crawl in their environments, but frogs and toads have adaptations for other kinds of movements. Perhaps you've tried to catch a frog or a toad only to have it leap away from you. The legs of frogs and toads have adaptations for leaping. Leaping requires powerful hind-leg muscles and a skeleton that can absorb the shock of landing. The feet of frogs and toads have adaptations, too, as you can see in Figure 16.

Lab zone Try This Activity

Webbing Along

1. Fill a sink or pail with water.
2. Spread your fingers and put your hand into the water just far enough so that only your fingers are under water. Drag your fingers back and forth through the water.
3. Now dry your hand and cover it with a small plastic bag. Secure the bag around your wrist with a rubber band.
4. Repeat Step 2. Note any difference in the way in which your fingers push the water.

Making Models Use your model to explain how a frog's webbed feet help it move through water.

Modeling Amphibian Circulation

Materials 25 red balloons

Time 15 minutes

Focus Have students trace the path of blood in Figure 15.

Teach Position students at five stations, representing parts of the circulatory system—lungs, body, right atrium, left atrium, ventricle. Place 25 balloons, representing oxygen, at the lungs station. Slowly clap your hands to indicate heartbeats. At each heartbeat, students change stations in the direction of blood flow. For example, students at the body station will move to the right atrium. Students at the ventricle move to the lungs or back to the body. As students pass the lungs station, they pick up a balloon. At the body station they drop a balloon. A student holding a balloon represents oxygen-rich blood. A student without a balloon represents oxygen-poor blood. Continue for about 4 minutes.

Apply Ask: **Where in an adult amphibian's circulatory system is oxygen acquired?** *(In the lungs and skin)* **Where does the mixing of oxygen-rich and oxygen-poor blood occur?** *(In the ventricle)* **learning modality: kinesthetic**

Lab zone Try This Activity

Skills Focus Making models L1

Materials plastic bags, heavy rubber bands, pail of water or sink

Time 15 minutes

Tips Make sure that students insert only their fingers into the water. No part of their palm should be under water as it will provide too much resistance. Encourage students to experiment with moving their bagged hands through the water with their fingers spread as wide as possible and with their hands balled into a fist.

Extend Ask: **How do some kinds of birds benefit from webbed feet?** *(Because these birds spend some part of their lives in water)* **learning modality: kinesthetic**

Monitor Progress L2

Writing Have students write a brief paragraph comparing and contrasting the characteristics of fishes and adult amphibians. *(Compare: Both lay eggs in water and have internal skeletons, a backbone, and a closed circulatory system. Contrast: Fishes have gills, most adult amphibians have lungs; amphibians have a two-loop circulatory system and fish have one loop.)* Students can save their paragraphs in their portfolios.

Portfolio

Answer

Figure 15 A mixture of oxygen-rich blood and oxygen-poor blood

Monitor Progress L2

Answers

Figure 17 Destruction of habitat and chemicals in the environment

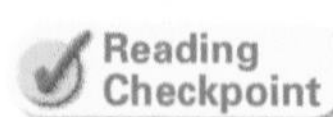
The specific environment in which the animal lives

Assess

Reviewing Key Concepts

1. a. An amphibian is an ectothermic vertebrate that spends its early life in water. **b.** Vertebrate, ectotherm, has double life (in water and on land). **c.** Salamander larvae resemble salamander adults. Larvae lose their gills during metamorphosis, but they do not undergo the dramatic physical changes seen in frog and toad metamorphosis.

2. a. Lungs, two-loop circulatory system and three-chambered heart, camouflage for stalking prey on land, strong skeletons and muscular limbs for movement on land
b. Crawling, leaping, climbing; each adaptation helps amphibian get around on land **c.** Sample answer: Blood leaves the ventricle and travels to the lungs, where it picks up oxygen. Then blood returns to the ventricle via the left atrium. Then it goes to the body and drops off oxygen to the body's cells. Finally, it returns to the ventricle via the right atrium and begins the cycle again.

Reteach L1

Call on students to give one characteristic of amphibians and tell how the characteristic helps the species survive in its environment.

Performance Assessment L2

Organizing Information Have students create a cycle diagram of the life cycle of a frog.

All in One Teaching Resources

- Section Summary: *Amphibians*
- Review and Reinforce: *Amphibians*
- Enrich: *Amphibians*

FIGURE 17
Golden Frog
Golden frogs, like the one shown here, are rarely seen anymore in their native habitat—the rain forests of Panama. Relating Cause and Effect *What are two possible causes for the decrease in the number of golden frogs?*

Amphibians in Danger Worldwide, amphibian populations are decreasing. One reason for the decrease is the destruction of amphibian habitats. An animal's **habitat** is the specific environment in which it lives. When a swamp is filled in or a forest is cut, an area that was moist becomes drier. Few amphibians can survive for long in dry, sunny areas. But habitat destruction does not account for the whole problem of population decrease. Amphibians are declining even in areas where their habitats have not been damaged. Because their skins are delicate and their eggs lack shells, amphibians are especially sensitive to changes in their environment. Poisons in the environment, such as pesticides and other chemicals, can pollute the waters that amphibians need to live and reproduce. Even small amounts of these chemicals can weaken adult amphibians, kill amphibian eggs, or cause tadpoles to become deformed.

What is a habitat?

Section 3 Assessment

Target Reading Skill Sequencing Review your cycle diagram about frog metamorphosis with a partner. Add any necessary information.

Reviewing Key Concepts

1. a. Defining What is an amphibian?
   b. Summarizing What are three main characteristics of amphibians?
   c. Comparing and Contrasting How is the metamorphosis of a salamander different from the metamorphosis of a frog?
2. a. Reviewing What are four adaptations of adult amphibians for living on land?
   b. Describing What are three adaptations frogs and toads have for moving? How does each adaptation help the amphibian survive in its environment?
   c. Sequencing How does blood move in the circulatory system of an amphibian? (*Hint:* Start with blood leaving the ventricle of the heart.)

Writing in Science

Web Site Design the home page of a Web site that introduces people to amphibians. First, come up with a catchy title for your Web site. Then, design your home page, the first page people will see. Consider these questions as you come up with your design: What information will you include? What will the illustrations or photos show? What links to specific topics relating to amphibians will you have?

Chapter Project

Keep Students on Track Review students' amphibian choices for appropriateness. Before students begin work on their amphibian models, review their fish models. Discuss with students ways in which amphibians differ from fish and how these differences will be reflected in their amphibian model.

Writing in Science

Design a Web Site Before students create their Web sites, choose good examples of professional Web sites for them to view. Have them discuss what makes the Web sites interesting to look at and easy to use.

Section 4 Reptiles

Reading Preview

Key Concepts

- What are some adaptations that allow reptiles to live on land?
- What are the characteristics of each of the three main groups of reptiles?
- What adaptation helped dinosaurs survive before they became extinct?

Key Terms

- reptile
- kidney
- urine
- amniotic egg

Target Reading Skill

Identifying Main Ideas As you read the information under the heading titled Adaptations for Life on Land, write the main idea in a graphic organizer like the one below. Then write three supporting details that give examples of the main idea.

Main Idea

Reptiles are adapted to conserve water.

Detail | Detail | Detail

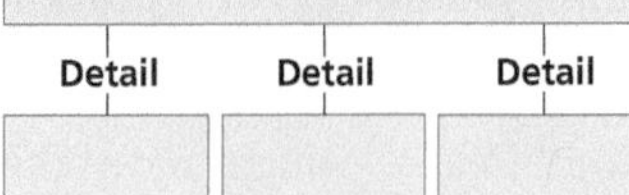

Lab zone Discover Activity

How Do Snakes Feed?

1. To model how a snake feeds, stretch a sock cuff over a grapefruit "prey" by first pulling on one side and then on the other. Work the grapefruit down into the "stomach." A snake's jawbones can spread apart like the sock cuff.
2. Remove the grapefruit and put a rubber band around the sock about 8 centimeters below the opening. The rubber band represents the firmly joined jawbones of a lizard. Now try to repeat Step 1.

Think It Over
Inferring What is the advantage of having jawbones like a snake's?

The king cobra of Southeast Asia is the world's longest venomous snake. It can grow to more than 4 meters long. When it encounters a predator, a king cobra flattens its neck and rears up. Its ropelike body sways back and forth, and its tongue flicks in and out.

A king cobra's fearsome behavior in response to a predator contrasts with the gentle way it treats its eggs. King cobras are one of the few snakes that build nests. The female builds a nest of grass and leaves on the forest floor. She lays her eggs inside the nest and guards them until they hatch.

King cobra ▶

Lab zone Discover Activity

Skills Focus Inferring

Materials sock with ribbed cuff, grapefruit, strong rubber band

Time 10 minutes

Tips Students can compare estimated diameters of the unstretched sock and the grapefruit. During Step 2, use a rubber band that is too small to fit around the grapefruit. Reinforce the lesson by showing students a picture of a snake skull, pointing out the lack of large regions of solid bone. L1

Think It Over Students should infer that the spreading jawbones of the snake allow it to eat larger prey than would be possible with firmly joined jawbones.

Section 4 Reptiles

Objectives

After completing the lesson, students will be able to

B.3.4.1 Identify adaptations that allow reptiles to live on land.

B.3.4.2 Contrast the characteristics of each of the three main groups of reptiles.

B.3.4.3 Describe one adaptation that helped dinosaurs survive before they became extinct.

Target Reading Skill

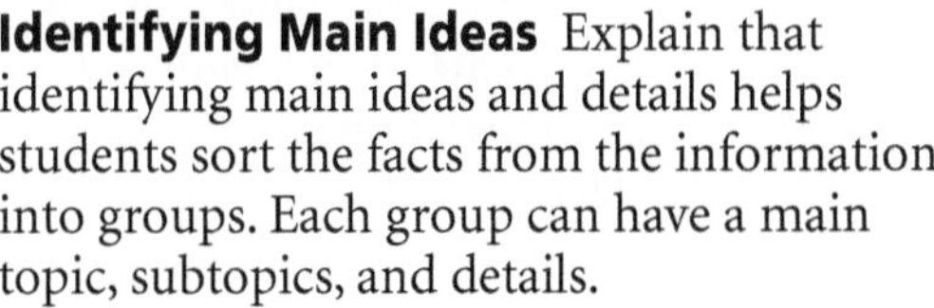

Identifying Main Ideas Explain that identifying main ideas and details helps students sort the facts from the information into groups. Each group can have a main topic, subtopics, and details.

Answers

Possible answers:

Main idea—Reptiles are adapted to conserve water.

Details—Reptiles have a thick, scaly skin that prevents water loss; reptile eggs have a shell and membranes that keep them from drying out; reptile's kidneys concentrate wastes before excreting them so that little water is lost.

All in One Teaching Resources

- Transparency B30

Preteach

Build Background Knowledge L2

Considering Snake Characteristics

Ask: **What are some characteristics of snakes?** *(Students may say no legs, poisonous, or fangs)* List students' answers on the board. After students have become familiar with the information in the section, revisit this list. Help students to decide which of the characteristics are facts, which are true of some snakes, and which are myths.

Instruct

Adaptations for Life on Land

Teach Key Concepts L2

Investigating Reptilian Adaptations

Focus Tell students that land animals are adapted to environmental conditions that differ from those of aquatic animals.

Teach Call on student volunteers to discuss how reptilian adaptations differ from those of amphibians. Ask: **How do the two groups differ in egg laying?** *(Reptiles lay eggs on land that are protected from drying out; amphibians lay eggs in water.)* **How and why are their skins different?** *(Amphibian skins are moist, because amphibians obtain oxygen through the skin; reptilian skins are dry and scaly—reptiles breathe solely with lungs—and are able to prevent water loss.)*

Apply Ask: **Do sea turtles have amphibian or reptilian adaptations?** *(Reptilian: sea turtles breathe with lungs and lay eggs out of water.)* **learning modality: verbal**

All in One Teaching Resources

- Transparency B31

Independent Practice L2

All in One Teaching Resources

- Guided Reading and Study Worksheet: *Reptiles*

For: More on reptiles
Visit: PHSchool.com
Web Code: ced-2034

Students can review reptiles in an online activity.

FIGURE 18
A Desert Tortoise
The tough, scaly skin of this desert tortoise helps it survive in a dry environment.

Adaptations for Life on Land

Like other reptiles, king cobras lay their eggs on land rather than in water. A **reptile** is an ectothermic vertebrate that has lungs and scaly skin. In addition to snakes such as the king cobra, lizards, turtles, and alligators are also reptiles. Unlike amphibians, reptiles can spend their entire lives on dry land.

The ancestors of modern reptiles were the first vertebrates adapted to life completely out of water. Reptiles get their oxygen from air and breathe entirely with lungs. Reptiles that live in water, such as sea turtles, evolved from reptiles that lived on land. So, even though they live in water, they still breathe with lungs and come ashore to lay eggs.

You can think of a land animal as a pocket of water held within a bag of skin. To thrive on land, an animal must have adaptations that keep the water within the "bag" from evaporating in the dry air. **The skin, kidneys, and eggs of reptiles are adapted to conserve water.**

Skin and Kidneys Unlike amphibians, which have thin, moist skin, reptiles have dry, tough skins covered with scales. This scaly skin protects reptiles and helps keep water in their bodies. Another adaptation that helps keep water inside a reptile's body is its **kidneys,** which are organs that filter wastes from the blood. The wastes are then excreted in a watery fluid called **urine.** The kidneys of reptiles concentrate the urine so that the reptiles lose very little water.

Reading Checkpoint What are two functions of a reptile's skin?

For: More on reptiles
Visit: PHSchool.com
Web Code: ced-2034

An Egg With a Shell Reptiles have internal fertilization and lay their eggs on land. While still inside a female's body, fertilized eggs are covered with membranes and a leathery shell. Unlike an amphibian's egg, a reptile's egg has a shell and membranes that protect the developing embryo and help keep it from drying out. An egg with a shell and internal membranes that keep the embryo moist is called an **amniotic egg.** Pores in the shell let oxygen gas in and carbon dioxide gas out.

Look at Figure 19 to see the membranes of a reptile's egg. One membrane holds a liquid that surrounds the embryo. The liquid protects the embryo and keeps it moist. A second membrane holds the yolk, or food for the embryo. A third membrane holds the embryo's wastes. Oxygen and carbon dioxide are exchanged across the fourth membrane.

FIGURE 19

The Amniotic Egg

The membranes and shell of an amniotic egg protect the developing embryo. Relating Cause and Effect *Which parts of an amniotic egg help keep the embryo from drying out?*

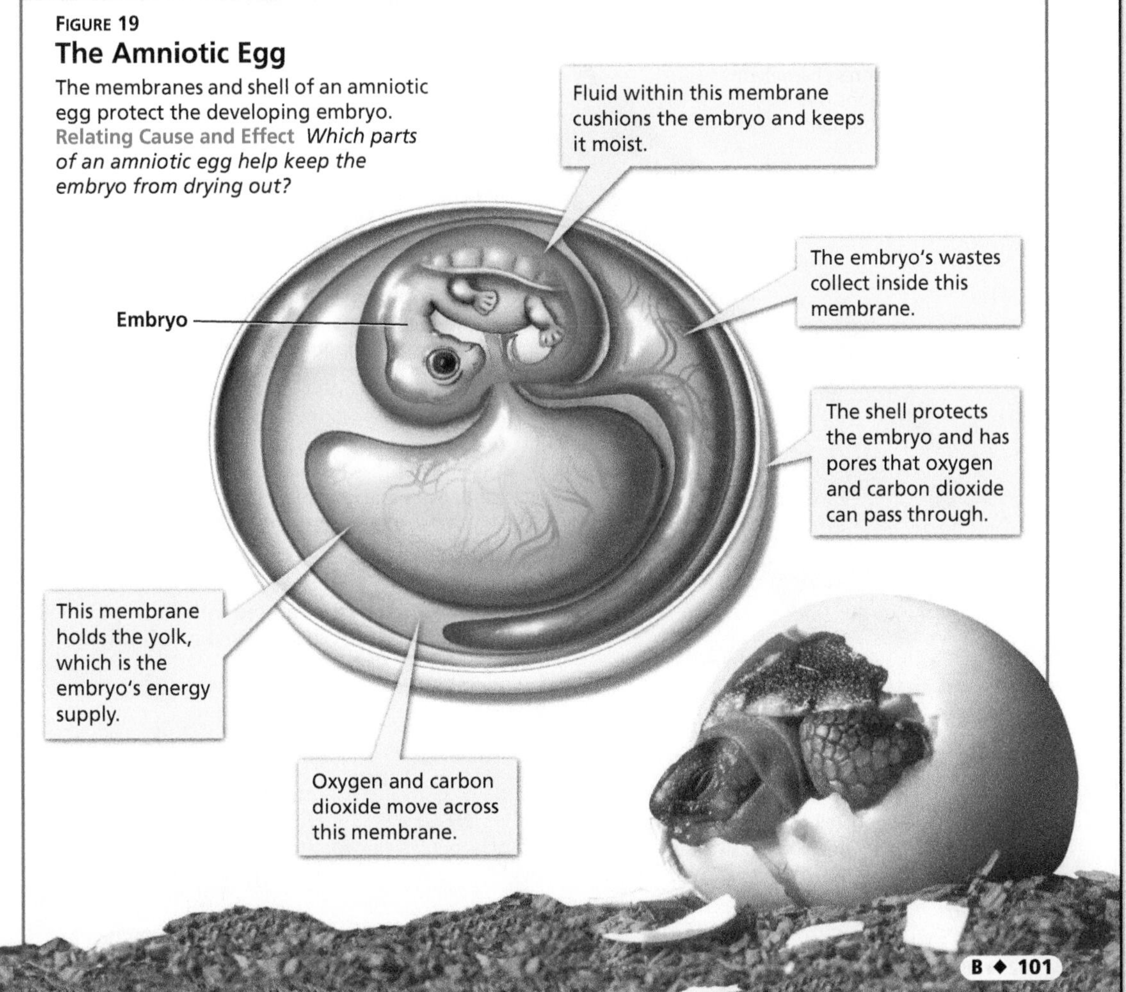
Fluid within this membrane cushions the embryo and keeps it moist.
Embryo
The embryo's wastes collect inside this membrane.
The shell protects the embryo and has pores that oxygen and carbon dioxide can pass through.
This membrane holds the yolk, which is the embryo's energy supply.
Oxygen and carbon dioxide move across this membrane.
B ◆ 101

Lab zone Build Inquiry L1

Making Inferences About Eggshells

Materials small, cut pieces of a sponge; plastic bag; water

Time 10 minutes over two class periods

Focus Challenge students to make inferences about how eggshells and membranes prevent fluid loss.

Teach Have students work in small groups; provide each group with two pieces of sponge and one resealable plastic bag that will model an egg's shell and membranes. Have students wet both sponge pieces thoroughly. Then put one piece in the plastic bag. They should place the other piece of sponge on top of the sealed bag and leave it overnight. The next day, ask students to describe the condition of their sponges. *(The sponge outside the bag is much drier and more rigid.)*

Apply Lead students to infer that the condition of the sponges left outside the bag is similar to what would happen to a developing embryo if the egg did not have a shell and membranes that retain moisture. **learning modality: visual**

Student Edition on Audio CD

Address Misconceptions

Investigating Snake Skin

Focus Snake skins are dry, not slimy.

Teach Some students may think snake skins are slimy. A snake's skin is actually quite dry, especially compared to that of a fish or amphibian. Under supervision, you may allow students to touch the scales of a molted snake skin. They should wash their hands afterward.

Monitor Progress L2

Skills Check Using Figure 19, point out the membranes of a tortoise egg and call on students to tell the function of each.

Answers

Figure 19 Shell; fluid within the membrane surrounding the embryo

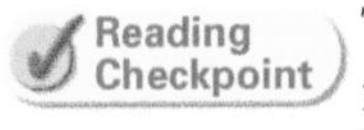
Reading Checkpoint: The scaly skin protects the reptile and prevents water loss.

Lizards and Snakes

Teach Key Concepts L2

Characteristics of Lizards and Snakes

Focus Direct students to Figure 20.

Teach Ask: **What are the chameleon's adaptations that make it a successful predator?** *(Sticky tongue that moves rapidly, claws that allow movement up trees, tail that grips, eyes that swivel, skin that changes color to match background)* **How is the chameleon's skin like that of all reptiles? Why is it like this?** *(Dry and scaly, to prevent water loss)* **Name two ways lizards differ from snakes.** *(Lizards have four legs, moveable eyelids, and two lungs; snakes have no legs or eyelids and only one lung.)*

Apply Ask: **What is the term for animals with a diet similar to most reptiles?** *(Carnivores)* **Besides assisting in obtaining food, what other benefit does the ability to blend into its surroundings offer a chameleon?** *(Makes it easier for chameleons to hide from their own predators)* **learning modality: visual**

Address Misconceptions L1

Investigating Venomous Snakes

Focus Tell students that venomous snakes are not necessarily aggressive.

Teach Students may mistakenly believe that venomous snakes are vicious and aggressive. Point out that although people rightly fear being bitten by venomous snakes, the most venomous snakes are not aggressive toward humans. Normally, they will bite a person only when cornered or startled. Snake venom is primarily an adaptation for capturing prey, not for defense.

Apply Ask: **If you do not know whether a snake you see is venomous, what should you do when you come upon it?** *(Possible answer: Move away in a nonthreatening manner.)* **learning modality: verbal**

Lizards and Snakes

Most reptiles alive today are either lizards or snakes. These two groups of reptiles share some important characteristics. **Both lizards and snakes are reptiles that have skin covered with overlapping scales.** As they grow, they shed their skin and scales, replacing the worn ones with new ones. Most lizards and snakes live in warm areas.

Lizards differ from snakes in an obvious way. Lizards have four legs, usually with claws on the toes, and snakes have no legs. In addition, lizards have long tails, external ears, movable eyelids, and two lungs. In contrast, snakes have streamlined bodies, no external ears, and no eyelids, and most have only one lung. You can see the characteristics of a lizard in Figure 20.

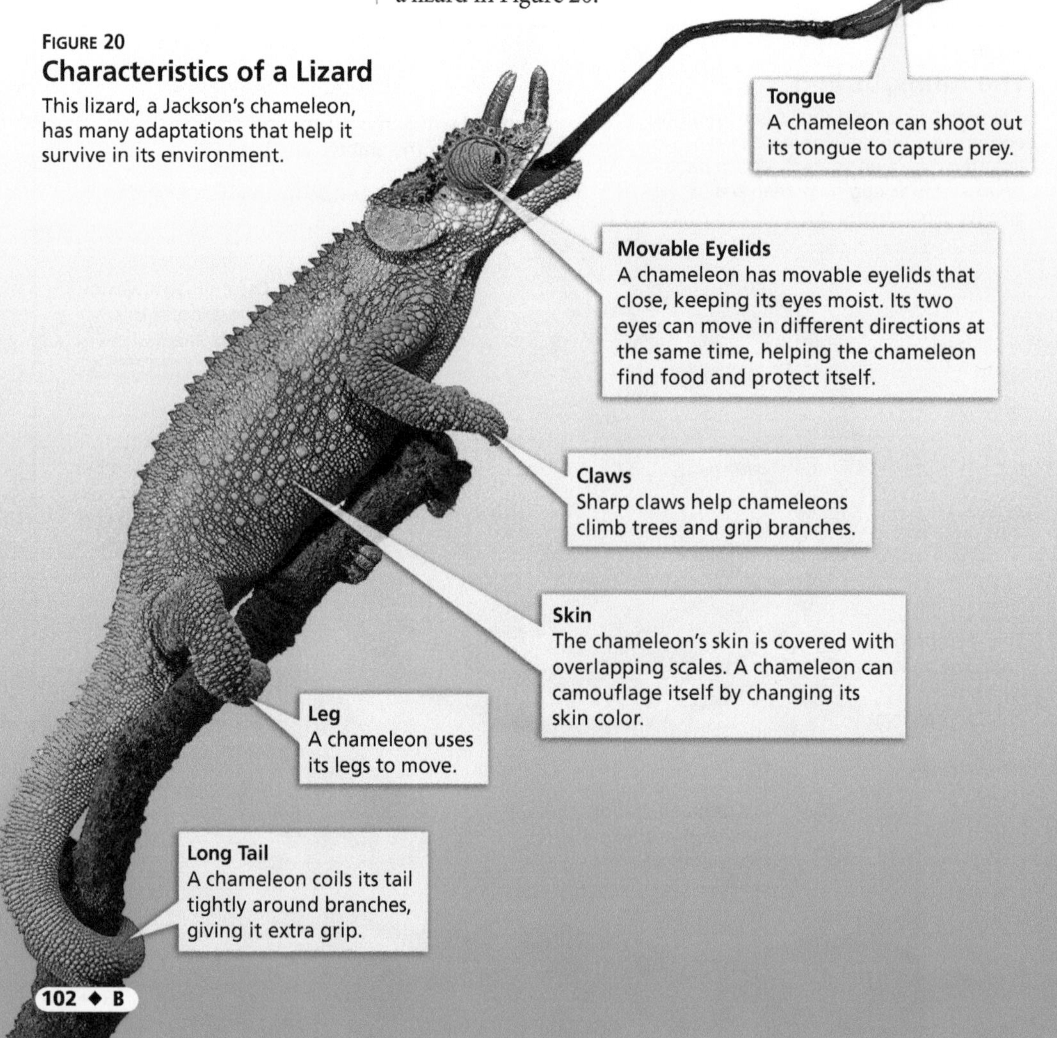

Tongue
A chameleon can shoot out its tongue to capture prey.
Movable Eyelids
A chameleon has movable eyelids that close, keeping its eyes moist. Its two eyes can move in different directions at the same time, helping the chameleon find food and protect itself.
Claws
Sharp claws help chameleons climb trees and grip branches.
Skin
The chameleon's skin is covered with overlapping scales. A chameleon can camouflage itself by changing its skin color.
Leg
A chameleon uses its legs to move.
Long Tail
A chameleon coils its tail tightly around branches, giving it extra grip.

FIGURE 20
Characteristics of a Lizard
This lizard, a Jackson's chameleon, has many adaptations that help it survive in its environment.

FIGURE 21
An Egg-Eating Snake
The jawbones of this snake's skull have moved to let the snake swallow an egg. Making Generalizations *How are snakes different from lizards?*

Obtaining Food A few lizards are herbivores that eat leaves. Most lizards, however, are carnivores that capture their prey by jumping at it. While some large lizards will eat frogs and birds, most smaller lizards are adapted to hunt insects. For example, chameleons have sticky tongues adapted for snaring insects.

All snakes are carnivores. Most snakes feed on small animals, such as mice, but some eat large prey. If you did the Discover Activity, you learned that a snake's jawbones can spread wide apart. In addition, the bones of a snake's skull can move to let the snake swallow an animal larger in diameter than itself. Snakes capture their prey in different ways. For example, some snakes have long, curved front teeth for hooking slippery prey. Other snakes, such as rattlesnakes and copperheads, have venom glands attached to hollow teeth called fangs. When these snakes bite their prey, venom flows down through the fangs and enters the prey.

Movement While lizards walk and run using their legs, snakes cannot move in this way. If you've ever seen a snake slither across the ground, you know that when it moves, its long, thin body bends into curves. Snakes move by contracting, or shortening, bands of muscles that are connected to their ribs and their backbones. Alternate contractions of muscles on the right and left sides produce a slithering side-to-side motion. Instead of slithering, sidewinder snakes, like the one shown in Figure 22, lift up their bodies as they move.

How do lizards move?

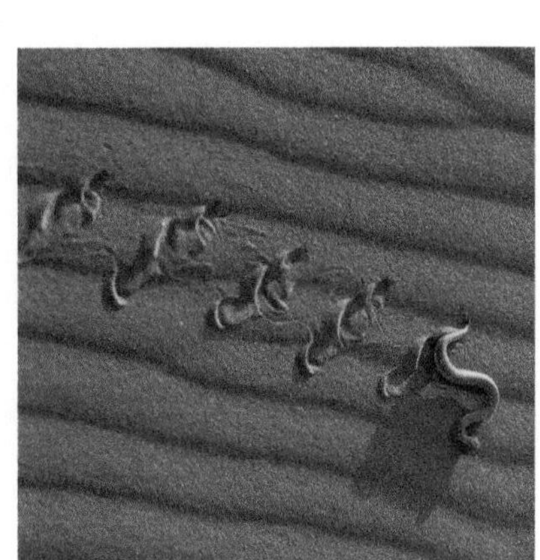

FIGURE 22
A Sidewinder Snake
This sidewinder snake lifts loops of its body off the desert sand as it moves along. Only a small part of its body touches the sand at one time.

Lab zone Build Inquiry L1

Gaining a Closer Perspective on Snakes

Materials live snake(s), skilled handler(s)

Time 40 minutes

Focus Arrange a presentation in which students can "meet a snake," either by taking students to a zoo, or by inviting a guest presenter to your class.

Teach Have students write a checklist of key features to observe. If possible, arrange for students to observe the movement of snakes across a variety of surfaces. Refer to Enrich: *Reptiles* in Teaching Resources for information on various types of snake movement. Ask students to describe the kinds of movement they observe. Some students may be fearful of snakes; allow fearful students to observe from a distance. Make sure the snakes are from nonvenomous and nonaggressive species. Garter and grass snakes are common and can be easily and safely handled.

Apply Ask: **Besides its movement, what snake or reptilian characteristics do you observe in the snake?** *(No legs, no eyelids, scaly skin.)* **learning modality: visual**

Differentiated Instruction

Gifted and Talented L3

Describing Reptiles Challenge students to create a crossword puzzle with answers gained from the figures and text covered under the *Lizards and Snakes* heading. *(Example: A chameleon catches prey on the ______ tip of its tongue [sticky].)* **learning modality: logical/mathematical**

Less Proficient Readers L1

Identifying Reptile Facts Pair up students needing help reading the section on reptiles with the Gifted and Talented students completing the crossword exercise. Have each of the less proficient readers review the text and figure descriptions to locate answers to their partners' crossword puzzle. **learning modality: visual**

Monitor Progress L2

Writing Ask students to write a paragraph that describes how snakes move. Students can save their paragraphs in their portfolios. Portfolio

Answers

Figure 21 Lizards—four legs, some are herbivores, all have two lungs and movable eyelids; Snakes—no legs, all are carnivores, most have only one lung, no eyelids.

They walk and run using their legs.

Alligators and Crocodiles

Teach Key Concepts L2

Investigating Large Reptilian Predators

Focus Tell students that alligators and crocodiles are known for their size, predator skills, and care of their young.

Teach Pace off 5 meters in your classroom to demonstrate to students the size of the largest alligators and crocodiles. Ask: **What traits make these animals successful predators?** *(Hunting at night when they are concealed, strong tail for rapid swimming, muscular jaws, many sharp teeth)*

Apply Ask: **Can you think of other vertebrate predators that share some of the alligator's and crocodile's traits?** *(Sharks are strong, fast, and large, have pointed teeth, and eat large prey; frogs and lizards sneak up on prey.)* **learning modality: verbal**

Turtles

Teach Key Concepts L2

Exploring Adaptations of Turtles

Focus Remind students that a turtle is a reptile.

Teach Ask: **Where do turtles live?** *(On land [tortoises] and in salt and fresh water)* **Do sea turtles have gills?** *(No, all turtles breathe with lungs.)* **What is a turtle shell made from?** *(The ribs and backbone)* **Without teeth, how do turtles feed?** *(Their sharp beaks tear food.)*

Apply Ask: **Do you think land turtles move quickly?** *(No)* **Then how do they escape predators?** *(By drawing into their protective shells)* **learning modality: verbal**

FIGURE 23
Alligator and Crocodile
Alligators and crocodiles are the largest reptiles still living on earth. They are similar in many ways, including appearance.
Comparing and Contrasting *How can you tell the difference between an alligator and a crocodile?*

Alligators and Crocodiles

If you walk along a lake in Florida, you just might see an alligator swimming silently in the water. Most of its body lies beneath the surface, but you can see its large, bulging eyes above the surface. Alligators, crocodiles, and their relatives are the largest living reptiles. **Both alligators and crocodiles are large, carnivorous reptiles that care for their young.** So, how do you tell an alligator from a crocodile? Alligators have broad, rounded snouts, with only a few teeth visible when their mouths are shut. In contrast, crocodiles have pointed snouts, with most of their teeth visible when their mouths are shut.

Obtaining Food Alligators and crocodiles are carnivores that often hunt at night. They have several adaptations for capturing prey. They use their strong, muscular tails to swim rapidly. Their jaws are equipped with many large, sharp, and pointed teeth. Their jaw muscles are extremely strong when biting down. Although alligators will eat dogs, raccoons, and deer, they usually do not attack humans.

Reproduction Unlike most other reptiles, crocodiles and alligators care for their eggs and newly hatched young. After laying eggs, the female stays near the nest. From time to time, she comes out of the water and crawls over the nest to keep it moist. After the tiny alligators or crocodiles hatch, the female scoops them up in her huge mouth. She carries them from the nest to a nursery area in the water where they will be safer. For as long as a year, she will stay near her young until they can feed and protect themselves.

When do alligators and crocodiles hunt?

Discovery
CHANNEL
SCHOOL
Fishes, Amphibians, and Reptiles
Video Preview
▶Video Field Trip
Video Assessment

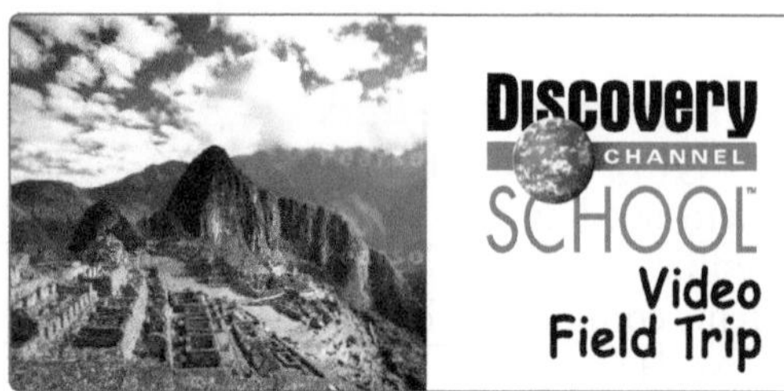

Fishes, Amphibians, and Reptiles

Show the Video Field Trip to help students understand reptile adaptations. Discussion question: **Describe two adaptations that allow crocodiles to remain underwater for long periods of time.** *(Their heart rates slow down; some of the valves that control blood flow close. This diverts blood away from the lungs, where it isn't needed and sends it to the brain and other organs where the blood is essential.)*

Math Analyzing Data

The Sex Ratio of Newly Hatched Alligators

The temperature of the developing eggs of the American alligator affects the sex ratio of the young. (Sex ratio is the number of females compared with the number of males.) The graph on the right shows the numbers of young of each sex that hatched from eggs in which the young developed at different temperatures.

Sex Ratio of Newly Hatched Alligators

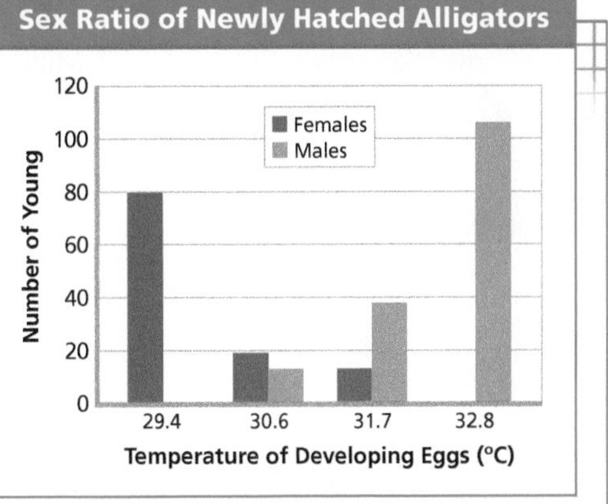

1. Reading Graphs At which temperature(s) did only females hatch?
2. Drawing Conclusions What effect does the temperature of developing eggs have on the sex of the baby alligators?
3. Calculating If 100 eggs developed at 31.7°C, about how many of the young would be male?

Turtles

Turtles live in the ocean, in fresh water, and on land. Turtles that live on land are commonly called "tortoises." **A turtle is a reptile whose body is covered by a protective shell that includes the ribs and the backbone.** The bony plates of the shell are covered by large scales made from the same material as the skin's scales. Some turtles have shells that are large enough to cover the whole body. A box turtle, for example, can draw its head, legs, and tail inside its shell for protection. Other turtles, like the snapping turtle, have much smaller shells. Turtle shells may be hard or as soft as pancakes.

Turtles feed in a variety of ways, but all have a sharp-edged beak instead of teeth for tearing food. Some turtles are carnivores, such as the largest turtles, the leatherbacks. Leatherbacks feed mainly on jellyfishes. Their tough skin protects them from the effects of the stinging cells. Other turtles, such as the Galápagos tortoise, are herbivores. They feed mainly on cacti, using their beaks to scrape off the prickly spines before swallowing the cactus.

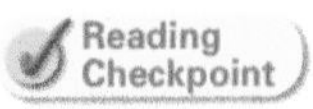

Reading Checkpoint **What are turtles that live on land called?**

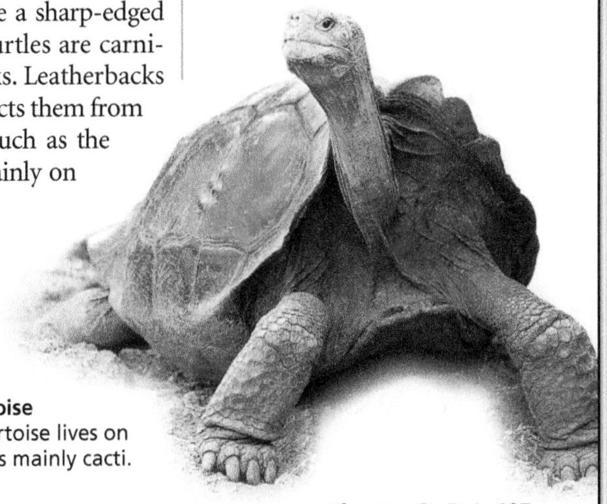

FIGURE 24
A Galápagos Tortoise
The Galápagos tortoise lives on land, where it eats mainly cacti.

Lab zone Teacher Demo

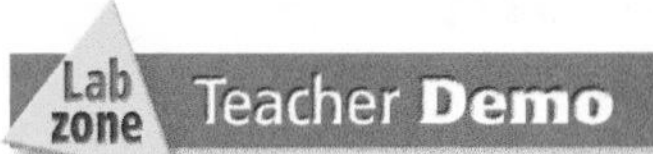

L1

Turtle Breathing

Materials live turtle, such as a box turtle

Time 5 minutes

Focus Challenge students to consider adaptations turtles have for breathing within the confines of a shell.

Teach Ask: **How does your chest move when you breathe?** *(In and out)* **If the turtle's chest moves like yours does, does its shell get in the way?** *(Yes)* Allow students to carefully observe the turtle as it breathes. Students should notice that the exposed soft tissue around the turtle's forelimbs and hind limbs moves.

Apply Ask: **What replaces the in-and-out motion of chests of vertebrates without shells?** *(The front-and-back motion of tissue around limbs)* **learning modality: visual**

Math Analyzing Data

Math Skill Making and interpreting graphs

Focus Compare bar graphs to determine the effect of incubation temperature on the sex of baby alligators.

Teach Make sure students understand that the answer to Question 2 is based on the ratio of males to females in the groups of eggs, not the absolute number.

Answers

1. 29.4°C
2. The warmer the incubation temperature, the greater the proportion of males.
3. According to the graph, out of the 50 alligators that were incubated at 31.7°C, 38 (or 76%) were males. So, I would expect about 76% of 100 eggs (76) to be males.

Monitor Progress

L2

Writing Have students compare the beaks of leatherback sea turtles with the teeth of alligators and crocodiles. Have them tell how each adaptation contributes to the animals' ability to successfully acquire food. Students can save their paragraphs in their portfolios.

Portfolio

Answers

Figure 23 An alligator has a broad rounded snout, and few of its teeth are visible when its mouth is shut. A crocodile has a pointed snout, and most of its teeth are visible when its mouth is shut.

Reading Checkpoint They hunt at night.

Reading Checkpoint Tortoises

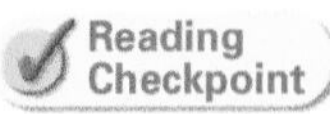

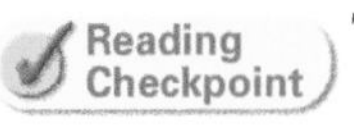

Extinct Reptiles—The Dinosaurs

Teach Key Concepts L2

Investigating Dinosaurs

Focus Review with students the meaning of the term *extinct.*

Teach Explain that before dinosaurs died out 65 million years ago, they occupied many of the habitats and played many of the roles of modern vertebrates. Ask: **What type of vertebrates are dinosaurs?** *(Reptiles)*

Apply Ask: **How were dinosaurs unlike modern reptiles?** *(Some were much larger; they might have been endothermic)* **learning modality: verbal**

Monitor Progress L2

Answers

Figure 25 Sample answer: The long neck may have allowed *Brachiosaurus,* which was a herbivore, to reach the leaves on tall trees.

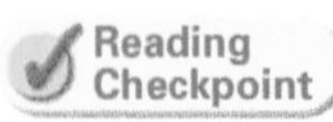
Tyrannosaurus rex

FIGURE 25
Brachiosaurus
Brachiosaurus grew to be more than 22.5 meters long—longer than two school buses put together end to end. Inferring *What advantage did a long neck give* Brachiosaurus*?*

Extinct Reptiles—The Dinosaurs

Millions of years ago, huge turtles and fish-eating reptiles swam in the oceans. Flying reptiles soared through the skies. Snakes and lizards basked on warm rocks. And there were dinosaurs of every description. Unlike today's reptiles, some dinosaurs may have been endothermic. Some dinosaurs, such as *Brachiosaurus* in Figure 25, were the largest land animals that ever lived.

Dinosaurs were the earliest vertebrates that had legs positioned directly beneath their bodies. This adaptation allowed them to move more easily than animals such as salamanders and lizards, whose legs stick out from the sides of their bodies. Most herbivorous dinosaurs, such as *Brachiosaurus,* walked on four legs. Most carnivores, such as the huge *Tyrannosaurus rex,* ran on two legs.

Dinosaurs became extinct, or disappeared from Earth, about 65 million years ago. No one is certain why. Today, it's only in movies that dinosaurs shake the ground with their footsteps. But the descendants of dinosaurs may still exist. Some biologists think that birds descended from certain small dinosaurs.

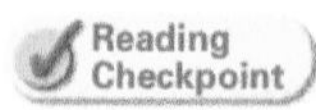
Give an example of a dinosaur that ran on two legs.

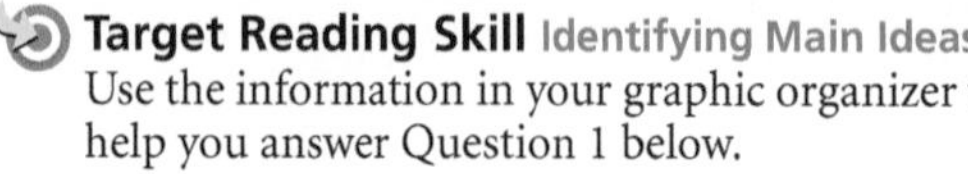

Section 4 Assessment

Target Reading Skill Identifying Main Ideas Use the information in your graphic organizer to help you answer Question 1 below.

Reviewing Key Concepts

1. a. Defining What is a reptile?
   b. Explaining What are three adaptations that allow reptiles to survive on land?
   c. Predicting What might happen to a reptile egg if part of its shell were removed?
2. a. Identifying What are the three main groups of reptiles?
   b. Classifying A gecko is a small reptile that has no shell protecting its body. It uses its legs to climb trees. Into which reptile group would you classify the gecko?
   c. Comparing and Contrasting Compare and contrast how alligators and turtles obtain food.
3. a. Reviewing When did the dinosaurs become extinct?
   b. Interpreting Diagrams What adaptation did the dinosaur in Figure 25 have that helped it survive?
   c. Inferring What advantage might a dinosaur that was an endotherm have had over other reptiles?

Writing in Science

Product Label Write a "packaging label" that will be pasted onto the eggshell of a reptile. Include on your label a list of the contents of the shell and a one-paragraph description of the egg's ability to survive in a dry environment.

Assess

Reviewing Key Concepts

1. a. Reptiles are ectothermic vertebrates with scaly skin that lay their eggs on land. **b.** Dry, scaly skin; amniotic egg; kidneys that concentrate urine **c.** It would dry out.
2. a. Lizards and snakes, alligators and crocodiles, turtles **b.** Lizards **c.** Alligators are carnivores that hunt at night, swimming rapidly towards prey and clamping down on prey with their huge, muscular jaws. Turtles are either herbivores or carnivores that use their beaks to scrape and tear their food.
3. a. 65 million years ago **b.** *Brachiosaurus,* like other dinosaurs, had legs positioned directly under its body, which allowed it to move more easily than other reptiles. **c.** Sample answer: It could have been more active at night and in colder climates.

Reteach L1

Call on students to describe the features of one of the three main groups of reptiles.

All in One Teaching Resources

- Section Summary: *Reptiles*
- Review and Reinforce: *Reptiles*
- Enrich: *Reptiles*

Lab zone Chapter Project

Keep Students on Track Check that students have chosen appropriate and safe materials for building their reptile model. Be sure that students are modeling the same adaptation in all three models.

Writing in Science

Writing Mode Exposition How-To

Scoring Rubric

4 Includes an accurate, detailed description; writing is clear
3 Includes accurate description; clear writing
2 Includes accurate description; unclear writing
1 Description is inaccurate and unclear

Section 5 Integrating Earth Science

Vertebrate History in Rocks

Reading Preview

Key Concepts

- Where are fossils most frequently found?
- What can scientists learn from studying fossils?

Key Terms

- fossil • sedimentary rock
- paleontologist

Target Reading Skill

Asking Questions Before you read, preview the red headings. In a graphic organizer like the one below, ask *what* and *how* questions for each heading. As you read, write the answers to your questions.

Vertebrate History in Rocks

Question	Answer
How do fossils form?	Fossils form by . . .

Lab zone Discover Activity

What Can You Tell From an Imprint?

1. Flatten some modeling clay into a thin sheet on a piece of paper.
2. Firmly press two or three small objects into different areas of the clay. The objects might include such things as a key, a feather, a postage stamp, or a flower. Don't let anyone see the objects you are using.
3. Carefully remove the objects from the clay, leaving only the objects' imprints.
4. Exchange your imprints with a partner. Try to identify the objects that made the imprints.

Think It Over

Observing What types of objects made the clearest imprints? If those imprints were fossils, what could you learn about the objects by looking at their "fossils"? What couldn't you learn?

Millions of years ago, in an ancient pond, some fishes died and their bodies settled into the mud on the bottom. Soon heavy rains fell, and more mud washed into the pond, covering the fishes. The soft tissues of the fishes decayed, but their bones remained. After many thousands of years, the mud hardened into rock, and the bones became the fossils shown here.

Fossilized fishes ▶

B ◆ 107

Section 5

Vertebrate History in Rocks

Objectives

After completing the lesson, students will be able to

B.3.5.1 Identify the kind of rock in which fossils are frequently found.

B.3.5.2 Describe what scientists can learn from studying fossils.

Target Reading Skill

Asking Questions Explain that changing a head into a question helps students anticipate the ideas, facts, and events they are going to read about.

Answers

Students' questions and answers might include: **How do fossils form?** *(Fossils form from imprints or the remains of organisms.)* **How are fossils interpreted?** *(Scientists examine fossil structure and make comparisons to present-day organisms.)*

All in One Teaching Resources

- Transparency B32

Preteach

Build Background Knowledge

L2

Identifying Fossils

Distribute some fossils. Ask: **What do you think made the patterns you see in the rocks?** *(Students may infer that the patterns are the remains or traces of dead animals or plants that lived long ago.)* **What can you infer about the organism that made the imprint and where it lived? Does it resemble any living organism that you know?** *(Answers will vary.)* Have students write brief descriptions of the fossils.

Lab zone Discover Activity

Skills Focus Observing L1

Materials modeling clay; paper; small objects of various textures and degrees of rigidity

Time 15 minutes

Tips Each student should use some objects that will make a clear impression, such as coins, and some that will not, such as feathers.

Expected Outcome Harder objects, such as a key, will be easiest to identify. Imprints of soft objects with recognizable outlines, such as a leaf, will also be easy to recognize.

Think It Over The objects that made the clearest imprints were firm and had distinct borders. If the imprints were fossils, you could learn the size and shape of the object that made them. You could not learn what was inside the object or organism, what it ate, or why it died.

Instruct

What Are Fossils?

Teach Key Concepts L2

Describing Types of Fossils

Focus Ask students to describe any fossils or pictures of fossils they have seen.

Teach Ask: **What chemical process is involved in forming fossils?** *(Tissues are replaced by minerals.)* **What is sedimentary rock?** *(Rock made from layers of sediment)*

Apply Ask: **Why aren't more organisms found as fossils?** *(Tissues of organisms decay rapidly, so they must be trapped quickly in appropriate conditions to be fossilized.)* **learning modality: verbal**

Independent Practice L2

All in One Teaching Resources

- Guided Reading and Study Worksheet: *Vertebrate History in Rocks*

Student Edition on Audio CD

Lab zone Build Inquiry L2

Calculating Sedimentary Rock Depths

Materials calculator

Time 10 minutes

Focus Explain that sedimentary rock is deposited slowly but can eventually be thousands of meters thick.

Teach Give an example of a thick sedimentary deposit: Part of the Florida peninsula consists of limestone deposits more than 4,000 meters thick. Ask: **Suppose this limestone accumulated at a rate of 1 cm every 50 years. How many years did it take for 4,000 meters of limestone to accumulate?** *(4,000 m × 100 cm/m × 50 yr/cm = 20 million years)*

Apply Ask: **Would dinosaur fossils be in this deposit?** *(No, dinosaurs became extinct 65 million years ago.)* **learning modality: logical/mathematical**

For: Links on fossils
Visit: www.SciLinks.org
Web Code: scn-0235

Download a worksheet that will guide students' review of Internet resources on fossils.

For: Links on fossils
Visit: www.SciLinks.org
Web Code: scn-0235

What Are Fossils?

A **fossil** is the hardened remains or other evidence of a living thing that existed a long time ago. Sometimes a fossil is an imprint in rock, such as an animal's footprint or the outline of a leaf. Other fossils are the remains of bones, shells, skeletons, or other parts of living things. Fossils are made when a chemical process takes place over time, during which an organism's tissues are replaced by hard minerals. Because most living tissues decay rapidly, only a very few organisms are preserved as fossils.

Fossils are found most frequently in sedimentary rock. Hardened layers of sediments make up **sedimentary rock.** Sediments contain particles of clay, sand, mud, or silt.

Science and History

Discovering Vertebrate Fossils

People have been discovering fossils since ancient times. Here are some especially important fossil discoveries.

1677 Dinosaur-Bone Illustration
Robert Plot, the head of a museum in England, published a book that had an illustration of a huge fossilized thighbone. Plot thought that the bone belonged to a giant human, but it probably was the thighbone of a dinosaur.

1811 Sea Reptile
Along the cliffs near Lyme Regis, England, 12-year-old Mary Anning discovered the fossilized remains of the giant sea reptile now called *Ichthyosaurus*. Mary became one of England's first professional fossil collectors.

1822 Dinosaur Tooth
In a quarry near Lewes, England, Mary Ann Mantell discovered a strange-looking tooth embedded in stone. Her husband Gideon drew the picture of the tooth shown here. The tooth belonged to the dinosaur *Iguanodon*.

1670 — 1760 — 1820

How do sediments build up into layers? Have you ever washed a dirty soccer ball and seen sand and mud settle in the sink? If you washed a dozen soccer balls, the sink bottom would be covered with layers of sediments. Sediments build up in many ways. For example, wind can blow a thick layer of sand onto dunes. Sediments can also form when muddy water stands in an area for a long time. Muddy sediment in the water eventually settles to the bottom and builds up.

Over a very long time, layers of sediments can be pressed and cemented together to form rock. As sedimentary rock forms, traces of living things that have been trapped in the sediments are sometimes preserved as fossils.

How does sedimentary rock form?

Writing in Science

Research and Write If you could interview the person who discovered one of the fossils, what questions would you ask about the fossil and how it was found? Write a list of those questions. Then use reference materials to try to find the answers to some of them.

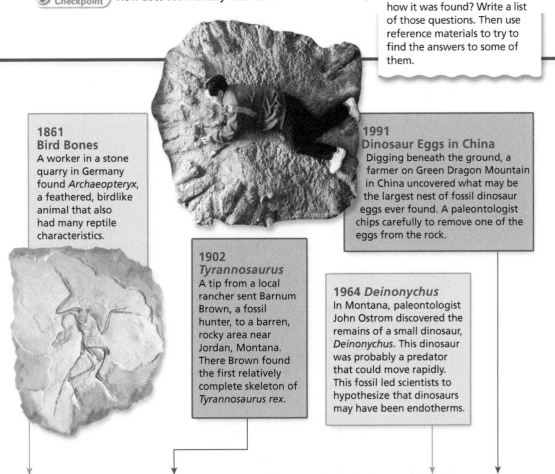

1861
Bird Bones
A worker in a stone quarry in Germany found *Archaeopteryx*, a feathered, birdlike animal that also had many reptile characteristics.

1902
Tyrannosaurus
A tip from a local rancher sent Barnum Brown, a fossil hunter, to a barren, rocky area near Jordan, Montana. There Brown found the first relatively complete skeleton of *Tyrannosaurus rex*.

1964 *Deinonychus*
In Montana, paleontologist John Ostrom discovered the remains of a small dinosaur, *Deinonychus*. This dinosaur was probably a predator that could move rapidly. This fossil led scientists to hypothesize that dinosaurs may have been endotherms.

1991
Dinosaur Eggs in China
Digging beneath the ground, a farmer on Green Dragon Mountain in China uncovered what may be the largest nest of fossil dinosaur eggs ever found. A paleontologist chips carefully to remove one of the eggs from the rock.

1880 1940 2000

Science and History

Focus Help students relate these major events in vertebrate paleontology to other events in world history.

Teach Have students reproduce the timeline without the descriptive paragraphs, and then add the following major events in world history:

- The signing of the Declaration of Independence (1776)
- The end of the Civil War (1865)
- The end of World War II (1945)
- The first moon landing (1969)
- The breakup of the Soviet Union (1991)

Extend News of paleontological discoveries is often reported in newspapers. Ask students if they have read of recent discoveries that they might include on the timeline. Suggest discoveries made in China since 1996 of feathered dinosaurs that might represent an intermediate form between dinosaurs and birds.

Writing in Science

Writing Mode Research

Scoring Rubric

4 Includes at least four questions that show an understanding of lesson content; answers are correct, detailed, and complete
3 Includes two or three questions; answers are correct and complete
2 Includes two questions; most answers are correct and complete
1 Includes only one question or answers are incorrect and incomplete

Differentiated Instruction

Less Proficient Readers L1

Following the Time Line Have students needing a review of the text to write down the dates on the timeline, leaving room for notes. Then have students listen to the *Student Edition on Audio* CD and record events occurring in each year noted. **learning modality: verbal**

Monitor Progress L2

Writing Have students write paragraphs describing how sedimentary rock is formed. Students can save their paragraphs in their portfolios.

Portfolio

Answer

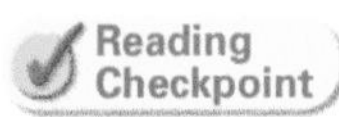
Particles of clay, sand, mud, or silt settle from the action of wind or water. The layers are pressed and cemented together over a long time.

Interpretation of Fossils

Teach Key Concepts L2

Examining the Fossil Record

Focus Tell students that scientists learn about how organisms change over time and how they are related to one another by studying fossils.

Teach Direct students to Figure 27. Ask: **Are mammals more closely related to fishes or to amphibians?** *(Amphibians)* **Which groups of vertebrates arose from reptiles?** *(Mammals and birds)*

Apply Ask: **What vertebrate fossils would be found in sediments 350 million years old but not in sediments 450 million years old?** *(Remains of amphibians)* **learning modality: visual**

All in One **Teaching Resources**

- Transparency B33

Build Inquiry L1

Understanding Sedimentary Rock Formation

Materials plastic jar with lid, marbles, pea gravel, sand, powdered clay

Time 10 minutes

Focus Help students understand how sedimentary rock forms and traps fossils.

Teach Students will simulate the effect of moving water on different sizes of rocks. Have students half-fill the jar with the pebbles, gravel, sand, and clay, which represent different-sized rocks. Have them then fill the jar, fasten its lid securely, and shake it until the solid contents are suspended. Then they should quickly set the jar down and record the order in which the materials settle to the bottom. *(Pebbles first, then the gravel, then the sand, then much later, the clay)*

Apply Ask: **What is the relationship between the size of the rock and the length of time it takes to settle?** *(The larger the rock, the faster it settles.)* **learning modality: kinesthetic**

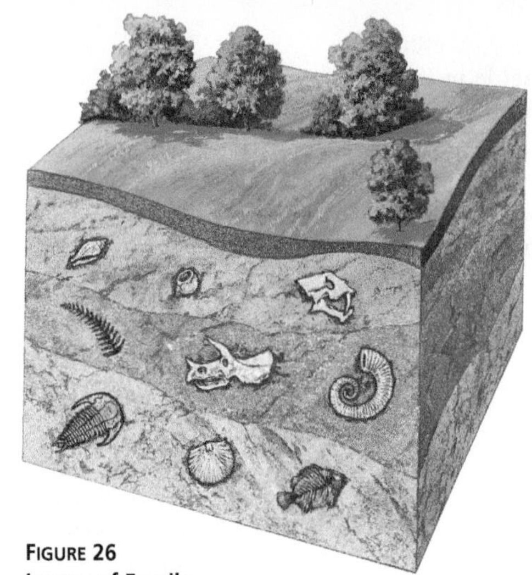

FIGURE 26
Layers of Fossils
Fossils most often form in layers of sedimentary rock.
Interpreting Diagrams *Which rock layer probably contains the oldest fossils?*

Interpretation of Fossils

What information can scientists learn from fossils? **Paleontologists** (pay lee un TAHL uh jists), the scientists who study extinct organisms, examine fossil structure and make comparisons to present-day organisms. **By studying fossils, paleontologists can infer how animals changed over time.** One important piece of information that paleontologists can learn from a fossil is its approximate age.

A Fossil's Age One method for estimating a fossil's age takes advantage of the process in which sediments form. Think about sediments settling out of water—the lowest layers are deposited first, and newer sediments settle on top of the older layers. Therefore, fossils in higher layers of rock are often younger than fossils in lower layers.

However, rock layers can become tilted or even turned upside down by events such as earthquakes. So, a fossil's position in rock is not always a good indication of its age. Scientists usually rely on other methods to help determine a fossil's age. For example, fossils—and the rocks in which they are found—contain some radioactive chemical elements. These radioactive elements decay, or change into other chemical elements, over a known period of time. The more there is of the decayed form of the element, the older the fossil.

Using Fossils Paleontologists have used fossils to determine a likely pattern of how vertebrates changed over time. You can see in Figure 27 that this pattern of vertebrate evolution looks something like a branching tree. Fossils show that the first vertebrates to live on Earth were fishes. Fishes first appeared on Earth about 530 million years ago. Amphibians, which appeared on Earth about 380 million years ago, are descended from fishes. Then, about 320 million years ago, amphibians gave rise to reptiles. Both mammals and birds, which you will learn about in the next chapter, are descended from reptiles. Based on the age of the oldest mammal fossils, mammals first lived on Earth about 220 million years ago. Birds were the latest group of vertebrates to arise. Their oldest fossils show that birds first appeared on Earth 150 million years ago.

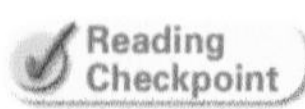

What is a paleontologist?

Differentiated Instruction

Gifted and Talented L3

Identifying Fossil Ages Challenge students to use library and Internet resources to investigate the actual processes that go into determining the ages of fossils, either by interpreting layers of sedimentary rock or carrying out radioactive dating. Students investigating fossil dating through examining sedimentary rock layers should prepare a visual display of the types and ages of fossils that could be found in rock layers in their area. Students exploring the details of radioactive dating should choose an example of a "famous" fossil whose age has been determined this way—such as an important dinosaur find—and provide a display presenting the steps involved in the technique. **learning modality: visual**

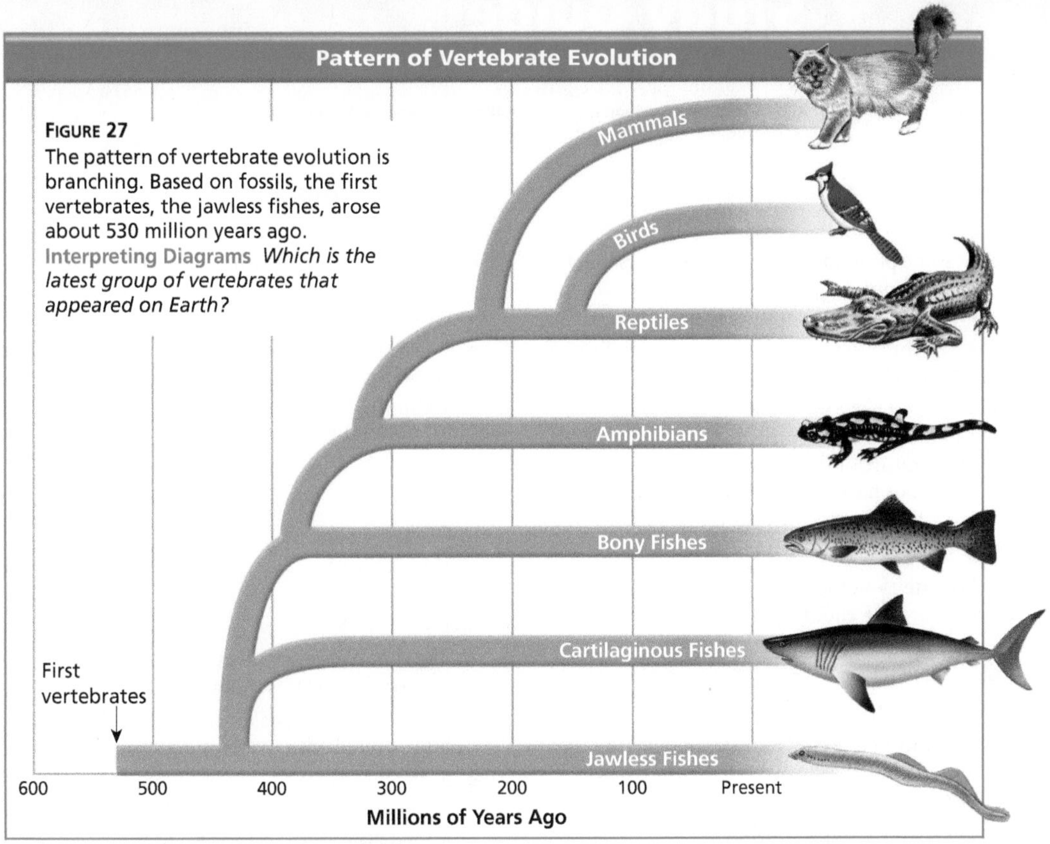

Pattern of Vertebrate Evolution

Mammals

Birds

Reptiles

Amphibians

Bony Fishes

Cartilaginous Fishes

Jawless Fishes

First vertebrates

600 500 400 300 200 100 Present

Millions of Years Ago

FIGURE 27
The pattern of vertebrate evolution is branching. Based on fossils, the first vertebrates, the jawless fishes, arose about 530 million years ago.
Interpreting Diagrams *Which is the latest group of vertebrates that appeared on Earth?*

Section 5 Assessment

Target Reading Skill Asking Questions Use your graphic organizer to answer the questions below.

Reviewing Key Concepts

1. a. Identifying Where are fossils most often found?
   b. Describing What are some types of fossils?
   c. Inferring How might a small fish that dies in a muddy pool become a fossil?
2. a. Reviewing What can be learned from studying fossils?
   b. Summarizing How does the measurement of radioactive elements help scientists calculate a fossil's age?
   c. Interpreting Diagrams Look at Figure 27. About how much time passed between the first appearance of vertebrates and the time birds appeared?

Lab zone At-Home Activity

Sedimentary Newspaper? If your family keeps newspapers in a stack, check the dates of the newspapers in the stack with a family member. Are the newspapers in any kind of order? If the oldest ones are on the bottom and the newest are on the top, you can relate this to the way in which sediments are laid down. Ask family members to imagine that two fossils were trapped in different newspapers. Explain which fossil would probably be older.

Lab zone At-Home Activity

Sedimentary Newspaper? L2
Ask: **What could you conclude if the newspapers in the top layer were older than those in the bottom layer?** *(Something must have disturbed the stack.)* **How is this similar to what can happen to rock layers?** *(Rock layers can be disturbed by natural events so that their original order is altered.)* **learning modality: verbal**

Monitor Progress L2

Answers
Figure 26 The lowest layer should contain the oldest fossils because it was deposited before the other layers.
Figure 27 Birds

Reading Checkpoint A scientist who studies extinct organisms, examines fossil structure, and makes comparisons to present-day organisms.

Assess

Reviewing Key Concepts

1. a. Sedimentary rock. **b.** Some fossils are imprints, such as a footprint, and some are remains of parts of living things. **c.** The fish is covered with mud and is buried. Over many thousands of years, the tissues are replaced with minerals.
2. a. How organisms changed over time
b. Scientists measure the ratio of decayed chemical element to nondecayed chemical element to find out a fossil's age.
c. 380 million years

Reteach L1

On the board draw a rough sketch of layers of sedimentary rock. Have students use the information in Figure 27 to place vertebrate fossils in their correct order.

Performance Assessment L2

Organizing Information Have students draw flowcharts that show the stages in the making of a fossil. Students can save their flowcharts in their portfolos.

Portfolio

All in One Teaching Resources
- Section Summary: *Vertebrate History in Rocks*
- Review and Reinforce: *Vertebrate History in Rocks*
- Enrich: *Vertebrate History in Rocks*

Study Guide

The BIG Idea

Have students read the answer to the Essential Question. Encourage them to evaluate and revise their own answers as needed.

Help Students Read

Building Vocabulary

Word-Part Analysis Tell students that the prefix *ecto* means "outside" or "external," *endo* means "inside" or "within," and the root word *thermo* means "heat." Thus an *ectotherm* uses heat from outside the body, and an *endotherm* generates heat from within.

Vocabulary Knowledge Rating Chart

Have students construct a chart with four columns: *Term, Can Define or Use It, Have Heard or Seen It, Don't Know*. Students should copy the Key Terms for the chapter under column 1. They should then check the appropriate column for each term, and use the chart to determine which terms to review.

Connecting Concepts

Concept Maps Help students develop one way to show how the information in this chapter is related. Fishes, amphibians, and reptiles are all adapted to their particular environments. The fossil record shows how these vertebrate groups are related. Have students brainstorm to identify the Key Concepts, Key Terms, details, and examples from this chapter. Then write each one on a sticky note and attach it at random on chart paper or on the board. Tell students that this concept map will be organized in hierarchical order and to begin at the top with the Key Concepts. Ask students these questions to guide them to categorize the information on the sticky notes: **What traits did these groups develop as they adapted to life on land? According to fossils, how are the groups related?** Prompt students by using connecting words or phrases, such as "led to," and "resulted in" to indicate the basis for the organization of the map. The phrases should form a sentence between or among a set of concepts.

Answer

Accept logical presentations by students.

All in One Teaching Resources

- Key Terms Review: *Fishes, Amphibians, and Reptiles*
- Connecting Concepts: *Fishes, Amphibians, and Reptiles*

Chapter 3 Study Guide

The BIG Idea **Structure and Function** Vertebrates have endoskeletons that include backbones. Backbones provide support and enable movement.

1 What Is a Vertebrate?

Key Concepts

- At some point in their lives, chordates will have a notochord, a nerve cord that runs down their back, and pouches in their throat area.
- A vertebrate has a backbone that is part of an internal skeleton.
- The body temperature of most fishes, amphibians, and reptiles is close to the temperature of their environment. Birds and mammals have a stable body temperature that is often warmer than their environment.

Key Terms

- chordate • notochord • vertebra
- ectotherm • endotherm

2 Fishes

Key Concepts

- In addition to living in water and having fins, most fishes are ectotherms, obtain oxygen through gills, and have scales.
- The major groups of fishes are jawless fishes, cartilagious fishes, and bony fishes.
- Jawless fishes are unlike other fishes in that they have no jaws and no scales.
- Cartilaginous fishes have jaws and scales, and skeletons made of cartilage.
- A bony fish has jaws, scales, a pocket on each side of the head that holds the gills, and a skeleton made of hard bone.

Key Terms

fish
cartilage
swim bladder

3 Amphibians

Key Concepts

- After beginning their lives in water, most amphibians spend their adulthood on land, returning to water to reproduce.
- The respiratory and circulatory systems of adult amphibians are adapted for life on land. In addition, adult amphibians have adaptations for obtaining food and moving.

Key Terms

amphibian, lung, ventricle, tadpole, atrium, habitat

4 Reptiles

Key Concepts

- The skin, kidneys, and eggs of reptiles are adapted to conserve water.
- Both lizards and snakes are reptiles that have skin covered with overlapping scales.
- Both alligators and crocodiles are large, carnivorous reptiles that care for their young.
- A turtle is a reptile whose body is covered by a protective shell that includes the ribs and the backbone.
- Dinosaurs were the earliest vertebrates that had legs positioned directly beneath their bodies.

Key Terms

- reptile • urine • kidney • amniotic egg

5 Vertebrate History in Rocks

Key Concepts

- Fossils are found most frequently in sedimentary rock.
- By studying fossils, paleontologists can infer how a species changed over time.

Key Terms

fossil, paleontologist, sedimentary rock

Review and Assessment

Go Online PHSchool.com
For: Self-Assessment
Visit: PHSchool.com
Web Code: cea-2030

Organizing Information

Identifying Main Ideas Copy the graphic organizer about amphibians onto a sheet of paper. Then complete it.

Main Idea

The larvae of amphibians are adapted for life in water, and adult amphibians are adapted for life on land.

Detail	Detail	Detail
a. ___?___	b. ___?___	c. ___?___

Reviewing Key Terms

Choose the letter of the best answer.

1. Vertebrates are a subgroup of
   a. chordates.
   b. fishes.
   c. amphibians.
   d. reptiles.
2. A fish
   a. is an endotherm.
   b. has fins.
   c. has lungs.
   d. has a three-chambered heart.
3. A tadpole is the larva of a
   a. fish.
   b. salamander.
   c. frog or toad.
   d. lizard or snake.
4. A reptile
   a. is an endotherm.
   b. lays eggs.
   c. has a swim bladder.
   d. has a thin skin.
5. Layers of clay, sand, mud, or silt harden and become
   a. radioactive chemicals.
   b. sedimentary rock.
   c. fossils.
   d. dinosaur bones.

If the statement is true, write *true.* If it is false, change the underlined word or words to make the statement true.

6. A notochord is replaced by a backbone in many vertebrates.
7. A bony fish uses its gills to stabilize its position in the water.
8. Amphibians obtain oxygen through gills and have scales.
9. An amniotic egg is a characteristic of reptiles.
10. Paleontologists are scientists who study fossils.

Writing in Science

Description Suppose you are a journalist for a nature magazine and you have spent a week observing crocodiles. Write a paragraph describing how crocodiles obtain their food.

Discovery Channel School

Fishes, Amphibians, and Reptiles
Video Preview
Video Field Trip
▶ Video Assessment

For: Self-Assessment
Visit: PHSchool.com
Web Code: cea-2030

Students can take a practice test online that is automatically scored.

All in One Teaching Resources

- Transparency B34
- Chapter Test
- Performance Assessment Teacher Notes
- Performance Assessment Student Worksheet
- Performance Assessment Scoring Rubric

ExamView® Computer Test Bank CD-ROM

Review and Assessment

Organizing Information

a. Larvae have tails for swimming; adults have legs for walking.
b. Larvae have gills; adults have lungs.
c. Larvae have one-loop circulatory system and two-chambered heart; adults have two-loop circulatory system and three-chambered heart.

Reviewing Key Terms

1. a **2.** b **3.** c **4.** b **5.** b
6. true
7. swim bladder
8. Fishes
9. true
10. true

Writing in Science

Writing Mode Description
Scoring Rubric
4 Description includes many events placed in proper context and accurately reflecting crocodile adaptations
3 Includes adequate number of events, accurately presented
2 Includes inadequate number of events or some inaccuracies
1 Includes inadequate and inaccurate description

Discovery Channel School Video Assessment

Fishes, Amphibians, and Reptiles

Show the Video Assessment to review chapter content and as a prompt for the writing assignment. Discussion questions: **Describe two adaptations of crocodiles that make them good predators.** *(Their muscular tail enables them to move very quickly in water and for short distances on land, and their strong jaw and long, sharp teeth help them eat their prey.)* **Describe how temperature is regulated in crocodile bodies.** *(Crocodiles rely on their environment to warm their bodies because they produce very little body heat of their own.)*

Checking Concepts

11. Chordates have a notochord, a nerve cord running down their back, and pouches in their throat area.

12. Fish reproduce sexually. Most have external fertilization.

13. A frog begins life as an egg laid in water or a moist environment. The egg hatches into a fishlike tadpole, which gradually develops into an adult frog. Hind legs appear, then front legs; lungs replace gills; tadpole loses its tail. The adult frog returns to the water to mate and lay eggs, completing the cycle.

14. A fish has a circulatory system with one loop and a simple, two-chambered heart. An adult amphibian has a circulatory system with two loops and a three-chambered heart.

15. An adult amphibian obtains oxygen with its internal lungs and through its thin, moist skin.

16. A snake alternates contractions of muscles on opposite sides of its body to produce a slithering motion.

17. A reptile's egg has a tough, leathery shell and membranes inside that protect, nourish, and allow gas exchange to and from the embryo.

18. Scientists consider the layer of sediment in which a fossil is found, knowing the relative ages of different layers; and scientists measure decay of radioactive elements found in fossils.

Thinking Critically

19. The endoskeleton grows as the animal grows. Also, its strength supports the animal against the pull of gravity.

20. The heart pumps blood in one continuous loop from the heart to the gills, from the gills to the rest of the body, and back to the heart; oxygen enters the blood at the gills.

21. Sample answer: Wrap the towel in a material such as foil or plastic wrap that will keep water from escaping.

22. Sharp, pointed teeth indicate that the fish was a predator and a carnivore; body and fin shape suggest that the fish chased its prey.

Review and Assessment

Checking Concepts

11. Describe the main characteristics of chordates.
12. How do fishes reproduce?
13. Describe the life cycle of a frog.
14. How is the circulatory system of an adult amphibian different from that of a fish?
15. Describe the adaptations of an adult amphibian for obtaining oxygen from the air.
16. How does a snake move?
17. Explain how the structure of a reptile's egg protects the embryo inside.
18. Describe two methods that scientists use to determine the age of a fossil.

Thinking Critically

19. **Relating Cause and Effect** Explain why an endoskeleton allows vertebrates to grow larger than animals without endoskeletons.
20. **Interpreting Diagrams** How does blood move in the circulatory system shown below?

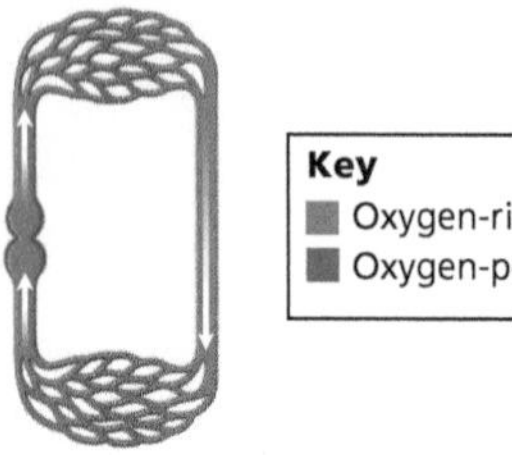

21. **Applying Concepts** Imagine that you are in a hot desert with a wet paper towel. You must keep the towel from drying out. What strategy can you copy from reptiles to keep the towel from drying out?
22. **Inferring** A scientist discovers a fossilized fish with a body streamlined for fast movement, a large tail fin, and sharp, pointed teeth. What could the scientist infer about the type of food that this fish ate and how it obtained its food? On what evidence is the inference based?

Applying Skills

Use the graph to answer Questions 23–25.

A scientist performed an experiment on five goldfishes to test the effect of water temperature on "breathing rate"—the rate at which the fishes open and close their gill covers. The graph shows the data that the scientist obtained at four different temperatures.

Fish Breathing Rate at Different Temperatures

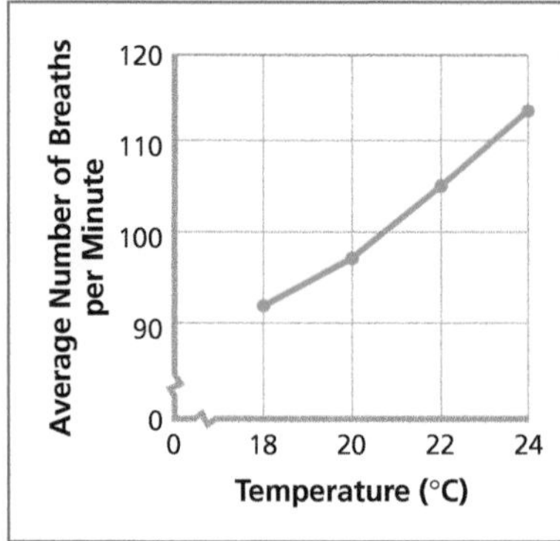

23. **Controlling Variables** Identify the manipulated variable and the responding variable in this experiment.
24. **Interpreting Data** How does the breathing rate at 18°C compare to the breathing rate at 22°C?
25. **Drawing Conclusions** Based on the data shown, what is the relationship between water temperature and fish breathing rate?

Lab zone Chapter Project

Performance Assessment Display your models in a creative and interesting way—for example, show the models in action and show details of the animals' habitats. Also display your poster. List all the adaptations you learned from your classmates' presentations. How did constructing a three-dimensional model help you understand the characteristics of these groups?

L3

Performance Assessment When students demonstrate their models for the class, some models may not perform the intended function as smoothly as they are designed to do. Locomotion can be a difficult adaptation to demonstrate successfully, but three-dimensional models should more accurately depict locomotion than would drawings. Look for realistic and thoughtful ideas.

Remind students that the poster, which can be a flowchart, can support their ideas. Guide students to record the adaptations that prompted their model choices. Also, have them record other adaptations modeled by classmates. After all students have presented their projects, you may wish to note which adaptations were modeled most often.

Standardized Test Prep

Test-Taking Tip

Interpreting Data Tables

Before you answer a question about a data table, read the title and the headings of the columns and rows. The title identifies the type of data the table contains. The headings reveal how the data are organized. For example, the table below shows that jawless fishes have skeletons made of cartilage. Read the questions about the table before you spend too much time studying the data.

Characteristics of Fishes

Group	Skeleton	Jaws	Scales
Jawless Fishes	Cartilage	None	None
Cartilaginous Fishes	Cartilage	Yes	Yes
Bony Fishes	Bone	Yes	Yes

Sample Question

Axel has found a fish washed up on the beach that has scales and a skeleton made of cartilage. According to the table, what kind of fish is it?

A a jawless fish
B a cartilaginous fish
C a bony fish
D The fish cannot be classified using this table.

Answer

The correct answer is **B**. Choices **A, C,** and **D** cannot be correct because only cartilaginous fishes have a cartilaginous skeleton and scales.

Choose the letter of the best answer.

1. If you monitored the body temperature of a snake in four different air temperatures, what would you notice about its body temperature?
A It rises or falls with the air temperature.
B It always stays at about 37°C .
C It is higher than the air temperature.
D It is lower than the air temperature.

Characteristics of Observed Animals

Animal	Skeleton	Scales	Outer Covering of Egg
1	Bone	None	Clear jelly
2	Bone	Yes	Leathery shell
3	Bone	Yes	Thin, moist membrane
4	Cartilage	Yes	No eggs observed

2. A scientist observed four different animals and recorded her data in the table shown above. Which of the animals is most likely a reptile?
F Animals 1 and 3
G Animal 2
H Animal 3
J Animal 4

3. Based on the data in the table above, what kind of animal can you infer Animal 3 might be?
A amphibian
B bony fish
C cartilaginous fish
D reptile

4. Suppose you are conducting an experiment that requires you to handle live bullfrogs. Which laboratory safety procedure should you carry out at the conclusion of each work session?
F Carefully clean the bullfrog's container.
G Put on gloves.
H Wash your hands thoroughly.
J Turn the heat on.

Constructed Response

5. Explain why amphibians can be said to have a "double life." Be sure to include details describing the two different phases in the life of a typical amphibian.

Applying Skills

23. The manipulated variable is the water temperature. The responding variable is the breathing rate of the fish.

24. The breathing rate at 18°C is lower than the breathing rate at 22°C.

25. The goldfish breathing rate is directly related to water temperature. The higher the water temperature, the faster the breathing rate.

Standardized Test Prep

1. A **2.** G **3.** B **4.** H

5. Amphibians can be said to have a "double life" because an amphibian typically spends its larval stage in water and its adult life on land. Eggs are coated with a jelly and the larvae wriggle out of the jelly after a few days and begin to swim. They undergo metamorphosis, causing them to lose their gills and develop lungs. They move onto land to live.

The BIG Idea

The Big Idea is the major scientific concept of the chapter. It is followed by the Essential Question. Read aloud the question to students. As students study the chapter, tell them to think about the Essential Question. Explain that they will discover the answer to the question as they read. The chapter Study Guide provides a sample answer.

Chapter 4 Birds and Mammals

The BIG Idea
Structure and Function

What key characteristics do birds and mammals share?

Chapter Preview

1 Birds
- *Discover* What Are Feathers Like?
- *Active Art* Respiration and Circulation
- *Try This* "Eggs-amination"
- *At-Home Activity* Count Down
- *Skills Lab* Looking at an Owl's Leftovers

2 The Physics of Bird Flight
- *Discover* What Lifts Airplanes and Birds Into the Air?
- *Try This* It's Plane to See

3 Mammals
- *Discover* What Are Mammals' Teeth Like?
- *Try This* Insulated Mammals
- *Analyzing Data* Mammal Diversity
- *At-Home Activity* Mammals' Milk
- *Consumer Lab* Keeping Warm

A three-toed sloth hangs from a tree branch in Costa Rica.

116 ◆ B

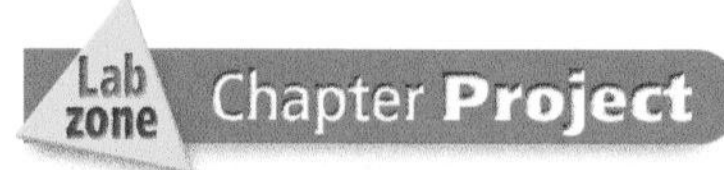

L3

Objectives
In this project, students will model the skills and observations required for the careful study of any group of animals. They will observe interactions between birds, and record feeding behavior and food preference of different birds. After this Chapter Project, students will be able to
- observe and identify birds at a feeder
- classify behaviors
- create data tables
- interpret data from their project

Skills Focus
Observing, classifying, recording and interpreting data

Project Time Line 2 to 3 weeks

All in One Teaching Resources
- Chapter Project Teacher Notes
- Chapter Project Overview
- Chapter Project Worksheet 1
- Chapter Project Worksheet 2
- Chapter Project Scoring Rubric

Developing a Plan
During the first week, students select a feeder location and begin observing and identifying visiting bird species. During the second week, students can list bird species observed and record common behaviors. In week three, students concentrate on feeding behaviors. Finally, students devise a way to present information they have collected.

Possible Materials
- To begin observations, each group will need a commercial bird feeder or materials to build a feeder. Students will need also string or wire to hang feeder.
- To attract the greatest variety of species, students may use an all-purpose bird feed mix, including hulled sunflower seeds, white millet, cracked corn, red millet, sunflower chips, peanut pieces, milo, thistle, and hulled millet.

Chapter at a Glance

Bird Watch

Technology

Video Preview

Local Standards

All in One Teaching Resources

- Chapter Project Teacher Notes, pp. 244–245
- Chapter Project Student Overview, pp. 246–247
- Chapter Project Student Worksheets, pp. 248–249
- Chapter Project Scoring Rubric, p. 250

2–3 periods
1–1 1/2 blocks

Birds

B.4.1.1 Identify the common characteristics of birds.

B.4.1.2 Explain how birds are adapted to their environments.

1–2 periods
1/2–1 block

The Physics of Bird Flight

B.4.2.1 Explain how a bird is able to fly.

B.4.2.2 Identify three types of flight birds use.

Video Field Trip

4–5 periods
2–2 1/2 blocks

Mammals

B.4.3.1 Describe the characteristics common to all mammals.

B.4.3.2 List the three main groups of mammals.

Review and Assessment

All in One Teaching Resources

- Key Terms Review, p. 276
- Transparency B42
- Performance Assessment Teacher Notes, p. 287
- Performance Assessment Scoring Rubric, p. 288
- Performance Assessment Student Worksheet, p. 289
- Chapter Test, pp. 290–293

Go Online PHSchool.com

Video Assessment

Test Preparation

Test Preparation Blackline Masters

Chapter Activities Planner

For more activities

Student Edition	Inquiry	Time	Materials	Skills	Resources
Chapter Project, p. 117	Open-Ended	2–3 weeks	All in One Teaching Resources See p. 244	Observing, classifying, recording and interpreting data	**Lab zone Easy Planner** All in One **Teaching Resources** Support, pp. 244–245
Section 1					
Discover Activity, p. 118	Directed	15 minutes	Feathers, hand lens	Observing	**Lab zone Easy Planner**
Try This Activity, p. 123	Directed	20 minutes	Bowl, hand lens, uncooked egg, water	Observing	**Lab zone Easy Planner**
Skills Lab, pp. 126–127	Guided	Prep: 20 minutes Class: 50 minutes	Owl pellet, hand lens, dissecting needle, metric ruler, forceps	Observing, drawing conclusions	**Lab zone Easy Planner** **Lab Activity Video** All in One **Teaching Resources** Skills Lab: *Looking at an Owl's Leftovers,* pp. 258–260
Section 2					
Discover Activity, p. 128	Directed	10 minutes	Notebook paper, scissors, metric ruler, book	Predicting	**Lab zone Easy Planner**
Try This Activity, p. 130	Open-Ended	30 minutes	Sheets of different kinds of paper (letter, construction, foil-covered), tape, glue, paper clips, string, rubber bands, staples	Making models	**Lab zone Easy Planner**
Section 3					
Discover Activity, p. 132	Guided	15 minutes	Cracker, hand mirror	Inferring	**Lab zone Easy Planner**
Try This Activity, p. 134	Directed	15 minutes	Bucket or sink full of cold water, paper towels, rubber gloves, shortening (from animal fat)	Inferring	**Lab zone Easy Planner**
Consumer Lab, p. 141	Directed	Prep: 15 minutes Class: 35 minutes	Hot tap water, scissors, 1-L beaker, 3 thermometers, clock or watch, graph paper, pair of wool socks, room-temperature tap water, 3 250-mL containers with lids	Graphing, interpreting data	**Lab zone Easy Planner** **Lab Activity Video** All in One **Teaching Resources** Consumer Lab: *Keeping Warm,* pp. 274–275

Section 1 Birds

 *2–3 periods, 1–1 1/2 blocks*

ABILITY LEVELS
- L1 Basic to Average
- L2 For All Students
- L3 Average to Advanced

Objectives

B.4.1.1 Identify the common characteristics of birds.

B.4.1.2 Explain how birds are adapted to their environments.

Key Terms

• bird • contour feather • down feather • crop • gizzard

Local Standards

Preteach

Build Background Knowledge

Students investigate the shape, structure, and texture of feathers.

 *What Are Feathers Like?* 

Targeted Print and Technology Resources

Teaching Resources
- L2 Reading Strategy Transparency B35: Previewing Visuals

Instruct

Characteristics of Birds Use pictures to teach characteristics of birds.

Birds in the Environment Use pictures to lead a discussion of the diversity of birds.

 *Looking at an Owl's Leftovers* 

Targeted Print and Technology Resources

All in One Teaching Resources
- L2 Guided Reading, pp. 253–255
- L2 Transparencies B36, B37, B38, B39
- L2 Skills Lab: *Looking at an Owl's Leftovers*, pp. 258–260

Lab Activity Video/DVD
Skills Lab: *Looking at an Owl's Leftovers*

PHSchool.com Web Code: cep-2041

Student Edition on Audio CD

Assess

Section Assesment Questions

Students can use their Previewing Visuals graphic organizers to answer the questions.

Reteach

Direct students to describe the kind of feathers that are used for flight.

Targeted Print and Technology Resources

All in One Teaching Resources
- Section Summary, p. 252
- L1 Review and Reinforce, p. 256
- L3 Enrich, p. 257

Section 2 The Physics of Bird Flight

 *1–2 periods, 1/2–1 block*

ABILITY LEVELS
L1 Basic to Average
L2 For All Students
L3 Average to Advanced

Objectives

B.4.2.1 Explain how a bird is able to fly.
B.4.2.2 Identify three types of flight birds use.

Key Term

• lift

Local Standards

Preteach

Build Background Knowledge

Have students investigate flight by imitating flapping wings or gliding.

 *What Lifts Airplanes and Birds Into the Air?* 

Targeted Print and Technology Resources

L2 Reading Strategy Transparency B40: Relating Cause and Effect

PresentationExpress™ CD-ROM

Instruct

Staying in the Air Draw labeled sketches to use as prompts for students to answer questions about how birds stay in the air.

Birds in Flight Ask leading questions for a discussion on ways birds fly.

Targeted Print and Technology Resources

All in One Teaching Resources

L2 Guided Reading, pp. 263–264
L2 Transparency B41

PHSchool.com Web Code: ced-2042

Video Field Trip

Student Edition on Audio CD

Assess

Section Assessment Questions

Students can use their Relating Cause and Effects graphic organizers to answer the questions.

Reteach

Use the figure *Wing Shape and Lift* to explain how wing shape enables a bird to fly.

Targeted Print and Technology Resources

• Section Summary, p. 262
L1 Review and Reinforce, p. 265
L3 Enrich, p. 266

Section 3 Mammals

 *4–5 periods, 2–2 1/2 blocks*

ABILITY LEVELS
L1 Basic to Average
L2 For All Students
L3 Average to Advanced

Objectives

B.4.3.1 Describe the characteristics common to all mammals.
B.4.3.2 List the three main groups of mammals.

Local Standards

Key Terms

• mammal • mammary gland • diaphragm • monotreme • marsupial
• gestation period • placental mammal • placenta

Preteach

Build Background Knowledge

Record students' generalizations about the characteristics of pet mammals.

 *What Are Mammals' Teeth Like?* 

Targeted Print and Technology Resources

L2 Reading Strategy: Building Vocabulary

PresentationExpress™ CD-ROM

Instruct

Characteristics of Mammals Relate characteristics of mammals to common organisms.

Diversity of Mammals Use pictures to discuss ways that mammals differ.

 *Keeping Warm* 

Targeted Print and Technology Resources

All in One Teaching Resources

L2 Guided Reading, pp. 269–271
L2 Consumer Lab: *Keeping Warm*, pp. 274–275

Lab Activity Video/DVD
Consumer Lab: *Keeping Warm*

www.SciLinks.org Web Code: scn-0243

Student Edition on Audio CD

Assess

Section Assessment Questions

Students can use their definitions to answer the questions.

Reteach

Create a chart listing five characteristics common to all three groups of mammals.

Targeted Print and Technology Resources

All in One Teaching Resources

• Section Summary, p. 268
L1 Review and Reinforce, p. 272
L3 Enrich, p. 273

Go Online
NSTA-PDLINKS
For: Professional development support
Visit: www.SciLinks.org/PDLinks
Web Code: scf-0240

Professional Development

Section 1 Birds

Feathers The textbook identifies two main types of feathers—down and contour—but there are subcategories within those types. Down feathers, which are generally fluffy and provide insulation, include the down feathers found on adult birds as well as those that cover the bodies of many kinds of newly hatched birds. In addition, some kinds of birds, including parrots, hawks, and herons, have powder-down feathers. Powder-down feathers have tips that disintegrate, forming a powder that provides waterproofing.

Address Misconceptions

Some students may think that any animal that flies is a bird. An animal is a bird if and only if it has feathers. For a strategy for overcoming this misconception, see **Address Misconceptions** in the section *Birds*.

Contour feathers have a central shaft with barbs attached. Many contour feathers are symmetrical. Flight feathers are often asymmetrical. This asymmetrical design contributes to the aerodynamics of the bird's wing during wing beats.

Types of Feathers

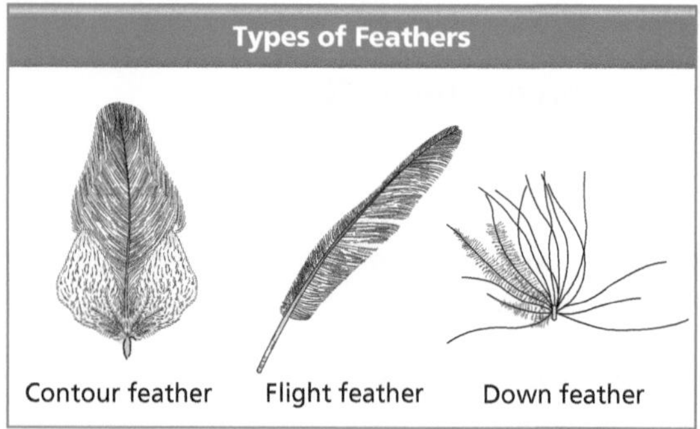

Contour feather   Flight feather   Down feather

Section 2 The Physics of Bird Flight

Aerodynamics of Bird Flight Winged flight basically involves two forces: thrust, which pushes the object forward, and lift, which makes the object rise. In birds, thrust is provided by the movement of the wings. Lift is provided by the shape and angle of the wings.

The leading edge of the wing is thicker than the trailing edge, and in its natural position the trailing edge curves downward. So, the wing shape is convex on its upper side and concave on its lower. The airfoil shape causes air to move faster over the wing than it does under, providing an area of lower pressure above and greater pressure below. Combined with forward thrust, this creates the lift.

In soaring, birds increase lift by tilting the wing upward. But in so doing, some thrust is lost, and the bird slows. But what happens if birds fly too slow? As airplane pilots know, slowing too much can produce turbulence above the wing, causing a complete loss of lift, or "stall," which can lead to a crash. One way in which soaring birds overcome the problem is by occasionally flapping the wings, which increases thrust.

Section 3 Mammals

Adaptations of Mammals' Digestive Tracts The digestive tract is similarly organized in all mammals. There's the mouth, esophagus, stomach, small intestine, and large intestine. The simplest versions are seen in omnivores and carnivores. The food they eat, consisting mostly of starches, proteins, and fats, is readily digested by enzymes released by the digestive glands. These mammals also digest a small amount of cellulose-laden plant fiber, but most cellulose passes through the gut unchanged. Herbivorous grazing mammals have more complex, very long digestive tracts, an adaptation to the slow and difficult task of breaking down cellulose, the main part of their diets.

These mammals cannot digest cellulose, however. They rely entirely on vast numbers of microorganisms that live in specialized chambers in the digestive tract. Herbivorous mammals fall into two categories: ruminants and nonruminants. The ruminants include cows, bison, goats, giraffes, and others, and are all named for the rumen, the first and largest chamber in their four-chambered stomachs. The rumen is a huge fermentation vat containing great numbers of microorganisms. It breaks down the tough cellulose material, yielding fatty acids, sugars, and starches. In nonruminants, including horses, rabbits, elephants, koalas, and others, cellulose digestion takes place in the cecum, a saclike organ found at the junction of the small and large intestine.

Help Students Read

Relate Text and Visuals

Strategy Show students how to use the text's illustrations to help clarify difficult concepts or to understand information.

Example

1. Choose a section in the chapter. Read the paragraphs aloud before students open their texts.
2. Have students open their books, reread the passage you read, and study the figure. Ask what parts of the passage now make more sense.

Discovery Channel School
Birds and Mammals
▶ Video Preview
Video Field Trip
Video Assessment

Lab zone™ Chapter Project

Bird Watch

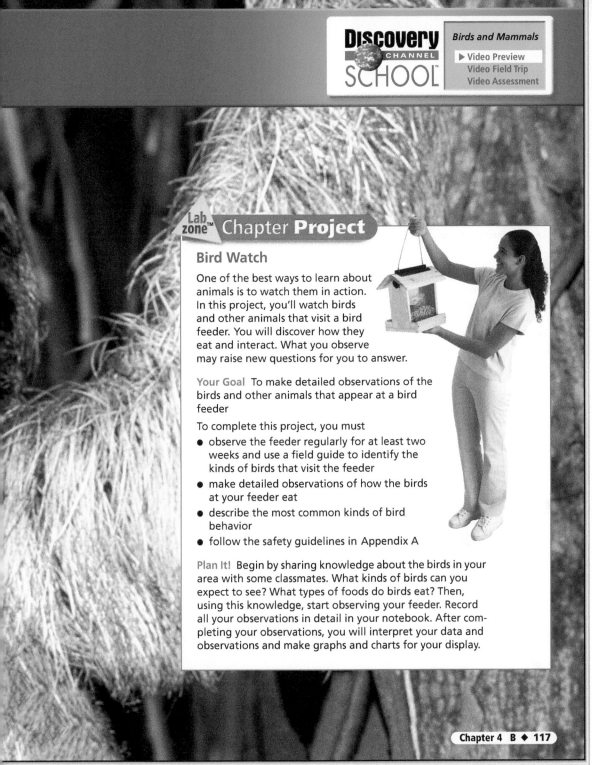

One of the best ways to learn about animals is to watch them in action. In this project, you'll watch birds and other animals that visit a bird feeder. You will discover how they eat and interact. What you observe may raise new questions for you to answer.

Your Goal To make detailed observations of the birds and other animals that appear at a bird feeder

To complete this project, you must

- observe the feeder regularly for at least two weeks and use a field guide to identify the kinds of birds that visit the feeder
- make detailed observations of how the birds at your feeder eat
- describe the most common kinds of bird behavior
- follow the safety guidelines in Appendix A

Plan It! Begin by sharing knowledge about the birds in your area with some classmates. What kinds of birds can you expect to see? What types of foods do birds eat? Then, using this knowledge, start observing your feeder. Record all your observations in detail in your notebook. After completing your observations, you will interpret your data and observations and make graphs and charts for your display.

Birds and Mammals

Show the Video Preview to introduce the Chapter Project and overview the chapter content. Discussion question: **What is the function of flight feathers?** *They help control flight, allowing the birds to steer and even brake before landing.*

- Students will need a field guide specific to your region of the country as well as guide to bird behaviors.
- Students will need art supplies to prepare their presentations. Cameras and videocassette recorders would be helpful, if available.

Launching the Project

To introduce the project, Ask: **How many different kinds of birds have you seen in your neighborhood?** *(Accept all responses at this time and encourage creative thinking.)* Encourage discussion of the different kinds of birds students have seen. Students could name source materials they found helpful for identifying unfamiliar species. Answer any initial questions that students may have. Discuss placement of the bird feeders so that they are easily refilled and observed while at the same time offering proximity to cover so birds can retreat if startled or threatened.

Performance Assessment

The Chapter Project Scoring Rubric will help you evaluate how well students complete the Chapter Project. You may want to share the scoring rubric with your students so they know what will be expected of them. Students will be assessed on

- thoroughness of research of the area's birds leading to the use of appropriate feeders, food, and location
- completeness of observation entries including: (1) what birds appeared, (2) their interactions, and (3) foods eaten
- application of chapter concepts to their observations
- thoroughness and organization of their presentations

Portfolio

Section 1 Birds

Objectives

After this lesson, students will be able to

B.4.1.1 Identify the common characteristics of birds.

B.4.1.2 Explain how birds are adapted to their environments.

Target Reading Skill

Previewing Visuals Explain that looking at the visuals before they read can help students activate prior knowledge and predict what subject they are beginning to read about.

Answers

Possible questions and answers include: **How are birds adapted for flight?** *(They have lightweight bones, wings, and contour feathers.)* **What is the function of contour feathers?** *(They give shape to the body and help the bird balance and steer during flight.)*

All in One Teaching Resources

- Transparency B35

Preteach

Build Background Knowledge

L2

Birds in Language

Invite students to generate a list of verbal expressions about birds; record each expression on the chalkboard. (*Samples: Birds of a feather flock together, eats like a bird, proud as a peacock*) Ask students if they think any of these have any basis in science. Again, record students' ideas. After students have read the section, have them reconsider the expressions, evaluating each on the basis of what they have learned.

Section 1 Birds

Reading Preview

Key Concepts

- What are the main characteristics of birds?
- How are birds adapted to their environments?

Key Terms

- bird
- contour feather
- down feather
- crop
- gizzard

Target Reading Skill

Previewing Visuals When you preview, you look ahead at the material to be read. Preview Figure 1. Then write two questions that you have about the diagram in a graphic organizer like the one below. As you read, answer your questions.

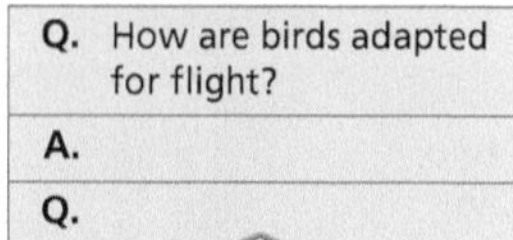

Adaptations for Flight

Q.	How are birds adapted for flight?
A.	
Q.	

Lab zone Discover Activity

What Are Feathers Like?

1. Observe the overall shape and structure of a feather. Then use a hand lens to examine the many hairlike barbs that project out from the feather's central shaft.
2. Gently separate two barbs in the middle of the feather. Rub the separated edges with your fingertip. How do they feel?
3. Use the hand lens to examine the edges of the two separated barbs. Draw a diagram of what you observe.
4. Rejoin the two separated barbs by gently pulling outward from the shaft. Then wash your hands.

Think It Over

Observing Once the barbs have been separated, is it easy to rejoin them? How might this be an advantage to the bird?

One day in 1861, in a limestone quarry in what is now Germany, Hermann von Meyer was inspecting rocks. Meyer, a fossil hunter, spotted something dark in a rock. It was the blackened imprint of a feather! Excited, he began searching for a fossil of an entire bird. He eventually found it—a skeleton surrounded by the imprint of many feathers. The fossil was given the scientific name *Archaeopteryx* (ahr kee AHP tur iks), meaning "ancient winged thing."

Paleontologists think that *Archaeopteryx* lived about 145 million years ago. *Archaeopteryx* didn't look much like the birds you know. It looked more like a reptile with wings. Unlike any modern bird, *Archaeopteryx* had a long, bony tail and a mouth full of teeth. But, unlike a reptile, it had feathers and wings. Paleontologists think that *Archaeopteryx* and modern birds descended from some kind of reptile, possibly a dinosaur.

◄ A model of *Archaeopteryx*

Lab zone Discover Activity

Skills Focus Observing L1

Materials feathers, hand lens

Time 15 minutes

Tips Try to have a variety of contour feathers. Good sources of feathers include pet stores and biological supply houses. Any fresh feathers should be frozen for 72 hours to kill any microorganisms. Point out the shaft and barbs of a feather.

Expected Outcome Students should observe that feathers have a central shaft with a vane made up of flexible barbs that link together but that can be pulled apart. The vanes of a flight feather are different widths.

Think It Over The barbs rejoin again, easily. This helps a bird quickly smooth its feathers in order to fly or swim.

Air spaces
No Teeth
Instead of heavy teeth, birds have a lightweight bill.
Lightweight Bones
Nearly hollow bones keep birds light in the air.
Wings
Bones of the forelimb are adapted as wings.
Hook
Barb
Contour Feathers
A series of hooks links the barbs of a feather together, keeping the feather smooth.

Characteristics of Birds

Modern **birds** all have certain characteristics in common. **A bird is an endothermic vertebrate that has feathers and a four-chambered heart. A bird also lays eggs.**

Adaptations for Flight The bodies of most birds are adapted for flight, as shown in Figure 1. Many of a bird's bones are nearly hollow, making the bird lightweight. In addition, the bones of a bird's forelimbs form wings. Flying birds have large chest muscles that move the wings. Finally, feathers help birds fly. Birds are the only animals with feathers.

Feathers are not all the same. If you have ever picked up a feather, it was probably a contour feather. A **contour feather** is one of the large feathers that give shape to a bird's body. The long contour feathers that extend beyond the body on the wings and tail are called flight feathers. When a bird flies, these feathers help it balance and steer. You can see in Figure 1 that a contour feather consists of a central shaft and many projections, called barbs. Hooks hold the barbs together. When birds fly, their barbs may pull apart, "unzipping" their feathers. Birds often pull the feathers through their bills to "zip" the barbs back together again.

In addition to contour feathers, birds have short, fluffy **down feathers** that are specialized to trap heat and keep the bird warm. Down feathers are found right next to the bird's skin, at the base of the contour feathers. Down feathers are soft and flexible, unlike contour feathers.

FIGURE 1
Adaptations for Flight
The bodies of most birds have adaptations for flight.
Interpreting Diagrams *What are two adaptations that make birds light?*

Instruct

Characteristics of Birds

Teach Key Concepts L2

Feather Facts

Focus Tell students that feathers distinguish birds from all other organisms.

Teach Point out that birds have different kinds of feathers. Ask: **Which feathers help shape a bird?** *(Contour feathers)* **Which feathers does a bird use for flight?** *(Contour)* **Describe down and explain its use.** *(Down feathers are short and fluffy and keep a bird warm.)*

Apply Some birds, such as ptarmigan and snowy owls, live within the Arctic and Antarctic circles. **What characteristic allows them to survive in such a cold environment?** *(Down feathers)* **learning modality: verbal**

All in One Teaching Resources

- Transparency B36

Address Misconceptions

Defining Characteristic

Focus Some students may think that "if it flies, it's a bird" or "if it lays eggs, it's a bird."

Teach Ask: **Give an example of an animal that can fly that is not a bird.** *(Bees and bats can fly.)* **Give an example of an animal that lays eggs but is not a bird.** *(Fishes, frogs, alligators, snakes)*

Apply Ask: **Why are egg-laying and flight not defining characteristics of birds?** *(Other animals can have these characteristics.)* **Why are feathers a defining characteristic of birds?** *(Only birds have feathers.)* **learning modality: logical/mathematical**

Independent Practice L2

All in One Teaching Resources

- Guided Reading and Study Worksheet: *Birds*

Student Edition on Audio CD

Monitor Progress L2

Oral Presentation Ask students to name at least four characteristics all birds share. *(Endothermic, vertebrates, feathers, four-chambered heart, lay eggs.)*

Answer

Figure 1 No teeth and nearly hollow bones

Differentiated Instruction

English Learners/Beginning L1

Vocabulary: Science Glossary Pair English learners with students proficient in English. Direct each pair to list terms such as *endothermic, vertebrate, feathers,* and *four-chambered heart*. Student pairs can compose a definition of each term and list two animals that share the characteristic. **learning modality: verbal**

English Learners/Intermediate L2

Vocabulary: Science Glossary After students write definitions for unfamiliar terms, direct them to write sentences in which they use each term. Have them rewrite the sentences on a separate sheet of paper, replacing key terms with a blank line. Partners can exchange papers and fill in the missing terms. **learning modality: verbal**

L2

Oxygen Delivery

Materials none

Time 10 minutes

Focus Tell students that birds need an efficient way to bring the additional oxygen they need for flying to their body cells.

Teach Have students find their resting pulse rates and count how many times they breathe in one minute. Suggest they record each of these figures. Next, have able students run in place for one minute. (**CAUTION:** *Students with medical problems that preclude running should be excused.*) Have students retake their pulse and breathing rates, record this information, and compare it to the "before run" data.

Apply Ask: **What happened to your heartbeat as you completed the physical activity?** *(The rate increased.)* **What do you think happens to a bird's heart and breathing rates when it flies?** *(They increase.)* **What features help birds get more oxygen to their muscles?** *(Air sacs and four-chambered heart)* **learning modality: kinesthetic**

For: Respiration and Circulation activity
Visit: PHSchool.com
Web Code: cep-2041

Compare and contrast the circulatory systems found in fishes, typical adult amphibians, and birds.

Go Online active art

For: Respiration and Circulation activity
Visit: PHSchool.com
Web Code: cep-2041

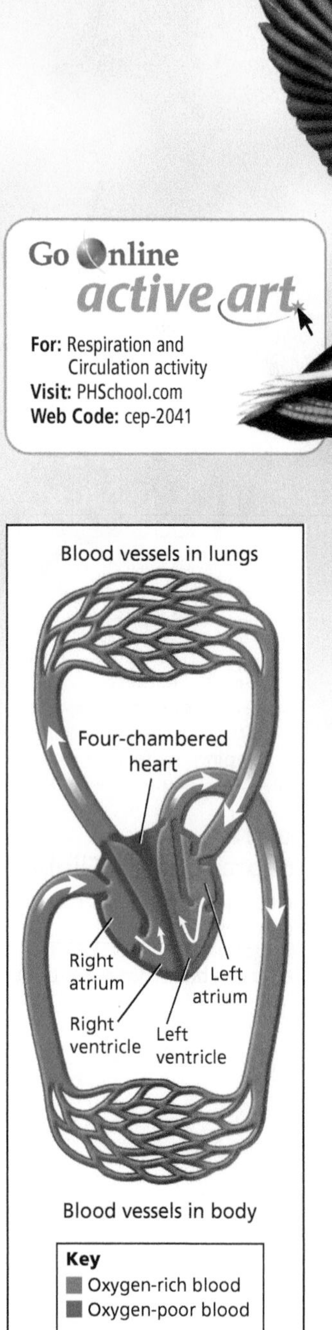

Air sacs
Lungs
Air sacs

Air Sacs
Multiple air sacs connect to the lungs.

Heart
The four-chambered heart keeps oxygen-rich blood separate from oxygen-poor blood.

FIGURE 2
Respiration and Circulation
Air sacs and a four-chambered heart help birds obtain oxygen and move it to their cells.
Applying Concepts *Why is a four-chambered heart efficient?*

Obtaining Oxygen Flying uses a lot of energy. Therefore, cells must receive plenty of oxygen to release the energy contained in food. Birds have a highly efficient way to get oxygen into their bodies and to their cells. Birds have a system of air sacs in their bodies. This system connects to the lungs. The air sacs enable birds to obtain more oxygen from each breath of air than other animals can.

The circulatory systems of birds are also efficient at getting oxygen to the cells. Birds have hearts with four chambers—two atria and two ventricles. Trace the path of blood through a bird's two-loop circulatory system in Figure 2. The right side of a bird's heart pumps oxygen-poor blood to the lungs, where oxygen is picked up. Oxygen-rich blood returns to the left side of the heart, which pumps it to the cells.

The advantage of a four-chambered heart over a three-chambered heart is that oxygen-rich blood does not mix with oxygen-poor blood. Therefore, blood carried to the cells of the body has plenty of oxygen.

Obtaining Food Birds must obtain a lot of food to provide the energy needed for flight. To capture, grip, and handle food, birds mainly use their bills. Bills are shaped to help birds feed quickly and efficiently. For example, the pointy, curved bill of a hawk acts like a meat hook to pull off bits of its prey. In contrast, a duck's bill acts like a kitchen strainer, separating out seeds and tiny animals from muddy pond water.

After a bird eats its food, digestion begins. Each organ in a bird's digestive system is adapted to process food. Many birds have an internal storage tank, or **crop,** for storing food inside the body after swallowing it. Find the crop in Figure 3. The crop is connected to the stomach.

The stomach has two parts. In the first part, food is bathed in chemicals that begin to break it down. Then the food moves to a thick-walled, muscular part of the stomach called the **gizzard.** The gizzard squeezes and grinds the partially digested food. Remember that birds do not have teeth. The gizzard does the same grinding function for birds that your teeth do for you. The gizzard may contain small stones that the bird has swallowed. These stones help grind the food by rubbing against it and crushing it.

What is a gizzard?

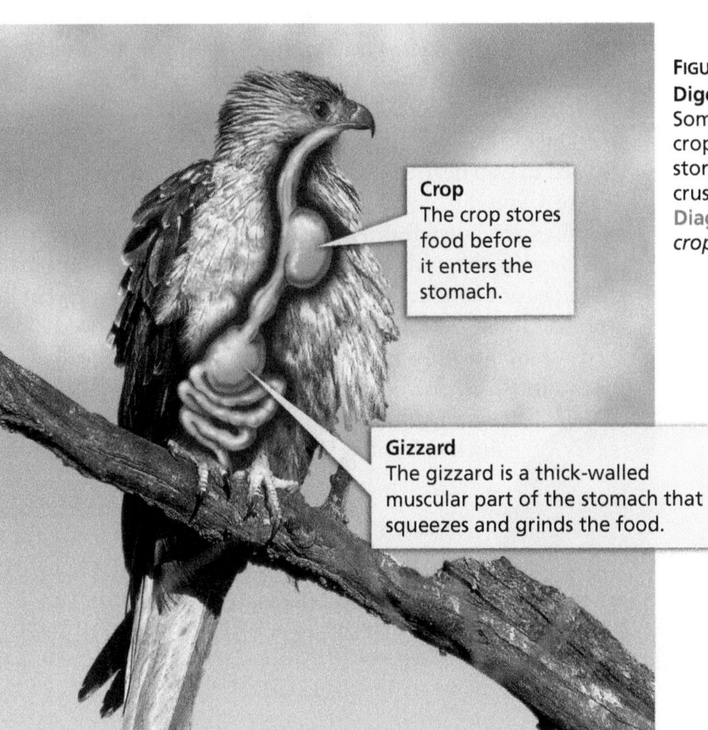
Crop
The crop stores food before it enters the stomach.
Gizzard
The gizzard is a thick-walled muscular part of the stomach that squeezes and grinds the food.

FIGURE 3
Digestive System of a Hawk
Some birds like this hawk have a crop and a gizzard. The crop stores food, and the gizzard crushes food. Interpreting Diagrams *Does food reach the crop or the gizzard first?*

L1

Model a Gizzard

Materials plastic jar, saltine cracker, several small pebbles

Time 10 minutes

Focus Tell students that occasionally they may see a bird swallow small pieces of stone and gravel. The small stones and gravel help a bird digest its food.

Teach Students can use saltines and pebbles to make a model of a bird's gizzard. Have students place the saltine, along with several small pebbles, in a plastic jar. Then have students put the lid on the jar and shake it for 30 seconds. Have students open the jar and observe the cracker. Students who are visually impaired can observe the results through tactile experience.

Apply Ask: **What has happened to the cracker?** *(It broke into smaller pieces.)* **How is the jar like a bird's gizzard?** *(They both use stones to grind the food.)* **How are they different?** *(A gizzard is a muscular wall that squeezes as it grinds food, the jar was a container that needed to be shaken.)* **learning modality: kinesthetic**

Help Students Read

L1

Relate Text and Visuals Refer to the Content Refresher, which provides the guidelines for Relating Text and Visuals. As students read about how a bird obtains oxygen, have them refer to Figure 2. Ask: **What does the illustration show you about the left and right chambers of the heart.** *(They are separate.)* **How do birds benefit from this characteristic?** *(Oxygen-rich and oxygen-poor blood do not mix. Therefore, the blood reaching cells is oxygen-rich.)*

All in One Teaching Resources
- Transparencies B37, B38, B39

Monitor Progress

L2

Skills Check Have students make a flowchart of the passage of food through a bird's digestive system. Students can save their flowcharts in their portfolio.

Portfolio

Answers

Figure 2 Oxygen-rich blood is kept separate from oxygen-poor blood.

Figure 3 The crop

Reading Checkpoint A gizzard is a thick-walled muscular part of the stomach in birds.

Build Inquiry

Keeping Warm L2

Materials 3 ice cubes, 3 plastic containers, aluminum foil, clock, cosmetic balls, down feathers, insulating materials such as shredded paper, plastic wrap, scrap of wool fabric

Time 35 minutes

Focus Show students the selection of insulators and ask them to rank the materials from least effective to most effective. Record the ranking so that students may check it when the activity is complete.

Teach Have students work in groups of four to test three different insulation materials. Each group should wrap an ice cube in one of the insulators, place it in a plastic container, and observe the container every 5 minutes for 30 minutes. Containers placed near a heat source or in sunlight may provide more dramatic results. Ask: **What variables must remain the same in order to test these materials properly?** *(Sample answer: The size and temperature of the ice cube and the container must be the same for all tested materials.)* Have groups describe and record their observations, for example: 10 minutes—beginning to melt; 20 minutes—nearly half melted; 25 minutes—all melted.

Apply Groups can compare data and draw conclusions about which materials are better insulators. Have students create a ranking according to their observations and compare it to the ranking they made at the beginning of the activity. Ask: **What can you conclude about down and its ability to insulate birds?** *(Down works well as an insulator.)* **learning modality: kinesthetic**

FIGURE 4
Keeping Warm
A pine grosbeak puffs out its feathers to trap air in the layer of down feathers next to its skin.

Keeping Conditions Stable Like all animals, birds use their food for energy. You know that birds need energy for flight. Because birds are endotherms, they also need a lot of energy to maintain their body temperature. Each day, an average bird eats food equal to about a quarter of its body weight. When people say, "You're eating like a bird," they usually mean that you're eating very little. But if you were actually eating as much as a bird does, you would be eating huge meals. You might be eating as many as 100 hamburger patties in one day!

To maintain their body temperature, birds use feathers as well as energy from food. As you read earlier, down feathers are specialized to trap heat. They are found right next to a bird's skin. In Figure 4, you can see what a down feather looks like. Unlike contour feathers, down feathers are soft and flexible. So, they mingle and overlap, trapping air. Air is a good insulator—a material that does not conduct heat well and therefore helps prevent heat from escaping. By trapping a blanket of warm air next to the bird's skin, down feathers slow the rate at which the skin loses heat. In effect, down feathers cover a bird in lightweight long underwear. Humans use down feathers from the eider duck to insulate jackets, sleeping bags, and bedding.

FIGURE 5
A Down-Filled Jacket
Wearing a jacket stuffed with down feathers helps this boy stay warm.
Applying Concepts *Why is his down jacket so puffy?*

Reproduction and Caring for Young Like reptiles, birds have internal fertilization and lay eggs. Bird eggs are similar to reptile eggs except that their shells are harder. In most bird species, the female lays the eggs in a nest that has been prepared by one or both parents.

Bird eggs will only develop at a temperature close to the body temperature of the parent bird. Thus, a parent bird usually incubates the eggs by sitting on them to keep them warm. In some species, incubating the eggs is the job of just one parent. For example, female robins incubate their eggs. In other species, such as pigeons, the parents take turns incubating the eggs. Chicks may take from 12 to 80 days to develop, depending on the species.

When it is ready to hatch, a chick pecks its way out of the eggshell. Some newly hatched chicks, such as ducks, chickens, and partridges, are covered with down and can run about soon after they have hatched. Other chicks, such as baby blue jays and robins, are featherless, blind, and so weak they can barely lift their heads to beg for food. Most parent birds feed and protect their young at least until they are able to fly.

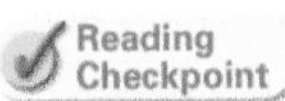

How is a bird egg different from a reptile egg?

Lab zone Try This **Activity**

"Eggs-amination"

1. Observe the surface of a chicken egg with a hand lens. Then gently crack the egg into a bowl. Do not break the yolk.
2. Note the membrane attached to the inside of the shell. Then look at the blunt end of the egg. What do you see?
3. Fill one part of the egg–shell with water. What do you observe?
4. Find the egg yolk. What is its function?
5. Look for a small white spot on the yolk. This marks the spot where the embryo would have developed if the egg had been fertilized.
6. Wash your hands with soap.

Observing Draw a labeled diagram of the egg that names each structure and describes its function.

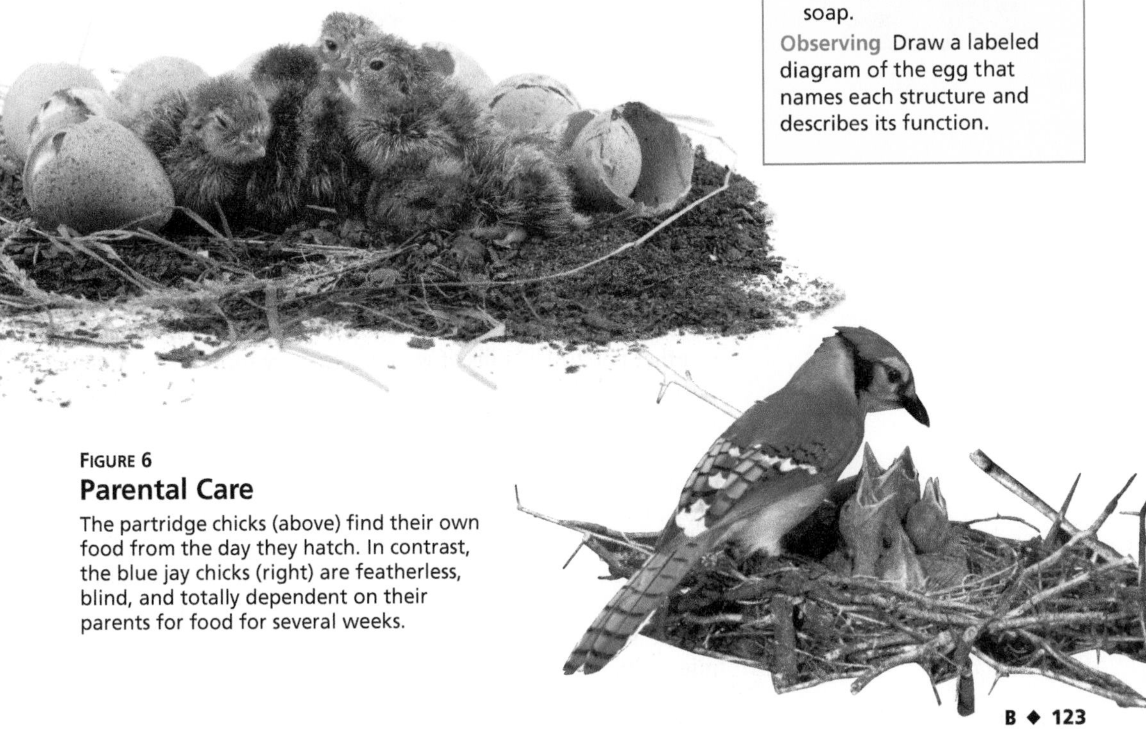

FIGURE 6
Parental Care
The partridge chicks (above) find their own food from the day they hatch. In contrast, the blue jay chicks (right) are featherless, blind, and totally dependent on their parents for food for several weeks.

Lab zone Teacher **Demo**

L1

Eggs' Shape and Strength

Materials 4 uncooked chicken eggs, clay, cosmetic balls, heavy book

Time 10 minutes

Focus Ask students to describe some characteristics an egg should have in order to decrease the risk of breaking. List students' suggestions on the chalkboard.

Teach Place the eggs in a triangular pattern, securing them with clay supports and placing the small end up. Place the cosmetic balls between the eggs so their sides do not touch. Ask: **What will happen when I place a book on the eggs?** *(Tally break/will not break on the chalkboard.)* Carefully place the book on the eggs to confirm students' observations.

Apply Ask: **How does the eggshell's strength benefit birds?** *(They will not break if they roll or when a bird sits on them.)* **learning modality: visual**

Lab zone Try This **Activity**

Skills Focus Observing L2

Materials bowl, hand lens, uncooked egg, water

Time 20 minutes

Tips Uncooked eggs can carry bacteria. Direct students not to put the eggs in their mouths.

Expected Outcome Step 2, air pocket between the shell and the membrane; Step 3, shell holds water; Step 4, yolk provides food. Diagrams should identify the white spot, shell, yolk, egg white, and membrane. Egg and shell keep the water inside, protect the embryo, and provide nourishment. **learning modality: visual**

Monitor Progress

L2

Oral Presentation Have students briefly describe activities related to parental care of unhatched and hatched young.

Answers

Figure 5 Down jackets are stuffed with down feathers. These feathers are good insulators because they are naturally fluffy so there can be many warm air pockets in the down. These pockets make the jacket puffy.

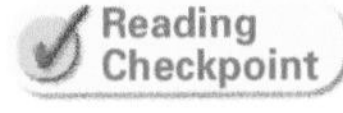

The eggshells of birds are harder than reptile shells.

Birds in the Environment

L2

Teach Key Concepts

Significant Adaptations

Focus Tell students that there are several characteristics they can use to group or classify birds.

Teach Indicate further that each characteristic is an adaptation so that the bird might feed, fly, build nests, or reproduce more easily. Ask: **How are long legs and toes helpful to birds that wade in water?** *(They allow birds to wade into waters as deep as their legs are long.)* **How is a duck's bill useful for feeding?** *(It filters many tiny plants and animals from the water.)* **How do sharp talons help hawks and eagles eat?** *(The talons allow the bird to grasp their prey firmly so that they can carry it to a nest and so that they can hold it while they tear the flesh.)*

Apply Invite students to think of another way they could use observable characteristics to group birds. *(Sample criteria: How and where they nest, how they communicate with one another, how they mark their territory)* **learning modality: logical/mathematical**

Help Students Read

L1

Summarize Summarizing the information presented in the text will help students focus on main ideas and remember what they read. Have students read the text related to the diversity of birds. Ask students to summarize the ways in which birds may be different from one another. **learning modality: verbal**

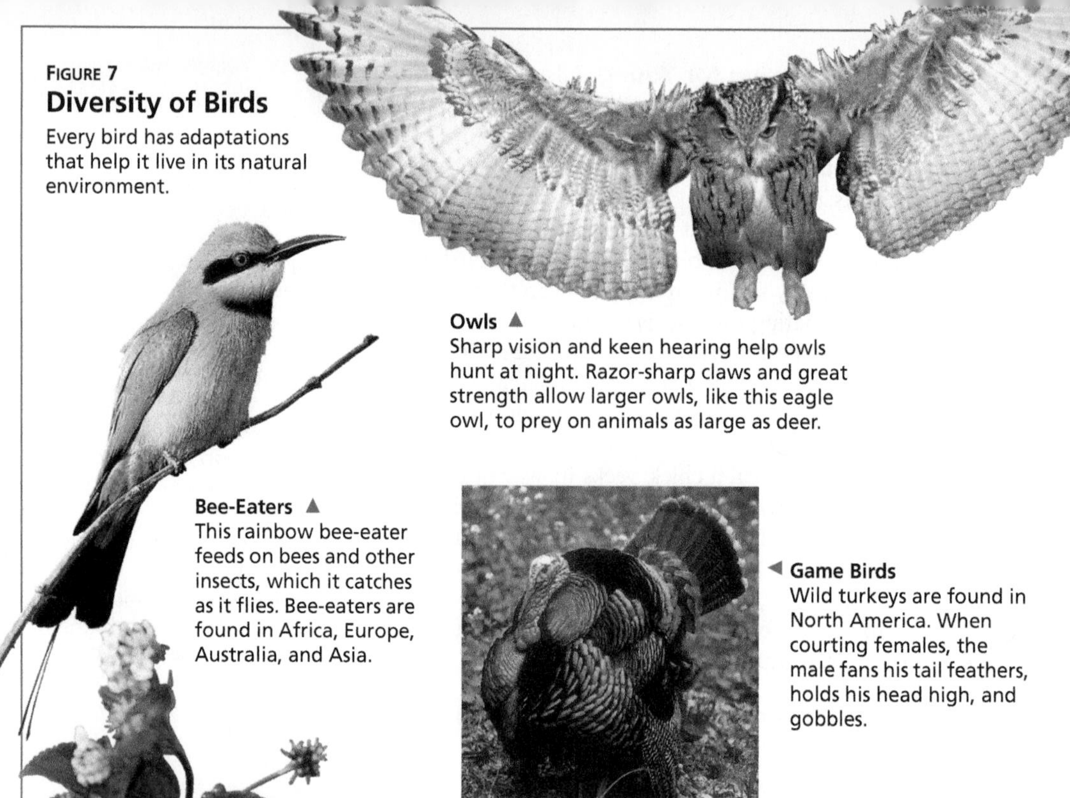

FIGURE 7
Diversity of Birds
Every bird has adaptations that help it live in its natural environment.

Owls ▲
Sharp vision and keen hearing help owls hunt at night. Razor-sharp claws and great strength allow larger owls, like this eagle owl, to prey on animals as large as deer.

Bee-Eaters ▲
This rainbow bee-eater feeds on bees and other insects, which it catches as it flies. Bee-eaters are found in Africa, Europe, Australia, and Asia.

◀ Game Birds
Wild turkeys are found in North America. When courting females, the male fans his tail feathers, holds his head high, and gobbles.

Birds in the Environment

With almost 10,000 species, birds are the most diverse land-dwelling vertebrates. **Birds are adapted for living in diverse environments. You can see some of these adaptations in the shapes of their legs, claws, and bills.** For example, the long legs and toes of wading birds, such as herons, cranes, and spoonbills, make wading easy. The claws of perching birds, such as goldfinches and mockingbirds, can lock onto a branch or other perch. The bills of woodpeckers are tools for chipping into the wood of trees. Birds also have adaptations for finding mates and caring for their young.

Birds play an important role in the environment. Nectar-eating birds, like hummingbirds, are pollinators. Seed-eating birds, like sparrows, carry the seeds of plants to new places. This happens when the birds eat the fruits or seeds of a plant, fly to a new location, and then eliminate some of the seeds in digestive wastes. In addition, birds are some of the chief predators of animals that may be pests. Hawks and owls eat rats and mice, while many perching birds feed on insect pests.

Ostriches ▼
The ostrich, found in Africa, is the largest living bird. It cannot fly, but it can run at speeds greater than 60 kilometers per hour. Its speed helps it escape from predators.

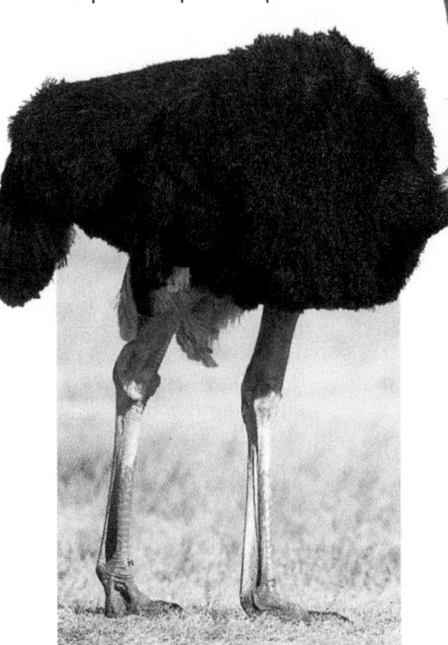

◀ Long-Legged Waders
The roseate spoonbill is found in the southern United States and throughout much of South America. The spoonbill catches small animals by sweeping its long, flattened bill back and forth under water.

Perching Birds ▶
Perching birds represent more than half of all the bird species in the world. The painted bunting, a seed-eating bird, lives in the southern United States and northern Mexico.

Section 1 Assessment

Target Reading Skill Previewing Visuals Refer to your questions and answers about Figure 1 to help you answer Question 1 below.

Reviewing Key Concepts

1. a. Identifying What characteristics do birds share?
   b. Explaining How is a bird's body adapted for flight?
   c. Relating Cause and Effect Why do birds need so much oxygen? What adaptation helps them obtain oxygen?
2. a. Listing What are three types of adaptations that allow birds to survive in diverse environments?
   b. Summarizing What are three roles birds play in the environment?
   c. Comparing and Contrasting Look at Figure 7. Compare and contrast the adaptations of an eagle owl and a roseate spoonbill for obtaining food.

Lab zone At-Home Activity

Count Down With the help of a family member, look for products in your home that contain down feathers. (*Hint:* Don't forget to check closets!) What kinds of items contain down feathers? What common purpose do these items have? Explain to your family member what down feathers look like and where they are found on a bird.

Assess

Reviewing Key Concepts

1. a. All birds are endothermic vertebrates with feathers and a four-chambered heart, and all lay eggs. **b.** Adaptations for flight include bones in the forelimbs modified as wings, lightweight bones, lack of teeth, large chest muscles, and feathers. **c.** Birds need a lot of oxygen to release the energy from food required for flying. Air sacs enable birds to obtain more oxygen per breath than other animals can. A four-chambered heart keeps oxygen-rich blood and oxygen-poor blood separate, so blood carried to the cells has more oxygen than if the blood were mixed.
2. a. Legs, claws, and bills **b.** Pollinators, seed-carriers, and predators of pests. **c.** The eagle owl has sharp vision and keen hearing for hunting at night. It also has sharp claws and great strength for killing large prey. The spoonbill has long legs so that it can wade in water; its bill is shaped to catch prey in water.

Reteach L1

Have students describe the kind of feathers used for flight.

Performance Assessment L2

Writing Have each student list and describe at least five adaptations of birds. Students should describe feathers, the four-chambered heart, feeding and digestive system adaptations, and reproductive adaptations. Students can save their descriptions in their portfolios. Portfolio

All in One Teaching Resources

- Section Summary: *Birds*
- Review and Reinforce: *Birds*
- Enrich: *Birds*

Lab zone Chapter Project

Keep Students on Track Provide field guides to help students identify visiting species. Suggest observing the feeders at different times of day. Cardinals, for instance, are early eaters while sparrows feed later. Check to see that students are recording appropriate observations. As students proceed with their observations, meet with them regularly to discuss their progress.

Lab zone At-Home Activity

Count Down L2 Tell students that all clothing and bedding materials must be labeled with the materials that they are made from. Students may find down in items such as bed pillows, comforters, furniture cushions, and winter coats.

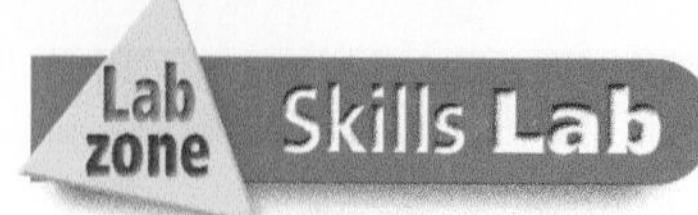

Looking at an Owl's Leftovers

Prepare for Inquiry

Key Concept

Students draw conclusions about an animal's diet by examining the parts of the diet not digested.

Skills Objectives

During this lab, students will be able to

- observe and analyze the components of an owl pellet
- draw conclusions about an owl's diet by studying the pellets it coughs up

Prep Time 20 minutes
Class Time 50 minutes

Advance Planning

Order owl pellets from a biological supply company. If possible, obtain one for each student and a few extras.

Safety

  Students should wear safety goggles and handle the sharp dissecting needles carefully. Remind students to wash their hands thoroughly after completing the dissection. Review the safety guidelines in Appendix A.

All in One Teaching Resources

- Lab Worksheet: *Looking at an Owl's Leftovers*

Guide Inquiry

Invitation

Have students think about what they discard when they eat. Ask: **What do you have left over when you eat a chicken wing? When you eat an apple?** *(Bones, apple core)* Tell students that other animals also leave behind parts of their food and these leftovers can be studied to determine the animal's diet.

Introduce the Procedure

Allow students time to practice with dissecting needles by examining a cookie with nuts, chips, or raisins. (**CAUTION:** *Tell students not to eat the cookies.*)

Encourage students to examine the outside of the pellet before making their predictions. Provide pictures of lizard, rat, and snake bones to help students identify them.

Lab zone Skills Lab

Looking at an Owl's Leftovers

Problem

What can you learn about owls' diets from studying the pellets that they cough up?

Skills Focus

observing, drawing conclusions

Materials

- owl pellet • hand lens • dissecting needle
- metric ruler • forceps

Procedure   

1. An owl pellet is a collection of undigested materials that an owl coughs up after a meal. Write a hypothesis describing what items you expect an owl pellet to contain. List the reasons for your hypothesis.
2. Use a hand lens to observe the outside of an owl pellet. Record your observations.
3. Use one hand to grasp the owl pellet with forceps. Hold a dissecting needle in your other hand, and use it to gently separate the pellet into pieces. **CAUTION:** *Dissecting needles are sharp. Never cut material toward you; always cut away from your body.*
4. Using the forceps and dissecting needle, carefully separate the bones from the rest of the pellet. Remove any fur that might be attached to bones.
5. Group similar bones together in separate piles. Observe the skulls, and draw them. Record the number of skulls, their length, and the number, shape, and color of the teeth.
6. Use the chart on the right to determine what kinds of skulls you found. If any skulls do not match the chart exactly, record which animal skulls they resemble most.

Skull Identification Key

Shrew 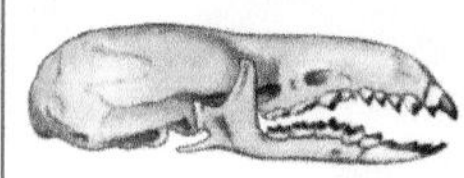	Upper jaw has at least 18 teeth; tips of the teeth are reddish brown. Skull length is 23 mm or less.
House mouse 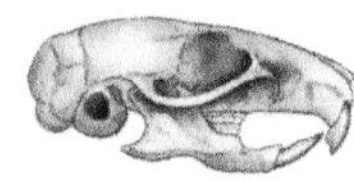	Upper jaw has two biting teeth and extends past lower jaw. Skull length is 22 mm or less.
Meadow vole 	Upper jaw has two biting teeth that are smooth, not grooved. Skull length is 23 mm or more.
Mole 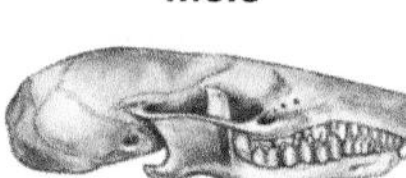	Upper jaw has at least 18 teeth. Skull length is 23 mm or more.
Rat 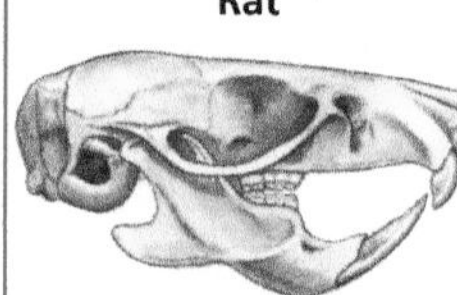	Upper jaw has two biting teeth. Upper jaw extends past lower jaw. Skull length is 22 mm or more.

7. Try to fit together any of the remaining bones to form complete or partial skeletons. Sketch your results.
8. Wash your hands thoroughly with soap when you are finished.

Analyze and Conclude

1. **Observing** How many animals' remains were in the pellet? What observations led you to that conclusion?
2. **Drawing Conclusions** Combine your results with the results of your classmates. Based on your class's data, which three animals were eaten most frequently? How do these results compare to your hypothesis?
3. **Calculating** Owls cough up about two pellets a day. Based on your class's data, what can you conclude about the number of animals an owl might eat in one month?
4. **Communicating** In this lab, you were able to examine only the part of the owl's diet that it did not digest. In a paragraph, explain how this fact might affect your confidence in the conclusions you reached.

Design an Experiment

Design an experiment to determine how an owl's diet varies at different times of the year. Give an example of a hypothesis you could test with such an experiment. What variables would you control? Before carrying out your experiment, obtain your teacher's approval of your plan.

Troubleshooting the Experiment

Explain that the pellets have been decontaminated. Reluctant students can work with a partner and perform data collection and record keeping. Break pellets into pieces and soak them in water to loosen materials before beginning the dissection.

Expected Outcome

Students should find varying numbers of identifiable animal remains in the pellets.

Analyze and Conclude

1. Answers will vary. Students should explain that the number of each type of bone could help determine the number of animals eaten. For example, each skull or each pair of femurs represents one animal.
2. Combined data should give an estimate of the total number and type of animals in the pellets.
3. The estimated total of animals found in all pellets divided by the number of pellets gives an average number of animals per pellet. Students can multiply this number by 2 to find the number of animals eaten per day. Then, multiplying the average number by 30 gives the average number of animals eaten in a month.
4. Students may explain that they are less confident in their results because they will probably underestimate the number of animals eaten each month.

Extend Inquiry

Design an Experiment A sample study might analyze pellets collected on the last two days of each month for a year. From this study, students would expect to conclude that an owl's diet varies during the year. In winter, hibernating animals will be absent. Animals such as house mice, which are always active, may be common in the diet all year.

Section 2

The Physics of Bird Flight

Objectives

After this lesson, students will be able to

B.4.2.1 Explain how a bird is able to fly.

B.4.2.2 Identify three types of flight birds use.

Target Reading Skill

Relating Cause and Effect Explain that *cause* is the reason why something happens. The *effect* is what happens as a result of the cause. Relating cause and effect helps students make a connection between the reason for what happens and the result.

Answers

Possible causes include: Air flows around wing; the shape of wing causes differences in air pressure that produces an upward force; contour feathers give wings a smooth shape.

All in One Teaching Resources

- Transparency B40

Preteach

Build Background Knowledge L1

Imitating Bird Flight

Ask students to demonstrate and describe birds in flight. *(Some students will flap their arms up and down, while others will glide with their arms outstretched.)* Call students' attention to this difference. Ask students to speculate about how some birds fly without seeming to put forth any effort.

Section 2

Integrating Physics

The Physics of Bird Flight

Reading Preview

Key Concepts

- What causes a bird to rise in the air?
- How may birds fly?

Key Term

- lift

Target Reading Skill

Relating Cause and Effect A cause makes something happen. An effect is what happens. As you read, identify the physical properties of a bird's wing that cause lift. Write them in a graphic organizer like the one below.

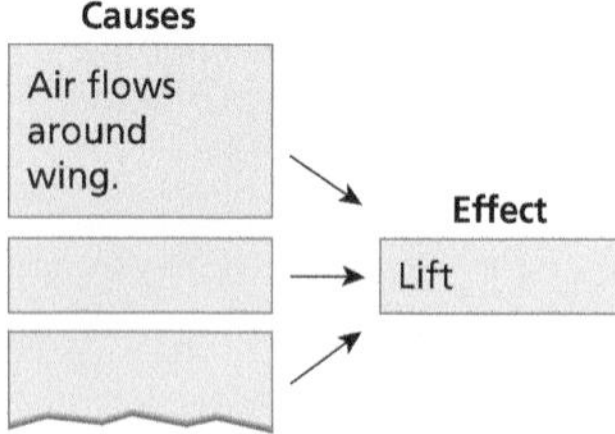

Lab zone Discover Activity

What Lifts Airplanes and Birds Into the Air?

1. Cut a strip of notebook paper 5 centimeters wide and 28 centimeters long. Insert about 5 centimeters of the paper strip into the middle of a book. The rest of the paper strip should hang over the edge.
2. Hold the book up so that the paper is below your mouth.
3. Blow gently across the top of the paper and watch what happens to the paper. Then blow harder.

Think It Over

Predicting If a strong current of air flowed across the top of a bird's outstretched wing, what might happen to the bird?

From ancient times, people have dreamed of soaring into the air like birds. When people first started experimenting with flying machines, they tried to glue feathers to their arms or to strap on feathered wings. Many failures, crash-landings, and broken bones later, these people had learned that feathers by themselves weren't the secret of flight.

Staying in the Air

All objects on land are surrounded by an invisible ocean of air. Air is a mixture of gas molecules that exert pressure on the objects they surround. Although you cannot see air pressure, you can see the results of air pressure. For example, when you blow into a balloon, it gets larger. The pressure of the air molecules pushing on the sides of the balloon makes it expand.

FIGURE 8
Bird Feather
Contour feathers give a smooth shape to a bird's body and wings. This smooth shape is helpful for flight.

Lab zone Discover Activity

Skills Focus Predicting L1

Materials notebook paper, scissors, metric ruler, book

Time 10 minutes

Tips The paper should be curled so that the free edge of the strip faces away from the student. Make certain students hold the book so that their breath flows across the top of the paper strip—not down on the paper. Before students complete Step 3, ask them to predict what will happen. Then have them complete Step 3 and determine if their predictions were accurate.

Expected Outcome When students blow gently across the paper, the paper lifts slightly. Blowing harder lifts the strip higher and it remains in a horizontal position.

Think It Over The air flowing over the bird's wing might lift the bird up into the air.

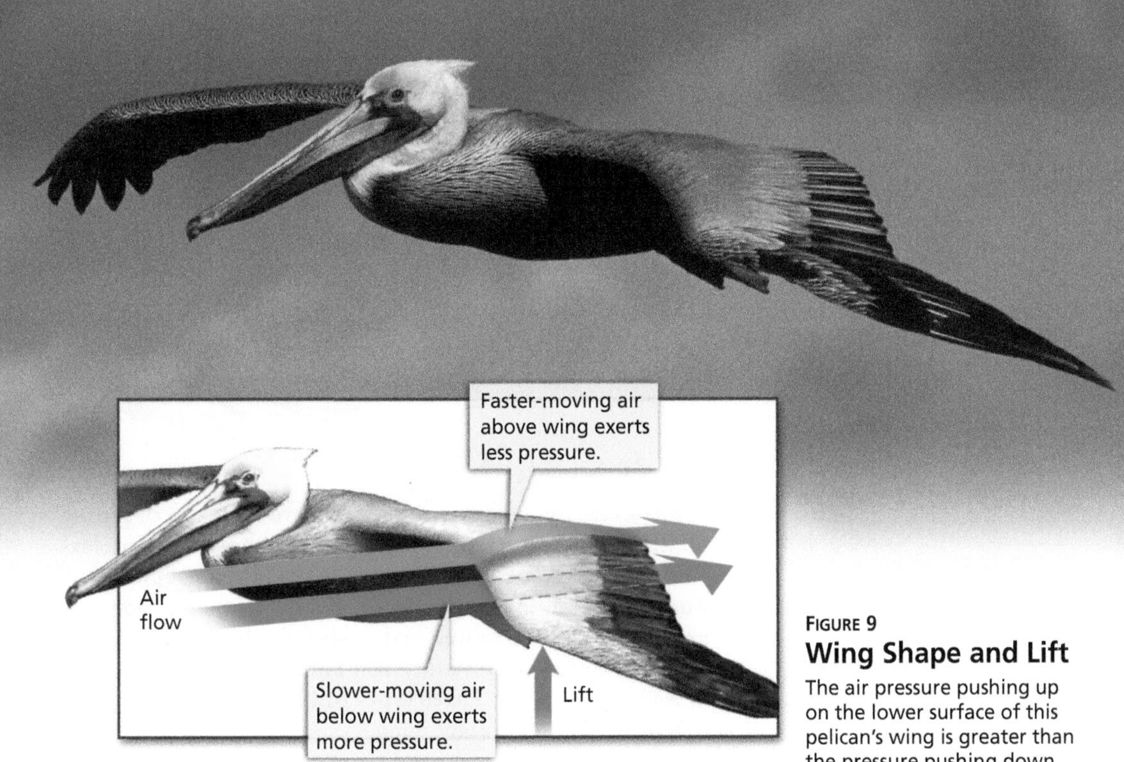

FIGURE 9
Wing Shape and Lift
The air pressure pushing up on the lower surface of this pelican's wing is greater than the pressure pushing down on its upper surface.
Relating Cause and Effect
How does the difference in pressure help a bird fly?

Movement and Air Pressure Air does not have to be inside a balloon to exert pressure. Moving air exerts pressure, too. The faster air moves, the less pressure it exerts. You saw this in the Discover Activity. The air blowing across the top of the paper was in motion. This moving air exerted less pressure on the paper than the air beneath it, so the paper rose.

Air Movement Around a Wing Like the paper, a flying bird's wing is surrounded by air molecules that exert pressure on the wing's surfaces. The wing allows air to flow smoothly over and under it. When a bird is between wing beats, the angle and shape of the wing cause the air to move faster above the wing than below it, as shown in Figure 9. The faster-moving air above the bird's wing exerts less pressure than the slower-moving air below it. **The difference in pressure above and below the wings as a bird moves through the air produces an upward force that causes the bird to rise.** That upward force is called **lift.**

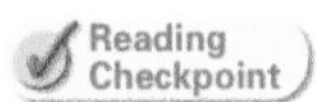

As air moves faster, what happens to the pressure it exerts?

Discovery
CHANNEL
SCHOOL
Birds and Mammals
Video Preview
▶Video Field Trip
Video Assessment

Instruct

Staying in the Air

Use Visuals: Figure 9 L2
Airfoils

Focus Direct students' attention to Figure 9.

Teach Point out that the angle and shape of a bird's wing allows air to flow around it in a specific manner. Ask: **Which exerts greater air pressure—moving air or air that is not moving?** *(Air that is not moving)* **How is air pressure affected when air moves faster?** *(Faster air produces less air pressure.)* **What is the result of faster-moving air above a bird's wing?** *(The pressure is less above the wing.)* **How does a difference in air pressure help a bird to fly?** *(It creates an upward force that lifts the bird.)* **learning modality: visual**

All in One Teaching Resources
- Transparency B41

All in One Teaching Resources
- Guided Reading and Study Worksheet: *The Physics of Bird Flight*

Student Edition on Audio CD

Birds and Mammals
Show the Video Field Trip to help students understand the adaptations of birds that enable them to fly. Discussion question: **Describe three adaptations for flight found in most birds.** *(Wing shape; strong chest muscles; nearly hollow bones; four-chambered hearts; two distinct pathways in the circulatory system.)*

Differentiated Instruction

Gifted and Talented L3
Relating Wing Shape and Flight Pattern Some students may be interested in comparing most efficient wing shape and specific flight mode. Encourage students to use available reference sources to produce a visual presentation relating wing shape, flight type, and example species. *(Examples: narrow, pointed wings for gliding long distances—seabirds, gulls, albatross; large surface area wings for soaring—eagles, storks, pelicans; short, rounded wings for rapid takeoffs, good maneuverability—pheasants, forest birds)* **learning modality: visual**

Monitor Progress L2

Answers

Figure 9 The difference in pressure creates lift.

As air moves faster, it exerts less pressure.

Birds in Flight

Teach Key Concepts

L2

Flying Is More Than Flapping

Focus Review the wing motions of a bird in flight. (Many students may indicate that a bird flaps its wings.)

Teach Indicate to students that some birds can cover great distances without flapping their wings. Ask: **How do some birds fly without flapping their wings?** (*They extend their wings and allow warm air currents to carry them upwards.*) **How can a bird fly without using lift?** (*By diving*) **What does a bird do with its wings when it dives?** (*Tucks them in*)

Apply Tell students that an albatross travels hundreds of miles over the ocean with no place to land. Ask: **Why is it useful for an albatross to be able to soar and glide?** (*Saves energy; the bird does not have to continuously flap its wings.*) Have students model the actual wing motions a bird uses while it flies. **learning modality: verbal**

Go Online PHSchool.com

For: More on bird adaptations
Visit: PHSchool.com
Web Code: ced-2042

Students can review bird adaptations in an online activity.

FIGURE 10
Types of Flight
Flapping, soaring and gliding, and diving are three types of flight. Applying Concepts *Which type of flight requires the most energy? Explain.*

Flapping allows these macaws to lift off and move forward through the air.

Birds in Flight

Before a bird can use lift to fly, it must have some way of getting off the ground. To get into the air, a bird pushes off with its legs and moves forward at the same time. The bird must move forward to make air move over its wings. Sharply pulling down its wings provides the power that pushes the bird forward. The forward motion creates lift. When birds are in the air, they fly in a variety of ways. **Three types of bird flight are flapping, soaring and gliding, and diving.**

Flapping Once in flight, all birds continue to flap their wings at least part of the time. To flap, a bird must sharply pull down its wings as it did when it pushed off the ground. Most small birds, such as sparrows, depend heavily on flapping flight. Canada geese and many other birds that travel long distances also use flapping flight. Flapping requires a lot of energy.

Soaring and Gliding Unlike flapping flight, soaring and gliding flight involve little wing movement. Birds soar and glide with their wings extended. When soaring, birds use rising currents of warm air to move upward. In contrast, when gliding, birds use falling currents of cool air to move downward. Soaring and gliding use less energy than flapping because they require less wing movement.

Sometimes birds fly using a combination of soaring and gliding. They "take the elevator up" by flying into a current of warm, rising air. The birds stretch their wings out and circle round and round, moving upward within the current of rising air. As the warm air rises it starts to cool. Finally, the air stops rising. At this point the bird begins gliding downward until it reaches another "up elevator" of rising air.

Lab zone Try This Activity

It's Plane to See

1. Work with a partner to design a paper airplane with wings shaped like those of a bird. You can use any of these materials: paper, tape, glue, paper clips, string, rubber bands, and staples. Draw a sketch of your design.
2. Construct your "birdplane" and make one or two trial flights. If necessary, modify your design and try again.
3. Compare your design with those of other groups. Which designs were most successful?

Making Models In what ways was the flight of your airplane like the flight of a bird? In what ways was it different?

130 ◆ B

Lab zone Try This Activity

Skills Focus Making models L3

Materials Sheets of different kinds of paper (letter, construction, foil-covered), tape, glue, paper clips, string, rubber bands, staples

Time 30 minutes

Tips Discuss with students their ideas for an airplane design that allows air to flow rapidly over the nose and wing.

Expected Outcome Both flights are the result of lift. However, a bird moves its wings, the airplane glides.

Extend Have students select a factor such as distance or time and compute the average for all their flights. **learning modality: kinesthetic**

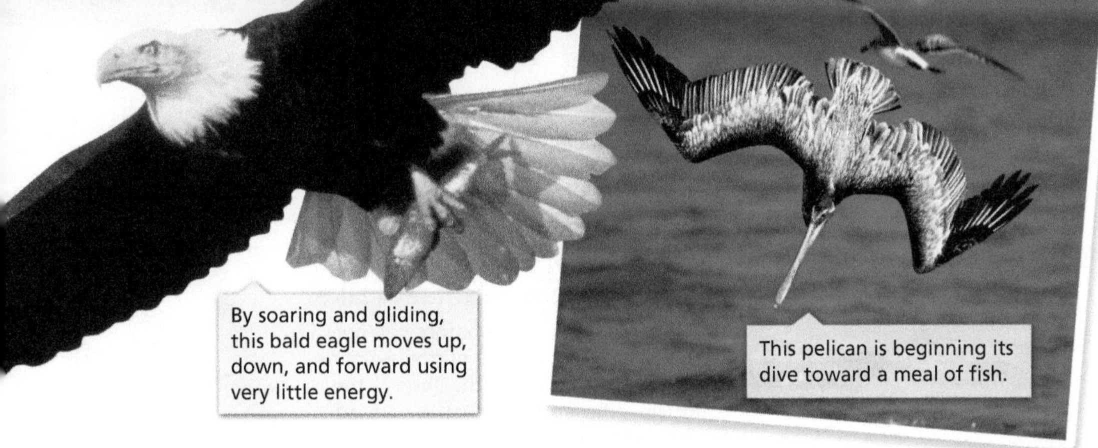

By soaring and gliding, this bald eagle moves up, down, and forward using very little energy.
This pelican is beginning its dive toward a meal of fish.

Diving A type of flight that doesn't use lift is diving. Birds that hunt their prey from the sky may use diving flight. For example, a brown pelican flies above the ocean, looking for schools of fish under the water's surface. Once it spots the fish, the pelican dives with great speed. As it dives, the pelican pulls its wings in close to its body. Pulling in the wings changes the pelican's body shape. The new body shape produces no lift at all. Without lift, the pelican falls from the sky headfirst into the ocean and hits the fish with enough force to stun them.

Some hawks and falcons dive from high in the sky towards their prey, too. Peregrine falcons can clock speeds up to 300 kilometers per hour while diving for pigeons or other prey.

 **Which type of bird flight is the fastest?**

For: More on bird adaptations
Visit: PHSchool.com
Web Code: ced-2042

Section 2 Assessment

Target Reading Skill Relating Cause and Effect Refer to your graphic organizer about lift to help you answer Question 1 below.

Reviewing Key Concepts

1. a. Defining What is lift?
   b. Explaining What effect does lift have on a flying bird?
   c. Applying Concepts What causes lift in an airplane?
2. a. Identifying What are three types of bird flight?
   b. Summarizing How does a bird take off from the ground to fly?
   c. Comparing and Contrasting How are soaring and gliding alike? How are they different?

Writing in Science

Advertisement You have been hired by an outdoor adventure company to write an exciting ad for one of their birdwatching hikes. In the ad, describe several interesting birds and types of bird flight that people will see on the hike.

Lab zone Chapter Project

Keep Students on Track At this point, students should have a list of the various species of birds that visit their feeders. While students continue general observations, they should also concentrate on observing specific feeding behaviors. Feeding behavior includes how birds perch while eating, how birds use their beaks, and rituals such as head bobbing. Review students' notebooks and monitor their progress.

Writing in Science

Writing Mode Persuasion

Scoring Rubric

4 Includes accurate, detailed descriptions of at least four birds

3 Includes accurate descriptions of two or three birds

2 Includes brief descriptions of two birds

1 Includes inaccurate or incomplete descriptions

Students can save their advertisements in their portfolios.

Monitor Progress L2

Answers

Figure 10 Flapping; it takes energy to push off from the ground, pull wings down, and flap during flight.

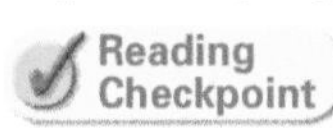 Diving

Assess

Reviewing Key Concepts

1. a. Lift is an upward force on a bird's wing. **b.** Lift keeps the flying bird up in the air. **c.** The angle and shape of an airplane's wing causes lift.

2. a. Flapping, soaring and gliding, diving **b.** To take off, a bird pushes off the ground with its legs and pulls its wings down at the same time. **c.** In both soaring and gliding, a bird's wings are extended and there is little wing movement. When soaring, birds use rising currents of warm air to move upward. When gliding, birds use falling currents of cool air to move downward.

Reteach L1

Have students use Figure 9 to explain how wing shape enables a bird to fly.

Performance Assessment L2

Drawing Have students draw and label the wing of a flying bird. Tell them to use arrows to show the direction in which the air moves over the wing, and clearly label areas of higher and lower pressure. *(Students' drawings should indicate that air moves over the wing from front to back. The area of lower pressure is over the wing, and the area of higher pressure is beneath the wing.)*

All in One Teaching Resources

- Section Summary: *The Physics of Bird Flight*
- Review and Reinforce: *The Physics of Bird Flight*
- Enrich: *The Physics of Bird Flight*

Section 3 Mammals

Objectives

After this lesson, students will be able to

B.4.3.1 Describe the characteristics common to all mammals.

B.4.3.2 List the three main groups of mammals.

Target Reading Skill

Building Vocabulary Explain that using vocabulary strategies, such as defining words by their context, helps students define Key Concept words.

Answers

Students' definitions will vary but should convey an accurate meaning for the context.

Preteach

Build Background Knowledge L2

Survey of Pet Mammals

Ask students who have mammals as pets to describe their pets' physical characteristics and behavior. Students can use their descriptions as a foundation for making generalizations about the characteristics of mammals. Record their generalizations on the chalkboard. After students complete the section, return to the generalizations and have students correct any incorrect statements.

Section 3 Mammals

Reading Preview

Key Concepts

- What characteristics do all mammals share?
- What are the main groups of mammals and how do they differ?

Key Terms

- mammal • mammary gland
- diaphragm • monotreme
- marsupial • gestation period
- placental mammal • placenta

Target Reading Skill

Building Vocabulary A definition states the meaning of a word or phrase by telling about its most important feature or function. After you read the section, reread the paragraphs that contain definitions of Key Terms. Use all the information you have learned to write a definition of each Key Term in your own words.

Lab zone Discover Activity

What Are Mammals' Teeth Like?

1. Wash your hands before you begin. Then, with a small mirror, examine the shapes of your teeth. Observe the incisors (the front teeth); the pointed canine teeth; the premolars behind the canine teeth; and the molars, which are the large teeth in the very back.
2. Compare and contrast the structures of the different kinds of teeth.
3. Use your tongue to feel the cutting surfaces of the different kinds of teeth in your mouth.
4. Bite off a piece of cracker and chew it. Observe the teeth that you use to bite and chew. Wash your hands when you are finished.

Think It Over

Inferring What is the advantage of having teeth with different shapes?

High in the Himalaya Mountains of Tibet, several yaks inch their way, single file, along a narrow cliff path. The cliff plunges thousands of meters to the valley below, so one false step can mean disaster. But the sure-footed yaks, carrying heavy loads of grain, slowly but steadily cross the cliff and make their way through the mountains.

▲ Himalayan yak

People who live in the mountains of central Asia have depended on yaks for thousands of years. Not only do yaks carry materials for trade, they also pull plows and provide milk. Mountain villagers weave blankets from yak hair and make shoes and ropes from yak hides.

The yak is a member of the group of vertebrates called **mammals.** Today about 4,000 different species of mammals exist. Some, like the yak and wildebeest, you may never have seen. But others, such as dogs, cats, and mice are very familiar to you. What characteristics do mammals share?

Lab zone Discover Activity

Skills Focus Inferring L1

Materials cracker, hand mirror

Time 15 minutes

Tips  Tell students that the tooth arrangement from the middle of the row to the back is 2 incisors, 1 canine, 2 premolars, and 3 molars.

Direct students to wash their hands before they feel their teeth with their fingers.

Think It Over Teeth with different shapes are adapted for different functions. A variety of teeth means that a variety of foods can be eaten.

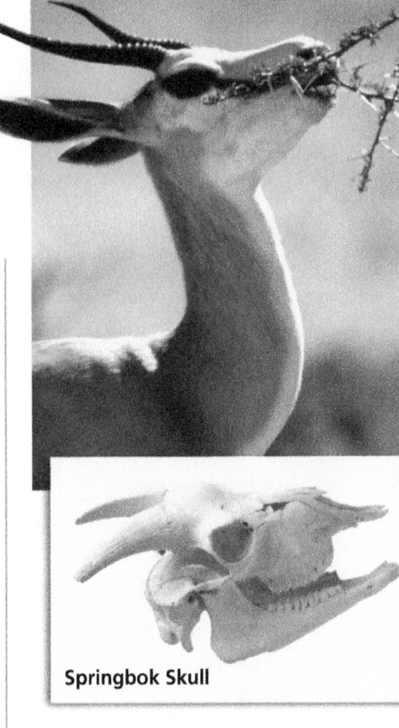

FIGURE 11
Teeth of Different Shapes
Lions have sharp, pointed canines. Springboks have broad molars.
Inferring *What kind of diet does each of these mammals eat?*

Characteristics of Mammals

All mammals are endothermic vertebrates that have a four-chambered heart and skin covered with fur or hair. Most mammals are born alive, and every young mammal is fed with milk produced by organs in its mother's body. These organs are called **mammary glands.** The word *mammal,* in fact, comes from the term *mammary.*

Obtaining Food In addition to their other characteristics, most mammals have teeth. Their teeth are adapted to chew their food, breaking it into small bits that make digestion easier. Most mammals have teeth with four different shapes. If you did the Discover Activity, you observed these shapes. Incisors are flat-edged teeth used to bite off and cut food. Canines are pointed teeth that stab food and tear into it. Premolars and molars have broad, flat upper surfaces for grinding and shredding food.

The size, shape, and hardness of a mammal's teeth reflect its diet. For example, the canines of carnivores are especially large and sharp. Large carnivores, such as the lion in Figure 11, use their canines to hold their prey while they kill it. In contrast, herbivores, such as a springbok, have molars for grinding and mashing plants.

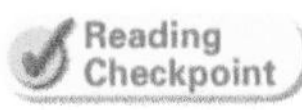

Which teeth stab and tear into food?

Instruct

Characteristics of Mammals

Teach Key Concepts L2

Size as an Advantage

Focus Remind students that size can play a role in an animal's survival.

Teach Tell students that small, early mammals lived at the same time as the dinosaurs. Ask: **What might be the advantage of being small at the time of the dinosaurs?** *(Sample answer: Small animals could hide in small spaces to avoid the dinosaurs. Small animals might be hard to see as they run along the ground.)*

Apply Ask: **If dinosaurs were active mostly during the day, what other characteristic might help a small mammal survive?** *(Sample answer: To be active at night)* **learning modality: logical/mathematical**

Independent Practice L2

All in One Teaching Resources

- Guided Reading and Study Worksheet: *Mammals*

Student Edition on Audio CD

Differentiated Instruction

Less Proficient Readers L1

Some students may need extra help remembering names for the types of teeth. Obtain a model or preserved jaw of an herbivore, such as a cow, and one of a carnivore, such as a cat. Label the four types of teeth present in each model. Have students identify each tooth as they touch it. Also, have students describe the shape of the tooth—long and sharp, broad and flat—and tell whether the tooth is best for tearing, chewing, or grinding.

Ask students how they can determine which jaw belongs to an herbivore and which to a carnivore. *(The herbivore will have broad and flat teeth for grinding up leaves. The carnivore will have sharp pointed teeth so it can tear pieces of flesh.)* **learning modality: visual**

Monitor Progress L2

Writing Have each student develop a chart that lists the four different shapes of teeth and the diet associated with each shape. Students can save their charts in their portfolios.

Portfolio

Answers

Figure 11 Lions are carnivores; springboks are herbivores.

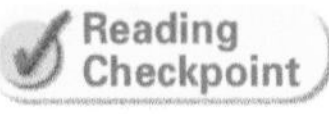

Canines

Use Visuals: Figures 12 and 14 L2

Fur, Hair, and Whiskers

Focus Direct students to look at the mammals in Figures 12 and 14 and compare the hair and fur they see.

Teach Ask: **Are there some kinds of hair common to all mammals?** *(Students should recognize that all the mammals shown have whiskers around the eyes, lips, and muzzle.)* Have students reexamine the wolf in Figure 12. Point out that some of the wolf's fur is long, some short. Ask: **What do you think is the function of the short, wooly hairs?** *(Insulation)* **What is the likely function of the longer, smooth hairs?** *(Protects the undercoat from water.)* **learning modality: visual**

FIGURE 12
Fur and Hair
A hippo has hardly any hair. In contrast, a wolf has a thick coat of fur.
Inferring *What can you infer about the environment each animal lives in?*

Obtaining Oxygen To release energy, food must combine with oxygen inside cells. Therefore, a mammal must have an efficient way to get oxygen into the body and to the cells that need it. Like reptiles and birds, all mammals breathe with lungs. Mammals breathe in and out because of the combined action of rib muscles and a large muscle called the **diaphragm** (DY uh fram). The diaphragm is located at the bottom of the ribs. The lungs have a huge, moist surface area where oxygen can move into the blood.

Like birds, mammals have a four-chambered heart and a two-loop circulatory system. This efficient system takes oxygen to the cells.

Keeping Conditions Stable Like birds, mammals are endotherms. They need the energy in food to keep a steady internal temperature. In addition, all mammals have fur or hair at some point in their lives that helps them keep their internal temperature stable. The amount of fur or hair that covers a mammal's skin varies greatly. Each strand of fur or hair is composed of dead cells strengthened with the same tough material that strengthens feathers. In general, animals that live in cold regions, like the wolf shown in Figure 12, have more fur than animals from warmer environments.

Fur is not the only adaptation that allows mammals to live in cold climates. Mammals also have a layer of fat beneath their skin. Like fur and feathers, fat is an insulator.

Lab zone Try This **Activity**

Insulated Mammals

Discover whether or not fat is an effective insulator.

1. Put on a pair of rubber gloves.
2. Spread a thick coating of solid white shortening on the outside of one of the gloves. Leave the other glove uncoated.
3. Put both hands in a bucket or sink filled with cold water.

Inferring Which hand got cold faster? Explain how this activity relates to mammalian adaptations.

Lab zone Try This **Activity**

Skills Focus Inferring L2

Materials bucket or sink full of cold water, paper towels, rubber gloves, shortening (from animal fat)

Time 15 minutes

Tips Explain to students that shortening is a form of animal fat that has been processed for cooking. Have students work in pairs to coat one another's gloves. When students are experimenting with reactions to temperature, be sure they do not use water that is dangerously cold.

Expected Outcome The hand in the glove without the shortening will feel the cold first. The glove with the shortening, which acts as an insulator, keeps heat in the hand just as animal fat keeps heat in the body of an animal.

Extend Have students coat the second glove with twice as much shortening as the first. Ask students to test whether more fat makes the hand less sensitive to cold. **learning modality: kinesthetic**

Movement In addition to adaptations for living in cold environments, mammals have adaptations that allow them to move in more ways than members of any other group of vertebrates. Most mammals walk or run on four limbs, but some have specialized ways of moving. For example, kangaroos hop, orangutans swing by their arms from branch to branch, and "flying" squirrels can spread their limbs and glide down from high perches. Bats have wings adapted from their front limbs. Whales, dolphins, and other sea mammals lack hind limbs, but their front limbs are adapted as flippers for swimming in water. These specialized ways of moving allow mammals to survive in many habitats.

Nervous System A mammal's nervous system coordinates its movements. In addition, the nervous system receives information about the environment. The brains of mammals enable them to learn, remember, and behave in complex ways. For example, in order for squirrels to eat nuts, they must crack the nutshell to get to the meat inside. Squirrels learn to use different methods to crack different kinds of nuts, depending on where the weak point in each kind of shell is located.

The senses of mammals are highly developed and adapted for the ways a species lives. Tarsiers, which are active at night, have huge eyes that enable them to see in the dark. Bats use a keen sense of hearing to navigate in the dark and catch prey. Dogs, cats, and bears often use smell to track their prey. Other mammals, such as antelopes, can smell approaching predators in time to flee.

What are three ways that mammals can move?

FIGURE 13
A Swinging Orangutan
This young orangutan can grasp branches with its limbs and swing from place to place.

FIGURE 14
The Senses of Seals
Seals can see under water in near darkness. Their long whiskers help them obtain food by detecting the movements of their prey.

B ◆ 135

L2

Compare and Contrast Movement

Materials photographs of porpoise, rabbit, gazelle, bat, and other mammals with interesting styles of movement

Time 10 minutes

Focus Remind students that movement is another defining characteristic of mammals; each mammal has a unique way of moving.

Teach Allow students time to study the photographs. Ask: **What adaptations does each animal have that helps or affects it movement?** *(The porpoise is streamlined for swimming in the sea. The rabbit has strong hind legs for hopping. The gazelle has long slender legs so that it can run fast. Bats have actual wings adapted from their front limbs.)* **learning modality: logical/mathematical**

Monitor Progress

L2

Skills Check Ask students to predict how the fur or hair of a mammal living in the Arctic tundra would differ from the fur or hair of a mammal living in the tropical rain forest.

Answers

Figure 12 The heavy fur of the wolf indicates that it lives in a cold environment; the hippo has little hair so it most likely lives in a warm environment.

Reading Checkpoint Accept any three of the following: Run, hop, swing, swim, fly, or glide.

Diversity of Mammals

Teach Key Concepts

L2

Unusual Mammals

Focus Tell students that comparing physical characteristics is one way to observe diversity and commonality among mammals.

Teach Ask: **What characteristics can you see that make the mammals in Figures 16 and 17 different?** *(Possible answers: Kangaroo—long, strong rear legs, very short front legs, carrying young in pouch, short thick neck; Giraffe—all four legs are long, young stands beside parent; long neck)* Ask: **What do these animals have in common that makes them mammals?** *(They are endothermic vertebrates with four-chambered hearts, skin with fur or hair and they produce milk.)* **learning modality: visual**

Help Students Read

L1

Identifying Main Ideas Have students read the main topic sentence in bold type under *Diversity of Mammals*. Ask: **Given this topic sentence, what are the main ideas that you should look for in this selection?** *(The characteristics of each type of mammal)* Have students work in groups to create index cards with the characteristics of each type of mammal. **learning modality: visual**

For: Links on mammals
Visit: www.SciLinks.org
Web Code: scn-0243

Download a worksheet that will guide students' review of Internet resources on mammals.

For: Links on mammals
Visit: www.SciLinks.org
Web Code: scn-0243

Diversity of Mammals

Mammals are a very diverse group. Look at the spiny anteater and the kangaroo shown on this page. Both are mammals that feed their young milk. But, in other ways, they are different. **There are three main groups of mammals—monotremes, marsupials, and placental mammals. The groups differ in how their young develop.**

FIGURE 15
A Spiny Anteater
The young of this spiny anteater, a monotreme, hatch from eggs.

Monotremes Egg-laying mammals are called **monotremes.** There are just three species of monotremes—two species of spiny anteaters and the duck-billed platypus. A female spiny anteater lays one to three leathery-shelled eggs directly into a pouch on her belly. After the young hatch, they stay in the pouch for six to eight weeks. There they drink milk that seeps out of pores on the mother's skin. In contrast, the duck-billed platypus lays her eggs in an underground nest. The tiny young feed by lapping at the milk that oozes from slits onto the fur of their mother's belly.

Marsupials Koalas, kangaroos, and opossums are some of the better-known marsupials. **Marsupials** are mammals whose young are born at an early stage of development, and they usually continue to develop in a pouch on their mother's body.

Marsupials have a very short **gestation period,** the length of time between fertilization and birth. For example, opossums have a gestation period of about 13 days. Newborn marsupials are tiny—some opossums are less than 1 centimeter long at birth! When they are born, marsupials are blind, hairless, and pink. They crawl along the wet fur of their mother's belly until they reach her pouch. Once inside, they find one of her nipples and attach to it. They remain in the pouch until they have grown enough to peer out of the pouch opening.

FIGURE 16
Kangaroos
This gray kangaroo, a marsupial, carries her offspring in a pouch.
Classifying *How do marsupials differ from monotremes?*

Placental Mammals Unlike a monotreme or a marsupial, a **placental mammal** develops inside its mother's body until its body systems can function independently. The name of this group comes from the **placenta,** an organ in pregnant female mammals that passes materials between the mother and the developing embryo. Food and oxygen pass from the mother to her young. Wastes pass from the young to the mother, who eliminates them. An umbilical cord connects the young to the mother's placenta. Most mammals, including humans, are placental mammals. Gestation periods of placental mammals are generally longer than those of marsupials. Usually, the larger the placental mammal, the longer the gestation period. The gestation period for an elephant, for example, averages about 21 months, but for a mouse, it's only about 20 days.

Placental mammals are classified into groups on the basis of characteristics such as how they eat and how their bodies move. You can see the diversity of placental mammals in Figure 18 on the next page.

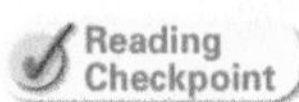
What is a placenta?

FIGURE 17 Mother and Baby Giraffe
This baby giraffe, a placental mammal, feeds on milk produced by its mother.

Math Analyzing Data

Mammal Diversity

This circle graph shows the percentage of species of some types of mammals.

1. Reading Graphs What percentage of species are bats?
2. Calculating What percentage of species are not bats?
3. Graphing Suppose you used the data shown in the circle graph to make a bar graph. Which bar would be tallest?
4. Predicting What total should all the percentages in the pie chart add up to? Do you have to add the percentages to obtain your answer? Explain.

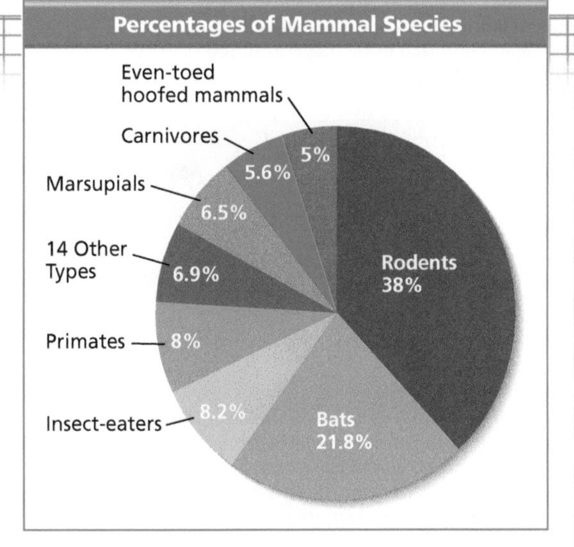

Math Analyzing Data

Math Skill Interpreting graphs

Focus For classification, mammals can be classed as: monotreme, marsupial, or placental. It is interesting to look at the number of species for each. Monotremes represent one tenth of one percent of all mammals, so do not have their own pie piece. They are lumped in the "14 Other Orders."

Teach Remind students that a circle graph shows how much of what kind goes to make up a whole class, group, or other entity. This circle graph, like most, is characterized by percents. Remind students that percentage means "per one hundred" Ask: **What information does each slice of the graph tell you?** *(What percentage of the whole is made up of each species)*

Answers

1. 21.8 percent
2. 78.2 percent
3. The group with the greatest number of species, the rodents, would be the tallest.
4. 100; In an accurate circle chart, the entire chart presents 100 percent of the items counted, in this case, mammal species.

Monitor Progress L2

Skills Check Ask students to identify three characteristics common to all mammals and one distinguishing characteristic for each group of mammals.

Answer

Figure 16 Monotremes lay eggs. Marsupials are born, not hatched, and then find their way to their mother's pouch to continue their development.

Reading Checkpoint An organ in pregnant female mammals that passes materials between the mother and the developing embryo.

Use Visuals: Figure 18 L1

Comparing Placental Mammals

Focus Review the definition of the term *placental mammal.*

Teach Explain that each of the animals pictured is a representative of a specific group of placental mammals that share several unique characteristics in addition to the characteristics shared by all placental mammals. Allow groups of four students to look at and discuss the photos. Encourage them to make comparisons using the photos and their accompanying captions. Then, have them list their observations about the characteristics of the mammals on these pages such as: *ocean dweller, able to fly.*

Extend Have students write the name of each mammal on the front of an index card and list several observable characteristics—including those common to all mammals—on the back of the card. Students may exchange cards and quiz one another.
learning modality: visual

FIGURE 18

Diversity of Placental Mammals

From tiny moles to huge elephants, placental mammals are diverse. They are grouped on the basis of how they eat and move as well as other characteristics.

Rabbits and Hares ▶
Leaping mammals like this black-tailed jack rabbit have long hind legs specialized for spectacular jumps. Rabbits and hares have long, curved incisors for gnawing.

Carnivores ▶
This river otter belongs to the group known as carnivores. Dogs, raccoons, and seals are other members of this group. Most carnivores have large canine teeth and clawed toes that help them catch and eat their prey.

Marine Mammals ▲
Whales, manatees, and these Atlantic spotted dolphins are ocean-dwelling mammals with a body shape adapted for swimming.

Rodents ▶
Rodents are gnawing mammals such as mice, rats, beavers, and the capybaras shown here. The incisor teeth of most rodents keep growing throughout their lives but are constantly worn down by gnawing.

Mammals With Trunks ▲
Elephants' noses are long trunks that they use for collecting food and water.

Insect-Eaters ▲
Moles and their relatives have sharp cutting surfaces on all of their teeth. This star-nosed mole spends much of its time searching for prey with its sensitive, tentacled snout.

◀ Flying Mammals
The wings of bats are made of a thin skin that stretches from their wrists to the tips of their long finger bones.

◀ Toothless Mammals
Armadillos, such as the one shown here, are toothless mammals. So are sloths. Although a few members of this group have small teeth, most have none.

Hoofed Mammals ▲
Some mammals with hooves have an even number of toes and some have an odd number of toes. Cows, deer, and pigs all have an even number of toes. Horses and zebras have an odd number of toes.

Primates ▼
This group of mammals with large brains and eyes that face forward includes humans, monkeys, and apes such as this chimpanzee.

L3

Mammal Classification

Materials colored markers, glue, magazines, poster board, scissors; magazines that contain pictures of animals

Time 20 minutes

Focus Tell students that the great diversity of placental mammals offers interesting challenges for classification.

Teach Direct groups of three students to look through the magazines and cut out as many pictures of mammals as they can find. Challenge students to observe and list as many traits—eating, moving, caring for young, and so on—about each mammal as they can. Next, have them use the traits to classify the mammal. Provide a place for students to post their work.

Apply Allow student groups to display their work and critique the work of others. Allow students to query one another's work. Discuss questions regarding the validity of any of the classifications. Work toward a class consensus. **learning modality: logical/mathematical**

Monitor Progress L2

Oral Presentation Ask students to name five mammals and state the group to which each belongs. Have them describe characteristics of the animal that place it in that group.

Monitor Progress L2

Answer

Reading Checkpoint The young are helpless—they may be furless, unable to open their eyes, or unable to feed themselves.

Assess

Reviewing Key Concepts

1. a. Four of the following: endothermic, vertebrates, four-chambered hearts, skin with fur or hair, produce milk, internal fertilization **b.** Mammals have teeth that are shaped to allow them to obtain food in particular ways. **c.** Fur or hair and fat help mammals live in colder environments than reptiles. Mammals are endotherms; reptiles are ectotherms.

2. a. Monotremes, marsupials, and placental mammals **b.** Monotremes lay eggs; marsupials are very immature when born and develop in a pouch; placental mammals develop inside the mother to a further extent than marsupials, with the aid of a placenta. **c.** Marine mammals have streamlined bodies for swimming, and flying mammals have wings made from thin skin that stretches from their wrists to the tips of their long finger bones.

Reteach L1

On the board create a chart listing five characteristics common to all three groups of mammals

Performance Assessment L2

Drawing Invite students to sketch a mammal or describe it in writing. They should then list the characteristics it has that are unique to mammals. Students can save their sketches in their portfolios.

Portfolio

All in One Teaching Resources

- Section Summary: *Mammals*
- Review and Reinforce: *Mammals*
- Enrich: *Mammals*

FIGURE 19
Parental Care by Dall's Sheep
Young mammals usually require much parental care. On a rocky slope in Alaska, this Dall's sheep, a placental mammal, keeps a close watch on her lamb.

Caring for Young Whether a monotreme, a marsupial, or a placental mammal, young mammals are usually quite helpless for a long time after being born. Many are born without a coat of insulating fur. Their eyes are often sealed and may not open for weeks. For example, black bear cubs are surprisingly tiny when they are born. The blind, nearly hairless cubs have a mass of only 240 to 330 grams—about the same mass as a grapefruit. The mass of an adult black bear, in contrast, ranges from about 120 to 150 kilograms—about 500 times as much as a newborn cub!

Young mammals usually stay with their mother or both parents for an extended time. After black bear cubs learn to walk, they follow their mother about for the next year, learning how to be a bear. They learn things that are important to their survival, such as which mushrooms and berries are good to eat and how to rip apart a rotten log and find good-tasting grubs within it. During the winter, when black bears go through a period of inactivity, the young bears stay with their mother. The following spring, she will usually force them to live independently.

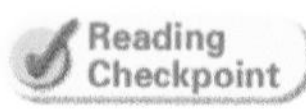
Why are most young mammals dependent on one or both parents after they are born?

Section 3 Assessment

Target Reading Skill Building Vocabulary Use your definitions to help answer the questions below.

Reviewing Key Concepts

1. a. Defining What characteristics do mammals share?
   b. Describing Describe the adaptation that most mammals have for obtaining food.
   c. Relating Cause and Effect What enables mammals to live in colder environments than reptiles? Explain.
2. a. Reviewing What are the three main groups of mammals?
   b. Explaining How do monotremes, marsupials, and placental mammals differ?
   c. Interpreting Photographs Look at Figure 18. Describe the adaptations for movement of marine mammals and flying mammals.

Lab zone At-Home Activity

Mammals' Milk With a family member, examine the nutrition label on a container of whole milk. What types of nutrients does whole milk contain? Discuss why milk is an ideal source of food for young, growing mammals.

Lab zone Chapter Project

Keep Students on Track While students continue to observe, they should begin to plan how their observations will be analyzed and presented. Review graphing techniques for the benefit of students who are unfamiliar with this method of organizing mathematical data. Suggest students group their observations to establish the habits of specific birds of related species.

Lab zone At-Home Activity

Mammals' Milk L2 Show students the nutrition facts listed on a milk label so that they will know where to look for the information.

Lab zone **Consumer Lab**

Keeping Warm

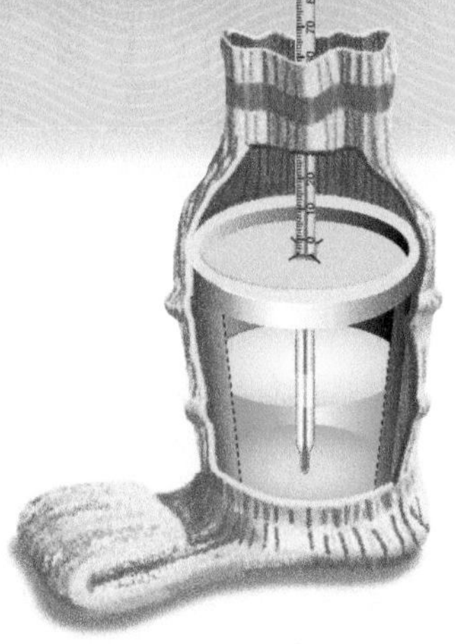

Problem

Do wool products provide insulation from the cold? How well does wool insulate when it is wet?

Skills Focus

graphing, interpreting data

Materials

- tap water, hot
- scissors
- beaker, 1-L
- 3 thermometers
- clock or watch
- graph paper
- a pair of wool socks
- tap water, room temperature
- 3 containers, 250-mL, with lids

Procedure   

1. Put one container into a dry woolen sock. Soak a second sock with water at room temperature, wring it out so it's not dripping, and then slide the second container into the wet sock. Both containers should stand upright. Leave the third container uncovered.
2. Create a data table in your notebook, listing the containers in the first column. Provide four more columns in which to record the water temperatures during the experiment.
3. Use scissors to carefully cut a small "X" in the center of each lid. Make the X just large enough for a thermometer to pass through.
4. Fill a beaker with about 800 mL of hot tap water. Then pour hot water nearly to the top of each of the three containers. **CAUTION:** *Avoid spilling hot water on yourself or others.*
5. Place a lid on each of the containers, and insert a thermometer into the water through the hole in each lid. Gather the socks around the thermometers above the first two containers so that the containers are completely covered.
6. Immediately measure the temperature of the water in each container, and record it in your data table. Take temperature readings every 5 minutes for at least 15 minutes.

Analyze and Conclude

1. **Graphing** Graph your results using a different color to represent each container. Graph time in minutes on the horizontal axis and temperature on the vertical axis.
2. **Interpreting Data** Compare the temperature changes in the three containers. Relate your findings to the insulation characteristics of mammal skin coverings.
3. **Communicating** Suppose a company claims that its wool socks keep you warm even if they get wet. Do your findings support this claim? Write a letter to the company explaining why or why not.

Design an Experiment

Design an experiment to compare how wool's insulating properties compare with those of other natural materials (such as cotton) or manufactured materials (such as acrylic). Obtain your teacher's permission before carrying out your investigation.

Keeping Warm 

Prepare for Inquiry

Key Concept

Wool is an insulator that helps conserve heat.

Skills Objectives

After this lab, students will be able to
- graph data
- interpret data to determine the insulation characteristics of various materials

Prep Time 15 minutes

Class Time 35 minutes

Advance Planning

Make sure groups use identical containers, such as plastic yogurt cups.

All in One Teaching Resources

- Lab Worksheet: *Keeping Warm*

Safety

Students should walk slowly when carrying glass containers or hot water to avoid breakage or spills. Students should be cautious when putting holes in lids with scissors. Students should be careful when handling glass thermometers and not force thermometers through the holes in the lids. They can make a larger hole if the thermometer does not fit. Review the safety guidelines in Appendix A.

Guide Inquiry

Invitation

Ask: **Name some ways we use insulation to conserve heat or keep heat in.** *(Sample answers: Wear warm clothes; use insulation to keep cold air out of houses)*

Introduce the Procedure

Before students begin, tell them that they will compare changes in temperature to find out which insulates better—dry wool or wet wool.

Troubleshooting the Experiment

Supply a large container of hot water so all groups will start with water around 40–45°C.

Expected Outcome

The containers should cool in this order: no sock, wet sock, dry sock.

Analyze and Conclude

1. Students should graph data with time along the x-axis, temperature along the y-axis.

2. The temperature changed the most in the container without a sock, then the wet sock, and then the dry sock. Wool keeps animals warm even when it is wet.

3. Sample answer: No. Wet socks will keep you warmer than no socks, but not as warm as dry socks.

Extend Inquiry

Design an Experiment Remind students to use materials of the same thickness.

Study Guide

The BIG Idea

Have students read the answer to the Essential Question. Encourage them to evaluate and revise their own answers as needed.

Help Students Read

Building Reading Literacy

Have students read the passage about the characteristics of birds. As they reach the bottom of a page, have them stop and write down the main ideas in the passage. Have them ask themselves: **Did I have any trouble reading this passage? If so, why?** Then, have them devise their own strategies to improve their understanding. Suggest they use the strategy as they continue reading.

Build Vocabulary

Word Forms Before students read the chapter, have them look up the words *circulate, digest,* and *adapt.* Then, have students write a prediction for the meanings of the terms *circulation, digestion,* and *adaptation.* After students study the section, have them look at their predictions and discuss any differences between their predictions and the way in which the term is used in the text.

Connecting Concepts

Concept Maps Help students develop one way to show how the information in this chapter is related. Birds and mammals each have their own set of common characteristics. Have students brainstorm to identify the key concepts, key terms, details, and examples. Then write each one on a sticky note and attach it at random to chart paper on to the board.

Tell students that this concept map will be organized in hierarchical order and to begin at the top with the key concepts. Ask students these questions to guide them to categorize the information on the stickies: **What are some characteristcs shared by all mammals? What are three main groups of mammals?**

Chapter 4 Study Guide

The BIG Idea **Structure and Function** Both birds and mammals are endothermic vertebrates with four-chambered hearts.

1 Birds

Key Concepts

- A bird is an endothermic vertebrate that has feathers and a four-chambered heart. A bird also lays eggs.
- Birds are adapted for living in diverse environments. You can see some of these adaptations in the shapes of their legs, claws, and bills.

Key Terms

bird
contour feather
down feather
crop
gizzard

2 The Physics of Bird Flight

Key Concepts

- The difference in pressure above and below the wings as the bird moves through the air produces an upward force that causes the bird to rise.
- Three types of bird flight are flapping, soaring and gliding, and diving.

Key Term

lift

3 Mammals

Key Concepts

- All mammals are endothermic vertebrates that have a four-chambered heart and skin covered with fur or hair. Most mammals are born alive, and every young mammal is fed with milk produced by organs in its mother's body.
- There are three main groups of mammals—monotremes, marsupials, and placental mammals. The groups differ in how their young develop.

Key Terms

• mammal • mammary gland • diaphragm
• monotreme • marsupial • gestation period
• placental mammal • placenta

Prompt students by using connecting words or phrases, such as "all have" and "can be divided into" to indicate the basis for the organization of the map. The phrases should form a sentence between or among a set of concepts.

Answers

Accept logical presentations by students.

All in One Teaching Resources

- Key Terms Review: *Birds and Mammals*
- Connecting Concepts: *Birds and Mammals*

Review and Assessment

Go Online PHSchool.com
For: Self-Assessment
Visit: PHSchool.com
Web Code: cea-2040

Organizing Information

Comparing and Contrasting Copy the table comparing mammal groups onto a sheet of paper. Then fill in the empty spaces and add a title.

Characteristic	Monotremes	Marsupials	Placental Mammals
How Young Begin Life	a. ___?___	b. ___?___	c. ___?___
How Young Are Fed	milk from pores or slits on mother's skin	d. ___?___	e. ___?___
Example	f. ___?___	g. ___?___	h. ___?___

Reviewing Key Terms

Choose the letter of the best answer.

1. Birds are the only animals with
   a. scales.
   b. wings.
   c. feathers.
   d. a four-chambered heart.
2. The gizzard of a bird
   a. stores air.
   b. removes oxygen from air.
   c. helps a bird fly.
   d. grinds food.
3. An organ that produces milk to feed the young is called a
   a. mammary gland.
   b. placenta.
   c. pouch.
   d. egg.
4. Which muscle helps mammals move air into and out of their lungs?
   a. air muscle
   b. diaphragm
   c. placenta
   d. gestation
5. A monotreme differs from a placental mammal because it
   a. has fur.
   b. has a placenta.
   c. lays eggs.
   d. feeds its young milk.

If the statement is true, write *true*. If it is false, change the underlined word or words to make the statement true.

6. Down feathers give shape to a bird's body.
7. A bird's crop stores food.
8. The upward force on a bird's moving wing is called lift.
9. The function of contour feathers is similar to the function of fur.
10. A diaphragm is the length of time between fertilization and birth.

Writing in Science

Cause and Effect Paragraph Which adaptations improve a bird's ability to fly? Write a paragraph in which you describe the effects of adaptations you learned about on the ability of a bird to fly. Be sure to include a topic sentence.

Birds and Mammals
Video Preview
Video Field Trip
▶ Video Assessment

For: Self-Assessment
Visit: PHSchool.com
Web Code: cea-2040

Students can take a practice test online that is automatically scored.

All in One Teaching Resources

- Transparency B42
- Chapter Test
- Performance Assessment Teacher Notes
- Performance Assessment Student Worksheet
- Performance Assessment Scoring Rubric

ExamView® Computer Test Bank CD-ROM

Review and Assessment

Organizing Information

a. hatch from egg
b. born live; crawl into mother's pouch
c. born live
d. feeds on milk produced by mother in her pouch
e. feeds on milk produced by mother
f. spiny anteater or duck-billed platypus
g. koala, kangaroo, or opossum
h. human, giraffe, bear, rabbit, whale, etc.
Sample title: Mammals

Reviewing Key Terms

1. c **2.** d **3.** a **4.** b **5.** c
6. Contour feathers
7. True
8. True
9. Down feathers
10. Gestation period

Writing in Science

Writing Mode Exposition: Cause and Effect

Scoring Rubric
4 Includes complete, accurate, detailed cause-and-effect relationships
3 Includes complete, accurate relationships
2 Includes incomplete but accurate relationships
1 Includes incomplete and inaccurate relationships

Video Assessment

Birds and Mammals

Show the Video Assessment to review chapter content and as a prompt for the writing assignment. Discussion question: **What is one adaptation of birds that helps provide the extra energy needed for flight?** *(Air sacs in the lungs extract extra oxygen; the two-loop circulatory system and four-chambered heart enable birds to pump oxygen-rich blood very efficiently.)*

Checking Concepts

11. The bones are lightweight, and the forelimb bones are modified into wings.

12. Air sacs allow birds to obtain more oxygen from each breath than other animals can.

13. A bird's four-chambered heart includes separate ventricles for the oxygen-rich blood and the oxygen-poor blood. By not allowing them to mix, a bird's circulatory system thus delivers oxygen more efficiently to the body's cells.

14. Lift is caused by the difference in pressure above and below a bird's wings (with greater pressure pushing up on the wing from below).

15. Warm air rises, and soaring birds are carried upward by the rising air. When the air cools, the birds glide downward until they find another column of rising air.

16. An incisor has a flat edge that makes it good for biting off and cutting food.

17. Accept any two: They are endotherms; their fur insulates them; they have a layer of insulating fat.

18. Mammals have complex nervous systems and senses that are capable of directing and coordinating complicated movements.

Thinking Critically

19. Endothermic animals have four-chambered hearts. In a four-chambered heart, oxygenated blood does not mix with deoxygenated blood, and therefore the blood that reaches the body tissues is carrying a large amount of oxygen. Oxygen is needed to release the energy that enables endothermy.

20. The faster-moving air above the wing exerts less pressure than the slow-moving air beneath the wing. The difference in pressure produces an upward force called lift.

21. These three mammals live in cold water and need a thick, insulating layer of fat to protect them from the cold.

22. Since rodents' front teeth grow constantly, they might continue to grow and become very long.

Review and Assessment

Checking Concepts

11. Explain how the skeleton of a bird is adapted for flight.
12. What adaptations help a bird obtain enough oxygen for flight? Explain.
13. Why is a bird's circulatory system efficient? Explain.
14. What causes lift?
15. Explain how soaring and gliding birds such as vultures use air currents in their flight.
16. How does the structure of an incisor relate to its function?
17. Identify and explain two ways in which mammals are adapted to live in climates that are very cold.
18. What is the function of a mammal's nervous system?

Thinking Critically

19. **Making Generalizations** What is the general relationship between whether an animal is an endotherm and whether it has a four-chambered heart? Relate this to the animal's need for energy.
20. **Relating Cause and Effect** Look at the diagram below. Explain how lift occurs and what effect it has on the bird.

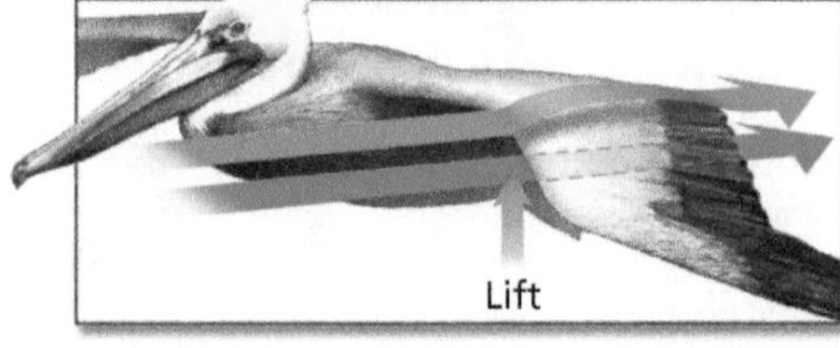

21. **Applying Concepts** Why do whales, polar bears, and seals have a thick layer of fat?
22. **Predicting** If a rodent were fed a diet consisting only of soft food that it did not need to gnaw, what might its front teeth look like after several months? Explain.

Applying Skills

Use the information in the table to answer Questions 23–25.

The data table below shows the approximate gestation period of several mammals and the approximate length of time that those mammals care for their young after birth.

Mammal	Gestation Period	Time Spent Caring for Young After Birth
Deer mouse	0.75 month	1 month
Chimpanzee	8 months	24 months
Harp seal	11 months	0.75 month
Elephant	21 months	24 months
Bobcat	2 months	8 months

23. **Graphing** Decide which kind of graph would be best for showing the data in the table. Then construct two graphs—one for gestation period and the other for time spent caring for young.
24. **Interpreting Data** Which mammals listed in the table care for their young for the longest time? The shortest time?
25. **Drawing Conclusions** How are the size of the mammal and the length of time it cares for its young related? Which animal is the exception to this pattern?

Lab zone Chapter Project

Performance Assessment When you present your bird-watch project, display your graphs, charts, and pictures. Describe the ways in which birds eat and the interesting examples of bird behavior you observed. Then, analyze how successful the project was. Was the bird feeder located in a good place for attracting and observing birds? Did many birds come to the feeder? If not, why might this have happened? What are the advantages and limitations of using field guides for identifying birds?

L3

Performance Assessment

Students can present their projects in a number of ways. They can turn in a written report with sketches and graphs, make posters that show the different birds that visited their feeders and their behaviors, or give an oral presentation that focuses on their observations or on the behavior of a single type of bird. Encourage students to be creative in the way they report their data. On their graphs, students could add illustrations of the different types of birds rather than just their names.

Reflect and Record Students should explain why they think the bird feeder was or was not placed in a good location.

Standardized Test Prep

Test-Taking Tip

Answering a Constructed Response Question

Be sure you understand the question before you begin. For example, are you being asked to write a description or to compare and contrast two items? Consider what information you should include in order to give a complete answer that addresses all the specific points asked for in the question. Your answer should also be organized. Take the time to decide how to best sequence the information in your response.

Sample Question

Both birds and mammals are endotherms. Compare and contrast how the two different groups of animals maintain their body temperatures. Consider the physical characteristics of each group in your response.

Answer

You might begin your answer with a brief review of the word *endotherm* and then continue by stating the similarities and differences in how birds and mammals maintain their body temperatures. Give specific examples that support your answer. For instance, if you state that birds and mammals have different body coverings to help keep them warm, you would state that down feathers help insulate a bird, whereas fur or hair helps insulate a mammal.

Choose the letter of the best answer.

1. Of the following structures found in a bird, which one's main function is to store food?
A stomach
B gizzard
C crop
D bill

2. Which characteristics do birds and mammals share?
F Both are endothermic vertebrates.
G Both have fur or hair.
H Both have a three-chambered heart.
J Both are vertebrates that produce milk.

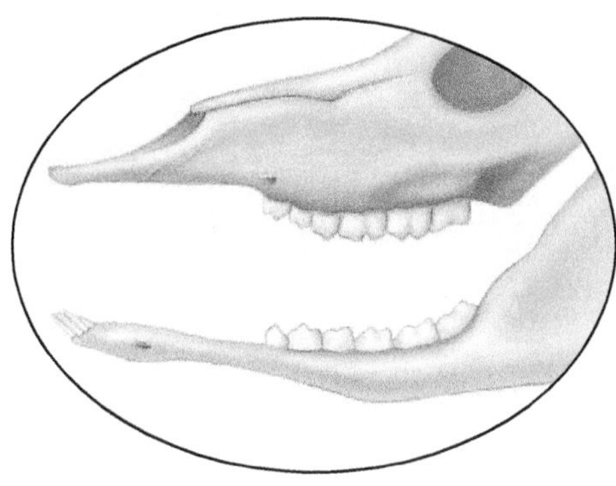

3. The diagram above shows the jawbone and teeth of an animal. The front of the mouth faces left. Which of the following best describes the teeth?
A many sharp canines
B broad molars at the back of the mouth
C molars at the front of the mouth
D flat incisors at the back of the mouth

4. Based on the kinds of teeth you observe in the diagram above, make your best inference about what this animal might be.
F bird
G cow
H rabbit
J bear

5. Which of the following best describes the function of the placenta?
A to deliver oxygen to the body's cells
B to store food inside the body before swallowing and digesting it
C to direct and coordinate a mammal's complex movements
D to pass materials between a mother and her offspring before it is born

Constructed Response

6. Describe how birds care for their eggs and newly hatched young. Your answer should include information about why this care is necessary.

Applying Skills

23. A bar graph would be best for showing this kind of data. Students' graphs should accurately reflect the data.

24. Longest — elephant and chimpanzee; Shortest — harp seal

25. In general, the larger the mammal, the more time it spends caring for its young. The harp seal is the exception.

Standardized Test Prep

1. C **2.** F **3.** B **4.** G **5.** D

6. Birds care for their eggs by sitting on them to keep the temperature close to that of the parent bird. The eggs need this warm temperature in order to develop. Bird parents feed and protect young birds until they are able to leave the nest and fly. This gives the birds time to develop feathers, sight, and strength.

The BIG Idea

The Big Idea is the major scientific concept of the chapter. It is followed by the Essential Question. Read aloud the question to students. As students study the chapter, tell them to think about the Essential Question. Explain that they will discover the answer to the question as they read. The chapter Study Guide provides a sample answer.

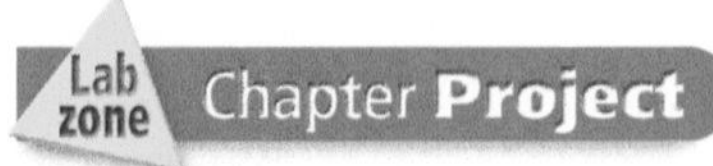

L3

Objectives

This project will enhance students' understanding of animal behavior, helping them differentiate between instinctive and learned behavior. After this project, students will be able to

- observe natural behavior patterns in an animal
- observe the animal's learning over a period of time
- draw conclusions about the animal's ability to learn new behaviors
- communicate their findings

Skills Focus

Observing, drawing conclusions, communicating

Project Time Line 2 to 3 weeks

All in One Teaching Resources

- Chapter Project Teacher Notes
- Chapter Project Overview
- Chapter Project Worksheet 1
- Chapter Project Worksheet 2
- Chapter Project Scoring Rubric

Safety

Be sure that students are not allergic to any animals with which they may be working. The animal's owner and, if the owner is a child, an adult should be present during the handling and training of the animal.

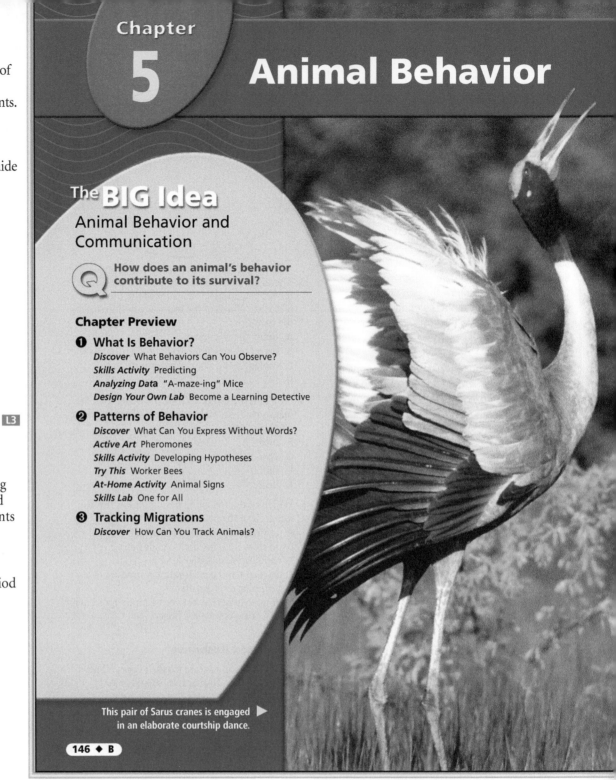

Chapter 5 Animal Behavior

The BIG Idea

Animal Behavior and Communication

How does an animal's behavior contribute to its survival?

Chapter Preview

This pair of Sarus cranes is engaged in an elaborate courtship dance.

146 ◆ B

Developing a Plan

During the first week, students should familiarize themselves with their animal's natural behaviors. They should also decide what behavior they plan to teach the animal and what method (trial and error or conditioning) they will use to train the animal. Students should allot about two weeks' time for training.

Possible Materials

Students will need animals. In addition, they may need:

- materials to construct a maze
- food to use as a reward
- glue or tape
- timer or stopwatch
- sketchbook, camera, or video camera to record behavior
- poster board and markers for their presentation

Chapter at a Glance

PRENTICE HALL TeacherEXPRESS™ Plan • Teach • Assess

Lab zone Chapter Project *Learning New Tricks*

Technology | **Local Standards**

All in One Teaching Resources
- Chapter Project Teacher Notes, pp. 302–303
- Chapter Project Student Overview, pp. 304–305
- Chapter Project Student Worksheets, pp. 306–307
- Chapter Project Scoring Rubric, p. 308

Video Preview

What Is Behavior?

3–4 periods
1 1/2–2 blocks

B.5.1.1 Explain what causes animal behavior.
B.5.1.2 Describe what instincts are.
B.5.1.3 Describe four types of learned behavior.

Video Field Trip

Patterns of Behavior

2–3 periods
1–1 1/2 blocks

B.5.2.1 List the three main ways animals communicate.
B.5.2.2 Give examples of competitive and cooperative behaviors.
B.5.2.3 Describe cyclic behavior.

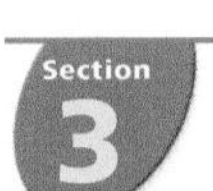

Tracking Migrations

1–2 periods
1/2–1 blocks

B.5.3.1 Explain how two electronic technologies help scientists track animals.
B.5.3.2 Explain the benefits of tracking animal migrations.

Review and Assessment

All in One Teaching Resources
- Key Terms Review, p. 333
- Transparency B48
- Performance Assessment Teacher Notes, p. 342
- Performance Assessment Scoring Rubric p. 343
- Performance Assessment Student Worksheet, p. 344
- Chapter Test, pp. 345–347

Video Assessment

Go Online PHSchool.com

Test Preparation

Test Preparation Blackline Masters

Chapter Activities Planner

For more activities

Student Edition	Inquiry	Time	Materials	Skills	Resources
Chapter Project, p.147	Open-ended	2 to 3 weeks	**All in One Teaching Resources** p. 302	Observing, drawing conclusions, communicating	**Lab zone Easy Planner** **All in One Teaching Resources** Support pp. 302–303
Section 1					
Discover Activity, p. 148	Guided	15 minutes	Small vertebrates, a cage or aquarium, food	Predicting	**Lab zone Easy Planner**
Skills Activity, p. 150	Guided	10 minutes	None	Predicting	**Lab zone Easy Planner**
Design Your Own Lab, p. 155	Open-ended	40 minutes	None	Posing questions, designing experiments, calculating	**Lab zone Easy Planner** **Lab Activity Video** **All in One Teaching Resources** Design Your Own Lab: *Become a Learning Detective*, pp. 316–317
Section 2					
Discover Activity, p. 156	Guided	15 minutes	None	Forming operational definitions	**Lab zone Easy Planner**
Skills Activity, p. 159	Open-ended	10 minutes	None	Developing hypotheses	**Lab zone Easy Planner**
Try This Activity, p. 161	Guided	15 minutes	22 × 28 cm sheets of paper; glue, stapler, or paste; scissors; timer	Calculating	**Lab zone Easy Planner**
Skills Lab, pp. 164–165	Directed	Prep: 30 minutes Class: 45 minutes plus a few minutes each day for two weeks	Large glass jar, water, hand lens, black paper, forceps, sandy soil, wire screen, bread crumbs, tape, large, thick rubber band, shallow pan, sponge, sugar, glass-marking pencil, 20–30 ants	Observing, inferring, posing questions	**Lab zone Easy Planner** **Lab Activity Video** **All in One Teaching Resources** Skills Lab: *One for All*, pp. 325–327
Section 3					
Discover Activity, p. 166	Directed	20 minutes	graph paper, clicker	Inferring	**Lab zone Easy Planner**

Section 1 What Is Behavior?

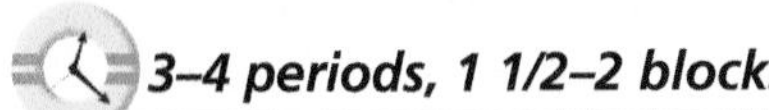
3–4 periods, 1 1/2–2 blocks

ABILITY LEVELS
- L1 Basic to Average
- L2 For All Students
- L3 Average to Advanced

Objectives

B.5.1.1 Explain what causes animal behavior.
B.5.1.2 Describe what instincts are.
B.5.1.3 Describe four types of learned behavior.

Local Standards

Key Terms

• behavior • stimulus • response • instinct • learning • imprinting • conditioning • trial-and-error learning • insight learning

Preteach

Build Background Knowledge

Use a chart to identify animal stimuli and responses.

 *What Behaviors Can You Observe?* 

Targeted Print and Technology Resources

All in One Teaching Resources
- L2 Reading Strategy Transparency B43: Outlining

PresentationExpress™ CD-ROM

Instruct

The Behavior of Animals Define *stimulus* and *response* and apply the terms to animal behavior.

Behavior by Instinct Use examples to teach about instinctive behavior.

Learned Behavior Use pictures to explain different kinds of learned behavior.

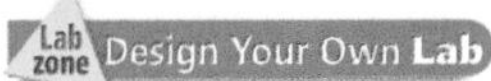 *Become a Learning Detective* 

Targeted Print and Technology Resources

All in One Teaching Resources
- L2 Guided Reading, pp. 311–313
- L2 Transparency B44
- L2 Design Your Own Lab: *Become a Learning Detective*, pp. 316–317

Design Your Own Lab: *Become a Learning Detective*

www.SciLinks.org Web Code: scn-0251

Video Field Trip

Student Edition on Audio CD

Assess

Section Assessment Questions

Have students use their completed Outlining graphic organizers to help answer the questions.

Reteach

Help students define and provide examples of the four types of learning.

Targeted Print and Technology Resources

All in One Teaching Resources
- Section Summary, p. 310
- L1 Review and Reinforce, p. 314
- L3 Enrich, p. 315

Section 2 Patterns of Behavior

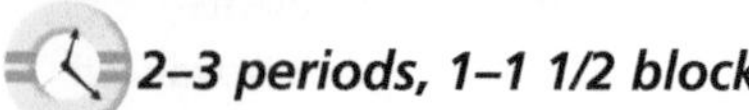
2–3 periods, 1–1 1/2 blocks

ABILITY LEVELS
- L1 Basic to Average
- L2 For All Students
- L3 Average to Advanced

Objectives

B.5.2.1 List the three main ways animals communicate.
B.5.2.2 Give examples of competitive and cooperative behaviors.
B.5.2.3 Describe cyclic behavior.

Local Standards

Key Terms

• pheromone • aggression • territory • courtship behavior • society • circadian rhythm • hibernation • migration

Preteach

Build Background Knowledge

Use question to explore student behavior.

Discover Activity *What Can You Express Without Words?*  L1

Targeted Print and Technology Resources

Teaching Resources
- L2 Reading Strategy Transparency B45: Using Prior Knowledge

PresentationExpress™ CD-ROM

Instruct

Communication Ask leading questions to discuss animal communication.

Competitive Behavior Use comparisons to help students understand competitive behavior.

Group Behavior Use an illustration to discuss animal societies.

Behavior Cycles Define cyclic behavior and have students give examples of each type.

Skills Lab *One for All* L2

Targeted Print and Technology Resources

All in One Teaching Resources
- L2 Guided Reading, pp. 320–322
- L2 Transparency B46
- L2 Skills Lab: *One for All*, pp. 325–327

Lab Activity Video/DVD
Skills Lab: *One for All*

PHSchool.com Web Code: cep-2052

Student Edition on Audio CD

Assess

Section Assessment Questions

Have students use their Using Prior Knowledge graphic organizers to help answer the questions.

Reteach

Use a concept map to organize information about cyclic behavior.

Targeted Print and Technology Resources

All in One Teaching Resources
- Section Summary, p. 319
- L1 Review and Reinforce, p. 323
- L3 Enrich, p. 324

Section 3 Tracking Migrations

1–2 periods, 1/2–1 block

ABILITY LEVELS
L1 Basic to Average
L2 For All Students
L3 Average to Advanced

Objectives

B.5.3.1 Describe how two electronic technologies help scientists track animals.
B.5.3.2 Explain the benefits of tracking animal migrations.

Local Standards

Key Terms

• transmitter • receiver • satellite

Preteach

Build Background Knowledge

Ask students to give examples of animals that migrate.

What Can More Data Points Tell You? 

Targeted Print and Technology Resources

L2 Reading Strategy Transparency B47: Comparing and Contrasting

Instruct

Technologies for Tracking Students review a brief history of tracking technologies.

Why Tracking Is Important Students discuss the benefits — for people, animals, the environment — of tracking animal migrations.

Targeted Print and Technology Resources

All in One Teaching Resources
L2 Guided Reading, p. 330

www.SciLinks.org Web Code: scn-0253

Assess

Section Assessment Questions

Have students use their Comparing and Contrasting graphic organizers to answer the questions.

Reteach

List the advantages and disadvantages of electronic tagging to track migration.

Targeted Print and Technology Resources

All in One Teaching Resources
• Section Summary, p. 329
L1 Review and Reinforce, p. 331
L3 Enrich, p. 332

Chapter 5 Content Refresher

Section 1 What Is Behavior?

Different Stimuli Animals respond to a variety of stimuli. The most familiar are visible and ultraviolet light, infrared radiation (heat), magnetic fields, vibrating air, physical touch, pressure, gravity, and chemicals. All are detected by sensory receptors. Sensory receptors can be as complex as the eye, which perceives light, and the inner ear, which senses air waves (sounds) and gravity. Receptors may also occur in organized clusters, such as those of taste, and smell, which perceive chemicals in the environment. The simplest receptors are plain nerve endings in the skin that perceive heat, touch, and pain. Stimulation of the receptors initiates nerve impulses that pass along neurons to the brain. There, they terminate in specific centers, where they are analyzed, and reactions initiated.

Address Misconceptions

Some students may think that only simple behaviors are instinctive. For a strategy for overcoming this misconception, see **Address Misconceptions** in the section *What Is Behavior?*

Section 2 Patterns of Behavior

Circadian Rhythms The cues for circadian rhythms can be both internal and external. Many circadian rhythms are determined by an internal biological clock that "keeps time." Experiments have shown that certain behaviors will continue on a regular cycle in the absence of any external cues. Even when kept in total darkness, almost all fruit fly larvae will hatch in the early morning. A single gene acts as the internal clock. Light is the most common external cue that influences daily rhythms. Under controlled conditions with no external cues, most human biological clocks run on a 25-hour daily schedule. The internal clocks can be easily reset to 24 hours with exposure to natural light.

Section 3 Tracking Migrations

Tagging Devices Improvements to the tags used to track monarch butterfly migration have led to better tracking with less impact on the butterflies. The old tagging method involved removing the scales on a portion of the forewing and placing an oblong or rectangular adhesive tag on that area. The new tagging method, which uses new, all-weather polypropylene tags, involves placing the adhesive tag on the underside of the butterfly's hind wing. No scales need to be removed to attach the tag. The new tags are round and only 9 millimeters in diameter. The recapture rate is two to three times higher with the new tags compared to rates with the older tags.

Tagging Methods

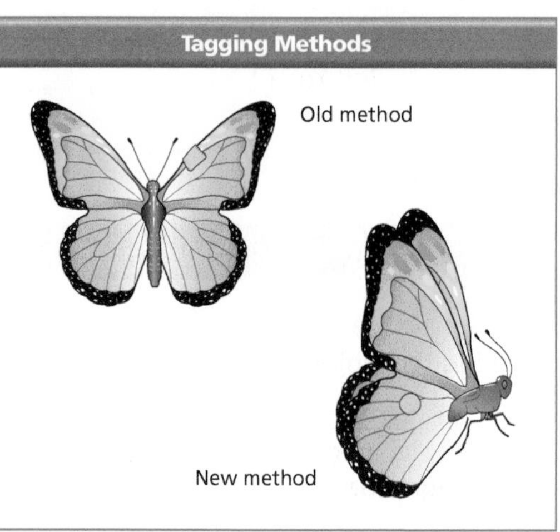

Help Students Read

Monitoring Your Understanding

Self-Questioning and Self-Adjusting

This strategy enables students to understand difficult material by focusing on their thought processes as they actively question and apply fix-up strategies to improve comprehension.

Example

1. Self-Question As students read, have them stop often to ask themselves questions such as "Do I understand this?"

2. Apply Fix-Up Strategies Have students use one of the following strategies when they do not understand a paragraph.

- Slowly reread what they do not understand, making sure they understand each sentence before continuing.
- Clarify by stating what they do not understand, talk through confusing points, or relate new information to concepts they are familiar with.
- Read ahead and use visuals and captions.

3. Self-Check After they read, have students summarize or restate the main idea of a paragraph or section.

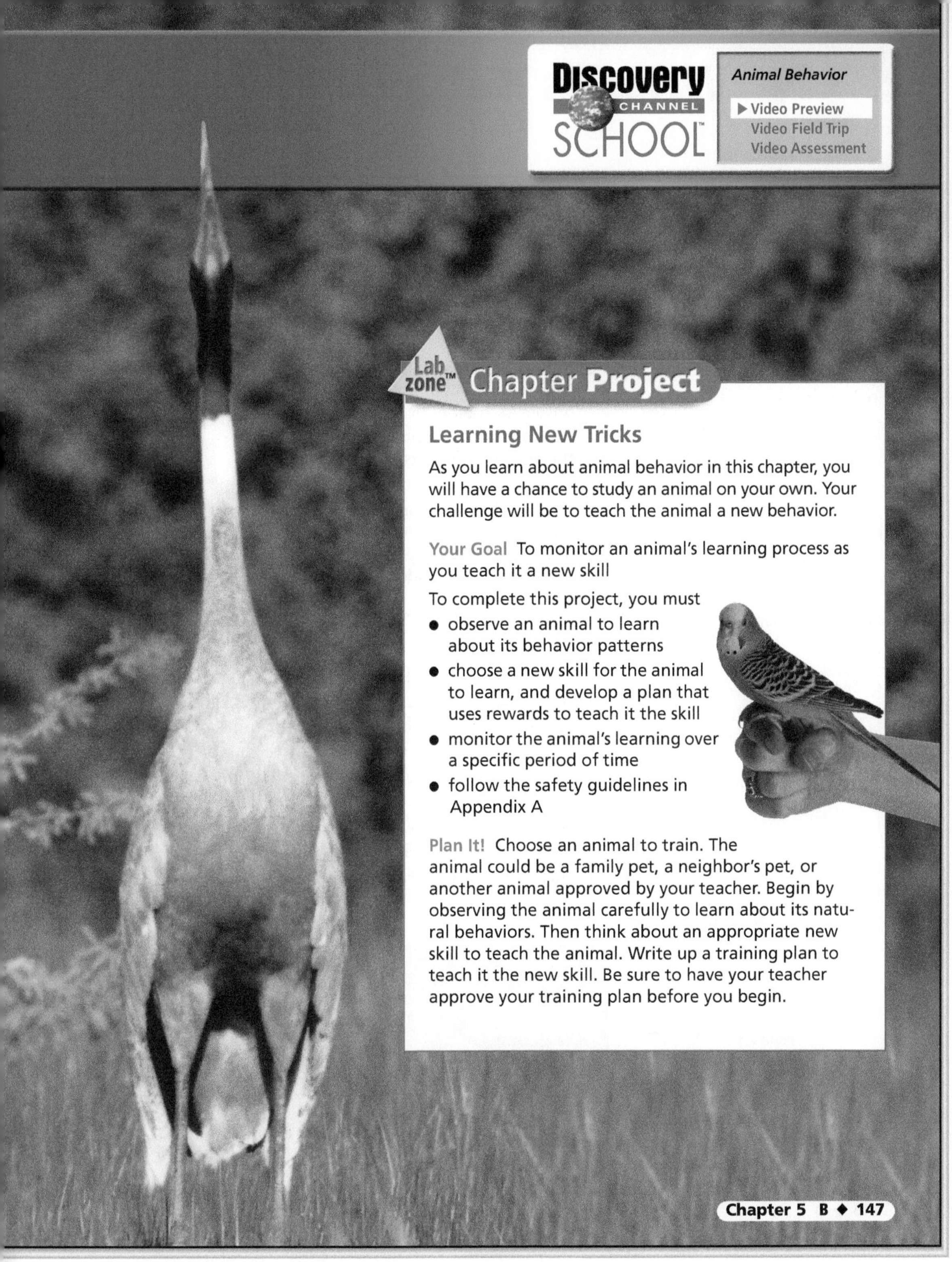

Lab zone™ Chapter Project

Learning New Tricks

As you learn about animal behavior in this chapter, you will have a chance to study an animal on your own. Your challenge will be to teach the animal a new behavior.

Your Goal To monitor an animal's learning process as you teach it a new skill

To complete this project, you must

- observe an animal to learn about its behavior patterns
- choose a new skill for the animal to learn, and develop a plan that uses rewards to teach it the skill
- monitor the animal's learning over a specific period of time
- follow the safety guidelines in Appendix A

Plan It! Choose an animal to train. The animal could be a family pet, a neighbor's pet, or another animal approved by your teacher. Begin by observing the animal carefully to learn about its natural behaviors. Then think about an appropriate new skill to teach the animal. Write up a training plan to teach it the new skill. Be sure to have your teacher approve your training plan before you begin.

Animal Behavior

Show the Video Preview to introduce the Chapter Project and overview the chapter content. Discussion question: **What rewards do dogs receive that condition their behavior?** *(Praise)*

Launching the Project

To introduce the project, bring an animal into the classroom and show students a behavior it has learned. Talk about who trained the animal, how it was trained, and any difficulties that were encountered during the training process.

Performance Assessment

The Chapter Project Scoring Rubric will help you evaluate how well students complete the Chapter Project. You might want to share the rubric with your students so they will know what is expected. Students will be assessed on

- how well they choose an appropriate behavior for the animal to learn, a stimulus, and a reward; how thoroughly they plan a workable regimen
- the completeness of their observation entries, including what their animals do during training and descriptions of external factors that may affect progress
- the thoroughness and organization of their presentation

Portfolio

Section 1 What Is Behavior?

Objectives

After completing this lesson, students will be able to

B.5.1.1 Explain what causes animal behavior.

B.5.1.2 Describe what instincts are.

B.5.1.3 Describe four types of learned behavior.

Target Reading Skill

Outlining Explain that using an outline format helps students organize information by main topic, subtopic, and details.

Answers

Possible answers:

I. The behavior of animals
  A. Behavior as response
  B. The functions of behavior
II. Behavior by instinct
III. Learned behavior
  A. Imprinting
  B. Conditioning
  C. Trial-and-error learning
  D. Insight learning

All in One Teaching Resources

- Transparency B43

Preteach

Build Background Knowledge L2

Animal Behavior

Make a two-column table on the board with the labels *Stimulus* and *Animal's Response*. List events in the first column that may produce a response in an animal. For example, a dog hears a doorbell, a cat or dog sees another animal, a cat sees a ball of yarn, or a fish sees food. Have students describe how the animal might respond in each case and list the responses in the second column.

Section 1 What Is Behavior?

Reading Preview

Key Concepts

- What causes animal behavior?
- What are instincts?
- What are four types of learned behaviors?

Key Terms

- behavior
- stimulus
- response
- instinct
- learning
- imprinting
- conditioning
- trial-and-error learning
- insight learning

Target Reading Skill

Outlining As you read, make an outline about behavior. Use the red headings for the main topics and the blue headings for the subtopics.

Understanding Behavior

I. Behavior of animals
  A. Behavior as response
  B.
II. Behavior by instinct
III.
  A.
  B.
  C.
  D.

Lab zone Discover Activity

What Behaviors Can You Observe?

1. Observe the behavior of a small vertebrate, such as a gerbil or a goldfish, for a few minutes. Write down your observations.
2. Place some food near the animal and observe the animal's behavior.
3. If there are other animals in the cage or aquarium, observe how the animals interact—for example, do they groom each other or ignore each other?
4. Note any other events that seem to make the animal change its behavior.

Think It Over

Predicting What are some circumstances under which you would expect an animal's behavior to change suddenly?

A male anole—a kind of lizard—stands in a patch of sun. As another male approaches, the first anole begins to lower and raise its head and chest in a series of quick push-ups. From beneath its neck a dewlap, a bright red flap of skin, flares out and then collapses, over and over. The anoles stare at one another, looking like miniature dinosaurs about to do battle. The first anole seems to be saying, "This area belongs to me. You'll have to leave or fight!"

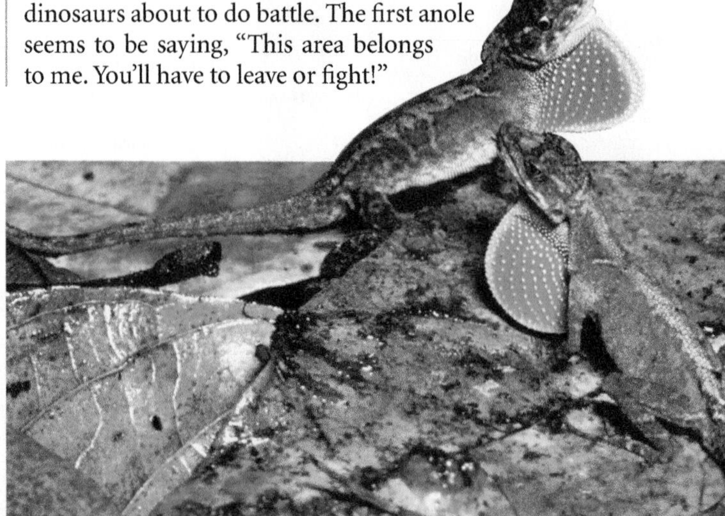

FIGURE 1
Dewlap Display
These two anoles are displaying their dewlaps in a dispute over space.

Lab zone Discover Activity

Skills Focus Predicting L1

Materials cage or aquarium, food, small vertebrates

Time 15 minutes

Tips Students should not handle the animals. Students must wash their hands afterwards. Remind students that tapping on the glass of a cage or aquarium may cause an animal stress.

Expected Outcome Animals will respond to different stimuli such as food, another animal, or disturbing sounds. Responses may include feeding, social interaction, hiding, or escape attempts.

Think It Over Possible answers include the addition of another animal, a loud noise, or the addition of food.

FIGURE 2
A Moth's Startling "Eyes"
Certain moths have markings on their underwings that resemble eyes. When the moth is poked by a predator, it raises its forewings to reveal the "eyes." **Predicting** *How is this behavior important to the moth's survival?*

The Behavior of Animals

The dewlap display by anole lizards is one example of behavior. An animal's **behavior** consists of all the actions it performs. For example, behaviors include actions an animal takes to obtain food, avoid predators, and find a mate. Like body structures, the behaviors of animals are adaptations that have evolved over long periods of time.

Most behavior is a complex process in which different parts of an animal's body work together. Consider what happens when a water current carries a small animal to a hydra's tentacles. After stinging cells on the tentacles catch the prey, the tentacles bend toward the hydra's mouth. At the same time, the hydra's mouth opens to receive the food.

Behavior as Response In the previous situation, the touch of the prey on the tentacles acts as a stimulus to the hydra. A **stimulus** (plural *stimuli*) is a signal that causes an organism to react in some way. The organism's reaction to the stimulus is called a **response.** The hydra's response to the prey is to sting it. **All animal behaviors are caused by stimuli.**

Some stimuli, such as prey brushing a hydra's tentacles, are outside the animal. Other stimuli, such as hunger, come from inside. An animal's response may include external actions or internal changes (such as a faster heartbeat), or both.

The Functions of Behavior Most behaviors help an animal survive or reproduce. When an animal looks for food or hides to avoid a predator, it is doing something that helps it stay alive. When animals search for mates and build nests for their young, they are behaving in ways that help them reproduce.

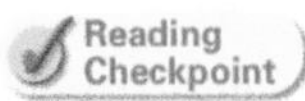

What is a stimulus?

For: Links on animal behavior
Visit: www.SciLinks.org
Web Code: scn-0251

Differentiated Instruction

English Learners/Beginning L1
Vocabulary: Science Glossary
Pronounce and define aloud the following: *behavior, stimulus, response*. For each word, give an example students will be familiar with. Have students write the definitions in their science glossaries. Students might draw a series of pictures depicting an animal responding to a stimulus. **learning modality: verbal**

English Learners/Intermediate L2
Vocabulary: Science Glossary Students can expand the Beginning activity (left) by adding the terms: *instinct, learning, conditioning, imprinting, trial-and-error learning, insight learning*. Students should record an example for each word. Call on individuals to share their examples for each word. **learning modality: logical/ mathematical**

Instruct

The Behavior of Animals

Teach Key Concepts L2

Complex Adaptations

Focus Ask: **What are some animal behaviors that you have observed?** *(Possible answers: Birds pecking at a tree or gerbils running on a wheel)* **How do you think the animals learned these behaviors?** *(Accept all reasonable answers at this time.)*

Teach Ask: **What is a stimulus?** *(A signal that causes an organism to react in some way)* **What is a response?** *(An organism's reaction to a stimulus)* Explain that most animal behaviors are complicated processes exhibited in response to an external or internal signal.

Apply Ask: **Give an example of an external signal that would produce a response from an animal.** *(Possible answers include seeing prey, seeing a predator, seeing a mate, seeing offspring, hearing a noise.)* **Give an example of an internal signal.** *(Possible answers include hunger, thirst, having to excrete wastes.)* **learning modality: logical/ mathematical**

Independent Practice L2

Teaching Resources

- Guided Reading and Study Worksheet: *What Is Behavior?*

Student Edition on Audio CD

For: Links on animal behavior
Visit: www.SciLinks.org
Web Code: scn-0251

Download a worksheet that will guide students' review of Internet resources on animal behavior.

Monitor Progress L2

Answers

Figure 2 The false "eyes" displayed on the wings of the moth look like the eyes of a much larger animal. A predator may be surprised by this display and hesitate, giving the moth time to escape.

Reading Checkpoint A signal that causes an organism to react

Behavior by Instinct

Teach Key Concepts L2

Behavior That Isn't Learned

Focus Remind students that behavior occurs in response to a stimulus.

Teach Explain that instinctive behavior is behavior that is inborn; the animal can perform the behavior correctly the first time a certain stimulus occurs. Instincts can occur in response to a certain stimulus without an animal having seen another animal of its species perform the behavior; an animal does not have to be taught instinctive behavior. Ask: **What are some examples of instincts?** *(A newborn kangaroo crawling into its mother's pouch; a spider spinning a web, a bird building a nest)*

Apply Ask: **How does instinctive behavior help an animal survive?** *(Possible answers: Instinctive behaviors may occur in response to a food stimulus or in response to predators or other threats.)* **learning modality: logical/ mathematical**

Address Misconceptions L2

Instinctive Behavior

Focus Some students may think that only simple behaviors are instinctive.

Teach Explain to students that many instinctive behaviors are complex. Spiders that spin an orb-web do so using different types of silk secreted by spinning glands. Some of the threads are non-adhesive, while others in the center of the web are sticky. When prey is trapped in the web, the spider responds to the vibrations it feels along the threads. The spider moves along the non-adhesive threads to inject venom into the prey. Other examples of complex behavior that is at least partly instinctive are seasonal migration and some elaborate courtship behaviors, such as cranes "dancing" for potential mates.

Apply When exposed to the stimulus of ultrasonic signals emitted by predatory bats, some moth species will automatically and instantly fold their wings and drop to the ground in response. Ask: **How is this instinctive behavior helpful to the moths?** *(Possible answer: The moths are less likely to be eaten the first time they encounter a predatory bat.)* **learning modality: logical/ mathematical**

FIGURE 3
A Web Built by Instinct
Most spiders know by instinct how to build elaborate webs.

Lab zone Skills Activity

Predicting

Hawks, which have short necks, prey on gull chicks. Geese, which have long necks, do not prey on the chicks. When newly hatched gull chicks see any bird's shadow, they instinctively crouch down. As the chicks become older, they continue to crouch when they see the shadow of a hawk, but they learn not to crouch when they see a goose's shadow. Predict how older gull chicks will behave when they see bird shadows shaped like A, B, and C. Explain your prediction.

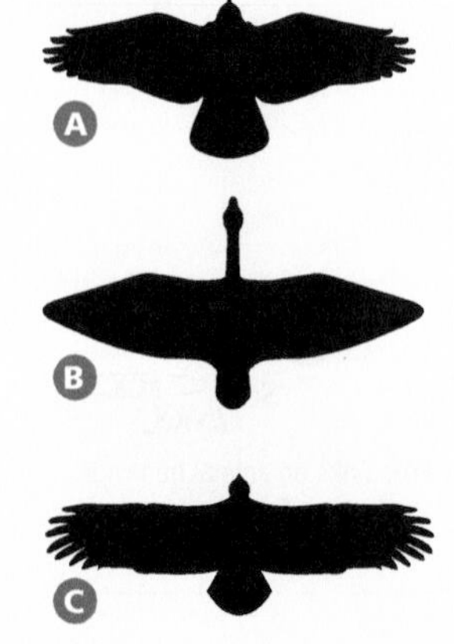

Behavior by Instinct

Animals perform some behaviors by **instinct,** without being taught. **An instinct is a response to a stimulus that is inborn and that an animal performs correctly the first time.** For example, a newborn kangaroo instinctively crawls into its mother's pouch and attaches itself to a nipple. Without this instinct, baby kangaroos could not obtain the milk they need to survive.

Some instincts are fairly simple. Earthworms, for example, crawl away from bright light. Other instincts are complex. Spiders spin complicated webs on their first try without making mistakes in the pattern. Most birds build their nests without ever being taught how.

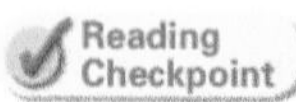

What is an instinct?

Learned Behavior

Recall the first time you rode a bicycle. It probably took a few tries before you did it well—you had to learn how. **Learning** is the process that leads to changes in behavior based on practice or experience. In general, the larger an animal's brain, the more the animal can learn. **Learned behaviors include imprinting, conditioning, trial-and-error learning, and insight learning.** Because learned behaviors result from an animal's experience, they are not usually done perfectly the first time.

All learned behaviors depend in part on inherited traits that have passed from parents to offspring. For example, lion cubs inherit physical features and instincts that are necessary for hunting. They are born with claws that help them capture prey. They also are born with the instinct to pounce on any object that attracts their attention. However, only through experience can they learn how to master hunting skills.

Lab zone Skills Activity

Skills Focus Predicting L1

Time 10 minutes

Tips Prepare students to predict the chicks' responses by asking them to compare the shadow shapes. Suggest they note similarities and differences that a chick might use as clues for distinguishing between the shadows.

Expected Outcome An older chick would learn not to crouch when it sees a shadow shaped like B, while shadows A and C would continue to elicit crouching behavior. This learning is a form of conditioning that modifies instinctive behavior. **learning modality: visual**

Imprinting Imprinting is a learned behavior. In **imprinting,** certain newly hatched birds and newborn mammals recognize and follow the first moving object they see. This object is usually the mother of the young animals. Imprinting involves a combination of instinct and learning. The young animal has an instinct to follow a moving object, but is not born knowing what its parent looks like. The young animal learns from experience what object to follow.

Once imprinting takes place, it cannot be changed. That is true even if the young animal has imprinted on something other than its mother. Young animals have imprinted on moving toys and even humans. Konrad Lorenz, an Austrian scientist, conducted experiments in which he, rather than the mother, was the first moving object that newly hatched birds saw. Figure 4 shows the result of one such experiment. Even as adults, the ducks followed Lorenz around.

Imprinting is valuable for two reasons. First, it keeps young animals close to their mothers, who know where to find food and how to avoid predators. Second, imprinting allows young animals to learn what other animals of their own species look like. This ability protects the animals while they are young. In later life, this ability is important when the animals search for mates.

FIGURE 4
Imprinting
Konrad Lorenz got these ducks to imprint on him by making himself the first moving object they ever saw.
Relating Cause and Effect *Why are the ducks following the swimmer?*

Learned Behavior

Teach Key Concepts L2

Learning

Focus Ask students to tell something they learned in the last week. *(Possible answers: examples from sporting activities, improving skills at computer or video games.)*

Teach Ask: **What is learning?** *(The process that leads to changes in behavior based on practice or experience.)* **What are some examples of learned behaviors?** *(Imprinting, conditioning, trial-and-error learning, insight learning)*

Apply Ask: **How does learning increase an animal's chance of survival?** *(Possible answer: An animal may learn to avoid predators and hunt for food more effectively.)* **learning modality: verbal**

L1

Automatic Responses

Materials clear plastic sheet, foam ball

Time 10 minutes

Focus Explain to students that some responses to stimuli are automatic or reflexive. The automatic "blink" response is common among most mammals.

Teach Have several volunteers come to the front of the classroom. Each volunteer should hold the clear plastic sheet in front of his or her face while another volunteer gently tosses the soft foam ball at the sheet. Most students will involuntarily blink, even though they know the ball can't hit them.

Apply Ask: **How does this automatic response aid a mammal's survival?** *(Possible answer: It helps avoid injury to the eye.)* **learning modality: kinesthetic**

Differentiated Instruction

Gifted and Talented L3

Researching Whooping Cranes Have students research the history and current status of the reintroduction of whooping cranes to eastern North America. Tell students to consider these questions: How does the reintroduction plan incorporate behaviors such as imprinting into the process? How do other whooping crane behaviors affect how the birds are handled by humans? Students should share the results of their research with the rest of the class in the form of a news report. **learning modality: logical/mathematical**

Monitor Progress L2

Skills Check Have students compare instinctive and learned behavior.

Answers

Figure 4 The ducks had imprinted on the swimmer when they were newly hatched ducklings.

Reading Checkpoint Behavior that is inborn and that an animal performs correctly the first time

L2

Designing a Behavior Experiment

Materials none

Time 15 minutes

Focus Remind students of the important steps in experimental design, such as posing a question, developing a hypothesis, controlling variables, and forming operational definitions before they begin the activity.

Teach Divide the class into cooperative groups. Instruct each group to design an experiment to investigate a particular animal's response to a stimulus, such as a dog's response to the ringing of a doorbell. Groups can assign the tasks of the designing process to specific students. Inform students that they must write a description of the procedure and remind them to think of ethical considerations, such as animal treatment and safety, as they outline the experiment.

Apply Have groups present their experimental designs to the rest of the class. Have the class review the experiments and ask questions. If possible allow students to do their experiments. **learning modality: logical/mathematical**

All in One Teaching Resources

- Transparency B44

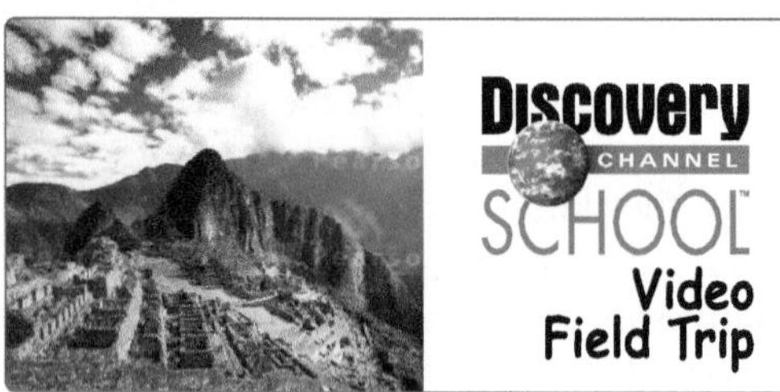

Animal Behavior

Show the Video Field Trip to introduce students to rescue and independence dogs and their training. Discussion question: **How do rescue and independence dogs learn to overcome their instincts?** *(By building up a dog's confidence in doing things it would normally avoid)*

FIGURE 5

Conditioning

Pavlov followed specific steps to condition a dog to salivate at the sound of a bell.

Predicting *Predict what the dog would do if it heard a bell ringing in another part of the house.*

Normal Stimulus Alone

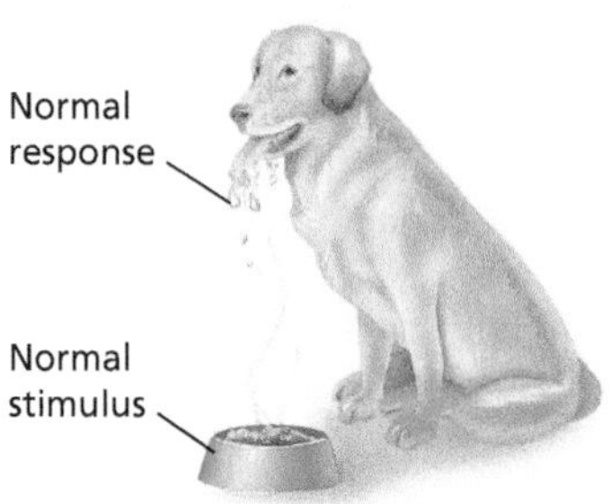

1 When a hungry dog sees or smells food, it produces saliva. Dogs do not usually salivate in response to other stimuli, such as the sound of a ringing bell.

Two Stimuli Together

2 For many days, Pavlov rang a bell every time that he fed the dog. The dog learned to associate the ringing of the bell with the sight and smell of food.

New Stimulus Only

3 Thus, when Pavlov rang a bell but did not give the dog food, the dog still produced saliva. The new stimulus produced the response that normally only food would produce.

Conditioning When a dog sees its owner approaching with a leash, the dog may jump up, eager to go for a walk. The dog has learned to associate the leash with a pleasant event—a brisk walk. Learning that a particular stimulus or response leads to a good or a bad outcome is called **conditioning.**

Pets are often trained using a form of conditioning. Suppose you want to train a puppy to come when you call it. The desired response is the puppy coming to you when it hears your call. The good outcome you will use is a food reward: a dog biscuit.

Here is how the conditioning works. At first, the puppy rarely comes when you call. But every now and then, the puppy runs to you in response to your call. Each time the puppy comes when you call, you give it a dog biscuit. Your puppy will soon learn to associate the desired response—coming when called—with the good outcome of a food reward. To get the reward, the puppy learns to come every time you call. After a while, the puppy will come to you even if you don't give it a dog biscuit.

During the early 1900s, the Russian scientist Ivan Pavlov performed experiments involving one kind of conditioning. Figure 5 shows the steps that Pavlov followed in his experiments.

Math Analyzing Data

"A-maze-ing" Mice

A scientist conducted an experiment to find out whether mice would learn to run a maze more quickly if they were given rewards. She set up two identical mazes. In one maze, cheese was placed at the end of the correct route through the maze. No cheese was placed in the second maze. Use the graph below to answer the questions.

1. **Reading Graphs** On Day 1, what was the average time it took mice with a cheese reward to complete the maze?
2. **Calculating** On Day 6, how much faster did mice with a reward complete the maze than mice without a reward?
3. **Interpreting Data** What was the manipulated variable in this experiment? Explain.

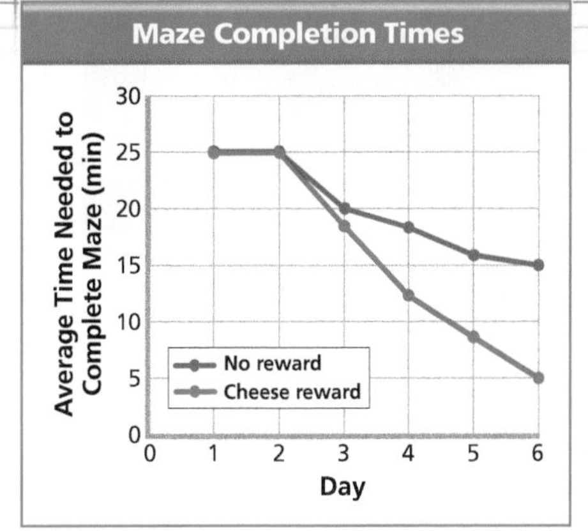

4. **Drawing Conclusions** Was the rate of learning faster for mice with the cheese reward or without the cheese reward? Explain.

Trial-and-Error Learning One form of conditioning is trial-and-error learning. In **trial-and-error learning,** an animal learns to perform a behavior more and more skillfully. Through repeated practice, an animal learns to repeat behaviors that result in rewards and avoid behaviors that result in punishment. When you learned to ride a bicycle, you did it by trial-and-error. You may have wobbled at first, but eventually you got better. You learned to move in ways that adjusted your balance and kept you from falling over.

Many animals learn by trial-and-error which methods are best for obtaining food. They also learn which methods to avoid. Think of what happens when a predator tries to attack a skunk. The skunk sprays the predator with a substance that stings and smells awful. In the future, the predator is likely to avoid skunks. The predator has learned to associate the sight of a skunk with its terrible spray.

FIGURE 6
Trial-and-Error Learning
After several failed attempts, this squirrel has finally figured out how to jump onto a hummingbird feeder, balance itself, and drink the water.

Math Analyzing Data

Math Skill Interpreting data

Focus Have students study the graph. Ask: **What does the graph show?** *(The differences in time for two groups of mice learning to run a maze)*

Teach Have students familiarize themselves with the line graph. Ask: **What does the *x*-axis show?** *(The number of days in the testing period)* **The *y*-axis?** *(The time it took the mice to complete each run)*

Answers

1. 25 minutes
2. 10 minutes
3. Whether a reward of cheese was given; the amount and kind of cheese for the reward should stay the same in repetitions.
4. After the second day, the rate of learning was faster with a reward given as positive reinforcement; rats learned to run the maze through trial and error; conditioning helped the rats learn that using the correct route through the maze would result in a reward, reinforcing and probably speeding up their response. **learning modality: logical/ mathematical**

Help Students Read L1

Comparing and Contrasting Have students read about trial-and-error and insight learning. Then have students construct a chart that compares and contrasts trial-and-error learning with insight learning. *(Possible answer: Both are types of learning that result in a particular behavior. In trial-and-error learning an animal learns to perform a behavior more skillfully through repeated practice. Insight learning involves solving a problem by applying prior knowledge, without a trial-and-error period.)*

Monitor Progress L2

Oral Presentation Ask students to describe an example of conditioning they have witnessed in themselves, another person, or in animals.

Answer

Figure 5 The dog would begin to salivate; it has been conditioned to salivate when it hears the bell.

Monitor Progress L2

Answer

Reading Checkpoint Chimpanzees use twigs to probe into insect nests; a raven can figure out how to bring a piece of meat dangling from a string close enough to eat.

Assess

Reviewing Key Concepts

1. a. Stimuli **b.** A response is an organism's reaction to a stimulus; example: hydra firing stinging cells in response to prey brushing against it. **c.** The functions of behavior are to help an animal survive or reproduce. The hydra's response helped it to stay alive by obtaining food.

2. a. An instinct is a response to a stimulus that is inborn and performed correctly the first time. Any two: Newborn kangaroo crawls into mother's pouch and attaches itself to a nipple, earthworms crawl away from bright light, spiders spin webs, birds build nests. **b.** No, instinctive behaviors are inborn and performed correctly the first time. **c.** Instinctive behaviors often have to do with basic survival such as finding food or avoiding predators. For animals capable of learning, instinct has to get them through the earliest stages of life so that they can become old enough to learn.

3. a. Imprinting, conditioning, trial-and-error learning, and insight learning.
b. During imprinting, an animal learns to recognize and follow the first moving object that it sees. **c.** The duckling will probably try to follow the child on the tricycle, because ducklings follow the first moving object they see after hatching. This behavior is called imprinting.

Reteach L2

Review the definitions of the four types of learning: imprinting, conditioning, trial-and-error, and insight. Have students provide an example for each type.

All in One Teaching Resources

- Section Summary: *What Is Behavior?*
- Review and Reinforce: *What Is Behavior?*
- Enrich: *What Is Behavior?*

FIGURE 7
Insight Learning
Using insight, this raven has figured out how to bring meat hanging from a string close enough to eat.

Insight Learning The first time you try out a new video game, you may not need someone to explain how to play it. Instead, you may use what you already know about other video games to figure out how the new one works. When you solve a problem or learn how to do something new by applying what you already know, without a period of trial-and-error, you are using **insight learning.**

Insight learning is most common in primates, such as gorillas, chimpanzees, and humans. For example, chimpanzees use twigs to probe into the nests of termites and other insects that they eat. The chimps use insight to bend or chew their twig "tools" into a shape that will best fit the holes.

In addition to primates, other kinds of animals have also shown insight learning. For example, you may be surprised to learn that the raven shown in Figure 7 is using insight learning to obtain food. The raven uses its beak to draw up a loop of string. Then, it holds the loop under its foot and draws up a second loop, and so on. Soon the food is within reach.

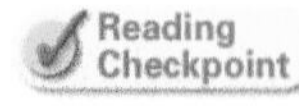

Reading Checkpoint **Give two examples of animals showing insight learning.**

Section 1 Assessment

Target Reading Skill Outlining Use the information in your outline about behavior to help you answer the questions below.

Reviewing Key Concepts

1. a. Defining What are signals that cause behavior called?
   b. Describing What is meant by *response?* Describe an example of a response.
   c. Relating Cause and Effect What are the functions of behavior? Think about the response you described. What function did that response serve?
2. a. Listing What are instincts? List two examples.
   b. Inferring Would instincts get better with practice? Explain.
   c. Developing Hypotheses Why do you think instincts are particularly important for newborn animals?
3. a. Identifying Identify the types of learned behaviors.
   b. Reviewing Describe what happens during imprinting.
   c. Predicting Right after hatching, before seeing anything else, a duckling sees a child riding a tricycle. What will probably happen the next time the child rides the tricycle in front of the duckling? Explain.

Writing in Science

List of Questions Suppose you could travel back in time and interview Dr. Pavlov and Dr. Lorenz. Formulate a list of five questions you would ask each scientist about his research on animal learning.

Lab zone Chapter Project

Keep Students on Track Review students' training plans. Check to make sure students have obtained permission from the owners of the animals. Also make sure that the skills students are planning to teach their animals are reasonable. Ensure that students have chosen appropriate rewards for the animals, and that the animals will not be harmed during the training process.

Writing in Science

List of Questions

Scoring Rubric

4 Questions are well thought out and probe key points about each scientist's work.
3 Questions are logical but not probing.
2 Questions are formulaic.
1 Questions reflect minimal preparation.

Lab zone Design Your Own Lab

Become a Learning Detective

Problem
What are some factors that make it easier for people to learn new things?

Skills Focus
calculating, posing questions, designing experiments

Materials
- paper
- pencil

Design a Plan
1. Look over the two lists of words shown in the diagram on this page. Researchers use groups of words like these to investigate how people learn. Notice the way the two groups differ. The words in List A have no meanings in ordinary English. List B contains familiar but unrelated words.
2. What do you think will happen if people try to learn the words in each list? Write a hypothesis about which list will be easier to learn. How much easier will it be to learn that list?
3. With a partner, design an experiment to test your hypothesis. Brainstorm a list of the variables you will need to control in order to make the results of your experiment reliable. Then write out your plan and present it to your teacher.
4. If necessary, revise your plan according to your teacher's instructions. Then perform your experiment using people your teacher has approved as test subjects. Keep careful records of your results.

List A	List B
zop	bug
rud	rag
tig	den
wab	hot
hev	fur
paf	wax
mel	beg
kib	cut
col	sip
nug	job

Analyze and Conclude
1. **Calculating** Find the average (mean) number of words people learned from each list. How do the results compare with your hypothesis?
2. **Posing Questions** What factors may have made one list easier to learn than the other? What other questions can you ask about your data?
3. **Designing Experiments** Look back at your experimental plan. Think about how well you were able to carry it out in the actual experiment. What difficulties did you encounter? What improvements could you make, either in your plan or in the way you carried it out?
4. **Communicating** Share your results with the rest of the class. How do the results of the different experiments in your class compare? What factors might explain the similarities or differences?

More to Explore
Plan an experiment to investigate how long people remember what they learn. Develop a hypothesis, and design an experiment to test your hypothesis.

Lab zone Design Your Own Lab

Become a Learning Detective 

Prepare for Inquiry

Key Concept
Various factors can make learning easier or harder.

Skills Objectives
After this lab, students will be able to
- pose questions about human learning
- design an experiment to answer their questions
- calculate the mean number of words learned

Prep Time none
Class Time 40 minutes

Advance Planning
To save class time, decide in advance who the test subjects will be.

Alternative Materials
If students conduct this experiment on classmates, they must generate new lists that are unfamiliar to the test subjects.

All in One Teaching Resources
- Lab Worksheet: *Become a Learning Detective*

Guide Inquiry

Invitation
Ask students to consider how the following factors may affect how easy it is to learn: It is a subject you enjoy; you are motivated by rewards; you are already familiar with the subject; there is much repetition.

Introduce the Procedure
Have students decide on a way to quantitatively measure learning. For example, each subject can examine the list of words for a given time. The subject then has a limited amount of time to write down all of the words he or she can remember. The subject will remember more words from the list that was easier to learn.

Troubleshooting the Experiment
Suggest that students have test subjects write down rather than speak words so that other groups will not overhear.

Expected Outcome
Familiar words are easier to learn than unfamiliar ones.

Analyze and Conclude
1. Most test subjects should learn more from list B than list A.
2. It is easier to remember meaningful words than nonsense words; additional questions might include: How does the age of the test subject affect the results? Does the order in which the lists are learned affect results?
3. Results will depend on student plans.
4. Possible answers: The number of words learned depends on the time allowed to learn.

Extend Inquiry

More to Explore Students might hypothesize that familiar concepts are remembered longer. Have several test subjects learn concepts that include familiar and unfamiliar words. Test the subjects after 1, 2, and 4 hours.

Section 2

Patterns of Behavior

Objectives

After completing this lesson, students will be able to

B.5.2.1 List the three main ways animals communicate.

B.5.2.2 Give examples of competitive and cooperative behaviors.

B.5.2.3 Describe cyclic behavior.

Target Reading Skill

Using Prior Knowledge Explain that using prior knowledge helps students connect what they already know to what they are about to read.

Answers

Possible answers:

What You Know

1. Dogs bark at intruders.
2. Different sounds an animal makes mean different things.
3. Animals communicate without words.

What You Learned

1. Animals use sounds to communicate warnings about predators, establish territories, or find a mate.
2. Animals communicate with chemicals called pheromones to mark territory and find mates.
3. Animals communicate through body movements to show aggression and courtship behavior.

All in One **Teaching Resources**

- Transparency B45

Preteach

Build Background Knowledge

L2

Purpose of Behavior

Instruct students to immediately stop what they are doing. Choose students at random and ask them what they were doing when you asked them to stop. Explain that whatever each student was doing was a part of his or her behavior. Ask: **What do you think was the purpose of your behavior?** *(Student answers will depend on what they were doing at the time of the exercise.)*

Section 2

Patterns of Behavior

Reading Preview

Key Concepts

- What are three main ways animals communicate?
- What are some examples of competitive behaviors and cooperative behaviors?
- What is a cyclic behavior?

Key Terms

- pheromone
- aggression
- territory
- courtship behavior
- society
- circadian rhythm
- hibernation
- migration

Target Reading Skill

Using Prior Knowledge Your prior knowledge is what you already know before you read about a topic. Before you read, write what you know about the different ways animals communicate in a graphic organizer like the one below. As you read, write what you learn.

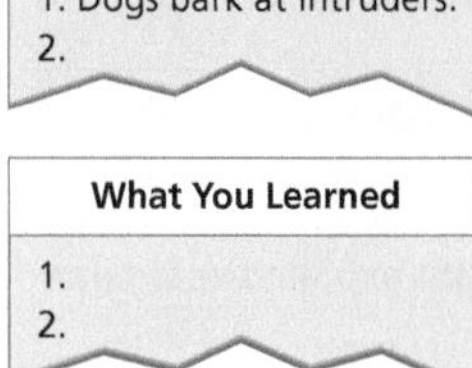

What You Know
1. Dogs bark at intruders.
2.
What You Learned
1.
2.

Lab zone Discover Activity

What Can You Express Without Words?

1. Use facial expressions and body movements, but no words, to show surprise or another emotion to your partner.
2. By observing your behavior, your partner should infer what you are communicating. Your partner should also note the behavior clues that led to this inference.
3. Now your partner should try to communicate a feeling or situation to you without words. Infer what your partner is trying to communicate, and note the behavior clues that led to your inference.

Think It Over

Forming Operational Definitions Write your own definition of *communication*. How did this activity change your idea of communication?

Oh no—ants have gotten into the sugar! As you watch in dismay, a stream of ants moves along the kitchen counter. They are heading right for the sugar bowl. Using their sense of smell, the ants follow a chemical trail that was first laid down by the ant that discovered the sugar. Each ant adds to the trail by depositing a tiny droplet of scent onto the counter. The droplet quickly evaporates, making an invisible cloud of scent above the path of the ants. The ants hold their antennae forward and use them to sniff their way to the sugar bowl. Then they turn around and follow the same chemical signal back to their nest.

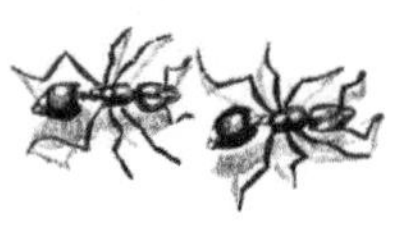

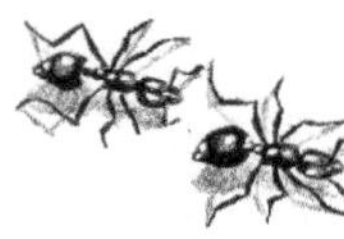

Lab zone Discover Activity

L1

Skills Focus Forming operational definitions

Materials none

Time 15 minutes

Tips Have students write the feeling or situation they are trying to convey. After their partner guesses what is being communicated, students can check their notebooks. Students should use natural facial expressions and simple movements.

Expected Outcome Emotions should be able to be communicated. Abstract ideas may be difficult to communicate nonverbally.

Think It Over Most students will include gestures and expressions in the definition of communication.

Communication

You've just read that ants can communicate the location of foods using scent. Animal communication comes in many forms. Perhaps you've seen a cat hissing and arching its back. It is using sound and body posture to communicate a message that seems to say, "Back off!" **Animals use mostly sounds, scents, and body movements to communicate with one another.** An animal's ability to communicate helps it interact with other animals.

Animals communicate many kinds of messages using sound. Some animals use sound to attract mates. Female crickets, for example, are attracted to the sound of a male's chirping. Animals may also communicate warnings with sound. When it sees a coyote or other predator approaching, a prairie dog makes a yipping sound that warns other prairie dogs to take cover in their burrows. The wolf in Figure 8 is warning wolves outside its pack to keep away.

Animals also communicate with chemical scents. A chemical released by one animal that affects the behavior of another animal of the same species is called a **pheromone** (FEHR uh mohn). For example, perhaps you have seen a male house cat spraying a tree. The musky scent he leaves contains pheromones that advertise his presence to other cats in the neighborhood. The scent trail that leads the ants to the sugar bowl in Figure 9 is also made of pheromones.

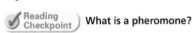

Reading Checkpoint What is a pheromone?

FIGURE 8
Howling Wolf
Wolves in a pack may howl all together to warn other packs to stay away.

Go Online active art
For: Pheromones activity
Visit: PHSchool.com
Web Code: cep-2052

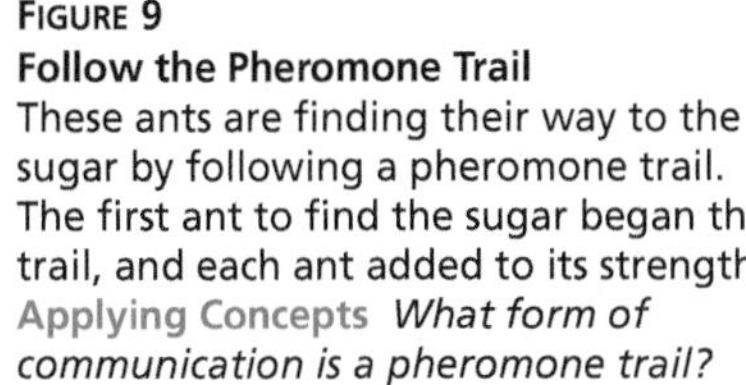

FIGURE 9
Follow the Pheromone Trail
These ants are finding their way to the sugar by following a pheromone trail. The first ant to find the sugar began the trail, and each ant added to its strength.
Applying Concepts *What form of communication is a pheromone trail?*

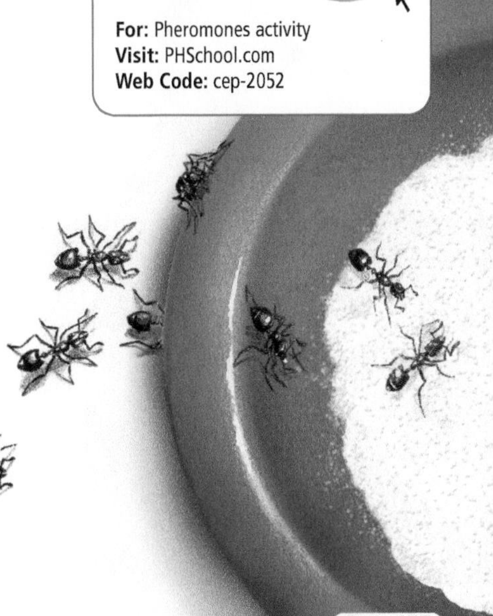

Instruct

Communication

Teach Key Concepts L2

Ways to Communicate

Focus Ask: **Give one example of animal communication. What message do you think the animal was trying to convey?** *(Answers will vary depending on the example students give.)*

Teach Ask: **What are three ways animals communicate?** *(Through sounds, scents, and body movements)* **What is a pheromone?** *(A chemical scent released by one animal that affects the behavior of another animal of the same species)*

Apply Ask: **Why is it important that animals be able to communicate with one another?** *(It is important to behavioral interactions; it allows animals to warn one another about predators or to attract mates.)* **learning modality: verbal**

Independent Practice L2

All in One Teaching Resources

- Guided Reading and Study Worksheet: *Patterns of Behavior*

Student Edition on Audio CD

For: Pheromones activity
Visit: PHSchool.com
Web Code: cep-2052

Students learn how ants use pheromones to communicate.

Differentiated Instruction

English Learners/Beginning L1
Comprehension: Key Concept Write the boldface sentence from this page on the board. Incorporate important information from the sentence into a concept map. The center of the map might be *Animals Communicate*. Each of three branches could be labeled *Using*. Fill in the blanks together. **learning modality: visual**

English Learners/Intermediate L2
Comprehension: Key Concept Provide students with the same sentence and concept map, and model by filling in one blank. Have students fill in the rest of the answers and then expand the map to include additional information from this section. **learning modality: logical/mathematical**

Monitor Progress L2

Answers

Figure 9 Communication by scent

Reading Checkpoint A pheromone is a chemical released by one animal that affects the behavior of another animal of the same species.

Competitive Behavior

Teach Key Concepts

L2

Animals Compete for Resources

Focus Explain that animals compete within a species and between species.

Teach Ask: **What resources might animals compete for?** *(Food, water, space, shelter, and mates)* **Why do animals show aggression?** *(To gain control over another animal)* **Why do animals have to compete for resources?** *(In most habitats resources are limited.)* **How does establishing a territory help an animal to survive and reproduce?** *(Within the territory, the animal has access to the resources, which include food, water and shelter. In many animal species a male cannot attract a female unless he holds a territory.)*

Apply Tell students that red-winged blackbirds display their red "epaulets" (red patches on the shoulder area of their wings) to defend a territory. Ask: **What would happen if a male blackbird's red patches were dyed black?** *(The male would probably lose its territory.)* **learning modality: logical/mathematical**

Teacher **Demo**

L2

Competition and Aggression

Materials 2 glass jars, 2 male bettas (Siamese fighting fish), opaque card, water

Time 15 minutes

Focus Explain to students that the males of this species are very aggressive toward other males.

Teach Place each fish in its own glass jar filled with water. Place the jars next to each other with the opaque card between them. Begin by allowing students to observe the behavior of the two fish for a few minutes with the card in place. Then, remove the card. Be sure each fish can clearly see the other. Have students record and observe the behaviors of the fish.

Apply Have students write short paragraphs to explain how they think these behaviors would benefit the bettas. *(The strongest and most aggressive males are those that survive and find mates.)* **learning modality: visual**

FIGURE 10
Boxing Hares
These Arctic hares are resolving their conflict by boxing. **Inferring** *What event might have led to this behavior?*

FIGURE 11
Aggressive Gorilla
This lowland gorilla needs no words to say, "Stay away!"

Competitive Behavior

Have you ever fed ducks in the park or pigeons on the street? Then you have probably seen how they fight over every crumb. These animals compete because there usually isn't enough food to go around. **Animals compete with one another for limited resources, such as food, water, space, shelter, and mates.**

Competition can occur among different species of animals. For example, a pride of lions may try to steal a prey from a troop of hyenas that has just killed the prey. Competition can also occur between members of the same species. A female aphid, a type of insect, kicks and shoves another female aphid while competing for the best leaf on which to lay eggs.

Showing Aggression When they compete, animals may display aggression. **Aggression** is a threatening behavior that one animal uses to gain control over another. Before a pride of lions settles down to eat its prey, individual lions show aggression by snapping, clawing, and snarling. First, the most aggressive members of the pride eat their fill. Then, the less aggressive and younger members of the pride get a chance to feed on the leftovers.

Aggression between members of the same species hardly ever results in the injury or death of any of the competitors. Typically, the loser communicates, "I give up" with its behavior. For example, to protect themselves from the aggressive attacks of older dogs, puppies often roll over on their backs, showing their bellies. This signal calms the older dog. The puppy can then creep away.

Differentiated Instruction

Less Proficient Readers L1

Using Visuals Have students use Figures 10, 11, and 12 to help them define and understand the concepts of competitive behavior, aggression, and courtship behavior, respectively. For each figure, have students write a description that tells what each animal is doing and identify the type of behavior being demonstrated.
learning modality: visual

Gifted and Talented L3

Establishing a Territory Have students research how an animal of their choice establishes and defends its territory. What is the size of its territory? What factors may influence how the animal chooses its territory? Have students share the results of their research with the rest of the class in the form of a multimedia presentation.
learning modality: logical/mathematical

Establishing a Territory On an early spring day, a male oriole fills the warm air with song. You may think the bird is singing just because it is a nice day. But in fact, he is alerting other orioles that he is the "owner" of a particular territory. A **territory** is an area that is occupied and defended by an animal or group of animals. If another animal of the same species enters the territory, the owner will attack the newcomer and try to drive it away. Birds use songs and aggressive behaviors to maintain their territories. Other animals may use calls, scratches, droppings, or pheromones.

By establishing a territory, an animal protects its access to resources such as food and possible mates. A territory also provides a safe area. Within it, animals can raise their young without competition from other members of their species. In most songbird species, and in many other animal species, a male cannot attract a mate unless he has a territory.

Attracting a Mate A male and female salamander swim gracefully in the water, moving around one another. They are engaging in **courtship behavior,** which is behavior in which males and females of the same species prepare for mating. Courtship behavior ensures that the males and females of the same species recognize one another, so that mating and reproduction can take place. Courtship behavior is typically also competitive. For example, in some species, several males may perform courtship behaviors for a single female. She then chooses one of them to mate with.

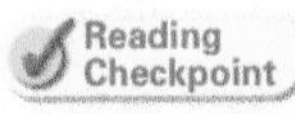
Reading Checkpoint How does having a territory help an animal survive?

Lab zone Skills Activity

Developing Hypotheses

The three-spined stickleback is a kind of fish in which the males' undersides turn red during the mating season. The males readily attack other male sticklebacks that enter their territory. In the laboratory, a biologist notices that males also show aggressive behavior whenever a red object passes their tank. What do you think is the stimulus for the stickleback's aggressive display in the wild? How could you test your hypothesis? Explain.

FIGURE 12
Kingfisher Courtship
These common kingfishers are engaged in courtship. The male on the left is offering the female a gift of food—a freshly caught fish.

Use Visuals: Figure 12 L2

Courtship Behavior

Focus Tell students that many species exhibit courtship behaviors.

Teach Ask: **Why is courtship behavior an important part of the reproductive process?** *(Courtship behavior ensures that males and females of the same species recognize one another so that mating and reproduction can take place.)* **What courting behavior is being exhibited by the male kingfisher?** *(The male has brought a freshly caught fish to the female.)*

Apply Ask: **Why is courtship behavior often competitive as well?** *(In some species, the males may have to compete with one another in order for a female to choose her mate.)* **learning modality: visual**

Lab zone Skills Activity

Skills Focus Developing hypotheses

Materials none

Time 10 minutes

Tips Remind students that a hypothesis must be testable. Make sure that students are only testing one variable, in this case color.

Expected Outcome Hypotheses should include the idea that the fish are responding to the red-color underside of the fish during the mating season. Procedures for testing hypotheses should identify all variables that need to be controlled. Students should also describe how they will measure and collect data. **learning modality: logical/mathematical**

Monitor Progress L2

Oral Presentation Have students form small groups and list three competitive or aggressive human behaviors they have observed in the school cafeteria. Classify each behavior and describe its purpose. One member of each group can present the group's ideas.

Answers

Figure 10 The hares may be fighting over food or a potential mate.

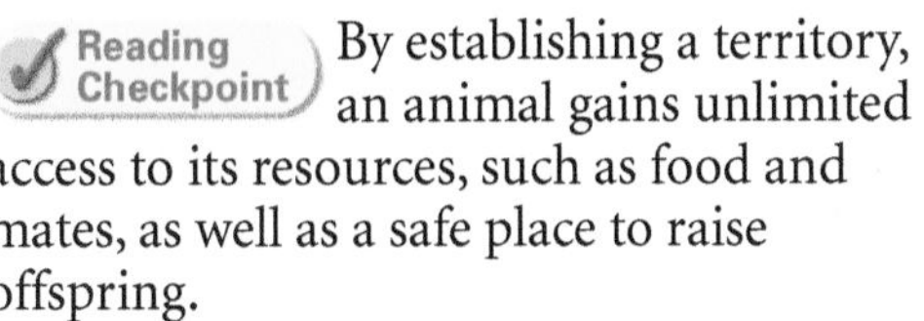
Reading Checkpoint By establishing a territory, an animal gains unlimited access to its resources, such as food and mates, as well as a safe place to raise offspring.

Group Behavior

Teach Key Concepts L2

Living in a Group

Focus Tell students that animals such as fish, insects, and hoofed mammals often live in groups.

Teach Ask: **What are some advantages to living in a group?** *(Group members protect one another and work together to find food.)* **What are some examples of animal societies?** *(Honeybees, ants, termites, naked mole rats, pistol shrimp)*

Apply Ask: **What disadvantage might there be for animals living in a group?** *(Possible answers: The group members must share resources; some groups have a leader that everyone must follow.)* **learning modality: logical/mathematical**

All in One Teaching Resources

- Transparency B46

L2

Group Safety

Materials Photos of groups of animals including large schools of fishes, a herd of zebra, and a herd of antelope

Time 10 minutes

Focus Tell students that when many individuals of the same species are in a large group, it may be confusing for a predator to see and select a single individual.

Teach Allow students to examine the photos of the groups of animals. Have them describe the markings or coloration of the animals in the group. Ask: **When a large group of individuals are together, what happens to individual markings? How might this confuse a predator?** *(The markings of an individual animal would blend in with the rest of the group. It may be difficult for a predator to pick out an individual in the group.)*

Apply Ask: **If you wanted to be inconspicuous in a large group of people all dressed in dark suits, what would you do? Explain.** *(Dress in a dark suit to blend in and not be noticeable.)* **learning modality: visual**

FIGURE 13
Safety in Groups
When a predator threatens, musk oxen form a horn-rimmed circle with their young sheltered in the center. Predicting *Would a potential predator be more or less likely to attack a group arranged in this way? Explain.*

Group Behavior

Not all animal behaviors are competitive. **Living in groups enables animals to cooperate.** Although many animals live alone and only rarely meet one of their own kind, other animals live in groups. Some fishes form schools, and some insects live in large groups. Hoofed mammals, such as bison and wild horses, often form herds. Living in a group usually helps animals survive. For example, group members may protect one another or work together to find food.

How can group members help one another? If an elephant gets stuck in a mudhole, for example, other members of its herd will dig it out. When animals such as lions hunt in a group, they usually can kill larger prey than a single hunter can.

Safety in Groups Living in groups often protects animals against predators. Fishes that swim in schools are often safer than fishes that swim alone. It is harder for predators to see and select an individual fish in a group. In a herd, some animals may watch for danger while others feed.

Animals in a group sometimes cooperate in fighting off a predator. For example, the North American musk oxen shown in Figure 13 make a defensive circle against a predator, such as a wolf. Their young calves are sheltered in the middle of the circle. The adult musk oxen stand with their horns lowered, ready to charge. The predator often gives up rather than face a whole herd of angry musk oxen.

Animal Societies Some animals, including ants, termites, honeybees, naked mole rats, and pistol shrimp, live in groups called societies. A **society** is a group of closely related animals of the same species that work together in a highly organized way. In a society, there is a division of labor—different individuals perform different tasks. In a honeybee society, for example, there are thousands of worker bees that take on different tasks in the beehive. Some workers feed larvae. Some bring back nectar and pollen from flowers as food for the hive. Other worker bees guard the entrance to the hive.

Reading Checkpoint What is a society?

Lab zone Try This Activity

Worker Bees

1. Make a paper chain by cutting paper strips for loops and gluing or taping the loops together. After 5 minutes, count the loops in the chain.
2. Now work in a small group to make a paper chain. Decide how to divide up the work before beginning. After 5 minutes, count the loops in the chain.

Calculating Find the difference between the number of loops in your individual and group chains. For Step 2, calculate the number of loops made per person by dividing the total number of loops by the number of people in your group. Was it more productive to work individually or as a group?

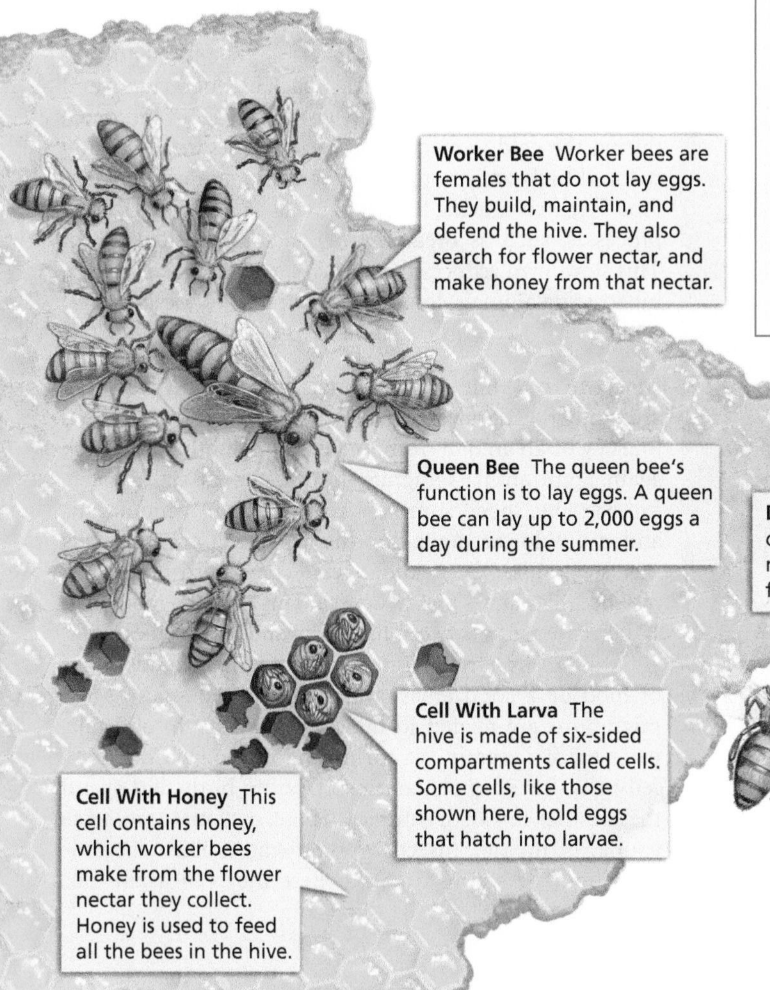

Worker Bee Worker bees are females that do not lay eggs. They build, maintain, and defend the hive. They also search for flower nectar, and make honey from that nectar.

Queen Bee The queen bee's function is to lay eggs. A queen bee can lay up to 2,000 eggs a day during the summer.

Drone The only function of the male drones is to mate with queen bees from other colonies.

Cell With Larva The hive is made of six-sided compartments called cells. Some cells, like those shown here, hold eggs that hatch into larvae.

Cell With Honey This cell contains honey, which worker bees make from the flower nectar they collect. Honey is used to feed all the bees in the hive.

FIGURE 14
A Honeybee Society
A honeybee hive usually consists of one queen bee, thousands of female worker bees, and a few hundred male drones.

Lab zone Try This Activity

Skills Focus Calculating L2

Materials 22 × 28 cm sheets of paper; glue, stapler, or paste; scissors; timer

Time 15 minutes

Tips When students work in groups, part of the planning should involve assigning tasks to each group member.

Expected Outcome By working cooperatively, students should have been able to make more paper-chain links. Group members can divide the work so that no one has to perform the whole task.

Extend Have students think about what kinds of tasks are probably performed more efficiently by one person than by a group. **learning modality: kinesthetic**

Use Visuals: Figure 14 L2

A Honeybee Society

Focus Tell students that different types of honeybees perform different tasks.

Teach After students read the description of the individuals in the honeybee society shown in Figure 14, ask: **Is any member of the honeybee society unimportant? Why?** *(None is unimportant. All members have their special tasks to perform.)*

Apply Have a volunteer list on the board the three types of honeybees and their duties. After reviewing the list, ask: **Why is it advantageous that there are more worker bees than other bees in the hive?** *(Worker bees have many different tasks to perform, such as caring for the hive, the queen, and the larvae, and finding and making food. The queens and the drones each have only one task.)* **learning modality: visual**

Address Misconceptions L2

Animal Societies

Focus Students may confuse human societies and animal societies.

Teach Explain to students that human societies may consist of associations of unrelated individuals. In animal societies such as those of ants, termites, honeybees, naked mole rats, and pistol shrimp, all individuals are close relatives, usually siblings. In addition, while roles in animal societies are usually rigid, roles in human societies are much more flexible.

Apply Ask: **What aspects of human society differ from those of an insect society?** *(Possible answers: In human society each individual can define his or her own role in society and complete an array of tasks related to survival.)* **learning modality: verbal**

Monitor Progress L2

Writing Have students form groups to make a list of the advantages of aggression, establishing a territory, and living in groups. Students can save their lists in their portfolios. Portfolio

Answers

Figure 13 A predator would be less likely to attack a group arranged this way because the predator's chance of success is limited.

Reading Checkpoint A society is a group of closely related animals of the same species that work together in a highly organized way.

Behavior Cycles

Teach Key Concepts L2

Circadian Rhythms

Focus Tell students that some animals have behaviors that change over time in regular patterns—usually over the course of a day or a season. Ask: **Give examples of regular changes in behavior in your own life.** *(Possible answers: Awake during the day, sleep at night; get hungry at same time each day)*

Teach Explain that circadian rhythms are behavior cycles that occur over a period of approximately one day. Explain to students that almost all animals display obvious circadian rhythms. Ask: **What are some behaviors that are related to seasons?** *(Hibernation and migration)*

Apply Ask: **How do migration and hibernation help animals survive?** *(Migration enables animals to move to favorable conditions as the seasons change; hibernation slows down an animal's processes, reducing the need for food when less is available.)* **learning modality: verbal**

Integrating Social Studies L2

Interpreting Maps Display several maps that show the migratory paths of different animals, such as monarch butterflies, golden plovers, starlings, humpback whales, or sea turtles. Allow students to examine the maps and the migratory routes. Have students describe the routes taken by the animals, including the names and areas of any relevant continents, countries, or islands. **learning modality: visual**

Behavior Cycles

Some animal behaviors, called cyclic behaviors, occur in regular, predictable patterns. **Cyclic behaviors usually change over the course of a day or a season.**

Daily Cycles Behavior cycles that occur over a period of approximately one day are called **circadian rhythms** (sur KAY dee un). For example, blowflies search for food during the day and rest at night. In contrast, field mice are active during the night and rest by day. Animals that are active during the day can take advantage of sunlight, which makes food easy to see. On the other hand, animals that are active at night do not encounter predators that are active during the day.

FIGURE 15
Hibernation
This common dormouse is hibernating for the winter.
Inferring *Why is hibernation during the winter a useful adaptation for animals?*

Hibernation Other behavior cycles are related to seasons. For example, some animals, such as woodchucks and chipmunks, are active during warm seasons but hibernate during the cold winter. **Hibernation** is a state of greatly reduced body activity that occurs during the winter when food is scarce. During hibernation, all of an animal's body processes, such as breathing and heartbeat, slow down. This slowdown reduces the animal's need for food. In fact, hibernating animals do not eat. Their bodies use stored fat to meet their reduced nutrition needs.

Migration While many animals live their lives in one area, others migrate. **Migration** is the regular, seasonal journey of an animal from one place to another and back again. Some animals migrate short distances. Dall's sheep, for example, spend summers near the tops of mountains and move lower down for the winters. Other animals migrate thousands of kilometers. The record-holder for distance migrated is the Arctic tern. This bird flies more than 17,000 kilometers between the North and South poles.

Animals usually migrate to an area that provides a lot of food or a good environment for reproduction. Most migrations are related to the changing seasons and take place twice a year, in the spring and in the fall. American redstarts, for example, are insect-eating birds that spend the summer in North America. There, they mate and raise young. In the fall, insects become scarce. Then the redstarts migrate south to areas where they can again find plenty of food.

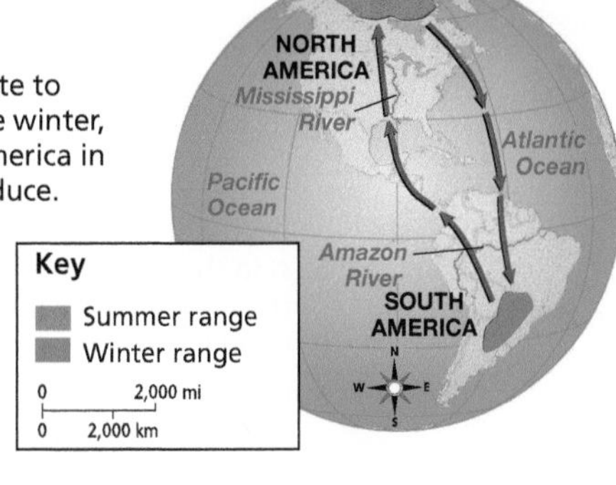

FIGURE 16
Migration
Golden plovers migrate to South America for the winter, and back to North America in the summer to reproduce.

Scientists are still learning about how migrating animals find their way. But they have discovered that animals use sight, taste, and other senses, including some that humans do not have. Some birds and sea turtles, for example, have a magnetic sense that acts something like a compass needle. Migrating birds also seem to navigate by using the positions of the sun, moon, and stars, as sailors have always done. Salmon use scent and taste to locate the streams where they were born, and return there to mate.

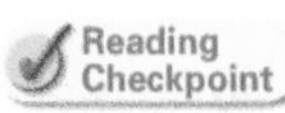 **What happens to an animal during hibernation?**

Section 2 Assessment

Target Reading Skill Using Prior Knowledge Review your graphic organizer and revise it based on what you just learned in the section.

Reviewing Key Concepts

1. a. Reviewing What are three main ways animals communicate?
   b. Explaining When house cats spray a tree with their scent, are they communicating? Explain.
   c. Developing Hypotheses What are some advantages of using pheromones to communicate instead of using sound?
2. a. Listing List examples of competitive behavior and cooperative behavior.
   b. Explaining Explain how competition is involved in establishing a territory.
   c. Predicting What might happen when a male mockingbird flies into the territory of another male mockingbird?
3. a. Reviewing What are behaviors that change over the course of a day or a season called?
   b. Comparing and Contrasting How are circadian rhythm and hibernation the same? How are they different?

Lab zone At-Home Activity

Animal Signs With a family member, spend some time making detailed observations of the behavior of an animal—a pet, an insect, a bird, or another animal. Watch the animal for signs of aggressive behavior or other communication. Try to figure out why the animal is behaving aggressively or what it is trying to communicate.

Monitor Progress L2

Answers

Figure 15 It reduces the animal's need for food when food is scarce.

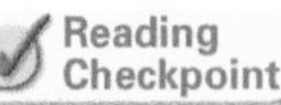 All of the animal's processes slow down.

Assess

Reviewing Key Concepts

1. a. Animals communicate through sounds, scents, and body movements.
b. Yes, they are marking territory and making other cats aware of their presence.
c. Communicating through pheromones rather than sounds is less likely to alert a predator to an animal's immediate location. Also, the animal does not have to be physically present to communicate.
2. a. Animals may compete for food, territory, or mates. Examples of cooperative behavior include hunting in groups and living in groups to help reduce the chance of an attack by a predator. Animals such as honeybees and ants that live in societies also exhibit cooperative behavior. **b.** An animal would compete with other animals; for example, by singing, calling, or leaving droppings, during establishment of its territory. **c.** The resident mockingbird may attack the second bird until it flies away.
3. a. Cyclic behaviors **b.** Both are cyclic behaviors, but hibernation is a cyclic behavior that is on an annual cycle, while a circadian rhythm is on a daily cycle.

Reteach L1

Ask students to make a concept map to organize the information about cyclic behavior. Branches may include *Daily cycle*, *Seasonal cycle*, *Journey*, and *Examples*.

Performance Assessment L2

Have students write a short paragraph explaining the advantages to animals living in a group. Students should include examples of group behavior in their explanations. Portfolio

All in One Teaching Resources

- Section Summary: *Patterns of Behavior*
- Review and Reinforce: *Patterns of Behavior*
- Enrich: *Patterns of Behavior*

Lab zone At-Home Activity

Animal Signs L2 Encourage students to observe active animals in a location where they are likely to interact with other animals. Caution students not to approach wild animals.

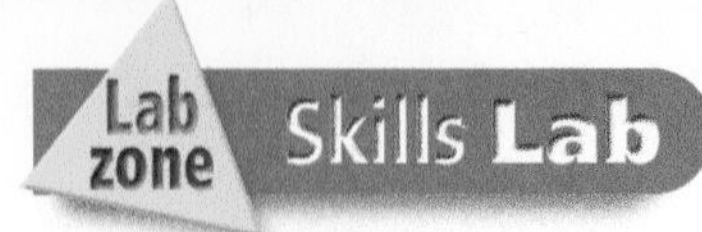

One for All

L2

Prepare for Inquiry

Key Concept

In ant colonies, individual members perform different tasks.

Skills Objectives

After this lab, students will be able to

- observe, infer, and pose questions to gather data about an assigned query.

Prep Time 30 minutes

Class Time 45 minutes plus a few minutes each day for two weeks

Advance Planning

Have students bring a glass jar to class a few days in advance. Large condiment jars work well. Ants can be collected from a colony in nature. **CAUTION:** *Avoid fire ants because they are extremely aggressive. To check if a colony contains fire ants, tap on the mound with a small straw or twig. If ants immediately swarm in large numbers, they are probably fire ants.* Collect sufficient soil from the area close to the colony for students to use in their jars. Try to collect ants of various sizes from the colony. Dig up only a small part of the colony. Place the container with the ants you have collected in the refrigerator to slow the ants down. Keep ants chilled before adding to students' jars. Place 20 to 30 ants directly into students' jars so that students do not handle ants. Caution students not to handle the ants at all. When finished, return all the ants to the refrigerator and then return them to their original colony.

Alternative Materials

Nylon screen can be substituted for the wire screen as it is easier to cut with scissors. You may prefer to purchase an "ant farm" from a scientific supply house.

All in One Teaching Resources

- Lab Worksheet: *One for All*

Guide Inquiry

Invitation

Review with students the information on animal societies. Have students study Figure 14 about honeybee societies. Have students predict how tasks such as getting food and building nests are accomplished in an ant society.

Introduce the Procedure

Tell students they may not observe some tasks. For example, there may be no eggs, larvae, or pupae for adult ants to care for. Students should think about how they will describe various behaviors. For example, ants may carry dirt grains (from digging), carry food, or interact with each other. Students should observe the tasks that ants of different sizes perform.

Students should look for tunnels, for food storage locations, and for a refuse pile in the jar.

Lab zone **Skills Lab**

One for All

Problem

How does an ant society show organization and cooperative behavior?

Skills Focus

observing, inferring

Materials

- large glass jar
- sandy soil
- shallow pan
- water
- wire screen
- sponge
- 20–30 ants
- hand lens
- bread crumbs
- sugar
- black paper
- tape
- glass-marking pencil
- forceps
- large, thick rubber band

Procedure   

1. Read over the entire lab to preview the kinds of observations you will be making. Copy the data table into your notebook. You may also want to leave space for sketches.
2. Mark the outside of a large jar with four evenly spaced vertical lines, as shown in the photograph on the next page. Label the sections with the letters A, B, C, and D. You can use these labels to identify the sections of soil on and below the surface.
3. Fill the jar about three-fourths full with soil. Place the jar in a shallow pan of water to prevent any ants from escaping. Place a wet sponge on the surface of the soil as a water source for the ants.
4. Observe the condition of the soil, both on the surface and along the sides of the jar. Record your observations.
5. Add the ants to the jar. Immediately cover the jar with the wire screen, using the rubber band to hold the screen firmly in place.
6. Observe the ants for at least 10 minutes. Look for differences in the appearance of adult ants, and look for eggs, larvae, and pupae. Examine both individual behavior and interactions between the ants.
7. Remove the screen cover and add small amounts of bread crumbs and sugar to the soil surface. Close the cover. Observe the ants for at least 10 more minutes.
8. Create dark conditions for the ants by covering the jar with black paper above the water line. Remove the paper only when you are making your observations.
9. Observe the ant colony every day for two weeks. Remove the dark paper, and make and record your observations. Look at the soil as well as the ants, and always examine the food. If any food has started to mold, use forceps to remove it. Place the moldy food in a plastic bag, seal the bag, and throw it away. Add more food as necessary, and keep the sponge moist. When you finish your observations, replace the dark paper.
10. At the end of the lab, follow your teacher's directions for returning the ants.

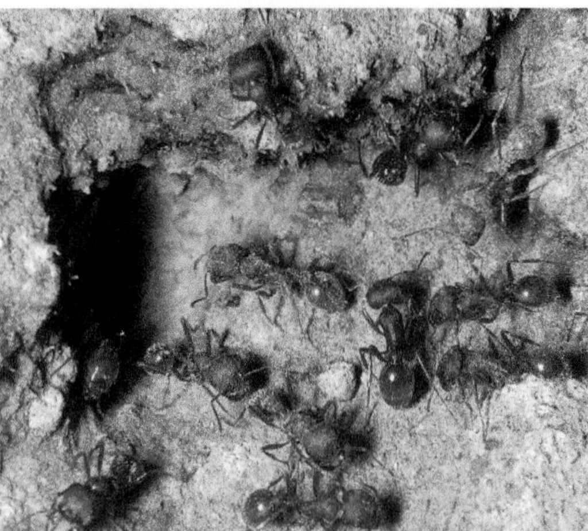

Data Table				
Date	Section A	Section B	Section C	Section D

Analyze and Conclude

1. Observing Describe the various types of ants you observed. What differences, if any, did you observe in their behavior? What evidence did you see of different kinds of ants performing different tasks?
2. Inferring How do the different behaviors you observed contribute to the survival of the colony?
3. Inferring How did the soil change over the period of your observations? What caused those changes? How do you know?
4. Communicating What kinds of environmental conditions do you think ant colonies need to thrive outdoors? Use the evidence you obtained in this lab to write a paragraph that supports your answer.

Design an Experiment

Design an experiment to investigate how an ant colony responds when there is a change in the ants' environment, such as the introduction of a new type of food. *Obtain your teacher's permission before carrying out your investigation.*

B ◆ 165

Troubleshooting the Experiment
Students should try not to touch the ants. Advise students to be very careful if they carry the glass jars around the room.

Expected Outcome
Ants will excavate tunnels and perform various tasks. Some will carry refuse to a pile. Other ants will place dead ants and dirt on this pile. Ants will retrieve food and place it in a storage tunnel. If eggs, larvae, and pupae are present, they will be stored in an underground location.

The main task for students will be to observe and describe the behaviors. Make sure that students infer how the behavior contributes to the colony's survival.

Analyze and Conclude
1. Possible answers: Some ants carried food to the food store; others dug tunnels; some took items to the refuse pile.
2. Possible answers: The behaviors result in a home being built, food stored, trash removed, offspring cared for, and protection set up.
3. Tunnels were dug through the soil over the course of the experiment. Ants must have caused these changes since no other organisms were present.
4. Possible answer: Ants require soil in which they can dig and a source of food and water.

Extend Inquiry

Design an Experiment Possible answer: students could decide to introduce a new kind of food or to present it in a different way.

Section 3 Tracking Migrations

Objectives

After completing this lesson, students will be able to

B.5.3.1 Describe how two electronic technologies help scientists track animals.

B.5.3.2 Explain the benefits of tracking animal migrations.

Target Reading Skill

Comparing and Contrasting Explain that comparing and contrasting information shows how ideas, facts, and events are similar and different. The results of the comparison can have importance.

Answers

Possible answers:

Simple Banding—no signal, inexpensive, lightweight; radio—radio signal, costly, prohibitive for small animals; satellite—electronic signal, costly, prohibitive for small animals

All in One Teaching Resources

- Transparency B47

Preteach

Build Background Knowledge L2

Animal Migrations

Ask students to give examples of animals that migrate. *(Birds, mammals such as caribou, whales, and manatees, sea turtles, some fishes such as salmon)* Ask: **Why do animals migrate?** *(To find food sources during winter months, to reproduce)*

Section 3 • Tech & Design •

Tracking Migrations

Reading Preview

Key Concepts

- How do electronic technologies help scientists track animals?
- What are the benefits of tracking animal migrations?

Key Terms

- transmitter
- receiver
- satellite

Target Reading Skill

Comparing and Contrasting As you read, compare and contrast three types of animal tags by completing a table like the one below.

Animal Tags

Feature	Simple Banding	Radio	Satellite
Kind of Signal	None		
Cost			
Weight			

Lab zone Discover Activity

How Can You Track Animals?

1. On a sheet of graph paper, sketch a map of your classroom.
2. Your teacher will produce a set of "signals" from a tracking device on an animal. Record the location of each signal on your map. Sketch the path of the animal you just tracked.
3. Your teacher will produce a second set of tracking signals. Record the location of each signal, then draw the animal's path. Compare the two pathways.

Think It Over

Inferring What does this activity show about actual animal tracking?

Have you ever changed your mind because of new information? Scientists who study manatees have done just that. The information came from a signaling device on a manatee.

Florida manatees are marine mammals that spend their winters in Florida and migrate north for the summer. Scientists once thought that the manatees didn't go any farther north than Virginia. Then they attached signaling devices to manatees to track their migration. They were quite surprised when they picked up a signal from a manatee swimming off the coast of Rhode Island, which is far north of Virginia.

FIGURE 17
Florida Manatee Migration
This map shows the long distance that at least one Florida manatee migrated one summer. Electronic tags like the one shown at the far right are used to track migrating manatees.

166 ♦ B

Lab zone Discover Activity

Skills Focus Inferring L2

Materials graph paper, clicker

Time 20 minutes

Tips For your first set of signals, move in a distinct path across the classroom, including several twists and turns. Move slowly so students have a chance to record their data. Click infrequently, only three times or so. Tell the students to note your location only when they hear a click, not what they see in between clicks, to graph the migratory path of the "animal" you represent. Then give students a second set of signals. Move along the exact path you took before, but click the clicker at least three times as often as before.

Think It Over Students should conclude that with more data points, they can draw better conclusions about the path traveled.

Technologies for Tracking

In the fall of 1803, American naturalist John James Audubon wondered whether migrating birds returned to the same place each year. So he tied a string around the leg of a bird before it flew south. The following spring, Audubon saw the bird with the string. He learned that the bird had indeed come back.

Scientists today still attach tags, such as metal bands, to track the movement of animals. But metal bands are not always useful tags. That is because the tagged animals have to be caught again for the scientists to get any data. Unfortunately, most tagged animals are never seen again.

Recent technologies have helped solve this problem. **Electronic tags give off repeating signals that are picked up by radio devices or satellites. Scientists can track the locations and movements of the tagged animals without recapturing them.** These electronic tags can provide a great deal of data. However, they are much more expensive than the "low-tech" tags that aren't electronic. Also, because of their weight, electronic tags may harm some animals by slowing them down.

FIGURE 18
Banded Puffin
Bands like the ones around the ankles of this Atlantic puffin are low-tech tags. **Inferring** *Why is a metal band tag useful?*

Radio Tracking Tracking an animal by radio involves two devices. A **transmitter** attached to the animal sends out a signal in the form of radio waves, just as a radio station does. A scientist might place the transmitter around an animal's ankle, neck, wing, or fin. A **receiver** picks up the signal, just like your radio at home picks up a station's signal. The receiver is usually in a truck or an airplane. To keep track of the signal, the scientist follows the animal in the truck or plane.

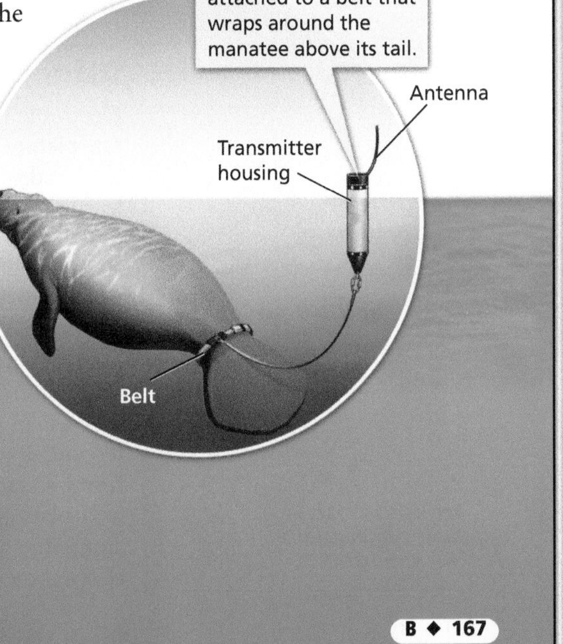

A radio transmitter is attached to a belt that wraps around the manatee above its tail.
Antenna
Transmitter housing
Belt

Instruct

Technologies for Tracking

Teach Key Concepts L2

Tracking Devices

Focus Tell students that scientists can use electronic tags to track animals.

Teach Ask: **What are some disadvantages of tracking migration by using a metal band that emits no signal?** *(Possible answers: Scientists have to capture the animal to tag, have to recapture the animal to read tag, cannot continuously track the animal's movements.)* Explain that radio and satellite transmissions allow scientists to learn more about migration paths without disrupting the animals. Ask: **How does radio tracking differ from satellite tracking?** *(With radio tracking, the transmitter sends a signal and the biologist's receiver picks up the signal. In satellite tracking, the receiver is a network of satellites in space.)*

Apply Ask: **How does using a radio tag satellite benefit the animal?** *(Animals do not need to be recaptured, less disturbance in natural habitat)* **learning modality: logical/mathematical**

Help Students Read L1

Monitor Your Understanding As students read Tracking Migrations, ask them to stop and monitor their understanding after each paragraph. Explain that if they have not fully understood the paragraph, they should apply one of the reading techniques that has worked for them in the past. In this case, outlining, summarizing, and/or identifying main ideas may be helpful strategies.

Independent Practice L2

All in One Teaching Resources

- Guided Reading and Study Worksheet: *Tracking Migrations*

Student Edition on Audio CD

Differentiated Instruction

Special Needs L1

Using Vocabulary Help students become familiar with the words *transmitter* and *receiver* in this section. Have them look up the verb form of each word and explain how the definition of the verb is related to the nouns used as vocabulary words. Students can then illustrate how a transmitter and receiver work together. **learning modality: visual**

Less Proficient Readers L1

Reading and Writing Have students write down the question "Why is tracking important?" As they read *Why Tracking Is Important,* have them stop each time they find an answer to the question. Students should record the answer, and then continue reading. When they are finished, have them report their answers aloud. **learning modality: verbal**

Monitor Progress L2

Oral Presentation Have students explain the difference between using a plain metal band and a radio tag as a tracking device.

Answer

Figure 18 Metal bands are an easy and inexpensive way to tag an animal to monitor where it goes.

Why Tracking Is Important

Teach Key Concepts L3

Tracking Migrations

Focus Tell students that electronic tracking is helping biologists learn more about animal migration.

Teach Ask: **Why is it important to track animal migrations?** *(Scientists can learn more about species and how to protect them.)* **How can tracking technologies benefit people?** *(It helps people whose work or recreation depends on the use of animal habitats.)*

Apply Ask: **Why is it important to know where animals migrate?** *(Scientists can then work to protect the habitats that animals depend on.)* **learning modality: logical/mathematical**

L3

Modeling Tagging Devices

Materials aluminum foil, cardboard, glue, letter and number crimper, mesh screen, photos of tagging devices to show as examples, wire

Time 20 minutes

Focus Tell students that they are going to design a tag for tracking the migration of an animal of their choice.

Teach Explain to students that the aluminum foil and cardboard are substitutes for other, more durable, materials they would use to make their tagging devices, such as plastic or metal. Show students photos of sample tags. Remind students that the tags should be safe for the animal and that they have to be durable for all kinds of environmental conditions.

Apply Have students present their devices to the rest of the class. They should explain what type of animal it will be used to track, whether it will be electronic, how they identify each animal, and how it will stay intact as the animal travels. **learning modality: kinesthetic**

FIGURE 19
Tracking Caribou
Scientists are fitting this caribou with a collar containing a satellite transmitter. **Inferring** *Why would it be difficult to track caribou without a satellite receiver?*

Satellite Tracking Receivers can be placed in satellites as well as in airplanes and trucks. A **satellite** is an instrument in orbit thousands of kilometers above Earth. Networks, or groups, of satellites are used to track animals. Each satellite in a network picks up electronic signals from a transmitter on an animal. Together, the signals from all the satellites determine the precise location of the animal.

Satellites can also track an animal's path as it moves. Satellite tracking is especially useful because the scientists do not have to follow after the animal. Satellite networks have tracked the migrations of many types of animals, including caribou, sea turtles, whales, seals, elephants, bald eagles, and ospreys.

Why Tracking Is Important

Electronic tracking tags are giving scientists a complete, accurate picture of migration patterns. For example, when scientists used radio transmitters to track one herd of caribou, they learned two important things. First, they learned that the herd moves over a larger area than previously thought. Second, they learned that each year the herd returns to about the same place to give birth to its young. This information would have been difficult to obtain with "low tech" tags.

Tracking migrations is an important tool to better understand and protect species. For example, Florida manatees are an endangered species, and therefore they need protection. Radio tracking showed that Florida manatees may travel as far north as Rhode Island when they migrate. This information suggests that the manatees may need protection along much of the Atlantic Coast of the United States. Previously, protection efforts focused mainly in the Florida area.

For: Links on migration
Visit: www.SciLinks.com
Web Code: scn-0253

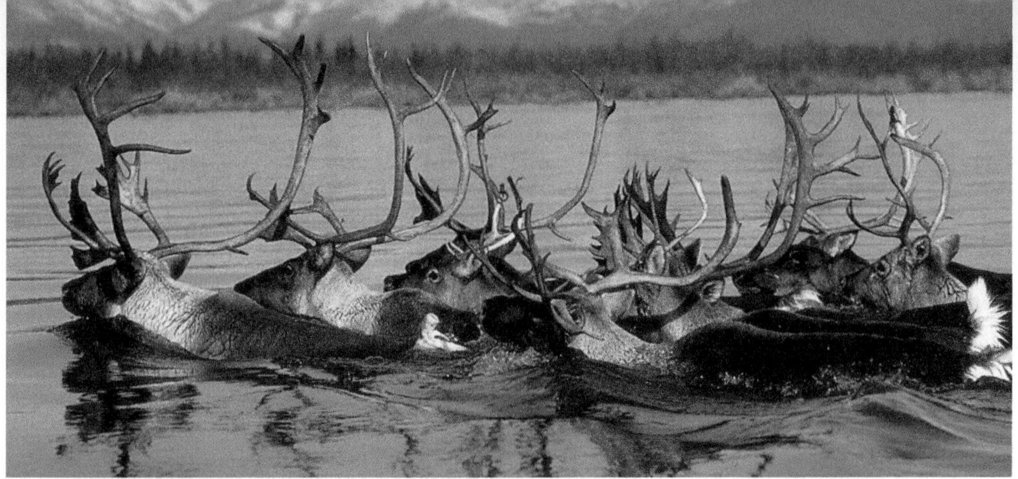

Technologies for tracking animals may also help people whose work or recreation affects animals. For example, suppose officials at a state park want to protect a group of migrating animals during the spring. The officials plan to ban fishing or boating for the entire spring season. Detailed migration information, however, might give the officials a better choice. They might be able to decrease the length of time the ban is in effect, or ban fishing and boating only in those few areas visited by the animals.

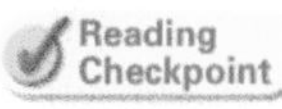 **What information did tracking provide biologists about a caribou herd?**

FIGURE 20
Caribou Migration
These caribou are migrating across Alaska on the same path used by caribou for thousands of years.

Section 3 Assessment

Target Reading Skill
Comparing and Contrasting Use the information in your table about animal tags to help you answer Question 1 below.

Reviewing Key Concepts

1. a. **Identifying** What are two methods of electronic animal tracking?
   b. **Comparing and Contrasting** How are electronic tracking methods similar? How are they different?
   c. **Making Judgments** Are electronic tags better than traditional tags?
2. a. **Reviewing** What are the benefits of tracking migrations?
   b. **Applying Concepts** Migrating birds are sometimes killed by crashing into cellular telephone towers. How could tracking bird migrations help people protect the birds?
   c. **Making Judgments** Should governments spend more money tracking migrations? Defend your position.

Writing in Science

Persuasive Letter Suppose you are a scientist who needs money to study the migrations of an endangered sea turtle species. Write a letter justifying why you need money for electronic tags.

For: Links on migration
Visit: www.SciLinks.com
Web Code: scn-0253

Download a worksheet that will guide students' review of Internet resources on migration.

Monitor Progress L2

Answers
Figure 19 Caribou travel through harsh weather and over difficult terrain.

 The herd migrates over a larger area than previously thought and returns to the same place to give birth.

Assess

Reviewing Key Concepts

a. Radio tagging and satellite tagging
b. Both radio and satellite tags emit a signal. Both allow scientists to continuously track the positions of tagged animals without needing to recapture them. A radio tag sends out radio waves that are picked up by a receiver. In satellite tagging the receiver is a network of satellites that work together to determine the exact location of the animal.
c. Sample answer: It depends on the situation and the type of animal being studied. Advantages include being able to continuously track an animal without having to recapture it. Disadvantages include greater cost and weight of tags.
5. a. By tracking animal migration, scientists can better understand and protect a species. Recreational officials can coordinate when areas in the path of a migration will be opened and closed. **b.** By knowing the path of migration, people could avoid building cell phone towers in those locations. **c.** Accept all well-defended arguments.

Reteach

As a class, list the advantages and disadvantages of electronic tagging to track animal migration.

All in One Teaching Resources

- Section Summary: *Tracking Migrations*
- Review and Reinforce: *Tracking Migrations*
- Enrich: *Tracking Migrations*

Lab zone Chapter Project

Keep Students on Track Review students' progress. Help students modify their training plans if they are having problems. If students cannot bring their animals into the classroom, discuss alternative presentations.

Writing in Science

Writing Mode Persuasion
Scoring Rubric
4 Includes two or three reasons for the grant and gives information to support the reasons
3 Includes one or two reasons and some supporting information
2 Includes only one reason and little supporting information
1 Includes only one reason and no supporting information

Study Guide

The BIG Idea

Have students read the answer to the Essential Question. Encourage them to evaluate and revise their own answers as needed.

Help Students Read

Building Vocabulary

Word Origins Point out to students that many science terms have Latin or Greek origins that give them their meaning. The word *aggression* is derived from the Latin *aggredi,* which means "to attack." The word *migrate* is derived from the Latin *migrare,* which means "to change." Have students explain how the Latin origins of these words relate to their modern meanings.

Vocabulary Rating Chart Have each student construct a chart with four columns labeled *Term, Can Define or Use It, Have Heard or Seen It,* and *Don't Know.* Have students copy the key terms from this chapter into the first column and rate their knowledge by putting a check in one of the other columns. Then have them reread the parts that pertain to the key terms in question.

Connecting Concepts

Concept Maps Help students develop one way to show how the information in this chapter is related. Most animal behaviors are complicated processes that help animals survive and reproduce. Have students brainstorm to identify the key concepts, key terms, details, and examples, and then write each one on a sticky note and attach it at random on chart paper or on the chalkboard.

Tell students that this concept map will be organized in a hierarchical order and to begin at the top with the key concepts. Ask students these questions to guide them to categorize the information in the stickers: **What causes behavior? How can animals learn new behavior? How do animals communicate?**

Prompt students by using such connecting words or phrases such as "caused by" and "through" to indicate the basis for the organization of the map. The phrases should form a sentence between or among a set of concepts.

Answer

Accept logical presentations by students.

All in One Teaching Resources

- Key Terms Review: *Animal Behavior*
- Connecting Concepts: *Animal Behavior*

Chapter 5 Study Guide

The BIG Idea **Animal Behavior and Communication** Most behaviors help animals to obtain food or mates, protect territory, or avoid predators.

1 What Is Behavior?

Key Concepts

- All animal behaviors are caused by stimuli.
- An instinct is a response to a stimulus that is inborn and that an animal performs correctly the first time.
- Learned behaviors include imprinting, conditioning, trial-and-error learning, and insight learning.

Key Terms

• behavior • stimulus • response • instinct • learning • imprinting • conditioning • trial-and-error learning • insight learning

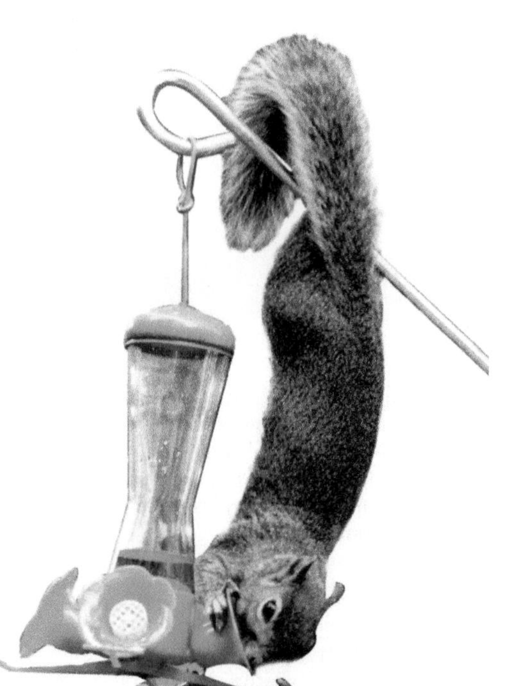

2 Patterns of Behavior

Key Concepts

- Animals use mostly sounds, scents, and body movements to communicate with one another.
- Animals compete with one another for limited resources, such as food, water, space, shelter, and mates.
- Living in groups enables animals to cooperate.
- Cyclic behaviors usually change over the course of a day or a season.

Key Terms

pheromone
aggression
territory
courtship behavior
society
circadian rhythm
hibernation
migration

3 Tracking Migrations

Key Concepts

- Electronic tags give off repeating signals that are picked up by radio devices or satellites. Scientists can track the locations and movements of the tagged animals without recapturing them.
- Tracking migrations is an important tool to better understand and protect species.

Key Terms

• transmitter • receiver • satellite

Review and Assessment

Go Online PHSchool.com
For: Self-Assessment
Visit: PHSchool.com
Web Code: cea-2050

Organizing Information

Concept Mapping Copy the concept map about behavior onto a separate sheet of paper. Then complete the map and add a title. (For more on Concept Mapping, see the Skills Handbook.)

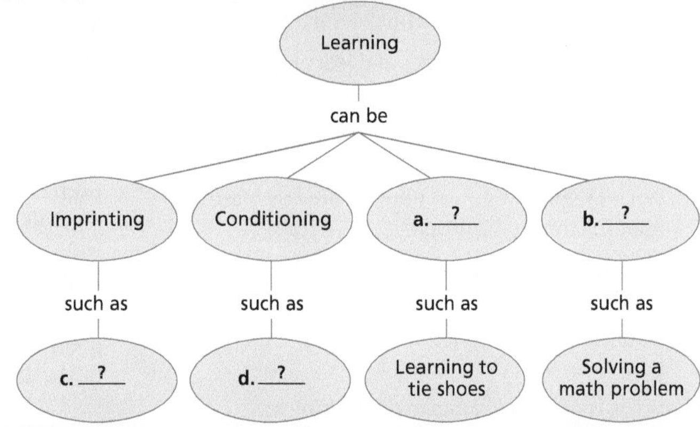

Reviewing Key Terms

Choose the letter of the best answer.

1. An organism's reaction to a signal is called
   a. a response. **b.** a stimulus.
   c. aggression. **d.** learning.
2. A process that leads to a change in behavior based on practice is called
   a. instinct. **b.** response.
   c. learning. **d.** behavior.
3. Learning that a particular stimulus or response leads to a good or a bad outcome is called
   a. instinct.
   b. imprinting.
   c. conditioning.
   d. insight learning.
4. A chemical released by one animal that affects the behavior of another animal of the same species is called a(n)
   a. stimulus.
   b. instinct.
   c. pheromone.
   d. circadian rhythm.
5. A threatening behavior that one animal uses to gain control over another is called
   a. courtship behavior.
   b. aggression.
   c. conditioning.
   d. cyclic behavior.
6. When a bird travels from its winter home in South America to its nesting area in New York, this is called
   a. learning.
   b. conditioning.
   c. migration.
   d. territorial behavior.
7. An instrument in orbit thousands of kilometers above Earth is called a
   a. pheromone. **b.** transmitter.
   c. receiver. **d.** satellite.

Writing in Science

Health Article Write a magazine article describing how dogs can be trained. Explain how trained dogs might assist people with special needs.

Animal Behavior
Video Preview
Video Field Trip
▶ Video Assessment

Review and Assessment

Organizing Information

a. Trial-and-Error
b. Insight Learning
c. Ducklings swimming by following their mother
d. A dog going to its master when called
Sample title: Types of Learning

Reviewing Key Terms

1. a **2.** c **3.** c **4.** c **5.** b **6.** c **7.** d

Writing in Science

Writing Skill Health Article

Scoring Rubric

4 Includes an engaging title and in-depth information about trained animal helpers
3 Includes the required information about the topic
2 Includes very general information, and specific and/or interesting examples are missing
1 Reflects minimal preparation

Video Assessment

Animal Behavior

Show the Video Assessment to review chapter content and as a prompt for the writing assignment.

Go Online PHSchool.com
For: Self-Assessment
Visit: PHSchool.com
Web Code: cea-2050

Students can take a practice test online that is automatically scored.

All in One Teaching Resources

- Transparency B48
- Chapter Test
- Performance Assessment Teacher Notes
- Performance Assessment Teacher Worksheet
- Performance Assessment Scoring Rubric

***ExamView*® Computer Test Bank CD-ROM**

Checking Concepts

8. The functions of behavior are to help an animal survive or reproduce.

9. Imprinting involves a combination of instinct and learning because the young animal has an instinct to follow a moving object, but it must learn from experience which object to follow.

10. In trial-and-error learning, an animal learns to perform a behavior more and more skillfully through repeated practice. An example is when a human learns to ride a bicycle.

11. Pheromones are chemicals released by an animal that affects the behavior of another animal of the same species. They may be used to signal the location of food, to attract mates, or to mark a territory, for example.

12. An animal may need to maintain a territory in order to attract mates. For example, if a male fights off other males that enter his territory, he can court females in his territory without much competition from other males.

13. Living in a group can help animals protect one another from predators, or to cooperate in finding food. For example, fishes that swim in schools are often safer than fishes that swim alone. When lions hunt in a group, they can kill larger prey than a single hunter can.

14. When tracking with a radio collar, the scientist must follow the animal with the receiver, usually in a vehicle or an airplane.

Review and Assessment

Checking Concepts

8. What are the functions of behavior?

9. Explain how both instinct and learning are involved in imprinting.

10. Explain what trial-and-error learning is. Describe an example.

11. What are pheromones? Explain how they are used in communication.

12. Explain how territorial behavior and courtship behavior are related.

13. Describe two examples of how living in a group can benefit an animal.

14. What is one disadvantage of tracking an animal by radio rather than by satellite?

Thinking Critically

15. Inferring Look at the photograph below. On its first try, this weaver bird is building a nest of grass with a hole at the bottom just the right size for the bird to enter. What kind of behavior is this? Explain.

16. Applying Concepts Explain how a racehorse's ability to win races is a combination of inherited and learned characteristics.

17. Problem Solving A dog keeps jumping onto a sofa. Describe how the owner might train the dog not to do this. The procedure must not involve any pain or harm to the dog.

18. Applying Concepts Give an example of something that you have learned by insight learning. Explain how you made use of your past knowledge and experience in learning it.

19. Drawing Conclusions How can hibernation help an animal survive the winter?

20. Applying Concepts Because a highway has been constructed through a forest, many animals have had to move to a different wooded area. Is their move an example of migration? Explain.

21. Making Judgments Is satellite tracking a good way to track the migration of monarch butterflies? Explain.

Applying Skills

Use the diagrams below, showing (A) a toad catching a bee and (B) the toad's reaction, to answer Questions 22–24.

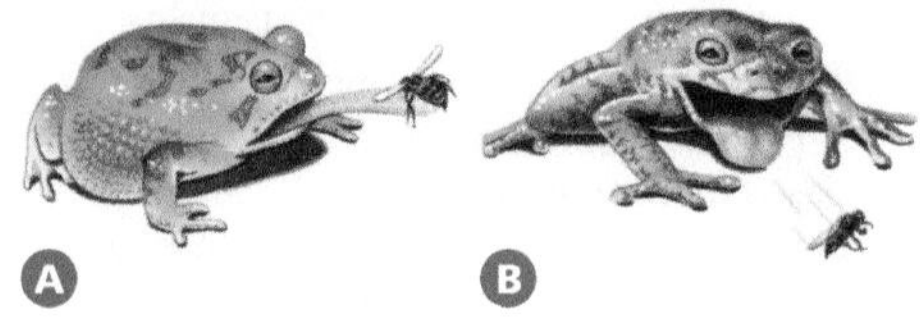

22. Inferring Explain why the toad probably behaves as it does in diagram B.

23. Predicting If another bee flies by, how will the toad probably behave? Explain.

24. Classifying What type of learning might result from the toad's experience? Explain.

Lab zone Chapter Project

Performance Assessment Obtain your teacher's permission before bringing an animal to class. You can also show photographs or illustrations of the animal's training. Describe your training plan. What did you discover about the animal's learning process? How could you have improved your plan?

172 ◆ B

L3

Performance Assessment Encourage each student to demonstrate how well his or her animal learned its trick. Students should explain how they trained their animals. Encourage students to use appropriate vocabulary from the text.

Reflect and Record It is likely that some, perhaps many, students will have been unable to train their animals. It is important that every student who made an honest attempt feel successful. Whether the animal was trained or not, students can still write about their experiences and think about ways of improving training.

Standardized Test Prep

Test-Taking Tip

Watching for Qualifiers *(Most, Least, Best)*

Multiple-choice questions often use qualifiers, words that change or limit the meaning of a phrase or sentence. Qualifiers include words such as *best*, *least*, and *most*. You need to read and compare all the answer choices carefully. While some of the answers may not be incorrect, another answer may be the best choice. Look for the best and most complete answer.

Sample Question

Which of the following is the best definition of *instinct*?

- **A** all the actions an animal performs
- **B** a behavior pattern that an animal performs
- **C** an inborn behavior pattern that an animal performs correctly the first time
- **D** a behavior pattern that an animal performs after practice and experience

Answer

C is the best answer. **A** is not a valid answer because it defines all behavior, not instinct, which is a specific type of behavior. **D** defines a learned behavior. **B** is not incorrect, but it does not completely describe instinct. As written, **B** could apply to several types of behavior.

Choose the letter of the best answer.

1. An enclosed cage at a university laboratory holds dozens of birds. When a biologist adjusts the light schedule and temperature in the cage to match fall conditions, she observes that the birds spend most of their time at the south end of the cage. What is the most likely explanation for the behavior?

- **A** The birds are forming a society.
- **B** There is more food at the south end of the cage.
- **C** The birds are exhibiting migratory behavior.
- **D** The scientist has conditioned the birds to prefer the south end of the cage.

2. The chimpanzee in the diagram below has learned a way to reach the bananas. What type of learning most likely applies to this situation?

- **F** instinct
- **G** conditioning
- **H** insight
- **J** imprinting

3. Ants have laid a pheromone trail to a food source. While the ants are in their nest at night, a researcher pours gasoline over the entire trail. Which of the following will probably happen the next morning?

- **A** The gasoline will have no effect on the ants.
- **B** The ants will find the food more rapidly.
- **C** The ants will eat the gasoline.
- **D** The ants will be unable to find the food.

4. You are awake during the day and asleep at night. This behavior is an example of

- **F** circadian rhythm.
- **G** aggression.
- **H** trail-and-error learning.
- **J** hibernation.

Constructed Response

5. Describe the organization of a honeybee society, including daily tasks.

Thinking Critically

15. The behavior is an instinct because the bird did not have to learn how to build the nest, but did it correctly on the first try.

16. A racehorse's ability to win races is based on a combination of the traits it inherits, such as strong limbs and lungs, and the training it receives. It may learn through conditioning to associate the event of the race with a stimulus such as a special treat. It may learn the stages of a successful race through trial and error.

17. Sample answer: The owner might use conditioning to train the dog. When the dog jumps on the couch, the owner would use a stimulus to get him off. A stimulus could be a command or an unpleasant sound.

18. Sample answer: I learned how to operate a friend's DVD player because it was similar to the one my family has.

19. By hibernating, an animal reduces its need for food when food is scarce in its environment.

20. This is not an example of migration because it is not a regular behavior that the animals would repeat each season. The animals are moving because of a disturbance, not to seek food or mates elsewhere.

21. Satellite tags would be a good choice because monarch butterflies migrate long distances, however, the tags may not be practical because they may be too big and heavy for the butterflies.

Applying Skills

22. The bee probably stung the toad, and the toad spat it out in an effort to get rid of it.

23. The toad will probably not try to catch the insect, because the toad will associate the bee with the sting.

24. Conditioning, because the toad has learned to connect a stimulus, the bee, with a bad event, being stung.

Standardized Test Prep

1. C **2.** H **3.** D **4.** F

5. Sample response: A honeybee society is highly organized. It is composed of a queen, whose function it is to mate and lay eggs for her lifetime; worker bees, females who do not reproduce but maintain the hive, search for nectar, and make honey; drones, males whose sole function it is to mate with queens.

Interdisciplinary Exploration

The Secret of Silk

This interdisciplinary feature presents the central theme of silk from four different curriculum perspectives: science, social studies, language arts, and mathematics. The four explorations are designed to capture students' interest and help them see how the content they are studying in science relates to other school subjects and real-world events. Share with others for a team-teaching experience.

All in One Teaching Resources

- Interdisciplinary Exploration: *Science*
- Interdisciplinary Exploration: *Social Studies*
- Interdisciplinary Exploration: *Language Arts*
- Interdisciplinary Exploration: *Mathematics*

Build Background Knowledge

Help students recall what they learned in the chapter Insects. Ask: **What is the name of the process by which an insect changes in form during its life cycle?** *(Metamorphosis)* **In which stage of metamorphosis does an insect look most like a worm?** *(Larval stage)*. Then ask: **What do you know about silkworms?** *(Accept all responses without comment at this time.)*

Introduce the Exploration

If possible, bring an item made of silk to show the class. You may not want students to touch the item as silk is easy to damage. If a silk item is not available, ask students who have seen items made of silk to describe how they look and feel. Point out that insects make silk thread that is woven into silk cloth. Ask: **What is a product we eat that insects make?** *(Honey)*

Interdisciplinary Exploration

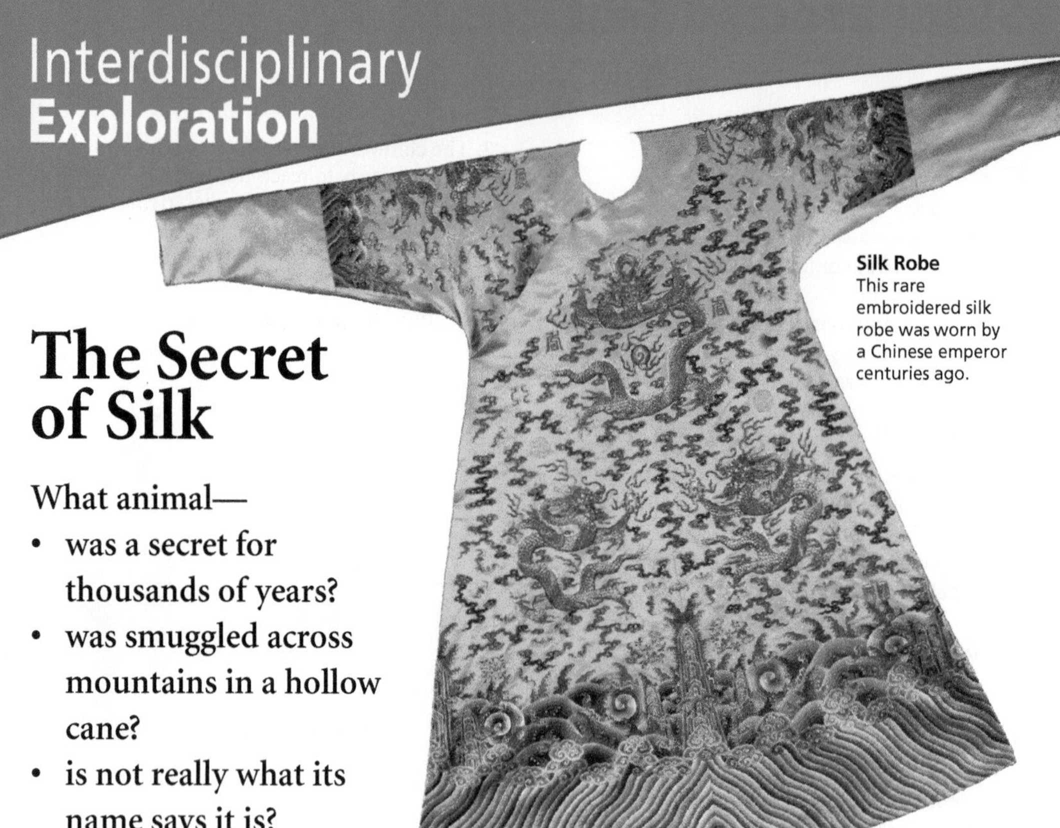

Silk Robe
This rare embroidered silk robe was worn by a Chinese emperor centuries ago.

The Secret of Silk

What animal—

- was a secret for thousands of years?
- was smuggled across mountains in a hollow cane?
- is not really what its name says it is?

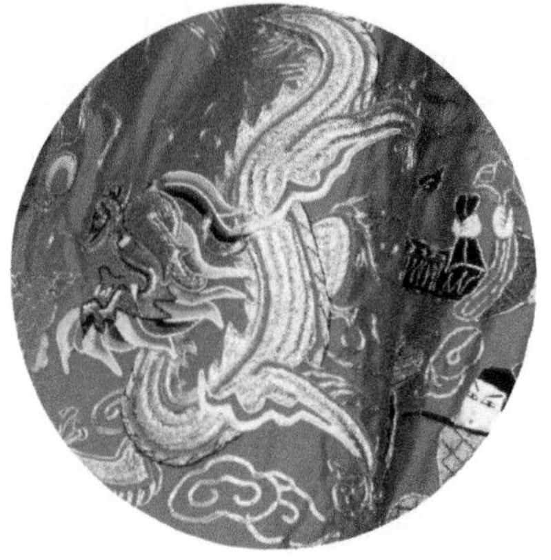

Modern Robe
This Chinese silk robe is embroidered with dragons from Chinese legends.

If you guessed that this amazing animal is the silkworm, you are right. The silk thread that this caterpillar spins is woven into silk cloth. For at least 4,000 years, people have treasured silk.

Chinese legends say that in 2640 B.C., a Chinese empress accidentally dropped a silkworm cocoon in warm water and watched the thread unravel. She had discovered silk. But for thousands of years, the Chinese people kept the work of silkworms a secret. Death was the penalty for telling the secret.

Then, it is said, in A.D. 552, two travelers from Persia visited China and returned to the West carrying silkworm eggs hidden in their hollow canes. Ever since then, the world has enjoyed the beauty of silk—its warmth, strength, softness, and shimmer.

Metamorphosis of the Silkworm

The silkworm is not really a worm; it's the larva of an insect—a moth named *Bombyx mori.* In its entire feeding period, this larva consumes about 20 times its own weight in mulberry leaves. The silkworm undergoes complete metamorphosis during its life.

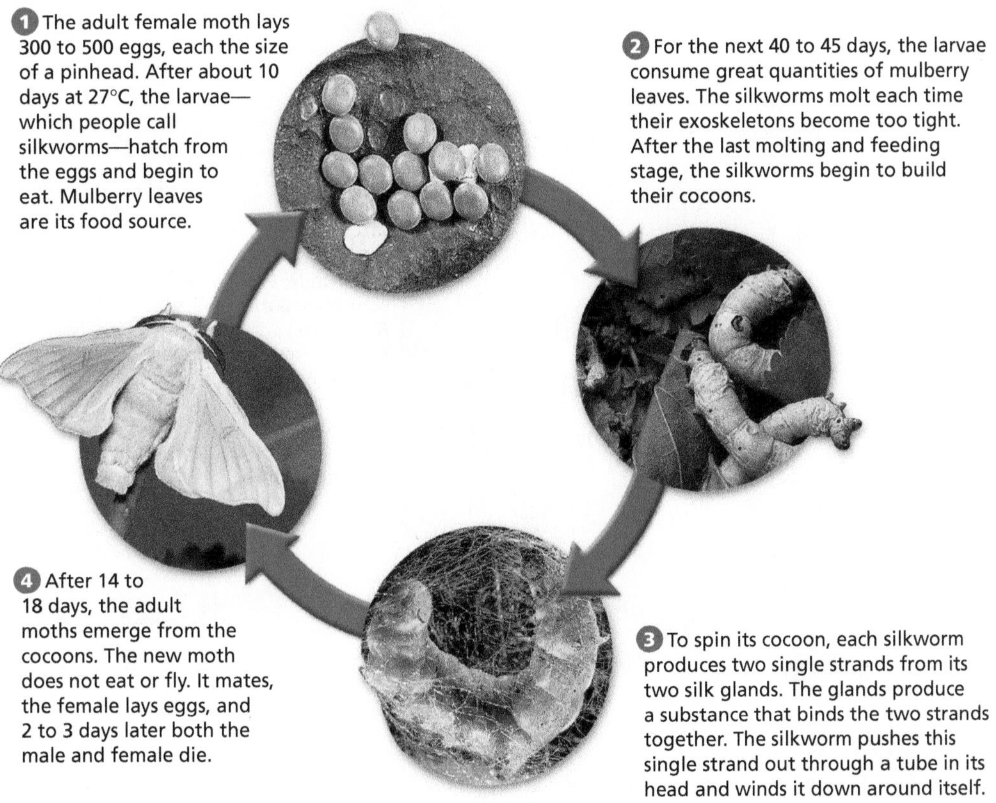

1 The adult female moth lays 300 to 500 eggs, each the size of a pinhead. After about 10 days at 27°C, the larvae—which people call silkworms—hatch from the eggs and begin to eat. Mulberry leaves are its food source.

2 For the next 40 to 45 days, the larvae consume great quantities of mulberry leaves. The silkworms molt each time their exoskeletons become too tight. After the last molting and feeding stage, the silkworms begin to build their cocoons.

3 To spin its cocoon, each silkworm produces two single strands from its two silk glands. The glands produce a substance that binds the two strands together. The silkworm pushes this single strand out through a tube in its head and winds it down around itself.

4 After 14 to 18 days, the adult moths emerge from the cocoons. The new moth does not eat or fly. It mates, the female lays eggs, and 2 to 3 days later both the male and female die.

Science Activity

Examine a silkworm cocoon. After softening the cocoon in water, find the end of the strand of silk. Pull this strand, wind it onto an index card, and measure its length.

With a partner, design an experiment to compare the strength of the silk thread you just collected to that of cotton and/or nylon thread of the same weight or thickness.

- Develop a hypothesis about the strength of the threads.
- Decide on the setup you will use to test the threads.
- Check your safety plan with your teacher.

Science

Explore Science Concepts

Use Diagrams Challenge students to make their own illustrated cycle diagrams showing the metamorphosis of a silkworm. After students have completed their diagrams, ask: **What is complete metamorphosis?** *(A type of metamorphosis with four stages: egg, larva, pupa, and adult)* **What is the other pattern of metamorphosis? How is it different from complete metamorphosis?** *(Gradual metamorphosis; an egg hatches into a nymph, which can look like an adult insect.)*

Research Have students choose another insect that goes through complete metamorphosis, such as a beetle, fly, or bee. Then have students create an illustrated cycle diagram with brief descriptions of each phase in the metamorphosis for the insect.

Extend Invite an entomologist to tell the class more about silkworms. If possible, ask the entomologist to bring some silkworms to show the class.

Science Activity

Materials silkworm cocoon, water, index card, ruler, cotton or nylon thread

Focus Ask: **How will you measure the length of the silk strand?** *(Measure the width of the card and multiply by 2. Multiply the answer by the number of times you wind the strand around the card.)*

Teach Make sure that students start with small weights so their planned experiments will not immediately fail by accidentally breaking all the threads they test. For students who are choosing to compare threads by width instead of weight, check that they describe a scientific method for measuring the width of the threads.

Scoring Rubric

4 Hypothesis is testable and relates to the question being answered; setup is appropriate to test hypothesis and includes a very accurate scale to measure the weight of the threads correctly.
3 Meets all criteria; scale is fairly accurate.
2 Meets all criteria; scale is barely accurate.
1 Hypothesis is untestable; setup does not include a scale to measure the weight of the threads correctly.

Explore Social Studies Concepts

Use Maps Show students a map of the United States and Canada. Challenge students to find two cities that are about 6,400 kilometers apart. Ask: **Start in Miami, Florida, and travel northwest. What city is about 6,400 kilometers from Miami?** *(Answers may vary; sample: Prince Rupert, British Columbia, Canada)* Help students appreciate how formidable a journey this would be traveling with pack animals such as camels, horses, or yaks.

Teach Key Concepts Ask: **Why did the Chinese "of course" keep the secret of the silkworm?** *(They were making a lot of money selling silk to Rome.)* **Do we keep similar secrets today?** *(Answers may vary. Lead students to recognize that patented formulas such as the formulas for soft drinks are similar to the secret of the silkworm.)* **What does it mean to control part of a route, as stated in point 6 on the map?** Explain that this most likely means that the Parthian traders were not allowing other traders to use a stretch of the route or were charging other traders to use it. By doing this, the Parthian traders could make a profit on goods traveling both east and west. **Why do you think the Roman soldiers surrendered when the Parthian army raised the cloth?** *(They may have been blinded or confused by the display or overwhelmed by the beauty of the cloth.)*

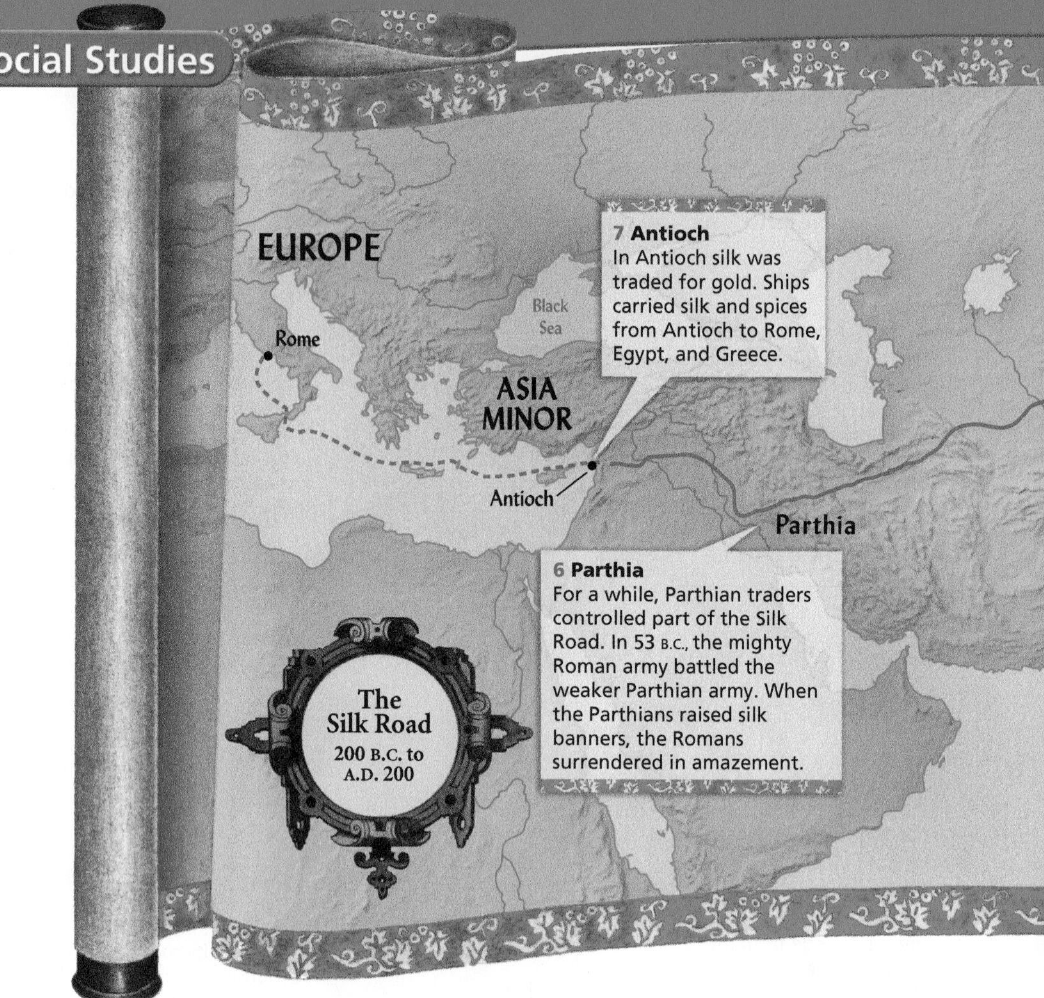

EUROPE
Rome
Black Sea
ASIA MINOR
Antioch
Parthia
7 Antioch
In Antioch silk was traded for gold. Ships carried silk and spices from Antioch to Rome, Egypt, and Greece.
6 Parthia
For a while, Parthian traders controlled part of the Silk Road. In 53 B.C., the mighty Roman army battled the weaker Parthian army. When the Parthians raised silk banners, the Romans surrendered in amazement.
The Silk Road
200 B.C. to A.D. 200

The Silk Road

Long before the rest of the world learned how silk was made, the Chinese were trading this treasured fabric with people west of China. Merchants who bought and sold silk traveled along a system of hazardous routes that came to be known as the Silk Road. The Silk Road stretched 6,400 kilometers from Ch'ang-an in China to the Mediterranean Sea. Silk, furs, and spices traveled west toward Rome along the road. Gold, wool, glass, grapes, garlic, and walnuts moved east toward China.

Travel along the Silk Road was treacherous and difficult. For safety, traders traveled in caravans of many people and animals. Some kinds of pack animals were better equipped to handle certain parts of the journey than others. Camels, for instance, were well suited to the desert; they could go without drinking for several days and withstand most sandstorms. Yaks were often used in the high mountains.

The entire journey along the Silk Road could take years. Many people and animals died along the way. Very few individuals or caravans traveled the length of the Silk Road.

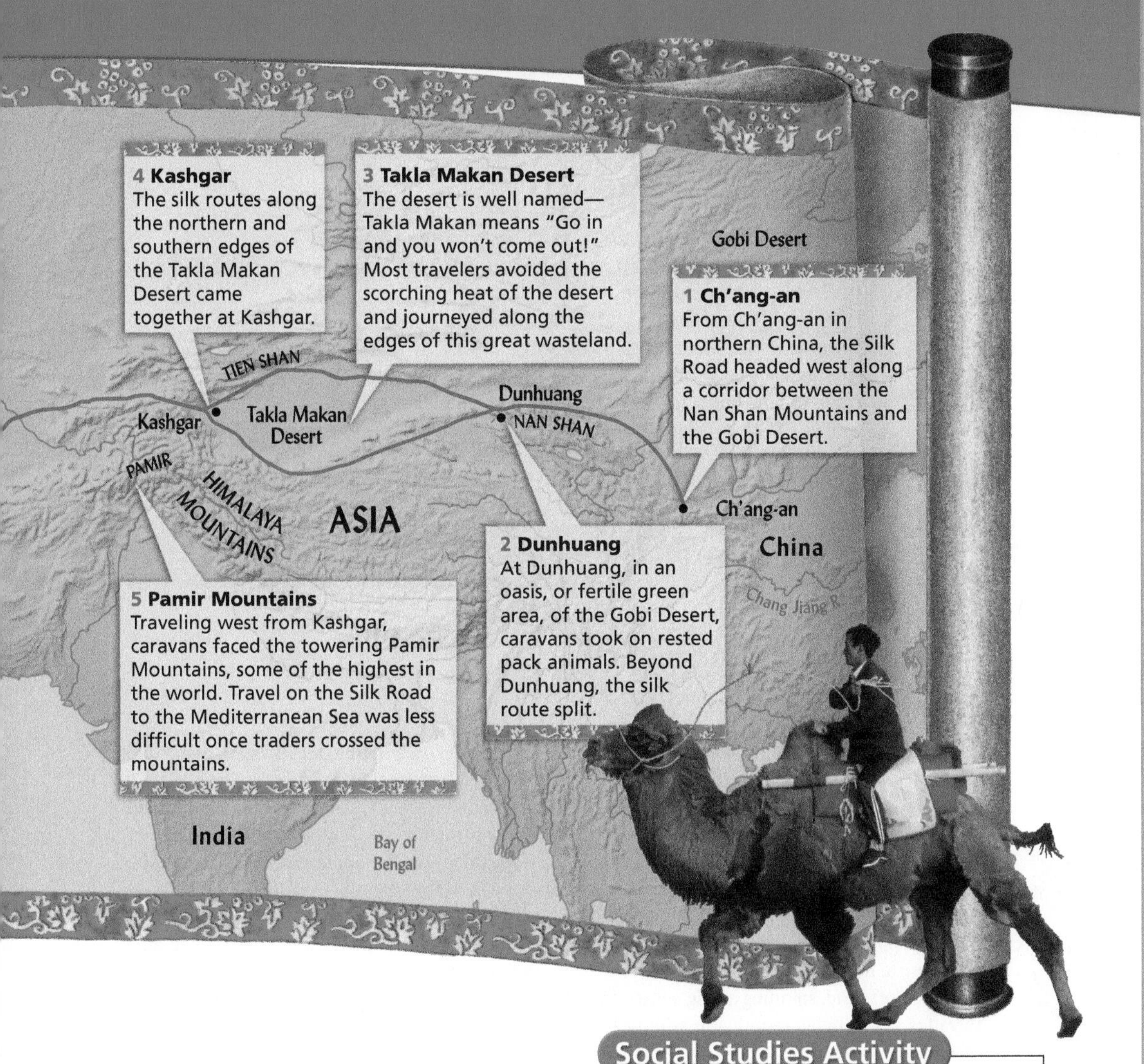

4 Kashgar
The silk routes along the northern and southern edges of the Takla Makan Desert came together at Kashgar.
3 Takla Makan Desert
The desert is well named—Takla Makan means "Go in and you won't come out!" Most travelers avoided the scorching heat of the desert and journeyed along the edges of this great wasteland.
Gobi Desert
1 Ch'ang-an
From Ch'ang-an in northern China, the Silk Road headed west along a corridor between the Nan Shan Mountains and the Gobi Desert.
TIEN SHAN
Kashgar
Takla Makan Desert
Dunhuang
NAN SHAN
PAMIR
HIMALAYA MOUNTAINS
ASIA
Ch'ang-an
China
Chang Jiang R.
2 Dunhuang
At Dunhuang, in an oasis, or fertile green area, of the Gobi Desert, caravans took on rested pack animals. Beyond Dunhuang, the silk route split.
5 Pamir Mountains
Traveling west from Kashgar, caravans faced the towering Pamir Mountains, some of the highest in the world. Travel on the Silk Road to the Mediterranean Sea was less difficult once traders crossed the mountains.
India
Bay of Bengal

Silk fabric became highly prized in Rome. In fact, it was said that the first silk products to reach Rome after 50 B.C. were worth their weight in gold. The Chinese, of course, kept the secret of the silkworm and controlled silk production. They were pleased that the Romans thought that silk grew on trees. It was not until about A.D. 550 that the Roman Empire learned the secret of silk.

In time, silk production spread around the world. The Silk Road, though, opened forever the exchange of goods and ideas between China and the West.

Social Studies Activity

You are a merchant traveling from Dunhuang to Kashgar and back. You will carry silk, furs, and cinnamon to Kashgar where you'll trade for gold, garlic, and glass. Plan your route and hire a guide.

- Look at the map to find the distances and the physical features you will see.
- Explain why you chose the route you did.
- List the animals and supplies you will take.
- Write a help-wanted ad for a guide to lead your caravan.

Social Studies Activity

Focus Invite interested students to research the typical weather conditions travelers could expect along their routes. Students may wish to sketch a map and add notations about the average maximum and minimum temperatures along the route.

Teach Make sure students understand how to read and use the map scale correctly. Remind students to read the captions by starting with number one in Ch'ang-an, where the Silk Road began. Assist students in finding the distance between two of the cities.

Extend Challenge interested students to research about the merchants who traveled the Silk Road. Have students find out the kinds of hardships the travelers encountered. Invite students to share their findings. Alternatively, find students who have experienced mountain hiking trips and primitive camping. Ask the students to share with the class what they learned about the kinds of clothes, equipment, and tools hikers take along. Ask them to describe the kinds of hardships and extreme conditions that hikers might have to deal with.

Scoring Rubric

4 Exceeds criteria; takes into consideration the length of the trip, the types of terrain, the types of weather, and temperature conditions.

3 Meets criteria; takes into consideration the length of the trip, the types of terrain, and the weather conditions.

2 Includes length of the trip and the types of terrain.

1 Is inaccurate or incomplete.

Background

Facts and Figures Yaks are huge animals that have thick hair and are native to the cold mountains of central Asia. Yaks are valuable as pack animals and for their milk, meat, hair, and hide.

Camels are native to the deserts of Asia and northern Africa. There are two kinds of camels: Arabian and Bactrian. Both have humps that store fat, enabling them to go without food for several days.

The Arabian camel is better adapted to desert conditions. Its feet can tolerate the heat of the sand, and its nostrils and eyes are protected from sandstorms.

The two-humped Bactrian camel is better suited for cooler mountain conditions. It has a furry coat that it sheds every year, allowing it to withstand a huge range of temperatures.

Explore Language Arts Concepts

Teach Key Concepts Before students read the story, tell them that this story is a myth. Ask: **What myths have you read?** *(Students may recall Greek or Roman myths of gods and goddesses.)*
Make sure students are familiar with the usage of the word *appears* that means "to come into sight," as used in the introduction. Ask : **Why do you think the girl lied to her father about what she had said to the horse?** *(Accept all reasonable answers.)*
Why do you think the horse was acting strangely and would not eat? *(Answers may vary; samples: the horse was confused or angry.)*

News Story Ask: **What did the other children see happen to the girl in the myth?** Challenge students to write a news story for a newspaper or for the evening news on television describing what happened. Students may wish to present a follow-up story covering what the neighbors found some days later.

Extend To extend this exploration, have students research other myths that explain natural phenomena. Have students retell the myths in class.

Language Arts

The Gift of Silk

A myth is a story handed down from past cultures—often to explain an event or natural phenomenon. Myths may be about gods and goddesses or about heroes.

The Yellow Emperor, Huang Di, who is mentioned in this Chinese myth, was a real person. Some stories say that he was the founder of the Chinese nation. He was thought to be a god who came to rule on Earth. Here the silkworm goddess appears to him at a victory celebration.

The Goddess of the Silkworm

A goddess descended from the heavens with a gift for the Yellow Emperor. Her body was covered with a horse's hide, and she presented two shining rolls of silk to the god. She was the "goddess of the silkworm", sometimes called the "lady with a horse's head". Long, long ago she had been a beautiful girl, but now a horse's skin grew over her body. If she pulled the two sides of the skin close to her body she became a silkworm with a horse's head, spinning a long, glittering thread of silk from her mouth. It is said she lived in a mulberry tree, producing silk day and night in the wild northern plain. This is her story.

Once in ancient times there lived a man, his daughter and their horse. Often the man had to travel, leaving his daughter alone at home to take care of the beast. And often the girl was lonely. One day, because she missed her father she teased the horse: "Dear long-nosed one, if you could bring my father home right how, I'd marry you and be your wife." At that the horse broke out of his harness. He galloped away and came quickly to the place where the master was doing business. The master, surprised to see his beast, grasped his mane and jumped up on his back. The horse stood mournfully staring in the direction he had come from, so the man decided there must be something amiss at home and hurried back.

When they arrived home, the daughter explained that she had only remarked that she missed her father and the horse had dashed off wildly. The man said nothing but was secretly pleased to own such a remarkable animal and fed him special sweet hay. But the horse would not touch it and whinnied and reared each time he saw the girl.

The man began to worry about the horse's strange behavior, and one day he said to the girl, "Why is it that our horse behaves so strangely whenever you are about?"

So the young girl confessed the teasing remark she had made.

When he heard this the father was enraged, "For shame to say such a thing to an animal! No one must know of this! You will stay locked in the house!"

Bronze Horse
This galloping horse was crafted in the second century.

Now the man had always liked this horse, but he would not hear of its becoming his son-in-law. That night, to prevent any more trouble, he crept quietly into the stable with his bow and arrow and shot the horse through the heart. Then he skinned it and hung up the hide in the courtyard.

Next day, when the father was away, the girl ran out of the house to join some other children playing in the courtyard near the horse hide. When she saw it she kicked it angrily and said, "Dirty horse hide! What made you think such an ugly long-snouted creature as you could become my . . . ."

But before she could finish, the hide suddenly flew up and wrapped itself around her, swift as the wind, and carried her away out of sight. The other children watched dumbfounded; there was nothing they could do but wait to tell the old man when he arrived home.

Her father set out immediately in search of his daughter, but in vain. Some days later a neighbouring family found the girl wrapped up in the hide in the branches of a mulberry tree. She had turned into a wormlike creature spinning a long thread of shining silk from her horse-shaped head, spinning it round and round her in a soft cocoon.

Such is the story of the goddess of the silkworm. The Yellow Emperor was delighted to receive her exquisite gift of silk . . . . He ordered his official tailor, Bo Yu, to create new ceremonial robes and hats. And Lei Zu, the revered queen mother of gods and people, wife of the Emperor, began then to collect silkworms and grow them. And so it was that the Chinese people learned of silk.

———Yuan Ke, *Dragons and Dynasties,* translated by Kim Echlin and Nie Zhixiong

Language Arts Activity

What two details in the myth tell you that silkworms were important to the Chinese people?

The girl in the myth gets into trouble because she breaks her promise. Write a story of your own using the idea of a broken promise.

- Decide on the place, time, and main characters.
- Think about the events that will happen and how your story will conclude.

Language Arts Activity

Focus Challenge students to write a myth to explain some natural phenomenon. For example, students could write a story that explains where fog or moss or lightning came from.

Teach Make sure students' stories include a broken promise. Remind students that, like many myths, their stories do not have to be factual.

Scoring Rubric

4 Exceeds criteria; includes a detailed description of place, time, and main characters and has a strong conclusion
3 Meets criteria; includes a fair description of place, time, and main characters and has a conclusion
2 Includes a weak description of place, time, and main characters and has a weak conclusion
1 Is inadequately developed and incomplete

Background

History Chinese tradition claims that the wife of the Yellow Emperor discovered silk around the 27th century B.C. The silkworm moth was originally native to China. The Chinese succeeded in guarding the secret of silk for about 3,000 years.

In A.D. 552, a Roman emperor sent two Persian monks to China. They risked their lives stealing mulberry seeds and silkworm eggs. They hid the seeds and eggs inside their walking staffs and smuggled them out of China.

Silk production spread gradually to many countries in Europe. However, the climate in England and the United States was not suitable for silkworms and they did not flourish in either country.

Mathematics

Explore Mathematics Concepts

Teach Key Concepts Before you work the problem, estimate aloud to demonstrate how to estimate to students. Write on the board "125 trees feed 6,000 silkworms." Write "100 trees" below 125 trees. Point out that 100 trees is about a fifth less than 125 trees. Explain that 1,000 is a bit more than one fifth of 6,000. So you estimate that the answer will be a little less than 5,000 silkworms.

Review proportions. Make sure students understand that the two ratios must be in the same form each time; for example $\frac{\text{trees}}{\text{silkworm}}$.

If students are not familiar with cross multiplication, or cannot recall why it works, show them with a simpler example, such as 1/2 = 2/4.

Once you have calculated the answer, compare it to your original estimate. Stress to students how estimating first can help them avoid mistakes.

Extend To extend this exploration, have pairs of students write problems for each other that can be solved using a proportion. Have students compare answers and work together to resolve any discrepancies.

Math Activity

Focus Group students in pairs. Remind them to estimate each answer before they calculate. Then they can compare the answer to the estimate to check their work.

Teach Remind students to keep the form the same in both ratios.

Expected Outcome

1. 16 sacks
2. 120 trays
3. (a) 1,824 centimeters per hour, (b) 109,440 centimeters
4. (a) 9 blouses; (b) 54 ties

Mathematics

Counting on Caterpillars

Lai opened the door to the silkworm room. She was greeted by the loud sound of thousands of silkworms crunching on fresh leaves from mulberry trees. Lai enjoyed raising silkworms, but it was hard work. Over its lifetime, each silkworm eats about twenty times its own weight.

Lai had a chance to care for more silkworms. But first she had to figure out how many more she could raise. She now had 6,000 silkworms that ate the leaves from 125 mulberry trees. Should she have her parents buy another piece of land with another 100 mulberry trees? If she had 100 more trees, how many more silkworms could she feed?

1 Analyze.

You know that 125 trees can feed 6,000 silkworms. You want to know the number of silkworms 100 trees will feed. Write a proportion, using n to represent the number of silkworms.

2 Write the proportion.

$$\frac{\text{Trees}}{\text{Silkworms}} \begin{matrix}\rightarrow\\\rightarrow\end{matrix} \frac{125}{6{,}000} = \frac{100}{n} \begin{matrix}\leftarrow\\\leftarrow\end{matrix} \frac{\text{Trees}}{\text{Silkworms}}$$

3 Cross multiply.

$125 \times n = 6{,}000 \times 100$

4 Simplify.

$125n = 600{,}000$

5 Solve.

$n = \frac{600{,}000}{125}$ $n = 4{,}800$

6 Think about it.

"Yes," she decided. She could raise 4,800 more silkworms!

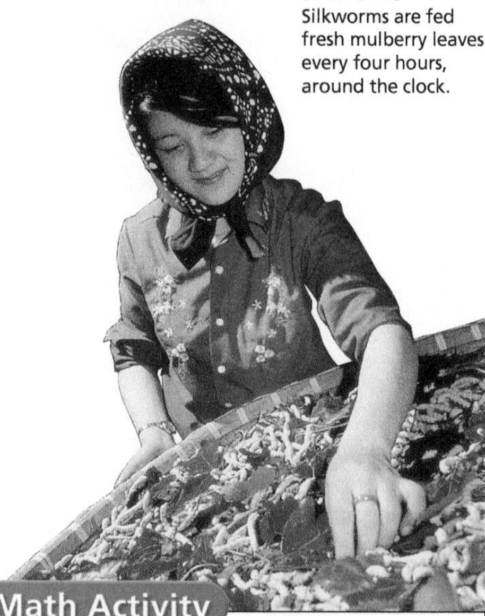

Silkworms
Silkworms are fed fresh mulberry leaves every four hours, around the clock.

Math Activity

Solve the following problems.

1. Lai's friend Cheng also raises silkworms. He buys mulberry leaves. If 20 sacks of leaves feed 12,000 silkworms a day, how many sacks of leaves will 9,600 silkworms eat per day?
2. When Lai's silkworms are ready to spin, she places them in trays. If 3 trays can hold 150 silkworms, how many trays does Lai use for her 6,000 silkworms?
3. A silkworm spins silk at a rate of about 30.4 centimeters per minute. (a) How many centimeters can it spin in an hour? (b) It takes a silkworm 60 hours to spin the entire cocoon. How many centimeters is that?
4. Lai's silk thread contributes to the creation of beautiful silk clothes. It takes the thread of 630 cocoons to make a blouse and the thread of 110 cocoons to make a tie.
   (a) If each of Lai's 6,000 silkworms produces a cocoon, how many blouses can be made from the thread? (b) How many ties can be made?

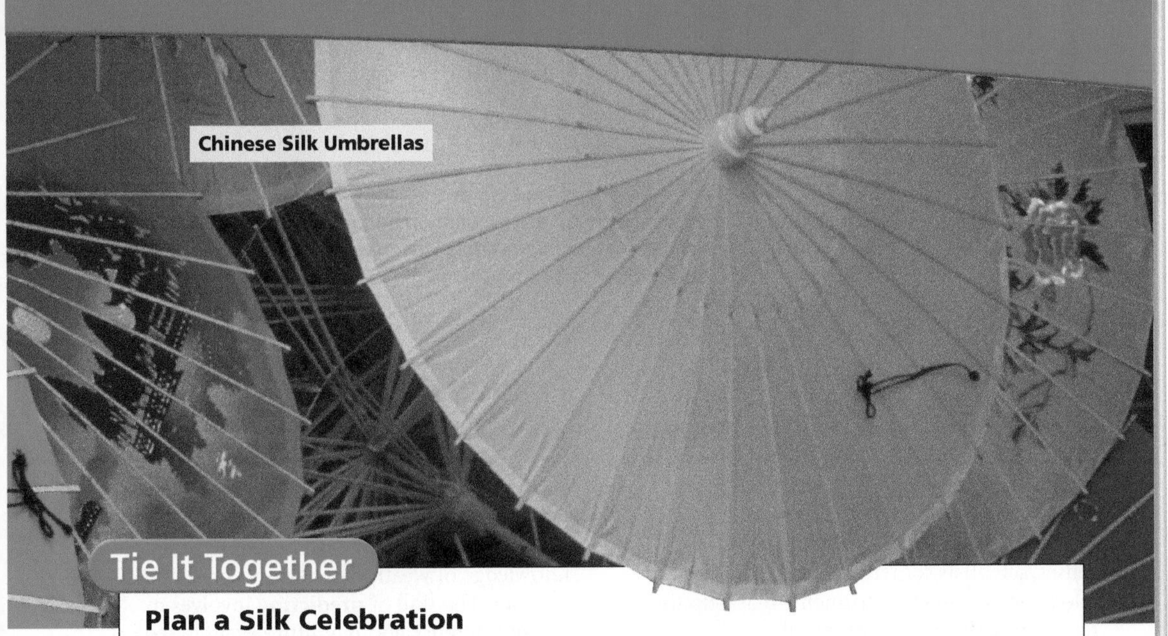
Chinese Silk Umbrellas

Tie It Together

Plan a Silk Celebration

People use silk in many ways other than just to make fine clothing. Did you know that silk was used for parachutes during World War II? Or that some bicycle racers choose tires containing silk because they provide good traction? Today, silk is used for a variety of purposes:

- recreation—fishing lines and nets, bicycle tires
- business—electrical insulations, typewriter and computer ribbons, surgical sutures
- decoration—some silkscreen printing, artificial flowers

Work in small groups to learn about one of the ways that people have used silk in the past or are using it today. Devise an interesting way to share your project with the class. Here are some ideas.

- a booth to display or advertise a silk product
- a skit in which you wear silk
- a historical presentation on the uses of silk in other countries
- a presentation about a process, such as silkscreen painting or silk flowers

Ask volunteers to bring pictures or silk products to class. After rehearsing or reviewing your presentation, work with other groups to decide how to organize your Silk Festival.

Tires of Silk
Professional bicycle racers such as Lance Armstrong often rely on tires containing silk. Silk gives the tires better traction, or grip, on the road.

Tie It Together

Plan a Silk Celebration

Time 1 week (2 days for research, 2 days for preparing the displays, 1 day for the Silk Festival)

Tips Have students work in groups of four or five. If possible, group students so that each group contains at least one student who knows how to research on the Internet or in science journals. Have groups each choose one bulleted item from the list on this page that they are most interested in. You may need to rearrange groups so that most students are working on the aspect of the project that most interests them.

- Most of the students' research should be readily available from encyclopedias. Groups who are researching innovative uses for silk may need to search in science journals or, with supervision, on the Internet.
- If students wish to bring a sample of silk to show the class, suggest that they bring it in a clear plastic bag so that it is less likely to be damaged.
- Encourage students to bring photocopies of interesting silk products or draw their own illustrations.

Extend Challenge students to find out how to raise silkworms. (Silkworm eggs and food can be obtained from biological supply companies.) Ask questions such as: **What kind of container do you need to keep silkworms in? What do they need besides mulberry leaves? Where do you get mulberry leaves? Do silkworms need water? What kind of temperature and humidity do they need? How much do silkworms eat? How do you get the moths to lay eggs? What conditions do the eggs need to hatch?**

Think Like a Scientist

The Skills Handbook is designed as a reference for students to use whenever they need to review inquiry, reading, or math skills. You can use the activities in this part of the Skills Handbook to teach or reinforce inquiry skills.

Observing

Focus Remind students that an observation is what they can see, hear, smell, taste, or feel.

Teach Invite students to make observations of the classroom. List these observations on the board. Challenge students to identify the senses they used to make each observation. Then, ask: **Which senses will you use to make observations from the photograph on this page?** *(Sight is the only sense that can be used to make observations from the photograph.)*

Activity

Some observations that students might make include that the boy is skateboarding, wearing a white helmet, and flying in the air. Make sure that students' observations are confined to only things that they can actually see in the photograph.

Inferring

Focus Choose one or two of the classroom observations listed on the board, and challenge students to interpret them. Guide students by asking why something appears as it does.

Teach Encourage students to describe their thought processes in making their inferences. Point out where they used their knowledge and experience to interpret the observations. Then invite students to suggest other possible interpretations for the observations. Ask: **How can you find out whether an inference is correct?** *(By further investigation)*

Activity

One possible inference is that the boy just skated off a ramp at a skate park. Invite students to share their experiences that helped them make the inference.

Predicting

Focus Discuss the weather forecast for the next day. Point out that this prediction is an inference about what will happen in the future based on observations and experience.

Teach Help students differentiate between a prediction and an inference. You might organize the similarities and differences in a Venn diagram on the board. Both are interpretations of observations using experience and knowledge, and both can be incorrect. Inferences describe current or past events. Predictions describe future events.

Activity

Students might predict that the boy will land and skate to the other side. Others might predict that the boy will fall. Students should also describe the evidence or experience on which they based their predictions.

SKILLS Handbook

Think Like a Scientist

Scientists have a particular way of looking at the world, or scientific habits of mind. Whenever you ask a question and explore possible answers, you use many of the same skills that scientists do. Some of these skills are described on this page.

Observing

When you use one or more of your five senses to gather information about the world, you are **observing.** Hearing a dog bark, counting twelve green seeds, and smelling smoke are all observations. To increase the power of their senses, scientists sometimes use microscopes, telescopes, or other instruments that help them make more detailed observations.

An observation must be an accurate report of what your senses detect. It is important to keep careful records of your observations in science class by writing or drawing in a notebook. The information collected through observations is called evidence, or data.

Inferring

When you interpret an observation, you are **inferring,** or making an inference. For example, if you hear your dog barking, you may infer that someone is at your front door. To make this inference, you combine the evidence—the barking dog—and your experience or knowledge—you know that your dog barks when strangers approach—to reach a logical conclusion.

Notice that an inference is not a fact; it is only one of many possible interpretations for an observation. For example, your dog may be barking because it wants to go for a walk. An inference may turn out to be incorrect even if it is based on accurate observations and logical reasoning. The only way to find out if an inference is correct is to investigate further.

Predicting

When you listen to the weather forecast, you hear many predictions about the next day's weather—what the temperature will be, whether it will rain, and how windy it will be. Weather forecasters use observations and knowledge of weather patterns to predict the weather. The skill of **predicting** involves making an inference about a future event based on current evidence or past experience.

Because a prediction is an inference, it may prove to be false. In science class, you can test some of your predictions by doing experiments. For example, suppose you predict that larger paper airplanes can fly farther than smaller airplanes. How could you test your prediction?

Activity

Use the photograph to answer the questions below.

Observing Look closely at the photograph. List at least three observations.

Inferring Use your observations to make an inference about what has happened. What experience or knowledge did you use to make the inference?

Predicting Predict what will happen next. On what evidence or experience do you base your prediction?

Classifying

Could you imagine searching for a book in the library if the books were shelved in no particular order? Your trip to the library would be an all-day event! Luckily, librarians group together books on similar topics or by the same author. Grouping together items that are alike in some way is called **classifying.** You can classify items in many ways: by size, by shape, by use, and by other important characteristics.

Like librarians, scientists use the skill of classifying to organize information and objects. When things are sorted into groups, the relationships among them become easier to understand.

Activity

Classify the objects in the photograph into two groups based on any characteristic you choose. Then use another characteristic to classify the objects into three groups.

Activity

This student is using a model to demonstrate what causes day and night on Earth. What do the flashlight and the tennis ball in the model represent?

Making Models

Have you ever drawn a picture to help someone understand what you were saying? Such a drawing is one type of model. A model is a picture, diagram, computer image, or other representation of a complex object or process. **Making models** helps people understand things that they cannot observe directly.

Scientists often use models to represent things that are either very large or very small, such as the planets in the solar system, or the parts of a cell. Such models are physical models—drawings or three-dimensional structures that look like the real thing. Other models are mental models—mathematical equations or words that describe how something works.

Communicating

Whenever you talk on the phone, write a report, or listen to your teacher at school, you are communicating. **Communicating** is the process of sharing ideas and information with other people. Communicating effectively requires many skills, including writing, reading, speaking, listening, and making models.

Scientists communicate to share results, information, and opinions. Scientists often communicate about their work in journals, over the telephone, in letters, and on the Internet. They also attend scientific meetings where they share their ideas with one another in person.

Activity

On a sheet of paper, write out clear, detailed directions for tying your shoe. Then exchange directions with a partner. Follow your partner's directions exactly. How successful were you at tying your shoe? How could your partner have communicated more clearly?

Inquiry Skills

Classifying

Focus Encourage students to think of common things that are classified.

Teach Ask: **What things at home are classified?** *(Clothing might be classified in order to place it in the appropriate dresser drawer; glasses, plates, and silverware are grouped in different parts of the kitchen; screws, nuts, bolts, washers, and nails might be separated into small containers.)* **What are some things that scientists classify?** *(Scientists classify many things they study, including organisms, geological features and processes, and kinds of machines.)*

Activity

Some characteristics students might use include color, pattern of color, use of balls, and size. Students' criteria for classification should clearly divide the balls into two, and then three, distinct groups.

Making Models

Focus Ask: **What are some models you have used to study science?** *(Students might have used human anatomical models, solar system models, maps, or stream tables.)* **How have these models helped you?** *(Models can help you learn about things that are difficult to study because they are very large, very small, or highly complex.)*

Teach Be sure students understand that a model does not have to be three-dimensional. For example, a map is a model, as is a mathematical equation. Have students look at the photograph of the student modeling the causes of day and night on Earth. Ask: **What quality of each item makes this a good model?** *(The flashlight gives off light, and the ball is round and can be rotated by the student.)*

Activity

The flashlight represents the sun and the ball represents Earth.

Communicating

Focus Have students identify the methods of communication they have used today.

Teach Ask: **How is the way you communicate with a friend similar to and different from the way scientists communicate about their work to other scientists?** *(Both may communicate using various methods, but scientists must be very detailed and precise, whereas communication between friends may be less detailed and precise.)* Encourage students to communicate like a scientist as they carry out the activity.

Activity

Students' answers will vary but should identify a step-by-step process for tying a shoe. Help students identify communication errors such as leaving out a step, putting steps in the wrong order, or disregarding the person's handedness.

Making Measurements

Students can refer to this part of the Skills Handbook whenever they need to review how to make measurements with SI units. You can use the activities here to teach or reinforce SI units.

Measuring in SI

Focus Review SI units with students. Begin by providing metric rulers, graduated cylinders, balances, and Celsius thermometers. Use these tools to reinforce that the meter is the unit of length, the liter is the unit of volume, the gram is the unit of mass, and the degree Celsius is the unit of temperature.

Teach Ask: **If you want to measure the length and the width of the classroom, which SI unit would you use?** *(Meter)* **Which unit would you use to measure the amount of mass in your textbook?** *(Gram)* **Which would you use to measure how much water a drinking glass holds?** *(Liter)* **When would you use the Celsius scale?** *(To measure the temperature of something)* Then use the measuring equipment to review SI prefixes. For example, ask: **What are the smallest units on the metric ruler?** *(Millimeters)* **How many millimeters are there in one centimeter?** *(10 millimeters)* **How many in 10 centimeters?** *(100 millimeters)* **How many centimeters are there in one meter?** *(100 centimeters)* **What does 1,000 meters equal?** *(One kilometer)*

Activity

Length The length of the shell is 7.8 centimeters, or 78 millimeters. If students need more practice measuring length, have them use meter sticks and metric rulers to measure various objects in the classroom.

Activity

Liquid Volume The volume of water in the graduated cylinder is 62 milliliters. If students need more practice, have them use a graduated cylinder to measure different volumes of water.

Making Measurements

By measuring, scientists can express their observations more precisely and communicate more information about what they observe.

Measuring in SI

The standard system of measurement used by scientists around the world is known as the International System of Units, which is abbreviated as SI (**Système International d'Unités,** in French). SI units are easy to use because they are based on powers of 10. Each unit is ten times larger than the next smallest unit and one tenth the size of the next largest unit. The table lists the prefixes used to name the most common SI units.

Common SI Prefixes		
Prefix	Symbol	Meaning
kilo-	k	1,000
hecto-	h	100
deka-	da	10
deci-	d	0.1 (one tenth)
centi-	c	0.01 (one hundredth)
milli-	m	0.001 (one thousandth)

Length To measure length, or the distance between two points, the unit of measure is the **meter (m).** The distance from the floor to a doorknob is approximately one meter. Long distances, such as the distance between two cities, are measured in kilometers (km). Small lengths are measured in centimeters (cm) or millimeters (mm). Scientists use metric rulers and meter sticks to measure length.

Common Conversions		
1 km	=	1,000 m
1 m	=	100 cm
1 m	=	1,000 mm
1 cm	=	10 mm

Activity

The larger lines on the metric ruler in the picture show centimeter divisions, while the smaller, unnumbered lines show millimeter divisions. How many centimeters long is the shell? How many millimeters long is it?

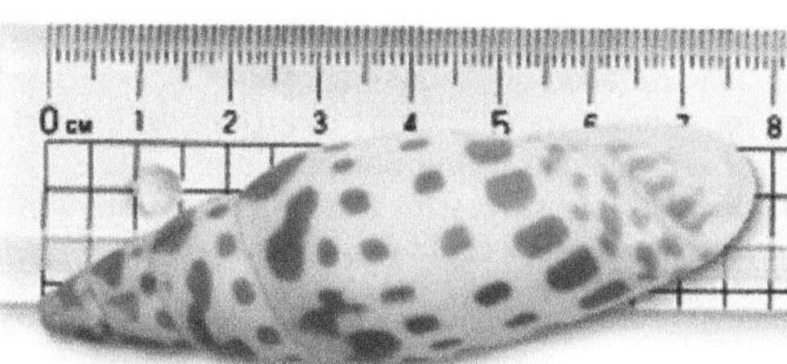

Liquid Volume To measure the volume of a liquid, or the amount of space it takes up, you will use a unit of measure known as the **liter (L).** One liter is the approximate volume of a medium-size carton of milk. Smaller volumes are measured in milliliters (mL). Scientists use graduated cylinders to measure liquid volume.

Common Conversion
1 L = 1,000 mL

Activity

The graduated cylinder in the picture is marked in milliliter divisions. Notice that the water in the cylinder has a curved surface. This curved surface is called the *meniscus*. To measure the volume, you must read the level at the lowest point of the meniscus. What is the volume of water in this graduated cylinder?

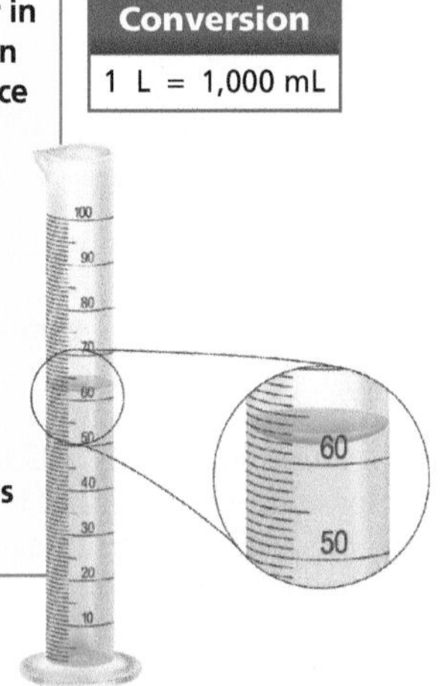

Mass To measure mass, or the amount of matter in an object, you will use a unit of measure known as the **gram (g).** One gram is approximately the mass of a paper clip. Larger masses are measured in kilograms (kg). Scientists use a balance to find the mass of an object.

Common Conversion

1 kg = 1,000 g

Activity

The mass of the potato in the picture is measured in kilograms. What is the mass of the potato? Suppose a recipe for potato salad called for one kilogram of potatoes. About how many potatoes would you need?

0.25 KG

Temperature To measure the temperature of a substance, you will use the **Celsius scale.** Temperature is measured in degrees Celsius (°C) using a Celsius thermometer. Water freezes at 0°C and boils at 100°C.

Time The unit scientists use to measure time is the **second (s).**

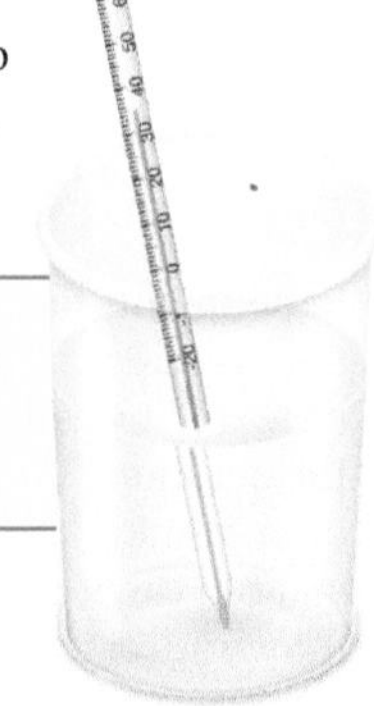

Activity

What is the temperature of the liquid in degrees Celsius?

Converting SI Units

To use the SI system, you must know how to convert between units. Converting from one unit to another involves the skill of **calculating,** or using mathematical operations. Converting between SI units is similar to converting between dollars and dimes because both systems are based on powers of ten.

Suppose you want to convert a length of 80 centimeters to meters. Follow these steps to convert between units.

1. Begin by writing down the measurement you want to convert—in this example, 80 centimeters.
2. Write a conversion factor that represents the relationship between the two units you are converting. In this example, the relationship is 1 meter = 100 centimeters. Write this conversion factor as a fraction, making sure to place the units you are converting from (centimeters, in this example) in the denominator.
3. Multiply the measurement you want to convert by the fraction. When you do this, the units in the first measurement will cancel out with the units in the denominator. Your answer will be in the units you are converting to (meters, in this example).

Example

80 centimeters = ■ meters

$$80 \text{ centimeters} \times \frac{1 \text{ meter}}{100 \text{ centimeters}} = \frac{80 \text{ meters}}{100}$$

$$= 0.8 \text{ meters}$$

Activity

Convert between the following units.

1. 600 millimeters = ■ meters
2. 0.35 liters = ■ milliliters
3. 1,050 grams = ■ kilograms

Inquiry Skills

Activity

Mass The mass of the potato is 0.25 kilograms. You would need 4 potatoes to make one kilogram. If students need more practice, give them various objects, such as coins, paper clips, and books, to measure mass.

Activity

Temperature The temperature of the liquid is 35°C. Students who need more practice can measure the temperatures of various water samples.

Converting SI Units

Focus Review the steps for converting SI units, and work through the example with students.

Teach Ask: **How many millimeters are in 80 centimeters?** *(With the relationship 10 millimeters = 1 centimeter, students should follow the steps to calculate that 80 centimeters is equal to 800 millimeters.)* Have students do the conversion problems in the activity.

Activity

1. *600 millimeters = 0.6 meters*
2. *0.35 liters = 350 milliliters*
3. *1,050 grams = 1.05 kilograms*

If students need more practice converting SI units, have them make up conversion problems to trade with partners.

Conducting a Scientific Investigation

Students can refer to this part of the Skills Handbook whenever they need to review the steps of a scientific investigation. You can use the activities here to teach or reinforce these steps.

Posing Questions

Focus Ask: **What do you do when you want to learn about something?** *(Answers might include asking questions about it or looking for information in books or on the Internet.)* Explain that scientists go through the same process to learn about something.

Teach Tell students that the questions scientists ask may have no answers or many different answers. To answer their questions, scientists often conduct experiments. Ask: **Why is a scientific question important to a scientific investigation?** *(It helps the scientist decide if an experiment is necessary; the answer might already be known. It also helps focus the idea so that the scientist can form a hypothesis.)* **What is the scientific question in the activity on the next page?** *(Is a ball's bounce affected by the height from which it is dropped?)*

Developing a Hypothesis

Focus Emphasize that a hypothesis is one possible explanation for a set of observations. It is *not* a guess. It is often based on an inference.

Teach Ask: **On what information do scientists base their hypotheses?** *(Their observations and previous knowledge or experience)* Point out that a hypothesis does not always turn out to be correct. Ask: **When a hypothesis turns out to be incorrect, do you think the scientist wasted his or her time? Explain.** *(No. The scientist learned from the investigation and will develop another hypothesis that could prove to be correct.)*

Designing an Experiment

Focus Have a volunteer read the Experimental Procedure in the box. Invite students to identify the manipulated variable *(amount of table salt)*, the variables kept constant *(amount and starting temperature of water, location of containers)*, the control *(Container 3)*, and the responding variable *(the temperature at which water freezes)*.

Conducting a Scientific Investigation

In some ways, scientists are like detectives, piecing together clues to learn about a process or event. One way that scientists gather clues is by carrying out experiments. An experiment tests an idea in a careful, orderly manner. Although experiments do not all follow the same steps in the same order, many follow a pattern similar to the one described here.

Posing Questions

Experiments begin by asking a scientific question. A scientific question is one that can be answered by gathering evidence. For example, the question "Which freezes faster—fresh water or salt water?" is a scientific question because you can carry out an investigation and gather information to answer the question.

Developing a Hypothesis

The next step is to form a hypothesis. A **hypothesis** is a possible explanation for a set of observations or answer to a scientific question. In science, a hypothesis must be something that can be tested. A hypothesis can be worded as an *If . . . then . . .* statement. For example, a hypothesis might be *"If I add table salt to fresh water, then the water will freeze at a lower temperature."* A hypothesis worded this way serves as a rough outline of the experiment you should perform.

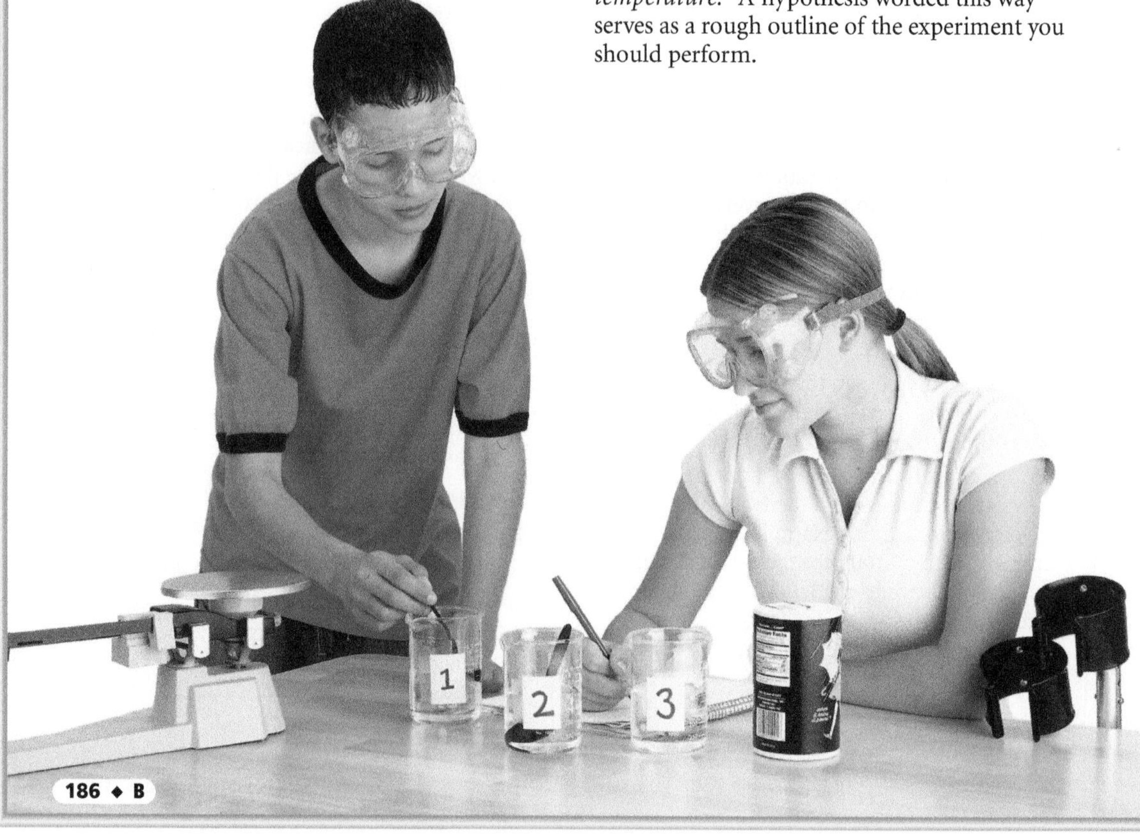

Teach Ask: **How might the experiment be affected if Container 1 had only 100 milliliters of water?** *(It wouldn't be an accurate comparison with the containers that have more water.)* Also make sure that students understand the importance of the control. Then, ask: **What operational definition is used in this experiment?** *("Frozen" means the condition when the wooden stick can no longer move in a container.)*

Designing an Experiment

Next you need to plan a way to test your hypothesis. Your plan should be written out as a step-by-step procedure and should describe the observations or measurements you will make.

Two important steps involved in designing an experiment are controlling variables and forming operational definitions.

Controlling Variables In a well-designed experiment, you need to keep all variables the same except for one. A **variable** is any factor that can change in an experiment. The factor that you change is called the **manipulated variable.** In this experiment, the manipulated variable is the amount of table salt added to the water. Other factors, such as the amount of water or the starting temperature, are kept constant.

The factor that changes as a result of the manipulated variable is called the **responding variable.** The responding variable is what you measure or observe to obtain your results. In this experiment, the responding variable is the temperature at which the water freezes.

An experiment in which all factors except one are kept constant is called a **controlled experiment.** Most controlled experiments include a test called the control. In this experiment, Container 3 is the control. Because no salt is added to Container 3, you can compare the results from the other containers to it. Any difference in results must be due to the addition of salt alone.

Forming Operational Definitions Another important aspect of a well-designed experiment is having clear operational definitions. An **operational definition** is a statement that describes how a particular variable is to be measured or how a term is to be defined. For example, in this experiment, how will you determine if the water has frozen? You might decide to insert a stick in each container at the start of the experiment. Your operational definition of "frozen" would be the time at which the stick can no longer move.

Experimental Procedure	
1.	Fill 3 containers with 300 milliliters of cold tap water.
2.	Add 10 grams of salt to Container 1; stir.
	Add 20 grams of salt to Container 2; stir.
	Add no salt to Container 3.
3.	Place the 3 containers in a freezer.
4.	Check the containers every 15 minutes.
	Record your observations.

Interpreting Data

The observations and measurements you make in an experiment are called **data.** At the end of an experiment, you need to analyze the data to look for any patterns or trends. Patterns often become clear if you organize your data in a data table or graph. Then think through what the data reveal. Do they support your hypothesis? Do they point out a flaw in your experiment? Do you need to collect more data?

Drawing Conclusions

A **conclusion** is a statement that sums up what you have learned from an experiment. When you draw a conclusion, you need to decide whether the data you collected support your hypothesis or not. You may need to repeat an experiment several times before you can draw any conclusions from it. Conclusions often lead you to pose new questions and plan new experiments to answer them.

Activity

Is a ball's bounce affected by the height from which it is dropped? Using the steps just described, plan a controlled experiment to investigate this problem.

Interpreting Data

Focus Ask: **What kind of data would you collect from the experiment with freezing salt water?** *(Amount of salt and temperature when the water freezes)*

Teach Ask: **What if you forgot to record some data during an investigation?** *(You wouldn't be able to draw valid conclusions because some data are missing.)* Then, ask: **Why are data tables and graphs a good way to organize data?** *(They make it easier to record data accurately, as well as compare and analyze data.)* **What kind of data table and graph might you use for this experiment?** *(A table would have a row for each container and a column in which the freezing temperature of the water is recorded. A bar graph would show the temperature at which the water froze in each container.)*

Drawing Conclusions

Focus Help students understand that a conclusion is not necessarily the end of a scientific investigation. A conclusion about one experiment may lead right into another experiment.

Teach Point out that in scientific investigations, a conclusion is a summary and explanation of the results of an experiment. For the Experimental Procedure described on this page, tell students to suppose that they obtained the following results: Container 3 froze at about 0°C, Container 1 froze at a slightly lower temperature, and Container 2 froze at the lowest temperature. Ask: **What conclusions can you draw from this experiment?** *(Students might conclude that the more table salt there is in the water, the lower the temperature at which the water freezes. The hypothesis is supported, and the question of which freezes at a lower temperature is answered—salt water.)*

Activity

You might wish to have students work in pairs to plan the controlled experiment. Students should develop a hypothesis, such as, "If I increase the height from which a ball is dropped, then the height of its bounce will increase." They can test the hypothesis by dropping a ball from varying heights (the manipulated variable). All trials should be done with the same kind of ball and on the same surface (constants). For each trial, they should measure the height of the bounce (responding variable). After students have designed the experiment, provide rubber balls, and invite them to carry out the experiment so they can collect and interpret data and draw conclusions.

Technology Design Skills

Students can refer to this part of the Skills Handbook whenever they need to review the process of designing new technologies. You can use the activities here to teach or reinforce the steps in this process.

Identify a Need

Focus Solicit from students any situations in which they have thought that a tool, machine, or other object would be really helpful to them or others. Explain that this is the first step in the design of new products.

Teach Point out that identifying specific needs is very important to the design process. Ask: **If it was specified that the toy boat be wind-powered, how might that affect the design?** *(The boat would likely be designed with sails.)*

Research the Problem

Focus Explain that research focuses the problem so that the design is more specific.

Teach Ask: **What might happen if you didn't research the problem before designing the solution?** *(Answers include developing a design that has already been found to fail, using materials that aren't the best, or designing a solution that already exists.)* **What would you research before designing your toy boat?** *(Students might research designs and materials.)*

Design a Solution

Focus Emphasize the importance of a design team. Ask: **Why are brainstorming sessions important in product design?** *(A group will propose more new ideas than one person.)*

Teach Divide the class into teams to design the toy boat. Instruct them to brainstorm design ideas. Then, ask: **Why do you think engineers evaluate constraints after brainstorming?** *(Evaluating constraints while brainstorming often stops the flow of new ideas.)* **What design constraints do you have for your toy boat?** *(Materials must be readily available and teacher-approved. The boat must be 15 centimeters or less in length and must travel 2 meters in a straight line carrying a load of 20 pennies.)*

Technology Design Skills

Engineers are people who use scientific and technological knowledge to solve practical problems. To design new products, engineers usually follow the process described here, even though they may not follow these steps in the exact order. As you read the steps, think about how you might apply them in technology labs.

Identify a Need

Before engineers begin designing a new product, they must first identify the need they are trying to meet. For example, suppose you are a member of a design team in a company that makes toys. Your team has identified a need: a toy boat that is inexpensive and easy to assemble.

Research the Problem

Engineers often begin by gathering information that will help them with their new design. This research may include finding articles in books, magazines, or on the Internet. It may also include talking to other engineers who have solved similar problems. Engineers often perform experiments related to the product they want to design.

For your toy boat, you could look at toys that are similar to the one you want to design. You might do research on the Internet. You could also test some materials to see whether they will work well in a toy boat.

Drawing for a boat design ▼

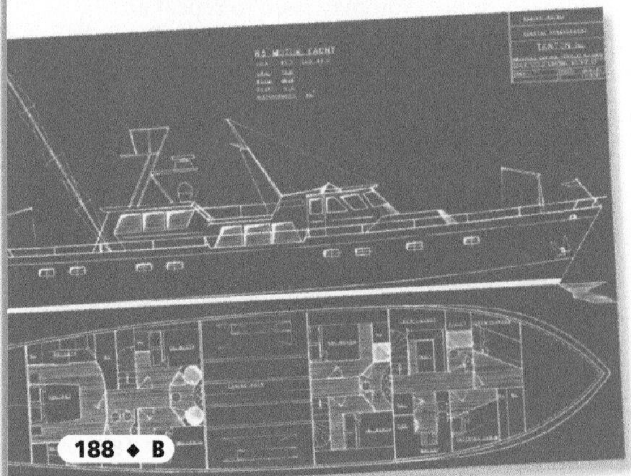

Design a Solution

Research gives engineers information that helps them design a product. When engineers design new products, they usually work in teams.

Generating Ideas Often design teams hold brainstorming meetings in which any team member can contribute ideas. **Brainstorming** is a creative process in which one team member's suggestions often spark ideas in other group members. Brainstorming can lead to new approaches to solving a design problem.

Evaluating Constraints During brainstorming, a design team will often come up with several possible designs. The team must then evaluate each one.

As part of their evaluation, engineers consider constraints. **Constraints** are factors that limit or restrict a product design. Physical characteristics, such as the properties of materials used to make your toy boat, are constraints. Money and time are also constraints. If the materials in a product cost a lot, or if the product takes a long time to make, the design may be impractical.

Making Trade-offs Design teams usually need to make trade-offs. In a **trade-off,** engineers give up one benefit of a proposed design in order to obtain another. In designing your toy boat, you will have to make trade-offs. For example, suppose one material is sturdy but not fully waterproof. Another material is more waterproof, but breakable. You may decide to give up the benefit of sturdiness in order to obtain the benefit of waterproofing.

Build and Evaluate a Prototype

Once the team has chosen a design plan, the engineers build a prototype of the product. A **prototype** is a working model used to test a design. Engineers evaluate the prototype to see whether it works well, is easy to operate, is safe to use, and holds up to repeated use.

Think of your toy boat. What would the prototype be like? Of what materials would it be made? How would you test it?

Troubleshoot and Redesign

Few prototypes work perfectly, which is why they need to be tested. Once a design team has tested a prototype, the members analyze the results and identify any problems. The team then tries to **troubleshoot,** or fix the design problems. For example, if your toy boat leaks or wobbles, the boat should be redesigned to eliminate those problems.

Communicate the Solution

A team needs to communicate the final design to the people who will manufacture and use the product. To do this, teams may use sketches, detailed drawings, computer simulations, and word descriptions.

Activity

You can use the technology design process to design and build a toy boat.

Research and Investigate

1. Visit the library or go online to research toy boats.
2. Investigate how a toy boat can be powered, including wind, rubber bands, or baking soda and vinegar.
3. Brainstorm materials, shapes, and steering for your boat.

Design and Build

4. Based on your research, design a toy boat that
   - is made of readily available materials
   - is no larger than 15 cm long and 10 cm wide
   - includes a power system, a rudder, and an area for cargo
   - travels 2 meters in a straight line carrying a load of 20 pennies
5. Sketch your design and write a step-by-step plan for building your boat. After your teacher approves your plan, build your boat.

Evaluate and Redesign

6. Test your boat, evaluate the results, and troubleshoot any problems.
7. Based on your evaluation, redesign your toy boat so it performs better.

Inquiry Skills

Build and Evaluate a Prototype

Focus Explain that building a prototype enables engineers to test design ideas.

Teach Relate building and testing a prototype to conducting an experiment. Explain that engineers set up controlled experiments to test the prototype. Ask: **Why do you think engineers set up controlled experiments?** *(From the data, they can determine which component of the design is working and which is failing.)* **How would you test your prototype of the toy boat?** *(Answers will vary depending on the toy boat's propulsion system.)*

Troubleshoot and Redesign

Focus Make sure students know what it means to troubleshoot. If necessary, give an example. One example is a stapler that isn't working. In that case, you would check to see if it is out of staples or if the staples are jammed. Then you would fix the problem and try stapling again. If it still didn't work, you might check the position of staples and try again.

Teach Explain that engineers often are not surprised if the prototype doesn't work. Ask: **Why isn't it a failure if the prototype doesn't work?** *(Engineers learn from the problems and make changes to address the problems. This process makes the design better.)* Emphasize that prototypes are completely tested before the product is made in the factory.

Communicate the Solution

Focus Inquire whether students have ever read the instruction manual that comes with a new toy or electronic device.

Teach Emphasize the importance of good communication in the design process. Ask: **What might happen if engineers did not communicate their design ideas clearly?** *(The product might not be manufactured correctly or used properly.)*

Activity

The design possibilities are endless. Students might use small plastic containers, wood, foil, or plastic drinking cups for the boat. Materials may also include toothpicks, straws, or small wooden dowels. Brainstorm with students the different ways in which a toy boat can be propelled. The boats may be any shape, but must be no longer than 15 centimeters.

As student groups follow the steps in the design process, have them record their sources, brainstorming ideas, and prototype design in a logbook. Also give them time to troubleshoot and redesign their boats. When students turn in their boats, they should include assembly directions with a diagram, as well as instructions for use.

Creating Data Tables and Graphs

Students can refer to this part of the Skills Handbook whenever they need to review the skills required to create data tables and graphs. You can use the activities provided here to teach or reinforce these skills.

Data Tables

Focus Emphasize the importance of organizing data. Ask: **What might happen if you didn't use a data table for an experiment?** *(Possible answers include that data might not be collected or they might be forgotten.)*

Teach Have students create a data table to show how much time they spend on different activities during one week. Suggest that students first list the main activities they do every week. Then they should determine the amount of time they spend on each activity each day. Remind students to give the data table a title. A sample data table is shown below.

Bar Graphs

Focus Have students compare and contrast the data table and the bar graph on this page. Ask: **Why would you make a bar graph if the data are already organized in a table?** *(The bar graph organizes the data in a visual way that makes them easier to interpret.)*

Teach Students can use the data from the data table they created to make a bar graph that shows the amount of time they spend on different activities during a week. The vertical axis should be divided into units of time, such as hours. Remind students to label both axes and give their graph a title. A sample bar graph is shown below.

Creating Data Tables and Graphs

How can you make sense of the data in a science experiment? The first step is to organize the data to help you understand them. Data tables and graphs are helpful tools for organizing data.

Data Tables

You have gathered your materials and set up your experiment. But before you start, you need to plan a way to record what happens during the experiment. By creating a data table, you can record your observations and measurements in an orderly way.

Suppose, for example, that a scientist conducted an experiment to find out how many Calories people of different body masses burn while doing various activities. The data table shows the results.

Notice in this data table that the manipulated variable (body mass) is the heading of one column. The responding variable (for Experiment 1, the number of Calories burned while bicycling) is the heading of the next column. Additional columns were added for related experiments.

Calories Burned in 30 Minutes

Body Mass	Experiment 1: Bicycling	Experiment 2: Playing Basketball	Experiment 3: Watching Television
30 kg	60 Calories	120 Calories	21 Calories
40 kg	77 Calories	164 Calories	27 Calories
50 kg	95 Calories	206 Calories	33 Calories
60 kg	114 Calories	248 Calories	38 Calories

Bar Graphs

To compare how many Calories a person burns doing various activities, you could create a bar graph. A bar graph is used to display data in a number of separate, or distinct, categories. In this example, bicycling, playing basketball, and watching television are the three categories.

To create a bar graph, follow these steps.

1. On graph paper, draw a horizontal, or *x*-, axis and a vertical, or *y*-, axis.
2. Write the names of the categories to be graphed along the horizontal axis. Include an overall label for the axis as well.
3. Label the vertical axis with the name of the responding variable. Include units of measurement. Then create a scale along the axis by marking off equally spaced numbers that cover the range of the data collected.
4. For each category, draw a solid bar using the scale on the vertical axis to determine the height. Make all the bars the same width.
5. Add a title that describes the graph.

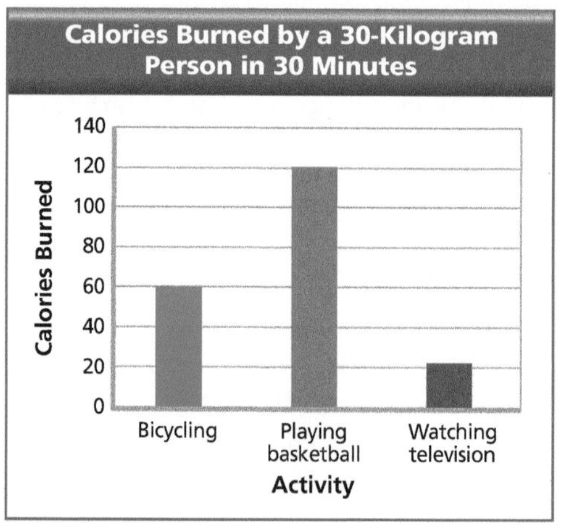

Time Spent on Different Activities in a Week				
	Going to Classes	Eating Meals	Playing Soccer	Watching Television
Monday	6	2	2	0.5
Tuesday	6	1.5	1.5	1.5
Wednesday	6	2	1	2
Thursday	6	2	2	1.5
Friday	6	2	2	0.5
Saturday	0	2.5	2.5	1
Sunday	0	3	1	2

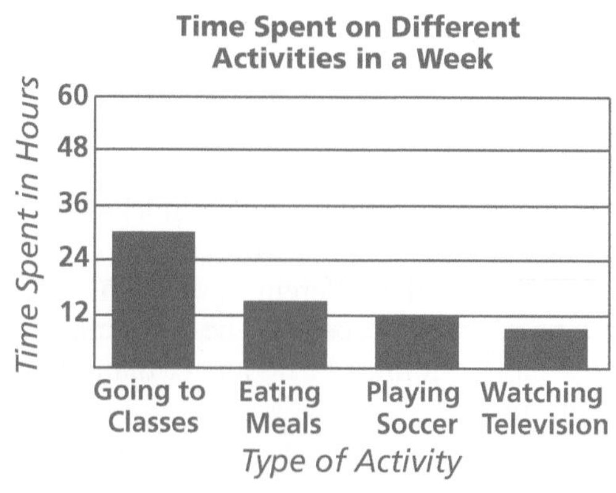

Line Graphs

To see whether a relationship exists between body mass and the number of Calories burned while bicycling, you could create a line graph. A line graph is used to display data that show how one variable (the responding variable) changes in response to another variable (the manipulated variable). You can use a line graph when your manipulated variable is **continuous,** that is, when there are other points between the ones that you tested. In this example, body mass is a continuous variable because there are other body masses between 30 and 40 kilograms (for example, 31 kilograms). Time is another example of a continuous variable.

Line graphs are powerful tools because they allow you to estimate values for conditions that you did not test in the experiment. For example, you can use the line graph to estimate that a 35-kilogram person would burn 68 Calories while bicycling.

To create a line graph, follow these steps.

1. On graph paper, draw a horizontal, or x-, axis and a vertical, or y-, axis.
2. Label the horizontal axis with the name of the manipulated variable. Label the vertical axis with the name of the responding variable. Include units of measurement.
3. Create a scale on each axis by marking off equally spaced numbers that cover the range of the data collected.
4. Plot a point on the graph for each piece of data. In the line graph above, the dotted lines show how to plot the first data point (30 kilograms and 60 Calories). Follow an imaginary vertical line extending up from the horizontal axis at the 30-kilogram mark. Then follow an imaginary horizontal line extending across from the vertical axis at the 60-Calorie mark. Plot the point where the two lines intersect.

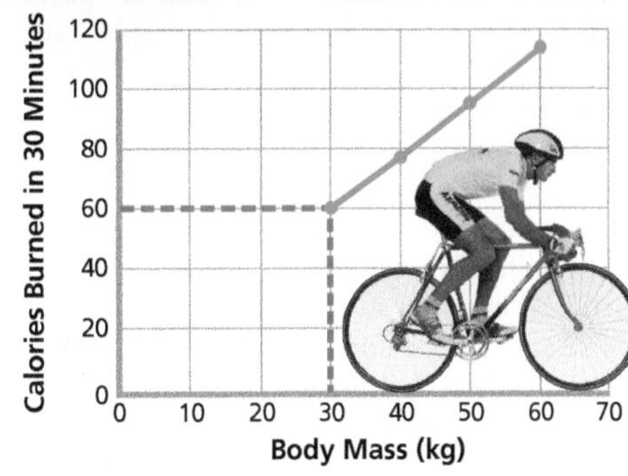

5. Connect the plotted points with a solid line. (In some cases, it may be more appropriate to draw a line that shows the general trend of the plotted points. In those cases, some of the points may fall above or below the line. Also, not all graphs are linear. It may be more appropriate to draw a curve to connect the points.)
6. Add a title that identifies the variables or relationship in the graph.

Activity

Create line graphs to display the data from Experiment 2 and Experiment 3 in the data table.

Activity

You read in the newspaper that a total of 4 centimeters of rain fell in your area in June, 2.5 centimeters fell in July, and 1.5 centimeters fell in August. What type of graph would you use to display these data? Use graph paper to create the graph.

Line Graphs

Focus Ask: **Would a bar graph show the relationship between body mass and the number of Calories burned in 30 minutes?** *(No. Bar graphs can only show data in distinct categories.)* Explain that line graphs are used to show how one variable changes in response to another variable.

Teach Walk students through the steps involved in creating a line graph using the example illustrated on the page. For example, ask: **What is the label on the horizontal axis? On the vertical axis?** *(Body Mass (kg); Calories Burned in 30 Minutes)* **What scale is used on each axis?** *(10 kg on the x-axis and 20 Calories on the y-axis)* **What does the second data point represent?** *(77 Calories burned for a body mass of 40 kg)* **What trend or pattern does the graph show?** *(The number of Calories burned in 30 minutes of cycling increases with body mass.)*

Activity

Students should make a different graph for each experiment. Each graph should have a different x-axis scale that is appropriate for the data. See sample graphs below.

Activity

Students should conclude that a bar graph would be best for displaying the data.

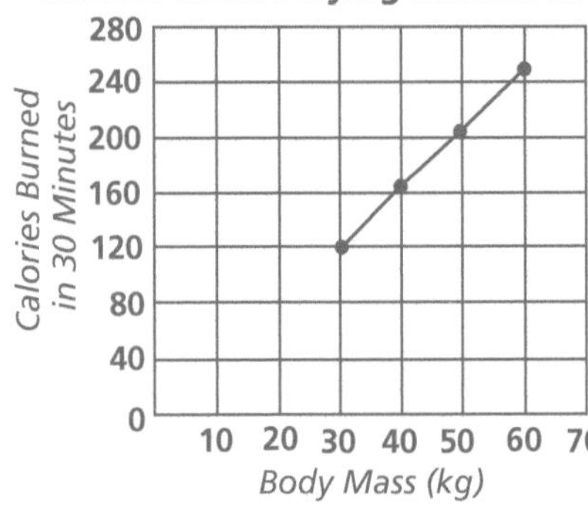

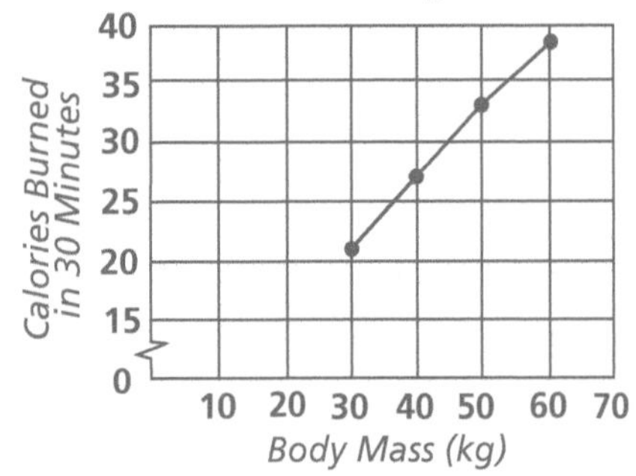

Circle Graphs

Focus Emphasize that a circle graph must include 100 percent of the categories for the topic being graphed. For example, ask: **Could the data in the bar graph titled "Calories Burned by a 30-kilogram Person in Various Activities" (on the previous page) be shown in a circle graph? Why or why not?** *(No. It does not include all the possible ways a 30-kilogram person can burn Calories.)*

Teach Walk students through the steps for making a circle graph. If necessary, help them with the compass and the protractor. Use the protractor to illustrate that a circle has 360 degrees. Make sure students understand the mathematical calculations involved in making a circle graph.

Activity

You might have students work in pairs to complete the activity. Students' circle graphs should look like the graph below.

Ways Students Get to School

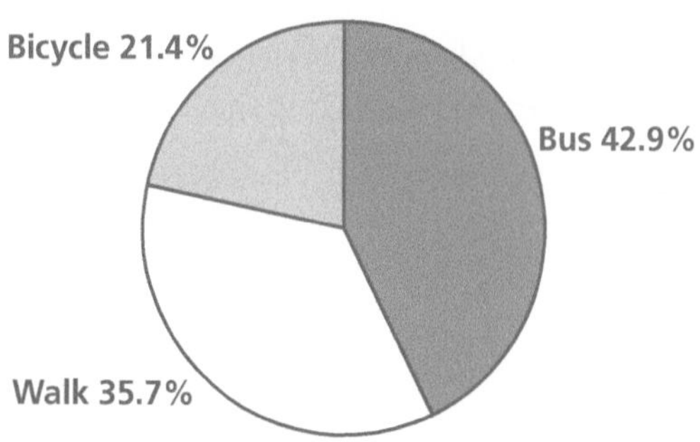

Circle Graphs

Like bar graphs, circle graphs can be used to display data in a number of separate categories. Unlike bar graphs, however, circle graphs can only be used when you have data for *all* the categories that make up a given topic. A circle graph is sometimes called a pie chart. The pie represents the entire topic, while the slices represent the individual categories. The size of a slice indicates what percentage of the whole a particular category makes up.

The data table below shows the results of a survey in which 24 teenagers were asked to identify their favorite sport. The data were then used to create the circle graph at the right.

Favorite Sports

Sport	Students
Soccer	8
Basketball	6
Bicycling	6
Swimming	4

To create a circle graph, follow these steps.

1. Use a compass to draw a circle. Mark the center with a point. Then draw a line from the center point to the top of the circle.
2. Determine the size of each "slice" by setting up a proportion where x equals the number of degrees in a slice. (*Note:* A circle contains 360 degrees.) For example, to find the number of degrees in the "soccer" slice, set up the following proportion:

$$\frac{\text{Students who prefer soccer}}{\text{Total number of students}} = \frac{x}{\text{Total number of degrees in a circle}}$$

$$\frac{8}{24} = \frac{x}{360}$$

Cross-multiply and solve for x.

$$24x = 8 \times 360$$
$$x = 120$$

The "soccer" slice should contain 120 degrees.

Sports That Teens Prefer

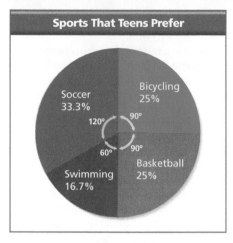

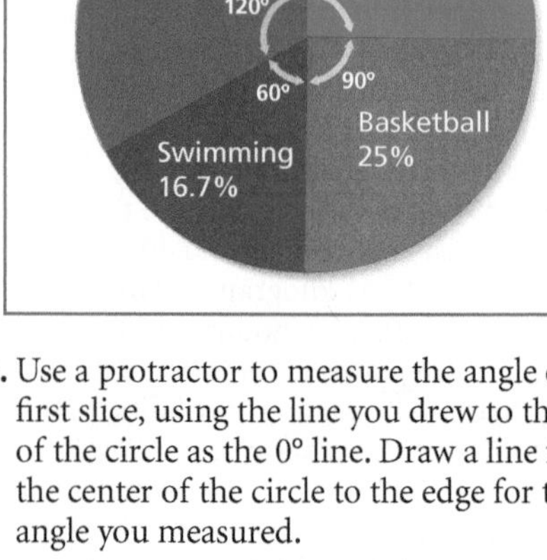

3. Use a protractor to measure the angle of the first slice, using the line you drew to the top of the circle as the 0° line. Draw a line from the center of the circle to the edge for the angle you measured.
4. Continue around the circle by measuring the size of each slice with the protractor. Start measuring from the edge of the previous slice so the wedges do not overlap. When you are done, the entire circle should be filled in.
5. Determine the percentage of the whole circle that each slice represents. To do this, divide the number of degrees in a slice by the total number of degrees in a circle (360), and multiply by 100%. For the "soccer" slice, you can find the percentage as follows:

$$\frac{120}{360} \times 100\% = 33.3\%$$

6. Use a different color for each slice. Label each slice with the category and with the percentage of the whole it represents.
7. Add a title to the circle graph.

Activity

In a class of 28 students, 12 students take the bus to school, 10 students walk, and 6 students ride their bicycles. Create a circle graph to display these data.

Math Review

Scientists use math to organize, analyze, and present data. This appendix will help you review some basic math skills.

Mean, Median, and Mode

The **mean** is the average, or the sum of the data divided by the number of data items. The middle number in a set of ordered data is called the **median.** The **mode** is the number that appears most often in a set of data.

Example

A scientist counted the number of distinct songs sung by seven different male birds and collected the data shown below.

Male Bird Songs

Bird	A	B	C	D	E	F	G
Number of Songs	36	29	40	35	28	36	27

To determine the mean number of songs, add the total number of songs and divide by the number of data items—in this case, the number of male birds.

$$\text{Mean} = \frac{231}{7} = 33 \text{ songs}$$

To find the median number of songs, arrange the data in numerical order and find the number in the middle of the series.

27 28 29 35 36 36 40

The number in the middle is 35, so the median number of songs is 35.

The mode is the value that appears most frequently. In the data, 36 appears twice, while each other item appears only once. Therefore, 36 songs is the mode.

Practice

Find out how many minutes it takes each student in your class to get to school. Then find the mean, median, and mode for the data.

Probability

Probability is the chance that an event will occur. Probability can be expressed as a ratio, a fraction, or a percentage. For example, when you flip a coin, the probability that the coin will land heads up is 1 in 2, or $\frac{1}{2}$, or 50 percent.

The probability that an event will happen can be expressed in the following formula.

$$P(\text{event}) = \frac{\text{Number of times the event can occur}}{\text{Total number of possible events}}$$

Example

A paper bag contains 25 blue marbles, 5 green marbles, 5 orange marbles, and 15 yellow marbles. If you close your eyes and pick a marble from the bag, what is the probability that it will be yellow?

$$P(\text{yellow marbles}) = \frac{\text{15 yellow marbles}}{\text{50 marbles total}}$$

$$P = \frac{15}{50}, \text{ or } \frac{3}{10}, \text{ or } 30\%$$

Practice

Each side of a cube has a letter on it. Two sides have *A*, three sides have *B*, and one side has *C*. If you roll the cube, what is the probability that *A* will land on top?

Math Review

Students can refer to this part of the Skills Handbook whenever they need to review some basic math skills. You can use the activities provided here to teach or reinforce these skills.

Mean, Median, and Mode

Focus Remind students that data from an experiment might consist of hundreds or thousands of numbers. Unless analyzed, the numbers likely will not be helpful.

Teach Work through the process of determining mean, median, and mode using the example in the book. Make sure students realize that these three numbers do not always equal each other. Point out that taken together, these three numbers give more information about the data than just one of the numbers alone.

Practice

Answers will vary based on class data. The mean should equal the total number of minutes divided by the number of students. The median should equal the number in the middle after arranging the data in numerical order. The mode should equal the number of minutes that is given most frequently.

Probability

Focus Show students a coin and ask: **What is the chance that I will get tails when I flip the coin?** *(Some students might know that there is a 1 in 2, or 50 percent, chance of getting tails.)*

Teach Set up a bag of marbles like the one in the example. Allow students to practice determining the probabilities of picking marbles of different colors. Then, encourage them to actually pick marbles and compare their actual results with those results predicted by probability.

Practice

$P(A) = 2 \text{ sides with } \frac{A}{6} \text{ sides total}$

$P = \frac{2}{6}, \text{ or } \frac{1}{3}, \text{ or } 33\%$

Area

Focus Ask: **Who knows what area is?** *(Area is equal to the number of square units needed to cover a certain shape or object.)* On the board, write the formulas for the area of a rectangle and a circle.

Teach Give students various objects of different shapes. Have them measure each object and determine its area based on the measurements. Point out that the units of the answer are squared because they are multiplied together. If students are interested, you might also explain that π is equal to the ratio of the circumference of a circle to its diameter. For circles of all sizes, π is approximately equal to the number 3.14, or $\frac{22}{7}$.

Practice

The area of the circle is equal to $21 \text{ m} \times 21 \text{ m} \times \frac{22}{7}$, or $1{,}386 \text{ m}^2$.

Circumference

Focus Draw a circle on the board. Then trace the outline with your finger and explain that this is the circumference of the circle, or the distance around it.

Teach Show students that the radius is equal to the distance from the center of the circle to any point on it. Point out that the diameter of a circle is equal to two times the radius. Give students paper circles of various sizes, and have them calculate the circumference of each.

Practice

The circumference is equal to $2 \times 28 \text{ m} \times \frac{22}{7}$, or 176 m.

Volume

Focus Fill a beaker with 100 milliliters of water. Ask: **What is the volume of water?** *(100 milliliters)* Explain that volume is the amount of space that something takes up. Then point out that one milliliter is equal to one cubic centimeter (cm^3).

Teach Write on the board the formulas for calculating the volumes of a rectangle and a cylinder. Point out that volume is equal to the area of an object multiplied by its height. Then measure the beaker to show students the relationship between liquid volume (100 milliliters) and the number of cubic units it contains (100 cubic centimeters).

Area

The **area** of a surface is the number of square units that cover it. The front cover of your textbook has an area of about 600 cm^2.

Area of a Rectangle and a Square To find the area of a rectangle, multiply its length times its width. The formula for the area of a rectangle is

$$A = \ell \times w, \text{ or } A = \ell w$$

Since all four sides of a square have the same length, the area of a square is the length of one side multiplied by itself, or squared.

$$A = s \times s, \text{ or } A = s^2$$

Example

A scientist is studying the plants in a field that measures 75 m × 45 m. What is the area of the field?

$$A = \ell \times w$$
$$A = 75 \text{ m} \times 45 \text{ m}$$
$$A = 3{,}375 \text{ m}^2$$

Area of a Circle The formula for the area of a circle is

$$A = \pi \times r \times r, \text{ or } A = \pi r^2$$

The length of the radius is represented by r, and the value of π is approximately $\frac{22}{7}$.

Example

Find the area of a circle with a radius of 14 cm.

$$A = \pi r^2$$
$$A = 14 \times 14 \times \frac{22}{7}$$
$$A = 616 \text{ cm}^2$$

Practice

Find the area of a circle that has a radius of 21 m.

Circumference

The distance around a circle is called the circumference. The formula for finding the circumference of a circle is

$$C = 2 \times \pi \times r, \text{ or } C = 2\pi r$$

Example

The radius of a circle is 35 cm. What is its circumference?

$$C = 2\pi r$$
$$C = 2 \times 35 \times \frac{22}{7}$$
$$C = 220 \text{ cm}$$

Practice

What is the circumference of a circle with a radius of 28 m?

Volume

The volume of an object is the number of cubic units it contains. The volume of a wastebasket, for example, might be about $26{,}000 \text{ cm}^3$.

Volume of a Rectangular Object To find the volume of a rectangular object, multiply the object's length times its width times its height.

$$V = \ell \times w \times h, \text{ or } V = \ell wh$$

Example

Find the volume of a box with length 24 cm, width 12 cm, and height 9 cm.

$$V = \ell wh$$
$$V = 24 \text{ cm} \times 12 \text{ cm} \times 9 \text{ cm}$$
$$V = 2{,}592 \text{ cm}^3$$

Practice

What is the volume of a rectangular object with length 17 cm, width 11 cm, and height 6 cm?

Practice

The volume of the rectangular object is equal to $17 \text{ cm} \times 11 \text{ cm} \times 6 \text{ cm}$, or $1{,}122 \text{ cm}^3$.

Fractions

A **fraction** is a way to express a part of a whole. In the fraction $\frac{4}{7}$, 4 is the numerator and 7 is the denominator.

Adding and Subtracting Fractions To add or subtract two or more fractions that have a common denominator, first add or subtract the numerators. Then write the sum or difference over the common denominator.

To find the sum or difference of fractions with different denominators, first find the least common multiple of the denominators. This is known as the least common denominator. Then convert each fraction to equivalent fractions with the least common denominator. Add or subtract the numerators. Then write the sum or difference over the common denominator.

Example

$$\frac{5}{6} - \frac{3}{4} = \frac{10}{12} - \frac{9}{12} = \frac{10 - 9}{12} = \frac{1}{12}$$

Multiplying Fractions To multiply two fractions, first multiply the two numerators, then multiply the two denominators.

Example

$$\frac{5}{6} \times \frac{2}{3} = \frac{5 \times 2}{6 \times 3} = \frac{10}{18} = \frac{5}{9}$$

Dividing Fractions Dividing by a fraction is the same as multiplying by its reciprocal. Reciprocals are numbers whose numerators and denominators have been switched. To divide one fraction by another, first invert the fraction you are dividing by—in other words, turn it upside down. Then multiply the two fractions.

Example

$$\frac{2}{5} \div \frac{7}{8} = \frac{2}{5} \times \frac{8}{7} = \frac{2 \times 8}{5 \times 7} = \frac{16}{35}$$

Practice

Solve the following: $\frac{3}{7} \div \frac{4}{5}$.

Decimals

Fractions whose denominators are 10, 100, or some other power of 10 are often expressed as decimals. For example, the fraction $\frac{9}{10}$ can be expressed as the decimal 0.9, and the fraction $\frac{7}{100}$ can be written as 0.07.

Adding and Subtracting With Decimals To add or subtract decimals, line up the decimal points before you carry out the operation.

Example

$$\begin{array}{r} 27.4 \\ +\ 6.19 \\ \hline 33.59 \end{array} \qquad \begin{array}{r} 278.635 \\ -\ 191.4 \\ \hline 87.235 \end{array}$$

Multiplying With Decimals When you multiply two numbers with decimals, the number of decimal places in the product is equal to the total number of decimal places in each number being multiplied.

Example

46.2 (one decimal place)
× 2.37 (two decimal places)
109.494 (three decimal places)

Dividing With Decimals To divide a decimal by a whole number, put the decimal point in the quotient above the decimal point in the dividend.

Example

15.5 ÷ 5

$$5\overline{)15.5} = 3.1$$

To divide a decimal by a decimal, you need to rewrite the divisor as a whole number. Do this by multiplying both the divisor and dividend by the same multiple of 10.

Example

1.68 ÷ 4.2 = 16.8 ÷ 42

$$42\overline{)16.8} = 0.4$$

Practice

Multiply 6.21 by 8.5.

Math Skills

Fractions

Focus Draw a circle on the board, and divide it into eight equal sections. Shade in one of the sections, and explain that one out of eight, or one eighth, of the sections is shaded. Also use the circle to show that four eighths is the same as one half.

Teach Write the fraction $\frac{3}{4}$ on the board. Ask: **What is the numerator?** *(Three)* **What is the denominator?** *(Four)* Emphasize that when adding and subtracting fractions, the denominators of the two fractions must be the same. If necessary, review how to find the least common denominator. Remind students that when multiplying and dividing, the denominators do not have to be the same.

Practice

$$\frac{3}{7} \div \frac{4}{5} = \frac{3}{7} \times \frac{5}{4} = \frac{15}{28}$$

Decimals

Focus Write the number *129.835* on the board. Ask: **What number is in the ones position?** *(9)* **The tenths position?** *(8)* **The hundredths position?** *(3)* Make sure students know that 0.8 is equal to $\frac{8}{10}$ and 0.03 is equal to $\frac{3}{100}$.

Teach Use the examples in the book to review addition, subtraction, multiplication, and division with decimals. Make up a worksheet of similar problems to give students additional practice. Also show students how a fraction is converted to a decimal by dividing the numerator by the denominator. For example, $\frac{1}{2}$ is equal to 0.5.

Practice

$6.21 \times 8.5 = 52.785$

Ratio and Proportion

Focus Differentiate a ratio from a fraction. Remind students that a fraction tells how many parts of the whole. In contrast, a ratio compares two different numbers. For example, $\frac{12}{22}$, or $\frac{6}{11}$, of a class are girls. But the ratio of boys to girls in the class is 10 to 12, or $\frac{5}{6}$.

Teach Use the example in the book to explain how to use a proportion to find an unknown quantity. Provide students with additional practice problems, if needed.

Practice

$6 \times 49 = 7x$
$294 = 7x$
$294 \div 7 = x$
$x = 42$

Percentage

Focus On the board, write $50\% = \frac{50}{100}$. Explain that a percentage is a ratio that compares a number to 100.

Teach Point out that when calculating percentages, you are usually using numbers other than 100. In this case, you set up a proportion. Go over the example in the book. Emphasize that the number representing the total goes on the bottom of the ratio, as does the 100%.

Practice

Students should set up the proportion

$$\frac{42 \text{ marbles}}{300 \text{ marbles}} = \frac{x\%}{100\%}$$

$42 \times 100 = 300x$

$4200 = 300x$

$4200 \div 300 = 14\%$

Ratio and Proportion

A **ratio** compares two numbers by division. For example, suppose a scientist counts 800 wolves and 1,200 moose on an island. The ratio of wolves to moose can be written as a fraction, $\frac{800}{1,200}$, which can be reduced to $\frac{2}{3}$. The same ratio can also be expressed as 2 to 3 or 2 : 3.

A **proportion** is a mathematical sentence saying that two ratios are equivalent. For example, a proportion could state that $\frac{800 \text{ wolves}}{1,200 \text{ moose}} = \frac{2 \text{ wolves}}{3 \text{ moose}}$. You can sometimes set up a proportion to determine or estimate an unknown quantity. For example, suppose a scientist counts 25 beetles in an area of 10 square meters. The scientist wants to estimate the number of beetles in 100 square meters.

Example

1. Express the relationship between beetles and area as a ratio: $\frac{25}{10}$, simplified to $\frac{5}{2}$.
2. Set up a proportion, with x representing the number of beetles. The proportion can be stated as $\frac{5}{2} = \frac{x}{100}$.
3. Begin by cross-multiplying. In other words, multiply each fraction's numerator by the other fraction's denominator.

   $$5 \times 100 = 2 \times x, \text{ or } 500 = 2x$$

4. To find the value of x, divide both sides by 2. The result is 250, or 250 beetles in 100 square meters.

Practice

Find the value of x in the following proportion: $\frac{6}{7} = \frac{x}{49}$.

Percentage

A **percentage** is a ratio that compares a number to 100. For example, there are 37 granite rocks in a collection that consists of 100 rocks. The ratio $\frac{37}{100}$ can be written as 37%. Granite rocks make up 37% of the rock collection.

You can calculate percentages of numbers other than 100 by setting up a proportion.

Example

Rain falls on 9 days out of 30 in June. What percentage of the days in June were rainy?

$$\frac{9 \text{ days}}{30 \text{ days}} = \frac{d\%}{100\%}$$

To find the value of d, begin by cross-multiplying, as for any proportion:

$9 \times 100 = 30 \times d \quad d = \frac{900}{30} \quad d = 30$

Practice

There are 300 marbles in a jar, and 42 of those marbles are blue. What percentage of the marbles are blue?

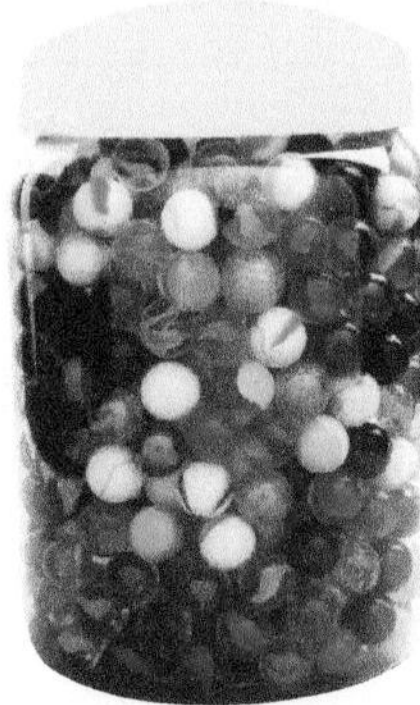

Significant Figures

The **precision** of a measurement depends on the instrument you use to take the measurement. For example, if the smallest unit on the ruler is millimeters, then the most precise measurement you can make will be in millimeters.

The sum or difference of measurements can only be as precise as the least precise measurement being added or subtracted. Round your answer so that it has the same number of digits after the decimal as the least precise measurement. Round up if the last digit is 5 or more, and round down if the last digit is 4 or less.

Example

Subtract a temperature of 5.2°C from the temperature 75.46°C.

$$75.46 - 5.2 = 70.26$$

5.2 has the fewest digits after the decimal, so it is the least precise measurement. Since the last digit of the answer is 6, round up to 3. The most precise difference between the measurements is 70.3°C.

Practice

Add 26.4 m to 8.37 m. Round your answer according to the precision of the measurements.

Significant figures are the number of nonzero digits in a measurement. Zeroes between nonzero digits are also significant. For example, the measurements 12,500 L, 0.125 cm, and 2.05 kg all have three significant figures. When you multiply and divide measurements, the one with the fewest significant figures determines the number of significant figures in your answer.

Example

Multiply 110 g by 5.75 g.

$$110 \times 5.75 = 632.5$$

Because 110 has only two significant figures, round the answer to 630 g.

Scientific Notation

A **factor** is a number that divides into another number with no remainder. In the example, the number 3 is used as a factor four times.

An **exponent** tells how many times a number is used as a factor. For example, $3 \times 3 \times 3 \times 3$ can be written as 3^4. The exponent ^{4} indicates that the number 3 is used as a factor four times. Another way of expressing this is to say that 81 is equal to 3 to the fourth power.

Example

$$3^4 = 3 \times 3 \times 3 \times 3 = 81$$

Scientific notation uses exponents and powers of ten to write very large or very small numbers in shorter form. When you write a number in scientific notation, you write the number as two factors. The first factor is any number between 1 and 10. The second factor is a power of 10, such as 10^3 or 10^6.

Example

The average distance between the planet Mercury and the sun is 58,000,000 km. To write the first factor in scientific notation, insert a decimal point in the original number so that you have a number between 1 and 10. In the case of 58,000,000, the number is 5.8.

To determine the power of 10, count the number of places that the decimal point moved. In this case, it moved 7 places.

$$58{,}000{,}000 \text{ km} = 5.8 \times 10^7 \text{ km}$$

Practice

Express 6,590,000 in scientific notation.

Significant Figures

Focus Measure the length of a paper clip using two different rulers. Use one ruler that is less precise than the other. Compare the two measurements. Ask: **Which measurement is more precise?** *(The ruler with the smallest units will give the more precise measurement.)*

Teach Give students the opportunity to take measurements of an object using tools with different precision. Encourage students to add and subtract their measurements, making sure that they round the answers to reflect the precision of the instruments. Go over the example for significant digits. Check for understanding by asking: **How many significant digits are in the number 324,000?** *(Three)* **In the number 5,901?** *(Four)* **In the number 0.706?** *(Three)* If students need additional practice, create a worksheet with problems in multiplying and dividing numbers with various significant digits.

Practice

26.4 m + 8.37 m = 34.77 m
This answer should be rounded to 34.8 m because the least precise measurement has only one digit after the decimal. This number is rounded up to 8 because the last digit is more than 5.

Scientific Notation

Focus Write a very large number on the board, such as 100 million, using all the zeros. Then, write the number using scientific notation. Ask: **Why do you think scientists prefer to write very large numbers using scientific notation?** *(Possible answers include that it is easier to do calculations, convert units, and make comparisons with other numbers.)*

Teach Go over the examples, and ask: **In the second example, which numbers are the factors?** *(5.8 and 10^7)* **Which number is the exponent?** *(^{7})* Explain that very small numbers have a negative exponent because the decimal point is moved to the right to produce the first factor. For example, 0.00000628 is equal to 6.28×10^{-6}.

Practice

$6{,}590{,}000 = 6.59 \times 10^6$

Reading Comprehension Skills

Students can refer to this part of the Skills Handbook whenever they need to review a reading skill. You can use the activities provided here to teach or reinforce these skills.

All in One Teaching Resources

- Target Reading Skills Handbook

Using Prior Knowledge

Focus Explain to students that using prior knowledge helps connect what they already know to what they are about to read.

Teach Point out that prior knowledge might not be accurate because memories have faded or perspectives have changed. Encourage students to ask questions to resolve discrepancies between their prior knowledge and what they have learned.

Asking Questions

Focus Demonstrate to students how to change a text heading into a question to help them anticipate the concepts, facts, and events they will read about.

Teach Encourage students to use this reading skill for the next section they read. Instruct them to turn the text headings into questions. Also challenge students to write at least four *what, how, why, who, when,* or *where* questions. Then, have students evaluate the skill. Ask: **Did asking questions about the text help you focus on the reading and remember what you read?** *(Answers will vary, but encourage honesty.)* If this reading skill didn't help, challenge them to assess why not.

Previewing Visuals

Focus Explain to students that looking at the visuals before reading will help them activate prior knowledge and predict what they are about to read.

Teach Assign a section for students to preview the visuals. First, instruct them to write a sentence describing what the section will be about. Then, encourage them to write one or two questions for each visual to give purpose to their reading. Also have them list any prior knowledge about the subject.

Reading Comprehension Skills

Each section in your textbook introduces a Target Reading Skill. You will improve your reading comprehension by using the Target Reading Skills described below.

Using Prior Knowledge

Your prior knowledge is what you already know before you begin to read about a topic. Building on what you already know gives you a head start on learning new information. Before you begin a new assignment, think about what you know. You might look at the headings and the visuals to spark your memory. You can list what you know. Then, as you read, consider questions like these.

- How does what you learn relate to what you know?
- How did something you already know help you learn something new?
- Did your original ideas agree with what you have just learned?

Asking Questions

Asking yourself questions is an excellent way to focus on and remember new information in your textbook. For example, you can turn the text headings into questions. Then your questions can guide you to identify the important information as you read. Look at these examples:

Heading: Using Seismographic Data
Question: How are seismographic data used?
Heading: Kinds of Faults
Question: What are the kinds of faults?

You do not have to limit your questions to text headings. Ask questions about anything that you need to clarify or that will help you understand the content. *What* and *how* are probably the most common question words, but you may also ask *why, who, when,* or *where* questions.

Previewing Visuals

Visuals are photographs, graphs, tables, diagrams, and illustrations. Visuals contain important information. Before you read, look at visuals and their labels and captions. This preview will help you prepare for what you will be reading.

Often you will be asked what you want to learn about a visual. For example, after you look at the normal fault diagram below, you might ask: What is the movement along a normal fault? Questions about visuals give you a purpose for reading—to answer your questions.

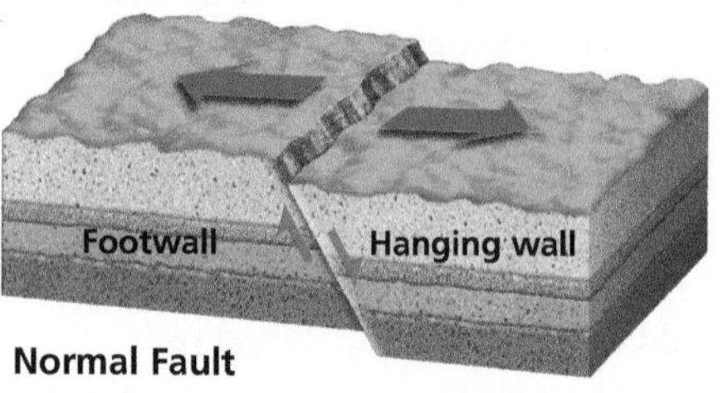

Normal Fault

Outlining

An outline shows the relationship between main ideas and supporting ideas. An outline has a formal structure. You write the main ideas, called topics, next to Roman numerals. The supporting ideas, called subtopics, are written under the main ideas and labeled A, B, C, and so on. An outline looks like this:

Technology and Society

I. Technology through history
II. The impact of technology on society
A.
B.

Outlining

Focus Explain that using an outline format helps organize information by main topic, subtopic, and details.

Teach Choose a section in the book, and demonstrate how to make an outline for it. Make sure students understand the structure of the outline by asking: **Is this a topic or a subtopic? Where does this information go in the outline? Would I write this heading next to a Roman numeral or a capital letter?** *(Answers depend on the section being outlined.)* Also show them how to indent and add details to the outline using numerals and lowercase letters.

Identifying Main Ideas

When you are reading science material, it is important to try to understand the ideas and concepts that are in a passage. Each paragraph has a lot of information and detail. Good readers try to identify the most important—or biggest—idea in every paragraph or section. That's the main idea. The other information in the paragraph supports or further explains the main idea.

Sometimes main ideas are stated directly. In this book, some main ideas are identified for you as key concepts. These are printed in boldface type. However, you must identify other main ideas yourself. In order to do this, you must identify all the ideas within a paragraph or section. Then ask yourself which idea is big enough to include all the other ideas.

Comparing and Contrasting

When you compare and contrast, you examine the similarities and differences between things. You can compare and contrast in a Venn diagram or in a table.

Venn Diagram A Venn diagram consists of two overlapping circles. In the space where the circles overlap, you write the characteristics that the two items have in common. In one of the circles outside the area of overlap, you write the differing features or characteristics of one of the items. In the other circle outside the area of overlap, you write the differing characteristics of the other item.

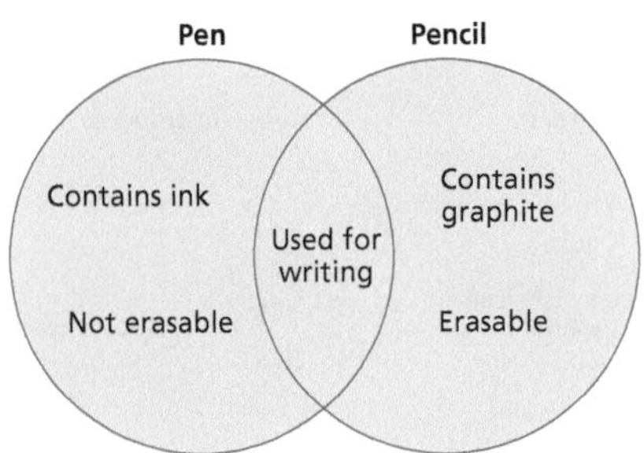

Table In a compare/contrast table, you list the characteristics or features to be compared across the top of the table. Then list the items to be compared in the left column. Complete the table by filling in information about each characteristic or feature.

Blood Vessel	Function	Structure of Wall
Artery	Carries blood away from heart	
Capillary		
Vein		

Identifying Supporting Evidence

A hypothesis is a possible explanation for observations made by scientists or an answer to a scientific question. Scientists must carry out investigations and gather evidence that either supports or disproves the hypothesis.

Identifying the supporting evidence for a hypothesis or theory can help you understand the hypothesis or theory. Evidence consists of facts—information whose accuracy can be confirmed by testing or observation.

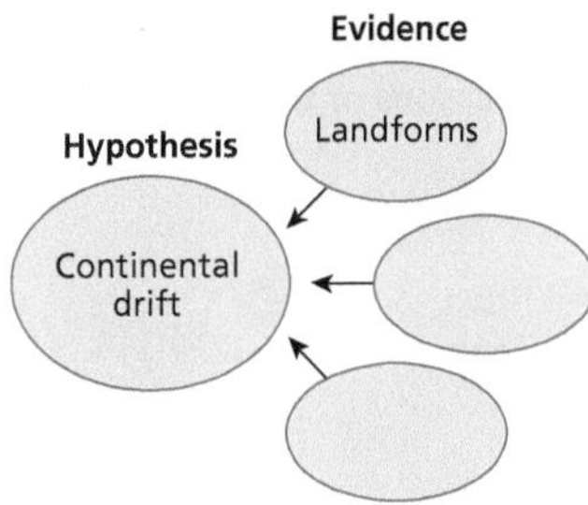

Reading Skills

Identifying Main Ideas

Focus Explain that identifying main ideas and details helps sort the facts from the information into groups. Each group can have a main topic, subtopics, and details.

Teach Tell students that paragraphs are often written so that the main idea is in the first or second sentence, or in the last sentence. Assign students a page in the book. Instruct them to write the main idea for each paragraph on that page. If students have difficulty finding the main idea, suggest that they list all of the ideas given in the paragraph, and then choose the idea that is big enough to include all the others.

Comparing and Contrasting

Focus Explain that comparing and contrasting information shows how concepts, facts, and events are similar or different. The results of the comparison can have importance.

Teach Point out that Venn diagrams work best when comparing two things. To compare more than two things, students should use a compare/contrast table. Have students make a Venn diagram or compare/contrast table using two or more different sports or other activities, such as playing musical instruments. Emphasize that students should select characteristics that highlight the similarities and differences in the activities.

Identifying Supporting Evidence

Focus Explain to students that identifying the supporting evidence will help them to understand the relationship between the facts and the hypothesis.

Teach Remind students that a hypothesis is neither right nor wrong, but it is either supported or not supported by the evidence from testing or observation. If evidence is found that does not support a hypothesis, the hypothesis can be changed to accommodate the new evidence, or it can be dropped.

Sequencing

Focus Tell students that organizing information from beginning to end will help them understand a step-by-step process.

Teach Encourage students to create a flowchart to show the things they did this morning to get ready for school. Remind students that a flowchart should show the correct order in which events occur. *(A typical flowchart might include: got up → took a shower → got dressed → ate breakfast → brushed teeth → gathered books and homework → put on jacket.)*

Then explain that a cycle diagram shows a sequence of events that is continuous. Point out the cycle diagram that shows how the weather changes with the seasons of the year. Ask: **Why is a cycle diagram used instead of a flowchart to show the sequence of the seasons?** *(A cycle diagram shows that the sequence is continuous, not just a series of events.)* Challenge students to make a sequence diagram for a section of the text. Have them explain why they chose either a cycle diagram or a flowchart. Remind them to include at least four steps in the sequence.

Relating Cause and Effect

Focus Explain to students that cause is the reason for what happens. The effect is what happens in response to the cause. Relating cause and effect helps students relate the reason for what happens to what happens as a result.

Teach Emphasize that not all events that occur together have a cause-and-effect relationship. For example, tell students that you went to the grocery store and your car stalled. Ask: **Is there a cause-and-effect relationship in this situation? Explain.** *(No. Going to the grocery store could not cause a car to stall. There must be another cause to make the car stall.)*

Sequencing

A sequence is the order in which a series of events occurs. A flowchart or a cycle diagram can help you visualize a sequence.

Flowchart To make a flowchart, write a brief description of each step or event in a box. Place the boxes in order, with the first event at the top of the chart. Then draw an arrow to connect each step or event to the next.

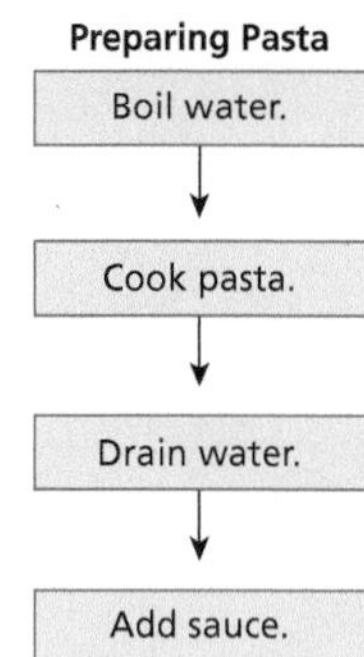

Cycle Diagram A cycle diagram shows a sequence that is continuous, or cyclical. A continuous sequence does not have an end because when the final event is over, the first event begins again. To create a cycle diagram, write the starting event in a box placed at the top of a page in the center. Then, moving in a clockwise direction, write each event in a box in its proper sequence. Draw arrows that connect each event to the one that occurs next.

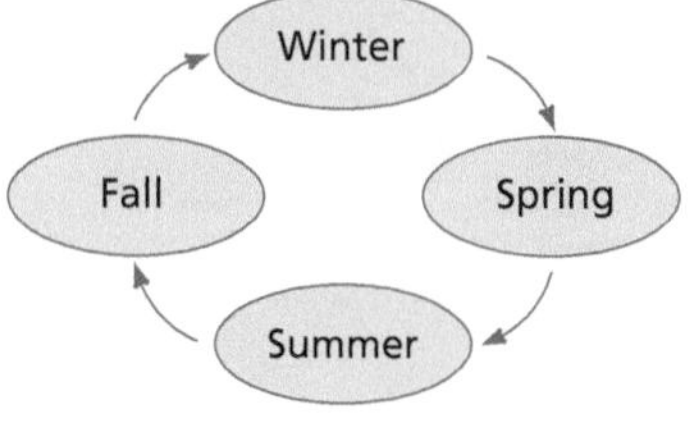

Relating Cause and Effect

Science involves many cause-and-effect relationships. A cause makes something happen. An effect is what happens. When you recognize that one event causes another, you are relating cause and effect.

Words like *cause, because, effect, affect,* and *result* often signal a cause or an effect. Sometimes an effect can have more than one cause, or a cause can produce several effects.

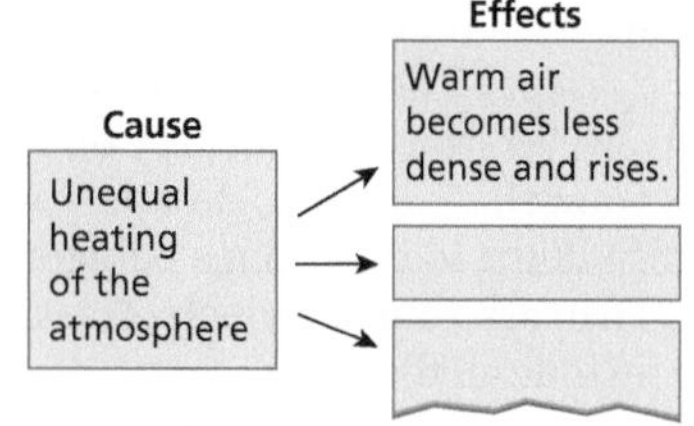

Concept Mapping

Concept maps are useful tools for organizing information on any topic. A concept map begins with a main idea or core concept and shows how the idea can be subdivided into related subconcepts or smaller ideas.

You construct a concept map by placing concepts (usually nouns) in ovals and connecting them with linking words (usually verbs). The biggest concept or idea is placed in an oval at the top of the map. Related concepts are arranged in ovals below the big idea. The linking words connect the ovals.

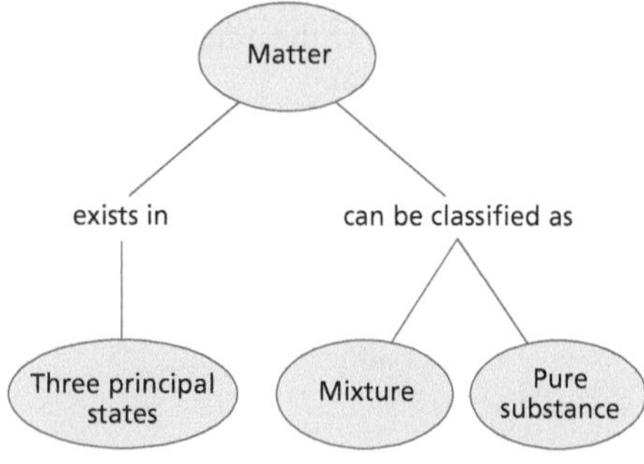

Concept Mapping

Focus Elicit from students how a map shows the relationship of one geographic area to another. Connect this idea to how a concept map shows the relationship between terms and concepts.

Teach Challenge students to make a concept map with at least three levels of concepts to organize information about types of transportation. All students should start with the phrase *Types of transportation* at the top of the concept map. After that point, their concepts may vary. *(For example, some students might place* private transportation *and* public transportation *at the next level, while other students might choose* human-powered *and* gas-powered.*)* Make sure students connect the concepts with linking words.

Building Vocabulary

Knowing the meaning of these prefixes, suffixes, and roots will help you understand the meaning of words you do not recognize.

Word Origins Many science words come to English from other languages, such as Greek and Latin. By learning the meaning of a few common Greek and Latin roots, you can determine the meaning of unfamiliar science words.

Prefixes A prefix is a word part that is added at the beginning of a root or base word to change its meaning.

Suffixes A suffix is a word part that is added at the end of a root word to change the meaning.

Greek and Latin Roots		
Greek Roots	**Meaning**	**Example**
ast-	star	astronaut
geo-	Earth	geology
metron-	measure	kilometer
opt-	eye	optician
photo-	light	photograph
scop-	see	microscope
therm-	heat	thermostat
Latin Roots	**Meaning**	**Example**
aqua-	water	aquarium
aud-	hear	auditorium
duc-, duct-	lead	conduct
flect-	bend	reflect
fract-, frag-	break	fracture
ject-	throw	reject
luc-	light	lucid
spec-	see	inspect

Prefixes and Suffixes		
Prefix	**Meaning**	**Example**
com-, con-	with	communicate, concert
de-	from; down	decay
di-	two	divide
ex-, exo-	out	exhaust
in-, im-	in, into; not	inject, impossible
re-	again; back	reflect, recall
trans-	across	transfer
Suffix	**Meaning**	**Example**
-al	relating to	natural
-er, -or	one who	teacher, doctor
-ist	one who practices	scientist
-ity	state of	equality
-ology	study of	biology
-tion, -sion	state or quality of	reaction, tension

Suffixes

Focus Explain to students that learning the meanings of common suffixes and recognizing them in words are two effective strategies for learning word meanings and building vocabulary.

Teach Remind students that a suffix is added to the end of a word to change its meaning. In addition, students can use suffixes to discover the part of speech of an unfamiliar word. On the chalkboard, draw a four-column chart. Label the columns Noun, Verb, Adjective, and Adverb. Choose a Key Term that has a familiar base word, such as *tension*. Ask: **What are the noun, verb, adjective, and adverb forms of this word?** *(Students should give all possible answers, which may include only two forms of the word.)* Ask: **What endings signal that the word is a noun, adjective, or adverb?** *(Students should list the suffixes.)* Challenge students to learn the meanings of suffixes and to use them to decode new words.

Building Vocabulary

Reading in a content area presents challenges different from those encountered when reading fiction. Science texts often have more new vocabulary and more unfamiliar concepts that place greater emphasis on inferential reasoning. Students who can apply vocabulary strategies will be more successful in reading and understanding a science textbook. Challenge students to use Greek and Latin word origins and the meanings of prefixes and suffixes to learn the Key Terms in each section.

Word Origins

Focus Explain that word origins describe the older, foreign words that many modern English words have come from. Many science words come from Greek and Latin.

Teach Tell students that most dictionaries give the word origin just before the definition. Choose a section that has a Key Term with a Greek or Latin word origin. Encourage students to learn the meaning of the root word. Ask: **How does knowing the word origin help you remember the meaning of the Key Term?** *(Answers will vary, but the meaning of the Latin or Greek root should provide a clue to the definition of the Key Term.)* Ask: **What other words do you know that come from the same word origin?** *(Students may mention other words related to the Key Term.)* Challenge students to use word origins to figure out the meanings of unfamiliar words as they read. Students should confirm their definitions as necessary by checking a dictionary.

Prefixes

Focus Tell students that learning the meaning of common prefixes can help them determine the meaning of words they don't recognize. They will also increase their vocabulary.

Teach Remind students that a prefix is a word part that is added at the beginning of a root word to change its meaning. List some of the familiar prefixes and meanings, such as *de-* and *re-*, on the chalkboard. Ask: **What words do you know that use these same prefixes?** *(Students should list at least two words for each prefix.)* Ask: **How does the prefix affect the meaning of the root word?** *(Students should explain how it changes the meaning.)* Challenge students to learn the meaning of common prefixes and to use the skill to increase their vocabulary.

- Complete student edition
- Video and audio
- Simulations and activities
- Section and chapter activities

Appendix A Laboratory Safety

Laboratory Safety

Laboratory safety is an essential element of a successful science class. Students need to understand exactly what is safe and unsafe behavior and what the rationale is behind each safety rule.

All in One Teaching Resources

- Laboratory Safety Teacher Notes
- Laboratory Safety Rules
- Laboratory Safety Symbols
- Laboratory Safety Contract

General Precautions

- Post safety rules in the classroom, and review them regularly with students before beginning every science activity.
- Familiarize yourself with the safety procedures for each activity before introducing it to your students.
- For open-ended activities like Chapter Projects, have students submit their procedures or design plans in writing and check them for safety considerations.
- Always act as an exemplary role model by displaying safe behavior.
- Know how to use safety equipment, such as fire extinguishers and fire blankets, and always have it accessible.
- Have students practice leaving the classroom quickly and orderly to prepare them for emergencies.
- Explain to students how to use the intercom or other available means of communication to get help during an emergency.
- Never leave students unattended while they are engaged in science activities.
- Provide enough space for students to safely carry out science activities.
- Instruct students to report all accidents and injuries to you immediately.

Safety Symbols

These symbols warn of possible dangers in the laboratory and remind you to work carefully.

Safety Goggles Wear safety goggles to protect your eyes in any activity involving chemicals, flames or heating, or glassware.

Lab Apron Wear a laboratory apron to protect your skin and clothing from damage.

Breakage Handle breakable materials, such as glassware, with care. Do not touch broken glassware.

Heat-Resistant Gloves Use an oven mitt or other hand protection when handling hot materials such as hot plates or hot glassware.

Plastic Gloves Wear disposable plastic gloves when working with harmful chemicals and organisms. Keep your hands away from your face, and dispose of the gloves according to your teacher's instructions.

Heating Use a clamp or tongs to pick up hot glassware. Do not touch hot objects with your bare hands.

Flames Before you work with flames, tie back loose hair and clothing. Follow instructions from your teacher about lighting and extinguishing flames.

No Flames When using flammable materials, make sure there are no flames, sparks, or other exposed heat sources present.

Corrosive Chemical Avoid getting acid or other corrosive chemicals on your skin or clothing or in your eyes. Do not inhale the vapors. Wash your hands after the activity.

Poison Do not let any poisonous chemical come into contact with your skin, and do not inhale its vapors. Wash your hands when you are finished with the activity.

Fumes Work in a ventilated area when harmful vapors may be involved. Avoid inhaling vapors directly. Only test an odor when directed to do so by your teacher, and use a wafting motion to direct the vapor toward your nose.

Sharp Object Scissors, scalpels, knives, needles, pins, and tacks can cut your skin. Always direct a sharp edge or point away from yourself and others.

Animal Safety Treat live or preserved animals or animal parts with care to avoid harming the animals or yourself. Wash your hands when you are finished with the activity.

Plant Safety Handle plants only as directed by your teacher. If you are allergic to certain plants, tell your teacher; do not do an activity involving those plants. Avoid touching harmful plants such as poison ivy. Wash your hands when you are finished with the activity.

Electric Shock To avoid electric shock, never use electrical equipment around water, or when the equipment is wet or your hands are wet. Be sure cords are untangled and cannot trip anyone. Unplug equipment not in use.

Physical Safety When an experiment involves physical activity, avoid injuring yourself or others. Alert your teacher if there is any reason you should not participate.

Disposal Dispose of chemicals and other laboratory materials safely. Follow the instructions from your teacher.

Hand Washing Wash your hands thoroughly when finished with the activity. Use soap and warm water. Rinse well.

General Safety Awareness When this symbol appears, follow the instructions provided. When you are asked to develop your own procedure in a lab, have your teacher approve your plan before you go further.

202 ◆ B

End-of-Experiment Rules

- Always have students use warm water and soap for washing their hands.

Heating and Fire Safety

- No flammable substances should be in use around hot plates, light bulbs, or open flames.
- Test tubes should be heated only in water baths.
- Students should be permitted to strike matches to light candles or burners *only* with strict supervision. When possible, you should light the flames, especially when working with younger students.
- Be sure to have proper ventilation when fumes are produced during a procedure.
- All electrical equipment used in the lab should have GFI (Ground Fault Interrupter) switches.

Science Safety Rules

General Precautions

Follow all instructions. Never perform activities without the approval and supervision of your teacher. Do not engage in horseplay. Never eat or drink in the laboratory. Keep work areas clean and uncluttered.

Dress Code

Wear safety goggles whenever you work with chemicals, glassware, heat sources such as burners, or any substance that might get into your eyes. If you wear contact lenses, notify your teacher.

Wear a lab apron or coat whenever you work with corrosive chemicals or substances that can stain. Wear disposable plastic gloves when working with organisms and harmful chemicals. Tie back long hair. Remove or tie back any article of clothing or jewelry that can hang down and touch chemicals, flames, or equipment. Roll up long sleeves. Never wear open shoes or sandals.

First Aid

Report all accidents, injuries, or fires to your teacher, no matter how minor. Be aware of the location of the first-aid kit, emergency equipment such as the fire extinguisher and fire blanket, and the nearest telephone. Know whom to contact in an emergency.

Heating and Fire Safety

Keep all combustible materials away from flames. When heating a substance in a test tube, make sure that the mouth of the tube is not pointed at you or anyone else. Never heat a liquid in a closed container. Use an oven mitt to pick up a container that has been heated.

Using Chemicals Safely

Never put your face near the mouth of a container that holds chemicals. Never touch, taste, or smell a chemical unless your teacher tells you to.

Use only those chemicals needed in the activity. Keep all containers closed when chemicals are not being used. Pour all chemicals over the sink or a container, not over your work surface. Dispose of excess chemicals as instructed by your teacher.

Be extra careful when working with acids or bases. When mixing an acid and water, always pour the water into the container first and then add the acid to the water. Never pour water into an acid. Wash chemical spills and splashes immediately with plenty of water.

Using Glassware Safely

If glassware is broken or chipped, notify your teacher immediately. Never handle broken or chipped glass with your bare hands.

Never force glass tubing or thermometers into a rubber stopper or rubber tubing. Have your teacher insert the glass tubing or thermometer if required for an activity.

Using Sharp Instruments

Handle sharp instruments with extreme care. Never cut material toward you; cut away from you.

Animal and Plant Safety

Never perform experiments that cause pain, discomfort, or harm to animals. Only handle animals if absolutely necessary. If you know that you are allergic to certain plants, molds, or animals, tell your teacher before doing an activity in which these are used. Wash your hands thoroughly after any activity involving animals, animal parts, plants, plant parts, or soil.

During field work, wear long pants, long sleeves, socks, and closed shoes. Avoid poisonous plants and fungi as well as plants with thorns.

End-of-Experiment Rules

Unplug all electrical equipment. Clean up your work area. Dispose of waste materials as instructed by your teacher. Wash your hands after every experiment.

Handling Organisms Safely

- In an activity where students are directed to taste something, be sure to store the material in clean, *nonscience* containers. Distribute the material to students in *new* plastic or paper dispensables, which should be discarded after the tasting. Tasting or eating should never be done in a lab classroom.
- When growing bacterial cultures, use only disposable petri dishes. After streaking, the dishes should be sealed and not opened again by students. After the lab, students should return the unopened dishes to you.
- Two methods are recommended for the safe disposal of bacterial cultures. *First method:* Autoclave the petri dishes and discard them without opening. *Second method:* If no autoclave is available, carefully open the dishes (never have a student do this), pour full-strength bleach into the dishes, and let them stand for a day. Then pour the bleach from the petri dishes down a drain, and flush the drain with lots of water. Tape the petri dishes back together, and place them in a sealed plastic bag. Wrap the plastic bag with a brown paper bag or newspaper, and tape securely. Throw the sealed package in the trash. Thoroughly disinfect the work area with bleach.
- To grow mold, use a new, sealable plastic bag that is two to three times larger than the material to be placed inside. Seal the bag and tape it shut. After the bag is sealed, students should not open it. To dispose of the bag and mold culture, make a small cut near an edge of the bag, and cook the bag in a microwave oven on a high setting for at least one minute. Discard the bag according to local ordinance, usually in the trash.
- Students should wear disposable nitrile, latex, or food-handling gloves when handling live animals or nonliving specimens.

Using Glassware Safely

- Use plastic containers, graduated cylinders, and beakers whenever possible. If using glass, students should wear safety goggles.
- Use only nonmercury thermometers with anti-roll protectors.

Using Chemicals Safely

- When students use both chemicals and microscopes in one activity, microscopes should be in a separate part of the room from the chemicals so that when students remove their goggles to use the microscopes, their eyes are not at risk.

English and Spanish Glossary

abdomen The hind section of an arthropod's body that contains its reproductive organs and part of its digestive tract. (p. 52)
abdomen Sección posterior del cuerpo de un artrópodo que contiene sus órganos reproductores y parte de su aparato digestivo.

adaptation A characteristic that helps an organism survive or reproduce in its environment. (p. 8)
adaptación Característica que ayuda a un organismo a sobrevivir o a reproducirse en su medio ambiente.

aggression A threatening behavior that one animal uses to gain control over another. (p. 158)
agresión Comportamiento amenazante que usa un animal para ganar el control sobre otro.

amniotic egg An egg with a shell and internal membranes that keep the embryo moist; a major adaptation to life on land characteristic of reptiles, birds, and egg-laying mammals. (p. 101)
huevo amniótico Huevo con cáscara y membranas internas que mantiene al embrión húmedo; adaptación principal a la vida en la tierra característica de los reptiles, las aves y los mamíferos que ponen huevos.

amphibian An ectothermic vertebrate that spends its early life in water and its adult life on land. (p. 94)
anfibio Vertebrado ectotérmico que pasa la primera etapa de su vida en el agua y la madurez en la tierra.

antenna An appendage on the head of an animal that contains sense organs. (p. 49)
antena Apéndice en la cabeza de un animal que contiene órganos sensoriales.

anus The opening at the end of an organism's digestive system through which wastes exit. (p. 30)
ano Abertura al final del sistema digestivo de un organismo a través del cual se eliminan los desechos.

arachnid An arthropod with two body sections, four pairs of legs, and no antennae. (p. 52)
arácnido Artrópodo con dos secciones corporales, cuatro pares de patas y sin antenas.

arthropod An invertebrate that has an external skeleton, a segmented body, and jointed appendages. (p. 47)
artrópodo Invertebrado que tiene esqueleto externo, cuerpo segmentado y apéndices anexos.

asexual reproduction The process by which a single organism produces a new organism identical to itself. (p. 9)
reproducción asexual Proceso por el cual un solo organismo produce un nuevo organismo idéntico a él.

atrium An upper chamber of the heart that receives blood. (p. 96)
aurícula Cámara superior del corazón que recibe la sangre.

behavior All the actions an animal performs. (p. 149)
comportamiento Todas las acciones que realiza un animal.

bilateral symmetry Line symmetry; the quality of being divisible into halves that are mirror images. (p. 13)
simetría bilateral Simetría lineal; la cualidad de ser divisible en mitades que son imágenes reflejas.

biological control A natural predator or disease released into an area to combat a pest insect. (p. 67)
control biológico Depredador o enfermedad natural liberada en un área para combatir una plaga de insectos.

bird An endothermic vertebrate that lays eggs and has feathers and a four-chambered heart. (p. 119)
ave Vertebrado endotérmico que pone huevos y tiene plumas y un corazón de cuatro cámaras.

bivalve A mollusk that has two shells held together by hinges and strong muscles. (p. 43)
bivalvo Molusco que tiene dos conchas unidas por charnelas y fuertes músculos.

carnivore An animal that eats only other animals. (p. 42)
carnívoro Animal que sólo come otros animales.

cartilage A tissue that is more flexible than bone. (p. 89)
cartílago Tejido que es más flexible que un hueso.

cell The basic unit of structure and function in living things. (p. 7)
célula Unidad básica de estructura y función en los seres vivos.

cephalopod An ocean-dwelling mollusk whose foot is adapted as tentacles that surround its mouth. (p. 44)
cefalópodo Molusco que vive en el océano, cuyas extremidades se adaptaron a la forma de tentáculos alrededor de su boca.

chordate The phylum whose members have a notochord, a nerve cord, and slits in their throat area at some point in their lives. (p. 80)
cordado Fílum cuyos miembros poseen un notocordio, un cordón nervioso y aberturas en el área de la garganta en alguna etapa de su vida.

circadian rhythm A behavior cycle that occurs over a period of about one day. (p. 162)
ritmo circadiano Ciclo de comportamiento que ocurre en un período de aproximadamente un día.

closed circulatory system A circulatory system in which blood moves only within a connected network of tubes called blood vessels. (p. 31)
sistema circulatorio cerrado Sistema circulatorio en el cual la sangre se mueve sólo dentro de una red conectada de conductos llamados vasos sanguíneos.

cnidarian An invertebrate animal that uses stinging cells to capture food and defend itself. (p. 19)
cnidario Animal invertebrado que usa células punzantes para capturar alimento y defenderse.

colony A group of many individual animals. (p. 22)
colonia Grupo de muchos animales individuales.

complete metamorphosis A type of metamorphosis characterized by four dramatically different stages. (p. 58)
metamorfosis completa Tipo de metamorfosis caracterizada por cuatro etapas muy diferentes.

conditioning The process of learning to connect a stimulus or a response with a good or bad event. (p. 152)
condicionamiento Proceso de aprendizaje que relaciona un estímulo o una respuesta con un suceso bueno o malo.

consumer An organism that obtains energy by feeding on other organisms. (p. 62)
consumidor Organismo que obtiene la energía alimentándose de otros organismos.

contour feather A large feather that helps give shape to a bird's body. (p. 119)
pluma remera Pluma grande que ayuda a dar forma al cuerpo del ave.

coral reef A diverse environment named for the coral animals that make up its stony structure. (p. 22)
arrecife de coral Medio ambiente diverso nombrado así por los animales coralinos que forman la estructura rocosa.

courtship behavior The behavior that animals of the same species engage in to prepare for mating. (p. 159)
comportamiento de cortejo Comportamiento en el que participan los animales de la misma especie en preparación para el apareamiento.

crop An internal organ of many birds that stores food. (p. 121)
buche Órgano interno de muchas aves, donde se almacena alimento.

crustacean An arthropod that has two or three body sections, five or more pairs of legs, and two pairs of antennae. (p. 50)
crustáceo Artrópodo que tiene dos o tres secciones corporales, cinco o más pares de patas y dos pares de antenas.

D

decomposer An organism that breaks down wastes and dead organisms. (p. 62)
descomponedor Organismo que degrada los desechos y organismos muertos.

diaphragm A large muscle located at the bottom of a mammal's rib cage that functions in breathing. (p. 134)
diafragma Músculo grande ubicado en la parte inferior de la caja torácica de un mamífero que participa en la respiración.

down feather A short, fluffy feather that traps heat and keeps a bird warm. (p. 119)
plumones Plumas cortas y mullidas que atrapan el calor y mantienen al ave abrigada.

E

echinoderm A radially symmetrical invertebrate that lives on the ocean floor and has an internal skeleton. (p. 70)
equinodermo Invertebrado con simetría radial que vive en el suelo oceánico y tienen esqueleto interno.

ecology The study of how organisms interact with their environment. (p. 62)
ecología El estudio de cómo interactúan los organismos con su medio ambiente.

ectotherm An animal whose body does not produce much internal heat. (p. 82)
ectotermo Animal cuyo cuerpo no produce mucho calor interno.

endoskeleton An internal skeleton. (p. 70)
endoesqueleto Esqueleto interno.

endotherm An animal whose body regulates its own temperature by controlling the internal heat it produces. (p. 83)
endotermo Animal cuyo cuerpo regula su propia temperatura controlando el calor interno que produce.

exoskeleton A waxy, waterproof outer shell or outer skeleton that protects the animal and helps prevent evaporation of water. (p. 48)
exoesqueleto Concha externa cerosa e impermeable o esqueleto externo que protege al animal y ayuda a evitar la evaporación del agua.

fertilization The joining of an egg cell and a sperm cell. (p. 9)
fecundación Unión de un espermatozoide y un óvulo.

fish An ectothermic vertebrate that lives in the water and has fins. (p. 87)
pez Vertebrado ectotérmico que vive en el agua y tiene branquias.

food chain A series of events in which one organism eats another and obtains energy. (p. 62)
cadena alimentaria Serie de sucesos en los que un organismo se come a otro y obtiene energía.

fossil The hardened remains or other evidence of a living thing that existed a long time ago. (p. 108)
fósil Restos endurecidos u otro vestigio de un ser vivo que existió hace mucho tiempo.

free-living organism An organism that does not live in or on other organisms. (p. 28)
organismo autónomo Organismo que no vive dentro o sobre otro organismo.

gastropod A mollusk with a single shell or no shell. (p. 42)
gasterópodo Molusco con una única concha o sin concha.

gestation period The length of time between fertilization and birth of a mammal. (p. 136)
período de gestación Tiempo entre la fecundación y el nacimiento del mamífero.

gill An organ that removes oxygen from water. (p. 41)
branquia Órgano que extrae el oxígeno del agua.

gizzard A muscular, thick-walled part of a bird's stomach that squeezes and grinds partially digested food.
molleja Parte muscular, de paredes gruesas del estómago del ave que exprime y muele parcialmente el alimento digerido. (p. 121)

gradual metamorphosis A type of metamorphosis in which an egg hatches into a nymph that resembles an adult, and which has no distinct larval stage. (p. 58)
metamorfosis gradual Tipo de metamorfosis en la que un huevo incubado pasa a la etapa de ninfa con aspecto de adulto, y no tiene una etapa de larva diferenciada.

habitat The specific environment in which an animal lives. (p. 98)
hábitat Medio ambiente específico en el que vive un animal.

herbivore An animal that eats only plants. (p. 42)
herbívoro Animal que sólo come plantas.

hibernation A state of greatly reduced body activity that occurs during the winter. (p. 162)
hibernación Estado de gran disminución de la actividad corporal que ocurre durante el invierno.

host An organism that provides food to a parasite that lives on or inside it. (p. 28)
huésped Organismo que proporciona alimento a un parásito que vive sobre o dentro de él.

imprinting A process in which newly hatched birds or newborn mammals learn to follow the first object they see. (p. 151)
impronta Proceso por el cual las aves o mamíferos recién nacidos aprenden a seguir al primero objeto que ven.

insect An arthropod with three body sections, six legs, one pair of antennae, and usually one or two pairs of wings. (p. 56)
insecto Artrópodo con tres secciones corporales, seis patas, un par de antenas y normalmente uno o dos pares de alas.

insight learning The process of learning how to solve a problem or do something new by applying what is already known. (p. 154)
aprendizaje por discernimiento Proceso de aprender cómo resolver un problema o hacer algo nuevo aplicando lo que ya se sabe.

instinct An inborn behavior pattern that an animal performs correctly the first time. (p. 150)
instinto Patrón innato de conducta que un animal ejecuta correctamente desde la primera vez.

invertebrate An animal that has no backbone. (p. 11)
invertebrado Animal que no posee columna vertebral.

kidney An organ that filters wastes from the blood. (p. 100)
riñón Órgano que filtra los desechos de la sangre.

larva The immature form of an animal that looks very different from the adult. (p. 17)
larva Forma inmadura de un animal que se ve muy diferente al adulto.

learning The process that leads to changes in behavior based on practice or experience. (p. 150)
aprendizaje Proceso que conduce a cambios en el comportamiento basados en la práctica o la experiencia.

lift The difference in pressure between the upper and lower surfaces of a bird's wings that produces an upward force that causes the bird to rise. (p. 129)
fuerza de elevación Diferencia de presión entre la superficie superior e inferior de las alas de un ave, que produce una fuerza ascendente que permite que el ave se eleve.

lung An organ found in air-breathing vertebrates that exchanges oxygen and carbon dioxide with the blood. (p. 96)
pulmón Órgano que se encuentra en los vertebrados que respiran aire, con el que intercambian oxígeno y dióxido de carbono con la sangre.

mammal An endothermic vertebrate with a four-chambered heart and skin covered with fur or hair, that feeds its young with milk from the mother's body. (p. 133)
mamífero Vertebrado endotérmico con un corazón de cuatro cámaras y piel cubierta de pelaje o pelo, que alimenta a sus crías con leche materna.

mammary gland An organ in female mammals that produces milk for the mammal's young. (p. 133)
glándula mamaria Órgano en los mamíferos hembra que produce leche para alimentar a las crías.

marsupial A mammal whose young are born at an early stage of development, and which usually continue to develop in a pouch on their mother's body. (p. 136)
marsupial Mamífero cuyas crías nacen en una etapa muy temprana del desarrollo, y que normalmente continúan el desarrollo en una bolsa del cuerpo de la madre.

medusa A cnidarian body plan characterized by a bowl shape and adapted for a free-swimming life.
medusa Cnidario cuyo cuerpo se caracteriza por tener forma de cuenco, y que está adaptado para nadar libremente en el agua. (p. 19)

metamorphosis A process in which an animal's body undergoes dramatic changes in form during its life cycle. (p. 51)
metamorfosis Proceso por el cual el cuerpo de un animal cambia de forma de manera drástica durante su ciclo de vida.

migration The regular, periodic journey of an animal from one place to another and back again for the purpose of feeding or reproduction. (p. 162)
migración Viaje regular y periódico de un animal de un lugar a otro y de regreso al mismo lugar con el propósito de alimentarse o reproducirse.

mollusk An invertebrate with a soft, unsegmented body; most are protected by a hard outer shell. (p. 41)
molusco Invertebrado con cuerpo blando y sin segmentos; la mayoría están protegidos por una concha exterior dura.

molting The process of shedding an outgrown exoskeleton. (p. 48)
muda Proceso de cambio de un exoesqueleto a otro.

monotreme A mammal that lays eggs. (p. 136)
monotrema Mamífero que pone huevos.

notochord A flexible rod that supports a chordate's back. (p. 80)
notocordio Bastoncillo flexible que sostiene el lomo de los cordados.

nymph A stage of gradual metamorphosis that usually resembles the adult insect. (p. 58)
ninfa Etapa de la metamorfosis gradual en la que normalmente el insecto se parece a un insecto adulto.

omnivore An animal that eats both plants and animals.
omnívoro Animal que come tanto plantas como animales. (p. 43)

open circulatory system A circulatory system in which the heart pumps blood into open spaces in the body and blood is not confined to blood vessels.
sistema circulatorio abierto Sistema circulatorio en el que el corazón bombea la sangre en espacios abiertos del cuerpo, y la sangre no se mantiene en vasos sanguíneos. (p. 41)

organ A structure that is composed of different kinds of tissue. (p. 7)
órgano Estructura compuesta de diferentes tipos de tejidos.

P

paleontologist A scientist who studies extinct organisms, examines fossil structure, and makes comparisons to present-day organisms. (p. 110)
paleontólogo Científico que estudia los organismos extintos, examina las estructuras de los fósiles y los compara con los organismos de la actualidad.

parasite An organism that lives inside or on another organism and takes food from the organism in or on which it lives. (p. 28)
parásito Organismo que vive dentro o sobre otro organismo y que se alimenta de él.

pesticide A chemical designed to kill a pest animal. (p. 67)
pesticida Sustancia química diseñada para matar una plaga animal.

pheromone A chemical released by one animal that affects the behavior of another animal of the same species. (p. 157)
feromona Sustancia química liberada por un animal que afecta el comportamiento de otro animal de la misma especie.

phylum One of about 35 major groups into which biologists classify members of the animal kingdom. (p. 10)
fílum Uno de alrededor de 35 grupos principales en los que los biólogos clasifican los miembros del reino animal.

placenta An organ in pregnant placental mammals that passes materials between the mother and the developing embryo. (p. 137)
placenta Órgano de la hembra embarazada del mamífero placentario que permite el paso de sustancias entre la madre y embrión en desarrollo.

placental mammal A mammal that develops inside its mother's body until its body systems can function independently. (p. 137)
mamífero placentario Mamífero que se desarrolla dentro del cuerpo de la madre hasta que sus sistemas corporales pueden funcionar por sí solos.

pollinator An animal that carries pollen from one plant to another of the same species, enabling plants to reproduce. (p. 66)
polinizador Animal que lleva polen de una planta a otra de la misma especie, permitiendo que las plantas se reproduzcan.

polyp A cnidarian body plan characterized by a vase-like shape and usually adapted for a life attached to an underwater surface. (p. 19)
pólipo Cnidario cuyo cuerpo se caracteriza por tener forma cilíndrica, y que generalmente está adaptado para vivir adherido a una superficie submarina.

producer An organism that can make its own food. (p. 62)
productor Organismo que puede producir su propio alimento.

pupa The third stage of complete metamorphosis, in which an insect changes from a larva to an adult. (p. 58)
pupa Tercera etapa de la metamorfosis completa, en la cual un insecto cambia de larva a adulto.

R

radial symmetry The quality of having many lines of symmetry that all pass through a central point. (p. 13)
simetría radial Cualidad de tener muchos ejes de simetría que pasan por un punto central.

radula A flexible ribbon of tiny teeth in mollusks. (p. 42)
rádula Hilera flexible de minúsculos dientes en los moluscos.

receiver A device that receives radio waves and converts them into a sound or light signal. (p. 167)
receptor Aparato que recibe las ondas de radio y las convierte en señales de sonido o de luz.

reptile An ectothermic vertebrate that lays eggs and has lungs and scaly skin. (p. 100)
reptil Vertebrado ectotérmico que pone huevos, y que tiene pulmones y piel con escamas.

response An organism's reaction to a stimulus. (p. 149)
respuesta Lo que un organismo hace como reacción a un estímulo.

S

satellite An instrument that orbits a celestial body, such as Earth. (p. 168)
satélite Instrumento que orbita un cuerpo celeste, como la Tierra.

scavenger An organism that feeds on dead or decaying material. (p. 28)
carroñero Organismo que se alimenta de materia muerta o en descomposición.

sedimentary rock Rock formed of hardened layers of sediments. (p. 108)
roca sedimentaria Roca formada por las capas endurecidas de sedimentos.

sexual reproduction The process by which a new organism develops from the joining of two sex cells. (p. 9)
reproducción sexual Proceso por el cual se forma un nuevo organismo a partir de la unión de dos células sexuales.

society A group of closely related animals of the same species that divide up the labor and work together in a highly organized way. (p. 161)
sociedad Grupo de animales de la misma especie estrechamente relacionados que se dividen el trabajo y lo realizan juntos de una manera altamente organizada.

stimulus A signal that causes an organism to react in some way. (p. 149)
estímulo Señal que hace que un organismo reaccione de alguna manera.

swim bladder An internal gas-filled organ that helps a bony fish stabilize its body at different water depths. (p. 91)
vejiga natatoria Órgano interno lleno de gas que ayuda a un pez con esqueleto a estabilizar su cuerpo a diferentes profundidades.

tadpole The larval form of a frog or toad. (p. 95)
renacuajo Estado de larva de una rana o un sapo.

territory An area that is occupied and defended by an animal or group of animals. (p. 159)
territorio Área que ocupa y defiende un animal o grupo de animales.

thorax An insect's midsection, to which its wings and legs are attached. (p. 56)
tórax Sección media de un insecto, a la que están unidas las alas y las patas.

tissue A group of similar cells that perform a specific function. (p. 7)
tejido Grupo de células semejantes que realizan una función específica.

transmitter A device that sends out signals in the form of radio waves. (p. 167)
transmisor Aparato que envía señales en forma de ondas de radio.

trial-and-error learning A form of conditioning in which an animal learns to perform a behavior more and more skillfully. (p. 153)
aprendizaje por ensayo y error Forma de condicionamiento en el cual un animal aprende a ejecutar un comportamiento más y más hábilmente.

tube feet Extensions of an echinoderm's water vascular system that stick out from the body and function in movement and obtaining food. (p. 71)
pies ambulacrales Extensiones del sistema vascular de agua de un equinodermo que sobresalen del cuerpo y sirven para la locomoción y la obtención de alimento.

urine A watery fluid produced by the kidneys that contains wastes. (p.100)
orina Fluido acuoso producido por los riñones que contiene desechos.

ventricle A lower chamber of the heart that pumps blood out to the lungs and body. (p. 96)
ventrículo Cámara inferior del corazón que bombea la sangre hacia los pulmones y el cuerpo.

vertebrae The bones that make up the backbone of an animal. (p. 81)
vértebras Huesos que forman la columna vertebral de un animal.

vertebrate An animal that has a backbone. (p. 11)
vertebrado Animal que posee columna vertebral.

water vascular system A system of fluid-filled tubes in an echinoderm's body. (p. 71)
sistema vascular de agua Sistema de vasos llenos de líquidos en el cuerpo de un equinodermo.

Index

Page numbers for key terms are printed in **boldface** type.
Page numbers for illustrations, maps, and charts are printed in *italics*.

Teacher's Edition entries appear in blue type. The page on which a term is defined is indicated in **boldface** type.

Index

Page numbers for key terms are printed in **boldface** type.
Page numbers for illustrations, maps, and charts are printed in *italics.*

Index

Page numbers for key terms are printed in **boldface** type.
Page numbers for illustrations, maps, and charts are printed in *italics*.

Acknowledgments

Acknowledgment for pages 178–179: Excerpt from *Dragons and Dynasties: An Introduction to Chinese Mythology* by Yuan Ke. Selected and translated by Kim Echlin and Nie Zhixiong and Penguin Books, 1993. First published in the People's Foreign Languages Press, 1991, 1992, 1993. Reprinted by permission of Penguin Books, Ltd., London.

Note: Every effort has been made to contact the copyright owner.

Staff Credits

Diane Alimena, Scott Andrews, Jennifer Angel, Michele Angelucci, Laura Baselice, Carolyn Belanger, Barbara A. Bertell, Suzanne Biron, Peggy Bliss, Stephanie Bradley, James Brady, Anne M. Bray, Sarah M. Carroll, Kerry Cashman, Jonathan Cheney, Joshua D. Clapper, Lisa J. Clark, Bob Craton, Patricia Cully, Patricia M. Dambry, Kathy Dempsey, Leanne Esterly, Emily Ellen, Thomas Ferreira, Jonathan Fisher, Patricia Fromkin, Paul Gagnon, Kathy Gavilanes, Holly Gordon, Robert Graham, Ellen Granter, Diane Grossman, Barbara Hollingdale, Linda Johnson, Anne Jones, John Judge, Kevin Keane, Kelly Kelliher, Toby Klang, Sue Langan, Russ Lappa, Carolyn Lock, Rebecca Loveys, Constance J. McCarty, Carolyn B. McGuire, Ranida Touranont McKneally, Anne McLaughlin, Eve Melnechuk, Natania Mlawer, Janet Morris, Karyl Murray, Francine Neumann, Baljit Nijjar, Marie Opera, Jill Ort, Kim Ortell, Joan Paley, Dorothy Preston, Maureen Raymond, Laura Ross, Rashid Ross, Siri Schwartzman, Melissa Shustyk, Laurel Smith, Emily Soltanoff, Jennifer A. Teece, Elizabeth Torjussen, Amanda M. Watters, Merce Wilczek, Amy Winchester, Char Lyn Yeakley. **Additional Credits** Tara Alamilla, Louise Gachet, Allen Gold, Andrea Golden, Terence Hegarty, Etta Jacobs, Meg Montgomery, Stephanie Rogers, Kim Schmidt, Adam Teller, Joan Tobin.

Illustration

Sally Bensusen: 56, 58–59; **Patrice Rossi Calkin:** 29, 145, 152; **Kerry Cashman:** 37, 184, 185; **Walter Cutler:** 95; **John Edwards and Associates:** 17, 20t, 21, 27, 36, 42, 43, 49, 76, 81, 101, 119, 120t, 121, 126, 129, 144, 167; **Foerster Interactive Arts:** 19; **Andrea Golden:** 33, 51; **Biruta Hansen:** 156–157; **Fran Milner:** 50, 91; **Karen Minot:** 41; **Paul Mirocha:** 173; **Morgan Cain & Associates:** 93, 141, 199; **Matthew Pippin:** 110; **Ortelius Design Inc.:** 163; **Walter Stuart:** 16, 46, 71, 106, 161; **J/B Woolsey Associates (Mark Desman):** 10, 80, 84–85, 172; **J/B Woolsey Associates:** 31, 150; **XNR Productions:** 166; **All charts and graphs by Matt Mayerchak**

Photography

Photo Research Sue McDermott

Cover Image top, Art Wolfe/Getty Images; bottom, Dale Wilson/Masterfile.

Page vi t, Douglas Faulkner/Corbis; **vi b,** Kim Taylor & Jane Burton/Dorling Kindersley; **vii,** Richard Haynes; **viii,** Richard Haynes; **x,** Claudio Vazquez; **1b,** Rob Walls/Alamy Images; **1t,** John Giustina/Getty Images, Inc.; **2 both,** Mary Ann McDonald/Corbis; **3,** Daniel Lyons/Bruce Coleman.

Chapter 1 Pages 4–5, Deep Sea Photos; **5 inset,** Richard Haynes; **6t,** Richard Haynes; **6bl,** Heather Angel/Natural Visions; **6br,** Heather Angel/Natural Visions; **7,** Neil Fletcher/Oxford University Museum; **8t,** Frank Greenaway/Dorling Kindersley; **8b,** Frank Oberle/Getty Images, Inc.; **9,** Michael Quinton/Minden Pictures; **11,** Wolfgang Bayer/Bruce Coleman, Inc.; **12,** Tom and Pat Leeson; **13tl,** Norbert Wu/Minden Pictures; **13tm,** Andrew J. Martinez/Photo Researchers, Inc.; **13tr,** James Watt/Visuals Unlimited; **13b,** Stuart Westmorland/Corbis; **14,** Tom Brakefield/Corbis; **15,** Michael DeFreitas/Bruce Coleman, Inc.; **19l,** Dale Sanders/Masterfile Corporation; **19r,** G. S. Grant/Photo Researchers, Inc.; **20tl,** Jeff Rotman/www.jeffrotman.com; **20b all,** Dorling Kindersley; **22,** Tim McKenna/Corbis; **22 inset,** Linda Pitkin/Masterfile Corporation; **23,** David B. Fleetham/Tom Stack & Associates, Inc.; **24t,** Richard Cummins/Corbis; **24–25,** Jeff Hunter/Getty Images, Inc.; **26t,** Richard Haynes; **26b,** Dr. Alan L. Yen; **28,** Hans Strand ; **28 inset,** David M. Dennis/Tom Stack & Associates, Inc.; **30,** Sinclair Stammers/Photo Researchers, Inc.; **32,** David Young-Wolff/PhotoEdit; **34t,** Dorling Kindersley; **34b,** Andrew J. Martinez/Photo Researchers, Inc.

Chapter 2 Pages 38–39, Barrett and MacKay; **39 inset,** Richard Haynes; **40b,** Richard Nowitz; **40t,** Corel Corp.; **42r,** Brandon Cole/Visuals Unlimited; **42l,** Digital Vision/Getty Images, Inc.; **44l,** Douglas Faulkner/Photo Researchers, Inc.; **44b,** Norbert Wu/Minden Pictures; **44t,** Ken Lucas/Visuals Unlimited; **45 both,** Dave Fleetham/Tom Stack & Associates; **46,** William Leonard/DRK Photo; **47b,** R.J. Erwin/Photo Researchers, Inc.; **47t,** Richard Haynes; **48b,** Robert A. Lubeck/Animals Animals; **48t,** John Gerlach/Tom Stack & Associates, Inc.; **51,** Dr. P. Wilson/FLAP/Bruce Coleman, Inc.; **52b,** Meckes/Ottawa/Eye of Science/Photo Researchers, Inc.; **52t,** Geoff Dann/Dorling Kindersley; **53b,** Robert Calentine/Visuals Unlimited; **53t,** Tim Flach/Getty Images, Inc.; **54l,** Marty Cordano/DRK Photo; **54r,** Simon D. Pollard/Photo Researchers, Inc.; **55b,** Valerie Hodgson/Visuals Unlimited; **55t,** Robert Calentine/Visuals Unlimited; **57l,** Dorling Kindersley; **57m,** Gregory G. Dimijian/Photo Researchers, Inc.; **57r,** Andrew Syred/SPL/Photo Researchers, Inc.; **60,** Robert A. Lubeck/Animals Animals; **61,** Richard Haynes; **62t,** Richard Haynes; **62–63b,** James P. Rowan/DRK Photo; **63l,** Bob Jensen/Bruce Coleman, Inc.; **63m,** Michael Edergerr/DRK Photo; **63r,** J. Fennell/Bruce Coleman, Inc.; **64l,** Bettmann/Corbis; **64r,** Aberdeen University Library, Scotland/Bridgeman Art Library; **65l,** Robert Frerck/Odyssey Productions; **65m,** Sergio Piumatti; **65r,** Darwin Dale/Photo Researchers, Inc.; **66b,** Geoff du Feu/Getty Images, Inc.; **66t,** John Trager/Visuals Unlimited; **67,** Anthony Bannister; Gallo Images/Corbis; **68–69,** Norm Thomas/Photo Researchers, Inc.; **69t,** Frank Whitney/Getty Images, Inc.; **70,** Richard Haynes; **72l,** Neil G. McDaniel/Photo Researchers, Inc.; **72r,** Brian Parker/Tom Stack & Associates, Inc.; **72–73t,** Kerrick James; **73l,** Brandon D. Cole/Corbis; **73r,** Ed Bravendam/Minden Pictures.

Chapter 3 Pages 78–79, Norbert Wu/Minden Pictures; **79 inset,** Richard Haynes; **80,** Russ Lappa; **81,** Tom Flach/Getty Images, Inc.; **82,** Dave King/Dorling Kindersley; **83l,** Michael Fogden/DRK Photo; **83r,** Frans Lanting/Minden Pictures; **86t,** Gerard Lacz/Animals Animals/Earth Scenes; **86b,** Brian Parker/Tom Stack & Associates; **87,** NHPA/Lutra; **88tl,** John D. Cunningham/Visuals Unlimited; **88tr,** Michael Patrick O'Neil/Photo Researchers, Inc.; **88b,** Animals Animals/Earth Scenes; **89t,** Bruce Coleman, Inc.; **89b,** Animals Animals/Earth Scenes; **89b inset,** Herve Berthoule Jacana/Photo Researchers, Inc.; **90t,** Frank Burek/Animals Animals/Earth Scenes; **90b,** Amos Nachoum/Corbis; **92tr,** Norbert Wu; **92m,** Stuart Westmorland/Getty Images, Inc.; **92bl,** Norbert Wu; **92br,** DRK Photo; **94,** Michael Fogden/Photo Researchers, Inc.; **96,** Gerry Ellis/Minden Pictures; **97l,** Visuals Unlimited; **97r,** Animals Animals/Earth Scenes; **98,** Michael Fogden/OSF/Animals Animals/Earth Scenes; **99t,** Richard Haynes; **99b,** Joe McDonald/Tom Stack & Associates, Inc.; **101,** Jay Ireland & Georgienne Bradley/Bradleyireland.com; **102,** Dorling Kindersley; **103t,** Kim Taylor & Jane Burton/Dorling Kindersley; **103b,** Art Wolfe/Getty Images, Inc.; **104l,** M.C. Chamberlain/DRK Photo; **104r,** Gerald & Buff Corsi/Tom Stack & Associates; **105,** T.A. Wiewandt/DRK Photo; **107t,** Richard Haynes; **107b,** Tom Bean/DRK Photo; **108t,** Ernst Mayr Library of the Museum of Comparative Zoology, Harvard University, ©President and Fellows of Harvard; **108m,** Natural History Museum, London; **108b,** Typ 605.77.700 F, Department of Printing and Graphic Arts, Houghton Library, Harvard College Library; **109t,** Louis Psihoyos/Matrix; **109b,** Andy Crawford/Dorling Kindersley; **112,** Stuart Westmorland/Getty Images, Inc.

Chapter 4 Pages 116–117, Barrett and MacKay; **117 inset,** Richard Haynes; **118t,** Richard Haynes; **118b,** John Downes/Dorling Kindersley; **119,** Russell & Martha Hansen; **121,** Geoff Higgings/PhotoLibrary.com; **122t,** Stephen J. Krasemann/DRK Photo; **122t inset,** Jerome Wexler/Photo Researchers, Inc.; **122b,** Nancy Sheehan/PhotoEdit; **123t,** Kim Taylor/Dorling Kindersley; **123b,** Richard Wagner; **124t,** NHPA/Manfred Danegger; **124bl,** Dave Watts/Tom Stack & Associates, Inc.; **124br,** Gary Griffen/Animals Animals/Earth Scenes; **125l,** D. Allen/Animals Animals/Earth Scenes; **125m,** Stephen J. Krasemann/DRK Photo; **125r,** Wayne Lankinen/DRK Photo; **127,** Richard Haynes; **128t,** Richard Haynes; **128b,** Darrell Gulin/DRK Photo; **129,** Thomas Mangelsen/Minden Pictures; **130,** Frans Lanting/Minden Pictures; **131l,** Michio Hoshino/Minden Pictures; **131r,** Arthur Morris/Visuals Unlimited; **132t,** Richard Haynes; **132b,** Eric Valli/Minden Pictures; **133t,** Hilary Pooley/Animals Animals/Earth Scenes; **133t inset,** Phillip Dowell/Dorling Kindersley; **133b,** Philip Dowell/Dorling Kindersley; **133b inset,** Dave King/Dorling Kindersley; **134l,** Daryl Balfour/Getty Images, Inc.; **134r,** Art Wolfe; **135 both,** Frans Lanting/Minden Pictures; **136t,** Tom McHugh/Photo Researchers; **136b,** Dave Watts/Tom Stack & Associates, Inc.; **137,** Joe McDonald/Visuals Unlimited; **138tr,** Roger Aitkenhead/Animals Animals/Earth Scenes; **138br,** Johnny Johnson/DRK Photo; **138tl,** Stephen J. Krasemann/DRK Photo; **138ml,** Chuck Davis/Getty Images, Inc.; **138bl,** Dave Welling; **139tl,** Dwight Kuhn; **139ml,** Charlie Heidecker/Visuals Unlimited; **139bl,** M.P. Kahl/DRK Photo; **139tr,** Art Wolfe/Getty Images, Inc.; **139br,** Renee Lynn/Getty Images, Inc.; **140,** Johnny Johnson/DRK Photo; **142l,** Dave Watts/Tom Stack & Associates, Inc.; **142r,** Joe McDonald/Visuals Unlimited.

Chapter 5 Pages 146–147, M. Philip Kahl Jr./Photo Researchers, Inc.; **147 inset,** Getty Images, Inc.; **148b,** Michael Fogden/DRK Photo; **148t,** Jerome Wexler/Photo Researchers, Inc.; **149 both,** Heather Angel/Natural Visions; **150,** Lawrence Stepanowicz/Alamy; **151,** Nina Leen/Time Life Pictures/Getty Images, Inc.; **153,** Steve Solum/Bruce Coleman Inc.; **154,** Bernd Heinrich; **156,** Richard Haynes; **157,** Natural Visions; **158b,** John Cancalosi/DRK Photo; **158t,** Art Wolfe; **159,** OSF/David Boag/Animals Animals; **160,** David E. Myers/Getty Images, Inc.; **162,** Kim Taylor/Bruce Coleman, Inc.; **163,** M.A. Chappell/Animals Animals; **164,** Doug Wechsler; **165,** Richard Haynes; **166–167b,** Douglas Faulkner/Corbis; **167t,** Arthur Morris/Visuals Unlimited; **168,** Natalie Fobes/Corbis; **169,** Michio Hoshino/Minden Pictures; **170l,** Steve Solum/Bruce Coleman Inc.; **170r,** Natural Visions; **172,** David Hosking/Getty Images, Inc. **174b,** Roy Parkes/Eye Ubiquitous/Corbis; **174t,** Christie's Images/Corbis; **175b,** Cary Wolinsky/Stock Boston; **175l,** Harry Rogers/Photo Researchers, Inc.; **175r,** Cary Wolinsky/Stock Boston; **175t,** E.R. Degginger/Animals Animals/Earth Scenes; **177,** Wolfgang Kaehler/Corbis; **178–179b,** Christie's Images, Inc./Christie's Images; **179t,** People's Republic of China Giraudon/Bridgeman Art Library; **180,** Xinhua/Liaison/Getty Images, Inc.; **181b,** Duomo/Corbis; **181t,** Keren Su/Corbis; **182,** Tony Freeman/PhotoEdit; **183t,** Russ Lappa; **183m,** Richard Haynes; **183b,** Russ Lappa; **184, 186,** Richard Haynes; **188,** Tanton Yachts; **189,** Richard Haynes; **191t,** Dorling Kinderlsey; **191b,** Richard Haynes; **193,** Image Stop/Phototake; **196, 203,** Richard Haynes.

Teacher's Edition

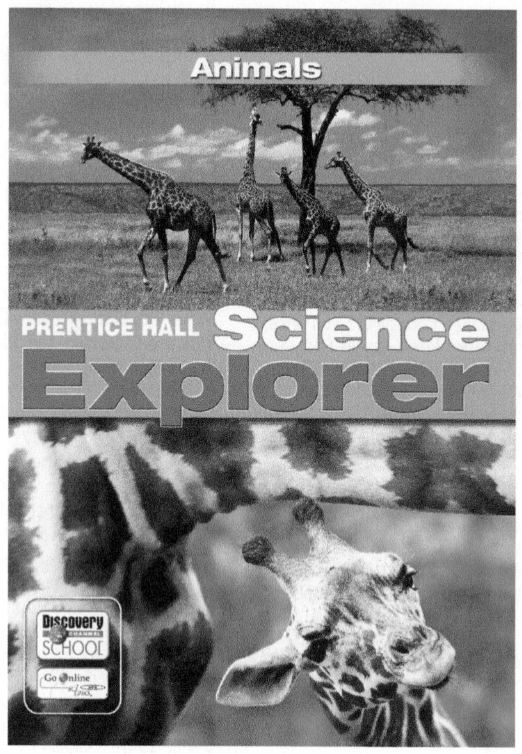

PEARSON

Boston, Massachusetts • Glenview, Illinois • Shoreview, Minnesota • Upper Saddle River, New Jersey

13-digit ISBN 978-0-13-365119-5
10-digit ISBN 0-13-365119-3
2 3 4 5 6 7 8 9 10 V092 12 11

Pacing Options

PRENTICE HALL TeacherEXPRESS™ Plan • Teach • Assess

Lab zone™

SCIENCE EXPLORER offers many aids to help you plan your instruction time, whether regular class periods or block scheduling. Section-by-section lesson plans for each chapter include suggested times for Student Edition activities. TeacherExpress™ and the Lab zone™ Easy Planner CD-ROM will help you manage your time electronically.

Pacing Chart

	PERIODS	BLOCKS
Careers in Science: An Alligator's Sensitive Side	1	1/2
Chapter 1 Sponges, Cnidarians, and Worms		
Chapter 1 Project *Design and Build an Animal Habitat*	Ongoing	Ongoing
1 What Is an Animal?	2–3	1–1 1/2
2 Integrating Mathematics: Animal Symmetry	2–3	1–1 1/2
3 Sponges and Cnidarians	2–3	1–1 1/2
4 Worms	2–3	1–1 1/2
Chapter 1 Review and Assessment	1	1/2
Chapter 2 Mollusks, Arthropods, and Echinoderms		
Chapter 2 Project *Going Through Changes*	Ongoing	Ongoing
1 Mollusks	2–3	1–1 1/2
2 Arthropods	3–4	1 1/2–2
3 Insects	2–3	1–1 1/2
4 Integrating Environmental Science: Insect Ecology	2–3	1–1 1/2
5 Echinoderms	1–2	1/2–1
Chapter 2 Review and Assessment	1	1/2
Chapter 3 Fishes, Amphibians, and Reptiles		
Chapter 3 Project *Animal Adaptations*	Ongoing	Ongoing
1 What Is a Vertebrate?	1–2	1/2–1
2 Fishes	2–3	1–1 1/2
3 Amphibians	1–2	1/2–1
4 Reptiles	3–4	1 1/2–2
5 Integrating Earth Science: Vertebrate History in Rocks	1–2	1/2–1
Chapter 3 Review and Assessment	1	1/2

	PERIODS	BLOCKS
Chapter 4 Birds and Mammals		
Chapter 4 Project *Bird Watch*	Ongoing	Ongoing
1 Birds	2–3	1–1 1/2
2 Integrating Physics: The Physics of Bird Flight	1–2	1/2–1
3 Mammals	4–5	2–2 1/2
Chapter 4 Review and Assessment	1	1/2
Chapter 5 Animal Behavior		
Chapter 5 Project *Learning New Tricks*	Ongoing	Ongoing
1 What Is Behavior?	3–4	1 1/2–2
2 Patterns of Behavior	2–3	1–1 1/2
3 Tech & Design: Tracking Migrations	1–2	1/2–1
Chapter 5 Review and Assessment	1	1/2
Interdisciplinary Exploration: The Secret of Silk	2–3	1–1 1/2

Research-Based and Proven to Work

As the originator of the small book concept in middle school science, and as the nation's number one science publisher, Prentice Hall takes pride in the fact that we've always listened closely to teachers. In doing so, we've developed programs that effectively meet the needs of your classroom.

As we continue to listen, we realize that raising the achievement level of all students is the number one challenge facing teachers today. To assist you in meeting this latest challenge, Prentice Hall has combined the very best author team with solid research to create a program that meets your high standards and will ensure that no child is left behind.

With Prentice Hall, you can be confident that your students will not only be motivated, inspired, and excited to learn science, but that they will also achieve the success needed in today's environment of the No Child Left Behind (NCLB) legislation and testing reform.

On the following pages, you will read about the key elements found throughout *Science Explorer* that truly set this program apart and ensure success for you and your students.

As we continue to listen, we realize that raising the achievement level of all students is the number one challenge facing teachers today.

A Science Program Backed by Research

In developing Prentice Hall *Science Explorer*, we used research studies as a central, guiding element. Research on *Science Explorer* indicated key elements of a textbook program that ensure students' success: support for reading and mathematics in science, consistent opportunities for inquiry, and an ongoing assessment strand. This research was conducted in phases and continues today.

1. Exploratory: Needs Assessment

Along with periodic surveys concerning state and national standards as well as curriculum issues and challenges, we conducted specific product development research, which included discussions with teachers and advisory panels, focus groups, and quantitative surveys. We explored the specific needs of teachers, students, and other educators regarding each book we developed in Prentice Hall *Science Explorer*.

2. Formative: Prototype Development and Field-Testing

During this phase of research, we worked to develop prototype materials. Then we tested the materials by field-testing with students and teachers and by performing qualitative and quantitative surveys. In our early prototype testing, we received feedback about our lesson structure. Results were channeled back into the program development for improvement.

3. Summative: Validation Research

Finally, we conducted and continue to conduct long-term research based on scientific, experimental designs under actual classroom conditions. This research identifies what works and what can be improved in the next revision of Prentice Hall *Science Explorer*. We also continue to monitor the program in the market. We talk to our users about what works, and then we begin the cycle over again. The next section contains highlights of this research.

A Science Program With Proven Results

In a year-long study in 2000–2001, students in six states using Prentice Hall *Science Explorer* outscored students using other science programs on a nationally normed standardized test.

The study investigated the effects of science textbook programs at the eighth-grade level. Twelve eighth-grade science classes with a total of 223 students participated in the study. The selected classes were of similar student ability levels.

Each class was tested at the beginning of the school year using the TerraNova CTBS Basic Battery Plus, and then retested at the end of the school year. The final results, shown in the graph, show a significant improvement in test scores from the pre-test to the post-test evaluation.

- All tests were scored by CTB/McGraw-Hill, the publisher of the TerraNova exam. Statistical analyses and conclusions were performed by an independent firm, Pulse Analytics, Inc.

In Japan, Lesson Study Research has been employed for a number of years as a tool for teachers to improve their curriculum. In April 2003, Prentice Hall adapted this methodology to focus on a lesson from this edition. Our goal was to test the effectiveness of lesson pedagogy and improve it while in the program development stage. In all three classrooms tested, student learning increased an average of 10 points from the pre- to the post-assessment.

- Detailed results of these studies can be obtained at **www.PHSchool.com/research.**

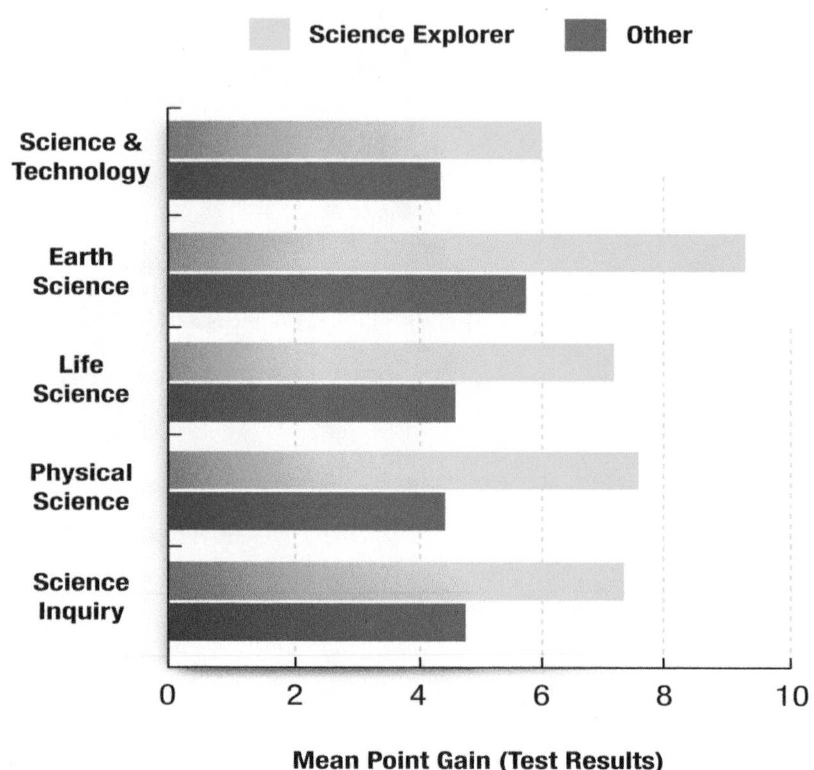

Foundational Research: Inquiry in the Science Classroom

"How do I know if my students are inquiring?" "If students are busy doing lots of hands-on activities, are they using inquiry?" "What is inquiry, anyway?" If you're confused, you are not alone. Inquiry is the heart and soul of science education, with most of us in continuous pursuit of achieving it with our students!

Michael J. Padilla, Ph.D.
Program Author of *Science Explorer*
Associate Dean and Director
Eugene T. Moore
School of Education
Clemson University
Clemson, South Carolina

"Because inquiry is an intellectual pursuit, it cannot merely be characterized by keeping students busy and active."

Defining Science Inquiry

What is it? Simply put, inquiry is the intellectual side of science. It is thinking like a scientist—being inquisitive, asking why, and searching for answers. The National Science Education Content Standards define inquiry as the process in which students begin with a question, design an investigation, gather evidence, formulate an answer to the original question, and communicate the investigative process and results. Since it is often difficult to accomplish all this in one class period, the standards also acknowledge that at times students need to practice only one or two inquiry components.

Understanding Inquiry

The National Research Council in Inquiry and the National Science Education Standards (2000) identified several "essential features" of classroom inquiry. We have modified these essential features into questions to guide you in your quest for enhanced and more thoughtful student inquiry.

1. ***Who asks the question?*** In most curricula, these focusing questions are an element given in the materials. As a teacher you can look for labs that, at least on a periodic basis, allow students to pursue their own questions.
2. ***Who designs the procedures?*** To gain experience with the logic underlying experimentation, students need continuous practice with designing procedures. Some labs in which the primary target is content acquisition designate procedures. But others should ask students to do so.
3. ***Who decides what data to collect?*** Students need practice in determining the data to collect.
4. ***Who formulates explanations based upon the data?*** Students should be challenged to think—to analyze and draw conclusions based on their data, not just copy answers from the text materials.
5. ***Who communicates and justifies the results?*** Activities should push students not only to communicate but also to justify their answers. Activities also should be thoughtfully designed and interesting so that students want to share their results and argue about conclusions.

Making Time for Inquiry

One last question—Must each and every activity have students do all of this? The answer is an obvious and emphatic "No." You will find a great variety of activities in *Science Explorer*. Some activities focus on content acquisition, and thus they specify the question and most of the procedures. But many others stress in-depth inquiry from start to finish. Because inquiry is an intellectual pursuit, it cannot merely be characterized by keeping students busy and active. Too many students have a knack for being physically but not intellectually engaged in science. It is our job to help them engage intellectually.

Evaluator's Checklist

Does your science program promote inquiry by—

- ✔ Enabling students to pursue their own questions
- ✔ Allowing students to design their own procedures
- ✔ Letting students determine what data are best to collect
- ✔ Challenging students to think critically
- ✔ Pushing students to justify their answers

Inquiry in *Science Explorer*

Science Explorer offers the most opportunities to get students to think like a scientist. By providing inquiry opportunities throughout the program, *Science Explorer* enables students to enhance their understanding by participating in the discovery.

Student Edition Inquiry

Six lab and activity options are included in every chapter, structured from directed to open-ended—providing you the flexibility to address all types of learners and accommodate your class time and equipment requirements. As Michael Padilla notes, some activities focus on content acquisition, and thus the question and most of the procedures are specified. But many others stress in-depth inquiry from start to finish. The graph below shows how, in general, inquiry levels are addressed in the Student Edition.

Science Explorer encourages students to develop inquiry skills across the spectrum from teacher-guided to open-ended. Even more opportunities for real-life applications of inquiry are included in Science & Society, Technology & Society, Careers in Science, and Interdisciplinary Exploration features.

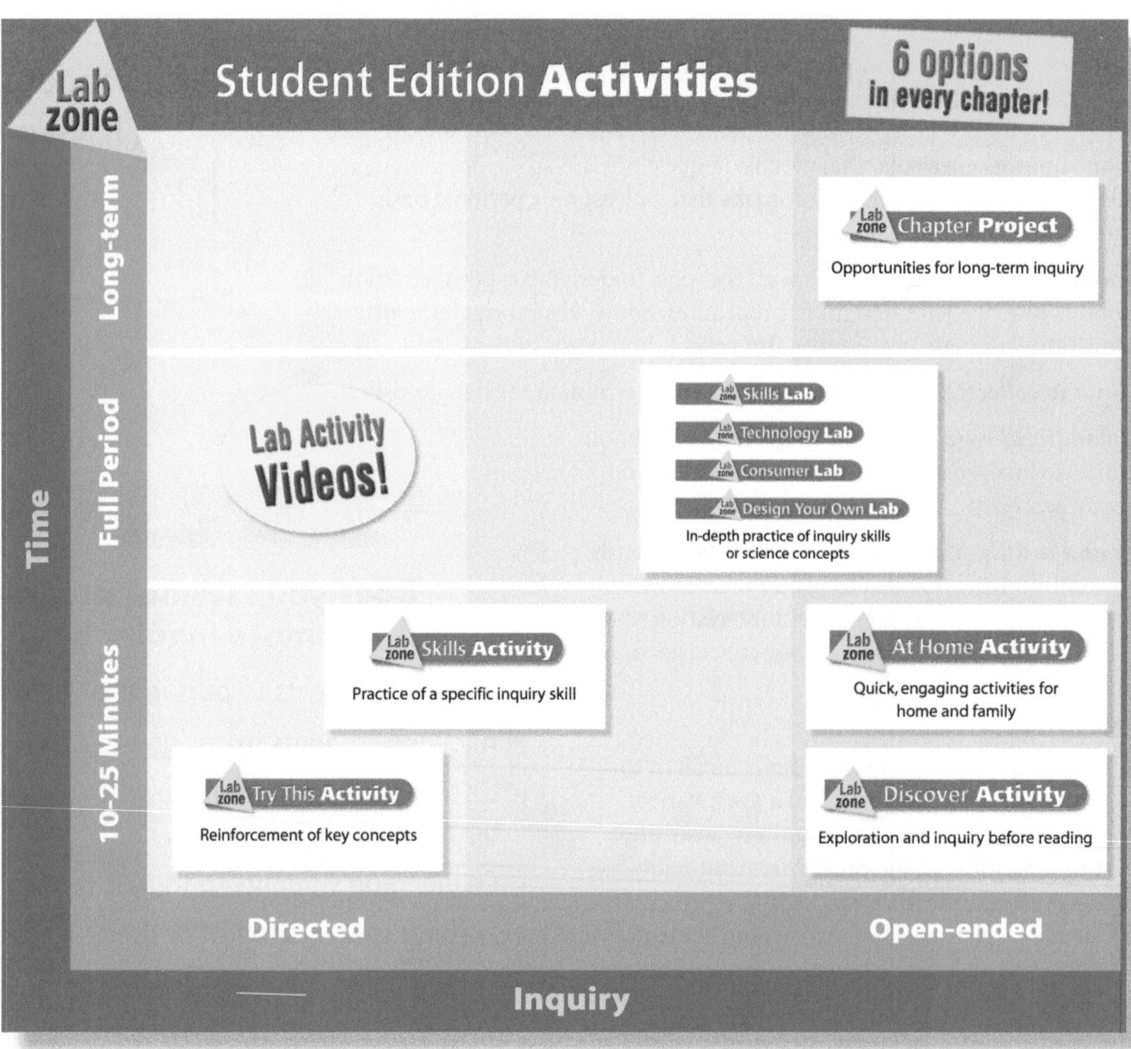

Inquiry Skills Chart

SCIENCE EXPLORER provides comprehensive teaching, practice, and assessment of science skills, with an emphasis on the process skills necessary for inquiry. This chart lists the skills covered in the program and cites the page numbers where each skill is covered.

Basic Process SKILLS				
	Student Text: Projects and Labs	Student Text: Activities	Student Text: Caption and Review Questions	Teacher's Edition: Extensions
Observing	4–5, 33, 38–39, 60–61, 93, 116–117, 126–127, 146–147, 164–165	14, 15, 26, 59, 86, 91, 107, 118, 123, 163	66	7, 12, 13, 16, 17, 29, 31, 42, 49, 56, 66, 81, 103, 104, 108, 134, 151
Inferring	60–61, 93, 164–165	40, 47, 55, 62, 80, 94, 99, 132, 134	57, 73, 83, 106, 114, 132, 134, 154, 172	8, 88, 101
Predicting	18, 46, 85	70, 128, 137, 148, 150	43, 67, 73, 81, 106, 144, 149, 152, 154, 160, 163, 172	123
Classifying	60–61, 116–117	12, 19, 43, 45	9, 32, 36, 45, 52, 76, 89, 136, 172	8, 10, 27, 63, 139
Making Models	78–79, 93	9, 97, 130		9, 17, 20, 44, 96, 110, 121, 168
Communicating	4–5, 18, 33, 60–61, 78–79, 84–85, 93, 141, 146–147, 155, 164–165	83, 125, 140		57
Measuring	46			
Calculating	18, 155	53, 63, 67, 105, 137, 153, 161	23, 36	108
Creating Data Tables	38–39, 116–117			
Graphing	46, 141	56, 137	76, 144	
Advanced Process SKILLS				
Posing Questions	155, 164–165			152
Developing Hypotheses	60–61, 155, 164–165		154, 163	152
Designing Experiments	18, 33, 38–39, 46, 60–61, 93 127, 141, 155, 165			152

Advanced Process SKILLS (continued)

	Student Text: Projects and Labs	Student Text: Activities	Student Text: Caption and Review Questions	Teacher's Edition: Extensions
Controlling Variables	141		36, 114	122, 152
Forming Operational Definitions	18	6, 156		121, 152
Interpreting Data	33, 46, 84–85, 116–117, 126–127, 146–147	51, 53, 153	76, 114, 144	
Drawing Conclusions	4–5, 18, 38–39, 46, 60–61, 84–85, 126–127, 146–147, 155, 164–165	30, 105, 111, 166	36, 76, 114	28, 81, 104
Critical Thinking SKILLS				
Comparing and Contrasting	78–79	14	14, 19, 23, 28, 45, 54, 67, 73, 76, 83, 92, 98, 106, 125, 131, 169	21, 22, 44, 49, 56, 80, 82, 88, 89, 90, 96, 122, 129, 135, 138, 153
Applying Concepts			12, 14, 48, 54, 59, 67, 76, 92, 95, 114, 122, 169, 172	30
Interpreting Diagrams, Graphs, Photographs, and Maps		30, 53, 105, 137, 153	10, 11, 16, 21, 31, 49, 50, 59, 67, 71, 87, 110, 111, 114, 140	10, 16, 19, 21, 56, 129, 134, 138, 160, 161, 162
Relating Cause and Effect		128	36, 98, 101, 114, 125, 144	
Making Generalizations		14	14, 59, 83, 103, 144	22
Making Judgments			23, 36, 76, 169, 172	
Problem Solving				
Informational Organizational SKILLS				
Concept Maps			75, 171	34, 74, 112, 142, 170
Compare/Contrast Tables		15, 40, 166	143	
Venn Diagrams				
Flowcharts				
Cycle Diagrams			35	21

The ***SCIENCE EXPLORER*** program provides additional teaching, reinforcement, and assessment of skills in the *Inquiry Skills Activities Book* and the *Integrated Science Laboratory Manual.*

NSES

A National Look at Science Education

Project 2061 was established by the American Association for the Advancement of Science (AAAS) as a long-term project to improve science education nationwide. A primary goal of Project 2061 is to define a "common core of learning"—the knowledge and skills we want all students to achieve. Project 2061 published *Science for All Americans* in 1989 and followed this with *Benchmarks for Science Literacy* in 1993. *Benchmarks* recommends what students should know and be able to do by the end of grades 2, 5, 8, and 12. Project 2061 clearly states that *Benchmarks* is not a curriculum but a tool for designing successful curricula.

The National Research Council (NRC) used *Science for All Americans* and *Benchmarks* to develop the National Science Education Standards (NSES), which were published in 1996. The NSES are organized into six categories (Content, Teaching, Assessment, Professional Development, Program, and System) to help schools establish the conditions necessary to achieve scientific literacy for all students.

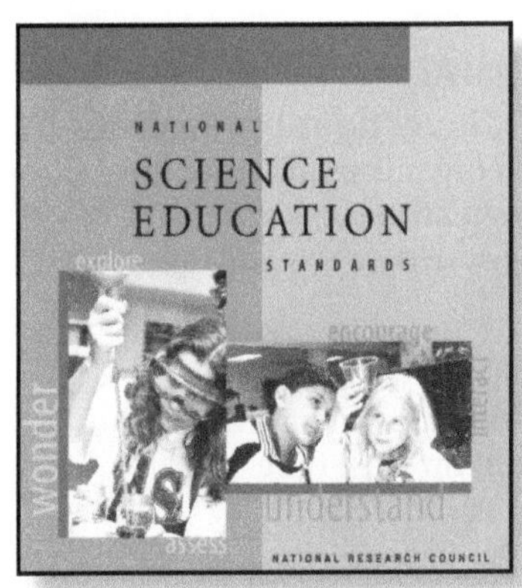

Michael Padilla, the program author of *Science Explorer,* guided one of six teams of teachers whose work led to the publication of *Benchmarks.* He also was a contributing writer of the National Science Education Standards. Under his guidance, *Science Explorer* has implemented these standards through its inquiry approach, a focus on student learning of important concepts and skills, and teacher support aligned with the NSES teaching standards.

Neither *Benchmarks* nor the NSES requires a single, uniform national curriculum, and in fact there is a great diversity nationwide in science curricula. The correlations that follow are designed to help you use the *Science Explorer* program to meet your particular curriculum needs.

Meeting the National Science Education Standards

SPONGES, CNIDARIANS, AND WORMS

Science as Inquiry (Content Standard A)

- **Ask questions that can be answered by scientific investigation** Do earthworms prefer dry or moist conditions? Do they prefer light or dark conditions? *(Skills Lab—Earthworm Responses)*
- **Design and conduct a scientific investigation** Students design a plan to investigate whether earthworms prefer smooth or rough surfaces. *(Skills Lab—Earthworm Responses)*

Life Science (Content Standard C)

- **Diversity and adaptations of organisms** Students learn the main characteristics of animals and some of the adaptations animals use to get food and escape predators. *(What Is an Animal?)* Students learn the characteristics and adaptations of sponges and cnidarians. *(Sponges and Cnidarians)* Students learn the characteristics and adaptations of the three main groups of worms. *(Worms)*
- **Populations and ecosystems** Students learn about effects humans can have on coral reefs. *(Sponges and Cnidarians)*
- **Structure and function of living systems** The bodies of complex animals all have either radial or bilateral symmetry. *(Animal Symmetry)*

MOLLUSKS, ARTHROPODS, AND ECHINODERMS

Science as Inquiry (Content Standard A)

- **Ask questions that can be answered by scientific investigation** How do changes in environmental temperature affect the activity level of a snail? How do different conditions affect mealworm development? *(Skills Lab—A Snail's Pace; Chapter Project—Going Through Changes)*
- **Design and conduct a scientific investigation** Students design a plan to investigate mealworm development. *(Chapter Project—Going Through Changes)*

Life Science (Content Standard C)

- **Diversity and adaptations of organisms** Students learn the characteristics and adaptations of mollusks, arthropods, insects, and echinoderms. *(Mollusks; Arthropods; Insects; Insect Ecology; Echinoderms)*
- **Populations and ecosystems** Insects play a key role in food chains because of the ways in which they obtain food and then become food for other animals. Students examine the animal life of a specific soil environment. *(Skills Lab—What's Living in the Soil?)*

A National Look at Science Education *(continued)*

FISHES, AMPHIBIANS, AND REPTILES

Science as Inquiry (Content Standard A)

- **Design and conduct a scientific investigation** Students create an artificial environment for two organisms and monitor the organisms' behavior. They also design an extension to the activity allowing more organisms to be added. *(Skills Lab—Home Sweet Home)*

Earth and Space Science (Content Standard D)

- **Earth's history** The fossils found in sedimentary rocks reveal the history of vertebrate evolution through time. *(Vertebrate History in Rocks)*

Life Science (Content Standard C)

- **Diversity and adaptations of organisms** The specialized characteristics of vertebrates reveal great diversity of form. Adaptations allow vertebrates to occupy many different habitats. *(What Is a Vertebrate?; Fishes; Amphibians; Reptiles)*
- **Structure and function of living systems** Vertebrates have similar structures to perform similar functions. Different vertebrate groups have specialized structures, such as a two-loop circulatory system and three-chambered heart. *(What Is a Vertebrate?; Fishes; Amphibians; Reptiles)*

BIRDS AND MAMMALS

Science as Inquiry (Content Standard A)

- **Recognize and analyze alternative explanations and predictions** Students may suggest explanations for observed animal behavior. *(Chapter Project—Bird Watch)*
- **Design and conduct a scientific investigation** Students implement a plan to investigate the effectiveness of wool as an insulator. Additionally, they will design their own experiment to test the insulation properties of wool to model fur as an adaptation to varying climates. *(Consumer Lab—Keeping Warm)*

Physical Science (Content Standard B)

- **Motions and forces** The flight of birds depends on lift and can be described using principles from physics. *(The Physics of Bird Flight)*

Life Science (Content Standard C)

- **Diversity and adaptations of organisms** Many characteristics of birds and mammals are adaptations that allow the animals to live in different environments. This is reflected in differences in physical and behavioral traits. *(Birds; The Physics of Bird Flight; Mammals)*
- **Structure and function** The structural features of both birds and mammals are related to their life-supporting functions. The physical adaptations of different animals, such as their brains and sense organs, enable them to behave in complex ways. *(Birds; The Physics of Bird Flight; Mammals)*

ANIMAL BEHAVIOR

Science as Inquiry (Content Standard A)

- **Ask questions that can be answered by scientific investigations** Students pose questions about teaching an animal and design a procedure to investigate their questions. *(Chapter Project—Learning New Tricks)*
- **Think critically and logically to make the relationships between evidence and explanations** Ants' social and group behavior provides a starting point from which scientific investigation and discussion can proceed. Evidence may be contrary to students' previous opinions and will be the source of lively scientific inquiry. *(Skills Lab—One for All)*

Life Science (Content Standard C)

- **Regulation and behavior** Behavior is a response to a stimulus. Behavior has an adaptive function, and it enables animals to meet basic needs such as finding food. Some animal behaviors, such as migration and hibernation, are related to seasonal and other environmental changes. *(What Is Behavior?; Patterns of Behavior; Tracking Migrations)*
- **Diversity and adaptations of organisms** Different animals behave in different ways, but most behaviors serve adaptive functions, such as reproduction or finding food. Different kinds of animals may exhibit similar behavior patterns, such as establishing a territory or living in groups. *(Patterns of Behavior; Tracking Migrations)*

Note: To see how the benchmarks are supported by *SCIENCE EXPLORER,* go to **PHSchool.com.**

Reading Comprehension in the Science Classroom

Q&A

Q: Why are science texts often difficult for students to read and comprehend?

A: In general, science texts make complex literacy and knowledge demands on learners. They have a more technical vocabulary and a more demanding syntax, and place a greater emphasis on inferential reasoning.

Q: What does research say about facilitating comprehension?

A: Studies comparing novices and experts show that the conceptual organization of experts' knowledge is very different from that of novices. For example, experts emphasize core concepts when organizing knowledge, while novices focus on superficial details. To facilitate comprehension, effective teaching strategies should support and scaffold students as they build an understanding of the key concepts and concept relationships within a text unit.

Q: What strategies can teachers use to facilitate comprehension?

A: Three complementary strategies are very important in facilitating student comprehension of science texts. First, guide student interaction with the text using the built-in strategies. Second, organize the curriculum in terms of core concepts (e.g., the **Key Concepts** in each section). Third, develop visual representations of the relationships among the key concepts and vocabulary that can be referred to during instruction.

Nancy Romance, Ph.D.
Professor of Science Education
Florida Atlantic University
Fort Lauderdale, Florida

"Effective teaching strategies should support and scaffold students as they build an understanding of the key concepts and concept relationships within a text unit."

Evaluator's Checklist

Does your science program promote reading comprehension with—

- ✔ Text structured in an outline format and key concepts highlighted in boldface type
- ✔ Real-world applications to activate prior knowledge
- ✔ Key concepts, critical vocabulary, and a reading skill for every section
- ✔ Sample graphic organizers for each section
- ✔ Relevant photos and carefully constructed graphics with questions
- ✔ Reading checkpoints that appear in each section
- ✔ Scaffolded questions in section assessments

Reading Support in *Science Explorer*

The latest research emphasizes the importance of activating learners' prior knowledge and teaching them to distinguish core concepts from less important information. These skills are now more important than ever, because success in science requires students to read, understand, and connect complex terms and concepts.

Before students read—

Reading Preview introduces students to the key concepts and key terms they'll find in each section. The **Target Reading Skill** is identified and applied with a graphic organizer.

During the section—

Boldface Sentences identify each key concept and encourage students to focus on the big ideas of science.

Reading Checkpoints reinforce students' understanding by slowing them down to review after every concept is discussed.

Caption Questions draw students into the art and photos, helping them connect the content to the images.

After students read—

Section Assessment revisits the **Target Reading Skill** and encourages students to use the graphic organizer.

Each review question is scaffolded and models the way students think, by first easing them into a review and then challenging them with increasingly more difficult questions.

Math in the Science Classroom

Why should students concern themselves with mathematics in your science class?

Good science requires good data from which to draw conclusions. Technology enhances the ability to measure in a variety of ways. Often the scientist must measure large amounts of data, and thus an aim of analysis is to reduce the data to a summary that makes sense and is consistent with established norms of communication—i.e., mathematics.

Calculating measures of central tendency (e.g., mean, median, or mode), variability (e.g., range), and shape (graphic representations) can effectively reduce 500 data points to 3 without losing the essential characteristics of the data. Scientists understand that a trade-off exists between precision and richness as data are folded into categories, and so margins of error can be quantified in mathematical terms and factored into all scientific findings.

Mathematics is the language used by scientists to model change in the world. Understanding change is a vital part of the inquiry process. Mathematics serves as a common language to communicate across the sciences. Fields of scientific research that originated as separate disciplines are now integrated, such as happened with bioengineering. What do the sciences have in common? Each uses the language of mathematics to communicate about data and the process of data analysis. Recognizing this need, *Science Explorer* integrates mathematics practice throughout the program and gives students ample opportunity to hone their math skills.

Clearly, mathematics plays an important role in your science classroom!

William Tate, Ph.D.
Professor of Education and Applied Statistics and Computation
Washington University
St. Louis, Missouri

"Mathematics is the language used by scientists to model change in the world."

Integrated Math Support

In the Student Edition

The math instruction is based on principles derived from Prentice Hall's research-based mathematics program.

Sample Problems, Math Practice, Analyzing Data, and a Math Skills Handbook all help to provide practice at point of use, encouraging students to Read and Understand, Plan and Solve, and then Look Back and Check.

Color-coded variables aid student navigation and help reinforce their comprehension.

In the Teacher's Edition

Math teaching notes enable the science teacher to support math instruction and math objectives on high-stakes tests.

In the Guided Reading and Study Workbook

These unique worksheets help students master reading and enhance their study and math skills. Students can create a record of their work for study and review.

Evaluator's Checklist

Does your science program promote math skills by—

- ✔ Giving students opportunities to collect data
- ✔ Providing students opportunities to analyze data
- ✔ Enabling students to practice math skills
- ✔ Helping students solve equations by using color-coded variables
- ✔ Using sample problems to apply science concepts

Technology and Design in the Science Classroom

Much of the world we live in is designed and made by humans. The buildings in which we live, the cars we drive, the medicines we take, and often the food we eat are products of technology. The knowledge and skills needed to understand the processes used to create these products should be a component of every student's basic literacy.

Some schools offer hands-on instruction on how technology development works through industrial arts curricula. Even then, there is a disconnect among science (understanding how nature works), mathematics (understanding data-driven models), and technology (understanding the human-made world). The link among these fields of study is the engineering design process—that process by which one identifies a human need and uses science knowledge and human ingenuity to create a technology to satisfy the need. Engineering gives students the problem-solving and design skills they will need to succeed in our sophisticated, three-dimensional, technological world.

As a complement to "science as inquiry," the National Science Education Standards (NRC, 1996) call for students at all age levels to develop the abilities related to "technology as design," including the ability to identify and frame a problem and then to design, implement, and evaluate a solution. At the 5–8 grade level, the standards call for students to be engaged in complex problem-solving and to learn more about how science and technology complement each other. It's also important for students to understand that there are often constraints involved in design as well as trade-offs and unintended consequences of technological solutions to problems.

As the *Standards for Technological Literacy* (ITEA, 2000) state, "Science and technology are like conjoined twins. While they have separate identities they must remain inextricably connected." Both sets of standards emphasize how progress in science leads to new developments in technology, while technological innovation in turn drives advances in science.

Ioannis Miaoulis, Ph.D.
President
Museum of Science
Boston, Massachusetts

"Engineering gives students the problem-solving and design skills they will need to succeed in our sophisticated, three-dimensional, technological world."

Evaluator's Checklist

Does your science program promote technology and design by—

- ✔ Incorporating technology and design concepts and skills into the science curriculum
- ✔ Giving students opportunities to identify and solve technological design problems
- ✔ Providing students opportunities to analyze the impact of technology on society
- ✔ Enabling students to practice technology and design skills

Technology and Design in *Science Explorer*

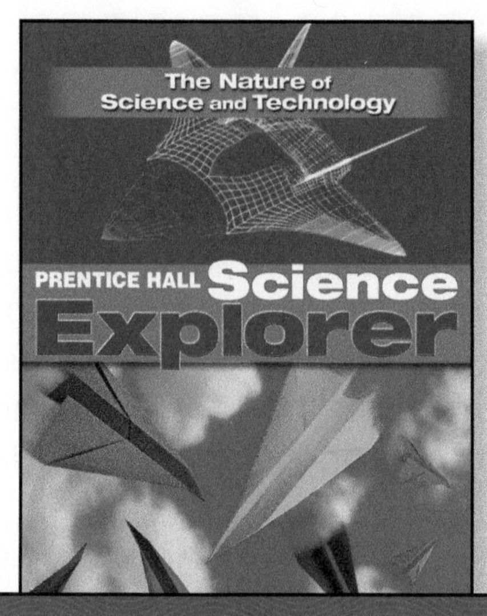

How often do you hear your students ask: "Why do I need to learn this?" Connecting them to the world of technology and design in their everyday life is one way to help answer this question. It is also why so many state science curricula are now emphasizing technology and design concepts and skills.

Science Explorer makes a special effort to include a technology and design strand that encourages students to not only identify a need but to take what they learned in science and apply it to design a possible solution, build a prototype, test and evaluate the design, and/or troubleshoot the design. This strand also provides definitions of technology and engineering and discusses the similarities and differences between these endeavors and science. Students will learn to analyze the risks and benefits of a new technology and to consider the tradeoffs, such as safety, costs, efficiency, and appearance.

In the Student Edition

Integrated Technology & Design Sections

Sections throughout *Science Explorer* specifically integrate technology and design with the content of the text. For example, students not only learn how seismographs work but also learn what role seismographs play in society and how people use the data that are gathered.

Technology Labs

These labs help students gain experience in designing and building a device or product that meets a particular need or solves a problem. Students follow a design process of Research and Investigate, Design and Build, and Evaluate and Redesign.

Chapter Projects

Chapter Projects work hand-in-hand with the chapter content. Students design, build, and test based on real-world situations. They have the opportunity to apply the knowledge and skills learned to building a product.

Special Features

This technology and design strand is also reflected in Technology & Society and Science & Society features as well as Science & History timelines and Tech & Design in History timelines. These highly visual features introduce a technology and its impact on society. For example, students learn how a hybrid car differs from a traditional car.

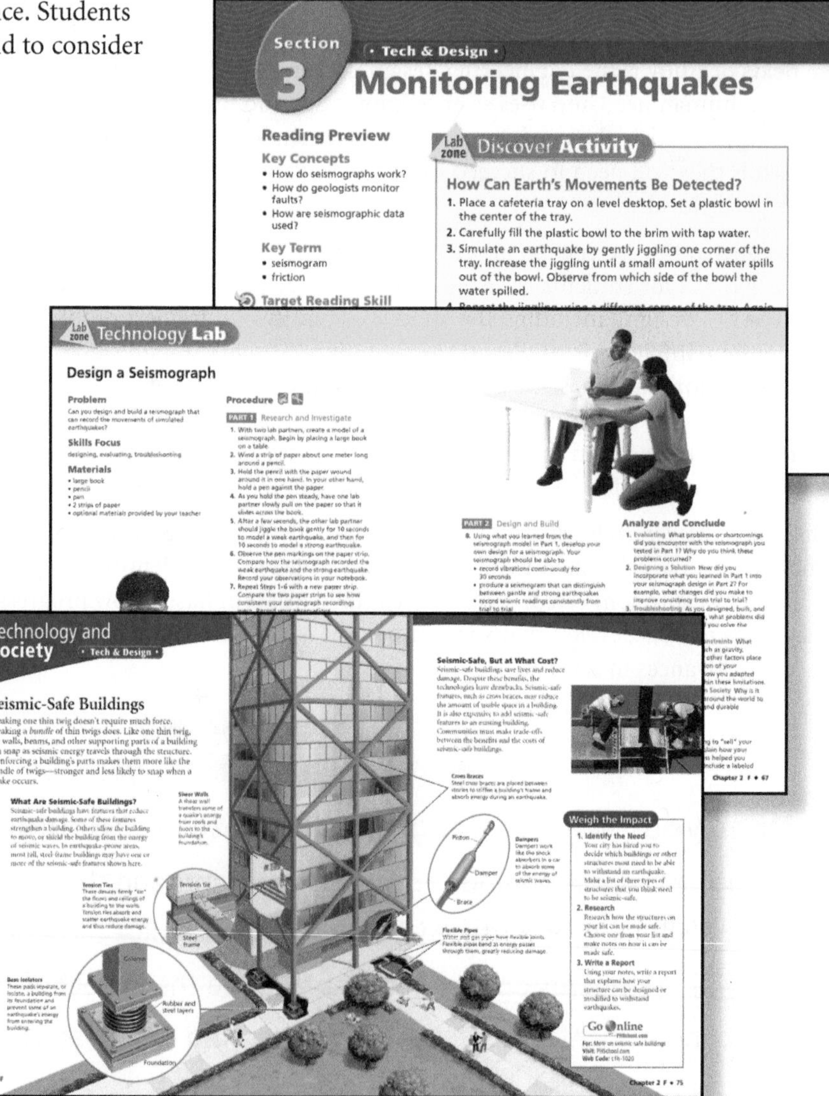

Assessment

Assessment in the Science Curriculum

No Child Left Behind clearly challenges school districts across the nation to raise expectations for all students with testing of student achievement in science beginning in 2007–2008.

A primary goal of NCLB is to provide classroom teachers with better data from scientifically valid assessments in order to inform instructional planning and to identify students who are at risk and require intervention. It has been a common practice to teach a science lesson, administer a test, grade it, and move on. This practice is a thing of the past. With the spotlight now on improving student performance, it is essential to use assessment results as a way to identify student strengths and challenges. Providing student feedback and obtaining student input is a valuable, essential part of the assessment process.

Assessment is a never-ending cycle, as is shown in the following diagram. Although you may begin at any point in the assessment cycle, the basic process is the same.

An important assessment strategy is to ensure that students have ample opportunities to check their understanding of skills and concepts before moving on to the next topic. Checking for understanding also includes asking appropriate, probing questions with each example presented. This enables students and teachers to know whether the skills or concepts being introduced are actually understood.

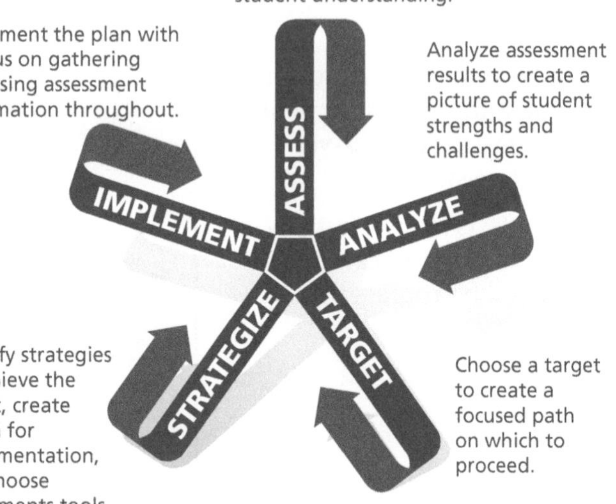

Use a variety of assessment tools to gain information and strengthen student understanding.
Analyze assessment results to create a picture of student strengths and challenges.
Choose a target to create a focused path on which to proceed.
Identify strategies to achieve the target, create a plan for implementation, and choose assessments tools.
Implement the plan with a focus on gathering and using assessment information throughout.
ASSESS
ANALYZE
TARGET
STRATEGIZE
IMPLEMENT

Eileen Depka
Supervisor of Standards and Assessment
Waukesha, Wisconsin

"Meeting the NCLB challenge will necessitate an integrated approach to assessment with a variety of assessment tools."

Evaluator's Checklist

Does your science program include assessments that—

- ✔ Are embedded before, during, and after lesson instruction
- ✔ Align to standards and to the instructional program
- ✔ Assess both skill acquisition and understanding
- ✔ Include meaningful rubrics to guide students
- ✔ Mirror the various formats of standardized tests

Prentice Hall *Science Explorer* now includes Success Tracker, an online tool to help teachers monitor and assess student progress with built-in remediation. Ask your sales rep about Success Tracker today!

Success  Tracker™
Online at PHSchool.com

Assessment in *Science Explorer*

Science Explorer's remarkable range of strategies for checking progress will help teachers find the right opportunity for reaching all their students.

The assessment strategies in *Science Explorer* will help both students and teachers alike ensure student success in content mastery as well as high-stakes test performance. A wealth of opportunities built into the Student Edition helps students monitor their own progress. Teachers are supported with ongoing assessment opportunities in the Teacher's Edition and an easy-to-use, editable test generator linked to content objectives. These integrated, ongoing assessment tools assure success.

Especially to support state and national testing objectives, Prentice Hall has developed test preparation materials that model the NCLB approach.

- **Diagnostic Assessment** tools provide in-depth analysis of strengths and weaknesses, areas of difficulty, and probable underlying causes that can help teachers make instructional decisions and plan intervention strategies.
- **Progress Monitoring** tools aligned with content objectives and state tests provide ongoing, longitudinal records of student achievement detailing individual student progress toward meeting end-of-year and end-of-schooling grade level, district, or state standards.
- **Outcomes** tools that mimic state and national tests show whether individual students have met the expected standards and can help a school system judge whether it has made adequate progress in improving its performance year by year.

Caption Questions enhance critical thinking skills.

Reading Checkpoints reinforce students' understanding.

Scaffolded Section Assessment Questions model the way students think.

Comprehensive Chapter Reviews and Assessments provide opportunities for students to check their own understanding and practice valuable high-stakes test-taking skills.

***ExamView®* Computer Test Bank CD-ROM** provides teachers access to thousands of modifiable test questions in English and Spanish.

Test Preparation Blackline Masters and Student Workbook include diagnostic and prescription tools, progress-monitoring aids, and practice tests that help teachers focus on improving test scores.

Section 3 Assessment

Target Reading Skill Sequencing Refer to your flowchart about seismographs as you answer Question 1.

Reviewing Key Concepts

1. a. Defining What is a seismogram?
   b. Explaining How can geologists tell apart the different types of seismic waves on a seismogram?
   c. Comparing and Contrasting Two identical seismographs are located 1,000 km and 1,200 km from an earthquake's epicenter. How would the two seismograms for the earthquake compare?
2. a. Reviewing What changes are measured by the instruments used to monitor faults?
   b. Describing How are satellites used to measure movements along a fault?
   c. Inferring A satellite that monitors a fault detects an increasing tilt in the land surface along the fault. What could this change in the land surface indicate?
3. a. Listing What are three ways in which geologists use seismographic data?
   b. Explaining How do geologists use seismographic data to make maps of faults?
   c. Making Generalizations Why is it difficult to predict earthquakes?

Writing in Science

Dialogue Geologists in Alaska have just detected an earthquake and located the earthquake's epicenter. Write a dialogue in which the geologists notify a disaster response team that will help people in the earthquake area.

Chapter 2 F ◆ 65

Standardized Test Prep

Test-Taking Tip
When answering questions about diagrams, read all parts of the diagram carefully, including title, captions, and labels. Make sure that you understand the meaning of arrows and other symbols. Determine exactly what the question asks. Then eliminate those answer choices that are not supported by the diagram.

Practice answering this question.
The diagram shows how stress affects a mass of rock in a process called
A compression.
B tension.
C squeezing.
D shearing.

The correct answer is **D** because the arrows show rock being pulled in opposite directions.

Choose the letter that best answers the question or completes the statement.

1. In a strike-slip fault, rock masses along the fault move
   A in the same direction.
   B down only.
   C together.
   D sideways past each other.
2. Stress will build until an earthquake occurs if friction along a fault is
   F decreasing. G high.
   H low. J changed to heat.

Use the information below and your knowledge of science to answer Questions 3 and 4.

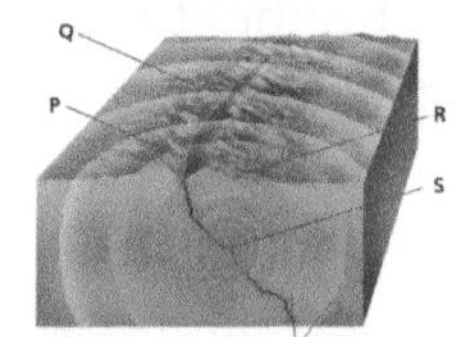

3. When an earthquake occurs, seismic waves travel
   A from P in all directions.
   B from R to S.
   C from S in all directions.
   D from Q to P.
4. At point R, seismic waves from an earthquake would be
   F weaker than at P.
   G likely to cause little damage.
   H weaker than at Q.
   J likely to cause the most damage.
5. To estimate the total energy released by an earthquake, a geologist should use the
   A Mercalli scale. B Richter scale.
   C epicenter scale. D moment magnitude scale.

Constructed Response

6. A geologist discovers a large fault beneath a major city. Why would this information be helpful in determining earthquake risk in the area? What three safety steps should the geologist recommend?

Chapter 2 F ◆ 79

Master Materials List

SCIENCE EXPLORER offers an abundance of activity options in the Student Edition so you can pick and choose those that suit your needs. Prentice Hall has worked with Science Kit to develop Consumable Kits and Nonconsumable Kits that precisely match the needs of the ***SCIENCE EXPLORER*** labs. Use this Master Materials List or contact your local Prentice Hall sales representative or Science Kit at 1-800-828-7777 or www.sciencekit.com/scienceexplorer.

Consumable Materials

Description	Textbook Section(s)	Quantity per Class
*Aluminum foil	2-2 (TT)	1
Ants -coupon	5-2 (Lab)	300
*Aquarium gravel, 5 lbs	3-2 (Lab)	1
Bag, plastic, 8"x 12'	1-3 (Lab), 3-3 (TT)	20
*Bottle, plastic, 2-L	2-3 (Lab)	5
*Bread crumbs	5-2 (Lab)	5
*Can, aluminum	1-1 (TT)	5
Cheesecloth, 2M piece	2-3 (Lab)	1
Container with lid, round, 250 mL	4-3 (Lab)	15
*Cornflakes	2-1 (CP)	1
Cotton swab, pkg/72	2-4 (DIS)	1
*Cracker	4-3 (DIS)	5
*Crickets	1-1 (DIS)	5
Cup, plastic	3-3 (DIS)	5
Cup, plastic, 16 oz./10	3-3 (DIS)	5
*Drawing materials	1-1 (TT)	5
Dropper, plastic 1 mL, pkg/20	1-4 (DIS), 1-4 (Lab), 2-5 (DIS)	2
Earthworms, live (12) - coupon	1-1 (DIS), 1-4 (Lab)	1
*Egg	4-1 (TT)	5
*Ferns	1-1 (DIS)	1
*Flowers, fresh	2-4 (DIS)	5
*Food, appropriate for chosen small vertebrate	5-1 (DIS)	
Glass-marking pencil	5-2 (Lab)	5
Gloves, disposable, pkg/100	3-2 (SA), 4-3 (TT)	1
*Glue, paper	4-2 (TT), 5-2 (TT)	1
*Goldfish, live	3-2 (DIS)	5
*Grapefruit	3-4 (DIS)	5
*Graph paper, sheet	2-1 (Lab), 4-3 (Lab), 5-3 (DIS)	15
*Guppies, live	3-2 (Lab)	5
*Guppy food	3-2 (Lab)	1
Hydra, brown, live -coupon	1-3 (TT)	1
Mealworms, live (30) -coupon	2-1 (CP)	1
*Minnows	1-1 (DIS)	5
Modeling clay, 1 lb	1-1 (TT), 3-5 (DIS)	4
Owl pellet	4-1 (Lab)	6
*Paper, assorted kinds	4-2 (TT)	1
Paper, construction (black)	1-1 (TT), 5-2 (Lab)	15
Paper, construction (green)	3-3 (DIS)	50
*Paper, white, ream	1-2 (DIS), 3-1 (Lab), 3-5 (DIS), 4-2 (DIS), 4-2 (TT), 5-1 (Lab), 5-2 (TT)	1
*Paper, tracing (tablet)	1-2 (DIS)	1
Paper clips, pkg/100	4-2 (TT)	1
*Paper towels, roll	1-4 (Lab), 2-2 (TT), 4-3 (TT)	3
Paste, paper	5-2 (TT)	
Peas, dried, green, 1 lb	3-3 (DIS)	1
Peas, dried, yellow, 1 lb	3-3 (DIS)	1
*Pencil	1-2 (DIS), 2-4 (DIS), 3-1 (Lab), 5-1 (Lab)	30
*Perch, preserved	3-2 (SA)	5
Pill bugs, live (30) - coupon	1-1 (DIS), 2-2 (TT)	1
Pipe cleaners, pkg/100	1-1 (TT)	1
Planaria, live - coupon	1-4 (DIS)	1
Rubber band, large	2-3 (Lab), 5-2 (Lab)	5
Rubber band, medium	3-3 (TT), 3-4 (DIS), 4-2 (TT)	20
Sandy soil, bag	5-2 (Lab)	1
*Shortening, solid	4-3 (TT)	1
*Small vertebrate	5-1 (DIS)	1

KEY: CP: Chapter Project; **DIS:** Discover; **SA:** Skills Activity; **TT:** Try This; **Lab:** Skills, Consumer, Design Your Own, and Tech & Design

* items are school supplied.

Quantities based on five groups of six students per class.

Master Materials List

Consumable Materials *(continued)*

Description	Textbook Section(s)	Quantity per Class
Snail, freshwater, live (12) - coupon	2-1 (Lab), 3-2 (Lab)	1
*Soil and leaf litter	2-3 (Lab)	5
Spoon, plastic	2-1 (CP)	5
*Staples, box	4-2 (TT)	1
Steel wool, coarse, pads	2-3 (Lab)	6
String, spool	4-2 (TT)	1
*Sugar	5-2 (Lab)	5
Tape, masking, roll	2-2 (DIS), 2-2 (TT), 4-2 (TT), 5-2 (Lab)	1
Toothpicks, box/250	1-3 (TT)	1
*Water plants	3-2 (Lab)	1
*Water, spring, 1 gallon	1-4 (DIS), 2-1 (Lab)	1

Nonconsumable Materials

Description	Textbook Section(s)	Quantity per Class
*Aquarium filter	3-2 (Lab)	1
*Aquarium heater	3-2 (Lab)	1
*Aquarium tank, 15 L with cover	3-2 (DIS), 3-2 (Lab)	1
*Aquarium thermometer	3-2 (Lab)	1
*Balance, triple beam	1-3 (Lab)	5
*Beaker, 1-L	4-3 (Lab)	5
Bird feeder	4-1 (CP)	1
*Bowl	1-3 (Lab), 4-1 (TT)	5
Cardboard, corrugated 12" x 12"	1-4 (Lab), 2-2 (DIS)	10
Choice chamber	2-1 (CP), 2-2 (TT)	5
Container, plastic (with lids)	1-3 (Lab), 2-1 (CP), 2-1 (Lab), 3-2 (Lab)	10
Dip net	3-2 (Lab)	5
Dissecting needle	4-1 (Lab)	5
Feather	4-1 (DIS)	5
Flashlight	1-4 (Lab)	5
Forceps	4-1 (Lab), 5-2 (Lab)	6
*Goggles	3-2 (SA)	30
Hand lens, pkg/6	1-3 (DIS), 1-3 (TT), 1-4 (DIS), 2-3 (DIS), 2-3 (Lab), 4-1 (DIS), 4-1 (TT), 4-1 (Lab), 5-2 (Lab)	1
*Insect collection	2-3 (DIS)	1
Jar, small	2-3 (Lab)	5
Jar, wide-mouthed	2-3 (Lab), 5-2 (Lab)	5
*Lamp, gooseneck	2-3 (Lab)	5
Mirror, small	4-3 (DIS)	6
*Pail	3-3 (TT), 4-3 (TT)	1
Paintbrush, small	1-4 (DIS)	5
Pan, round, aluminum	5-2 (Lab)	5
Petri dishes pkg/6	1-3 (TT), 1-4 (DIS), 2-1 (Lab)	1
Plants, potted	1-1 (DIS)	3
Ruler, 30 cm	1-3 (Lab), 2-1 (Lab), 3-2 (Lab), 4-2 (DIS), 4-1 (Lab)	5
*Scissors	1-2 (DIS), 1-3 (DIS), 2-3 (Lab), 4-2 (DIS), 4-3 (Lab), 5-2 (TT)	5
Shells, assorted, pkg/30	2-1 (DIS)	1
Socks, ribbed	3-4 (DIS)	5
*Socks, wool	4-3 (Lab)	5
Sponge, artificial	1-3 (DIS), 1-3 (Lab), 5-2 (Lab)	5
Sponge, natural	1-1 (DIS), 1-3 (DIS), 1-3 (Lab)	1
Stapler	4-2 (TT), 5-2 (TT)	1
Sea star, shell	1-1 (DIS)	5
*Stopwatch	1-3 (Lab), 1-4 (Lab), 2-1 (Lab), 3-3 (DIS), 4-3 (Lab), 4-3 (Lab), 5-2 (TT)	5
*Terrarium	5-1 (DIS)	1
Thermometer, -25°C to 100°C	2-1 (Lab), 3-2 (Lab), 4-3 (lab)	15
Tray	1-4 (Lab)	5
*Trowel	2-3 (Lab)	5
*Umbrella	3-1 (DIS)	5
Wire screen, 6" x 6"	5-2 (Lab)	5

KEY: CP: Chapter Project; **DIS:** Discover; **SA:** Skills Activity; **TT:** Try This; **Lab:** Skills, Consumer, Design Your Own, and Tech & Design

* items are school supplied.

Quantities based on five groups of six students per class.